COLLEGE
TRIGONOMETRY
A NARRATIVE APPROACH

Stephen Majewicz

Second Edition

Custom Publishing

New York   Boston   San Francisco
London   Toronto   Sydney   Tokyo   Singapore   Madrid
Mexico City   Munich   Paris   Cape Town   Hong Kong   Montreal

**Pearson
Custom Publishing**
is a division of

PEARSON

www.pearsonhighered.com

ISBN 10: 0-536-78388-8
ISBN 13: 978-0-536-78388-2

19 2023

To my in-laws, Anthony and Anne Santoro

A Note to the Instructor

College Trigonometry: *A Narrative Approach* is written to help students succeed in Mat 10 and prepare them for future mathematics courses. Mat 10 is a one-semester course in Trigonometry which contains most of the topics traditionally taught. There are two fundamental qualities of any mathematics course which every student needs in order to succeed: a good instructor and a good textbook. It is your job to be a good instructor. The job of the textbook is to supply clear explanations of worked out examples, plenty of exercises for the students to work on, and comfortable reading material which the student can understand. This book has it all.

In addition, it provides the student with material, which supplements the notes given by the instructor. Whenever a new topic is introduced in the text, it is accompanied by numerous worked out examples and in-depth detailed explanations of these problems. Explanations of the steps taken in solving such examples are given as well. Throughout the text, there are sets of examples (called 'Try These') for the student to try out, and the solutions to them are given at the end of the text. Each chapter (or section) concludes with numerous exercise problems varying in their level of difficulty. The solutions to the odd numbered exercises are given at the end of the text. The text is reader friendly, and when read by the student, he/she will feel as if he/she is being taught by the instructor one-on-one.

This textbook has numerous exercise problems, which make excellent homework problems. The 'Try These' problems should be assigned to the students as well. It will provide you with the adequate teaching material for Mat 10. It is important that your students get enough practice in order to succeed in Mat 10. Since there is only so much that we can do in the classroom, the text is the students' instructor outside of the classroom. By providing them with homework problems and reading material, they will be guided in the right direction.

A Note to the Student

Trigonometry (Mat 10) is a mathematics course which will be useful in studying advanced mathematics courses such as Calculus, Linear Algebra, and Differential Equations. Trigonometric functions are very important, and they appear in many applications. The course begins with a discussion of angles, their measures, and right triangle trigonometry. Some of this material may be new to you, so it is important to do plenty of homework problems that pertain to these topics. After this, you will learn how to do trigonometry for any angle. Many relationships between the different trigonometric functions are given, as well as some properties of these functions. You will learn that the definitions of the trigonometric functions can also be easily developed by using the unit circle. These properties come in handy in graphing trigonometric functions. After doing some graphing, you will learn how to do algebraic manipulations with the trigonometric functions. This will help you solve trigonometric equations and prove different trigonometric identities. In particular, formulas for the sum of angles, the difference of angles, etc. will be developed. Once you have mastered these formulas and their uses, you will learn how to solve a triangle. This requires the knowledge of the Law of Sines and the Law of Cosines, two formulas which will be discussed in the last chapter of the text. In case you need a review of Algebra or Precalculus used in the course, see Chapter R for all of the necessary prerequisite material.

The two resources at your disposal which will aid you in doing well in this course are the lectures and the textbook. It is important to attend class regularly and take notes. The instructor will be able to explain something to you that you do not understand. Ask questions if an explanation is not clear. Don't be afraid and don't ever think that your question is stupid. Every question is a good one. Remember that the instructor is there to help you. The textbook contains all of the material that you will need to learn in the course. It has plenty of worked out examples for you to read. After looking over the examples, you should do the 'Try These' examples to convince yourself that you understand the material. Make sure that you do all of the homework assignments your instructor assigns. Homework can be time consuming, but it is given to you for a reason. By doing your homework, you will strengthen your mathematics skills, as well as become a disciplined student. Such skills and discipline are key necessities for success in your college career, as well as in your life. After completing each chapter of the text, you should do the 'Try These' examples once more. If you read over your notes, read the book, and do your homework regularly, you will do well in the class.

I wish you the best of luck in Mat 10. Remember to have confidence and patience. You will succeed!

Professor Stephen Majewicz

TABLE OF CONTENTS

Acknowledgements

I would like to thank Ms. Mariya Petrova of Kingsborough Community College for reviewing several sections of the book and for her helpful suggestions and comments. I would also like to thank Mr. Marcos Perez for preparing many sketches for this text. His contribution is highly appreciated.

I would like to thank Mr. Alex Gindes, Ms. Lena Juraev, Ms. Anastasia Kagan, and Ms. Oksana Voronetska for pointing out several errors in the first edition of the text.

I would like to thank the members of the Mathematics 10 committee of Kingsborough Community College for supporting my work and adapting my text for the Mathematics 10 course. The members are Professors Aleksandr Davydov, Susan Hom, Robert Putz, Stanley Rabinowitz, Dale Siegel, Richard Staum, and Rachel Sturm.

I would like to extend a special thank you to Professor Rina Yarmish, Chair of the Department of Mathematics and Computer Science at Kingsborough Community College for her encouragement and strong support throughout this endeavor.

Chapter R: Functions and their Graphs

This chapter contains material which you should already be familiar with. You should take some time to look over the topics in this chapter and review what you don't remember. Much of this material will be used when learning about trigonometric functions.

Section R.1   The Cartesian Plane and Analytic Geometry

The Cartesian Plane

Let's begin with the construction of the Cartesian Plane. On a piece of paper (which, geometrically speaking, is a two-dimensional object), draw two real number lines: one vertical and the other horizontal. These real number lines are called the **coordinate axes** for our plane. The **vertical axis** will be labeled the **y-axis** and the **horizontal axis** will be labeled the x-**axis**. The place where both axes intersect is where both the x-axis and the y-axis have the point 0. Label the x-axis in such a way that the numbers are increasing from left to right. Label the y-axis in such a way that the numbers are increasing as you go upward. You will obtain the following picture:

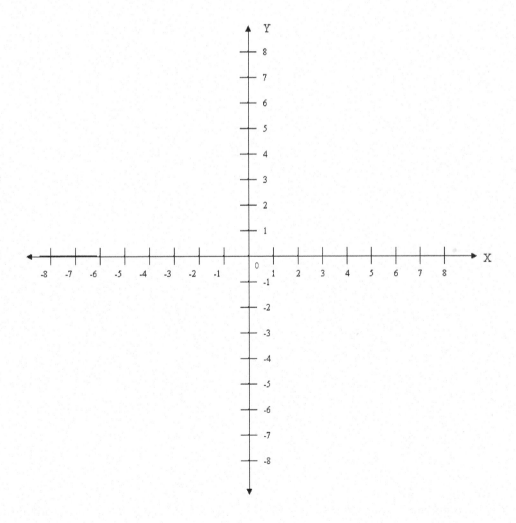

Notice that I have labeled only the integers on each axis. Of course, I could locate **any** real number on each axis since an axis is just a real number line. The object drawn above is called the **Cartesian Plane** (or **Rectangular Coordinate System**, or the xy-**plane**).

Definition 1: An **ordered pair** is a pair of real numbers, written as (x, y), where x is the x-**coordinate** (or the **abscissa**) and y is the y-**coordinate** (or the **ordinate**).

For example, $(1, -3)$ is an ordered pair with x-coordinate 1 and y-coordinate -3. To draw a picture of this ordered pair, you begin at the place where the axes meet and go one unit to the right (along the positive x-axis since 1 is the x-coordinate and it is positive). Then you go down by three units (since -3 is the y-coordinate and it is negative). After you do this, you draw a dot. This is the **graph** of the ordered pair $(1, -3)$. Before we graph this, we have the following definitions:

Definition 2: The graph of an ordered pair is called a **point** in the Cartesian Plane. The process of graphing an ordered pair is called **point plotting**.

Definition 3: The point with ordered pair $(0, 0)$ is called the **origin**.

Now we will plot the point whose ordered pair is $(1, -3)$. In other words, we will plot the point whose coordinates are $x = 1$ and $y = -3$. We will identify a point in the Cartesian Plane with its ordered pair. For example, if I say 'the point $(-5, 0)$', I refer to the point whose ordered pair is $(-5, 0)$. Below, I have plotted several points for you to look at, including $(1, -3)$ and $(-5, 0)$.

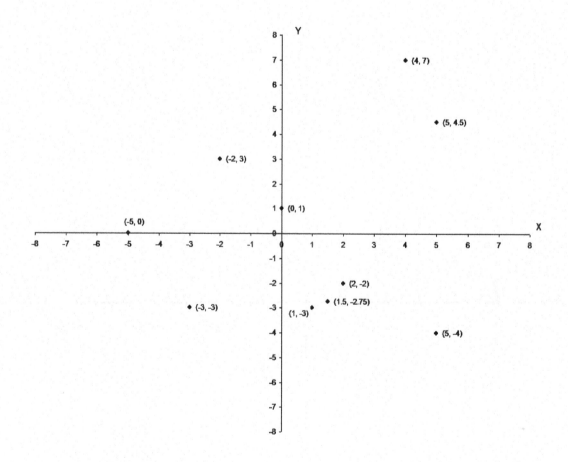

Notice that the coordinate axes divide the xy-plane into four pieces. We call them the **quadrants** of the Cartesian Plane. Below, I have labeled the quadrants using Roman numerals. I've also mentioned the sign of each variable in each quadrant. Notice that the points which lie on the x- or y-axis do not lie in a quadrant.

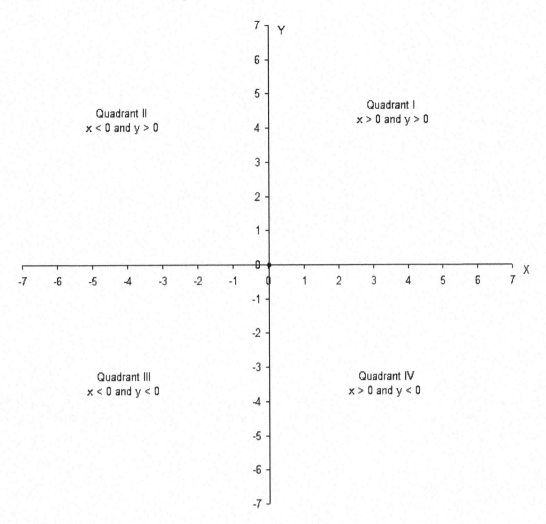

The Distance Formula and the Midpoint Formula

Let's recall two formulas which often arise in the study of analytic geometry, the **distance formula** and the **midpoint formula**. First let's take a look at the distance formula.

The Distance Formula

The **distance** between the two points $(x_1,\ y_1)$ and $(x_2,\ y_2)$ is given by

$$d = \sqrt{(x_2 - x_1)^2 + (y_2 - y_1)^2}.$$

It is good to know where this formula comes from, just in case you forget what it is. Take a look at the next figure.

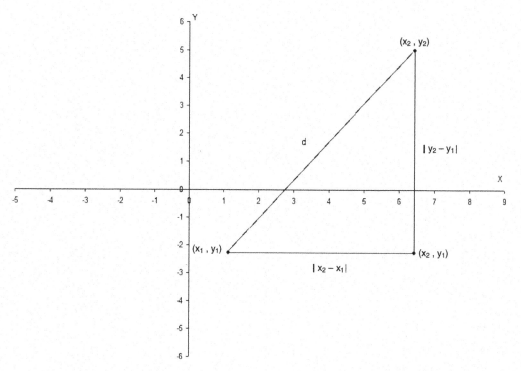

Notice that the distance between (x_1, y_1) and (x_2, y_2) is the same as the length of the line segment whose endpoints are (x_1, y_1) and (x_2, y_2). So I've constructed a right triangle whose legs are parallel to the coordinate axes and whose hypotenuse is the line segment whose length we want to find. Well, by the Pythagorean Theorem, we have

$$|x_2 - x_1|^2 + |y_2 - y_1|^2 = d^2.$$

And, by a property of absolute value we have

$$(x_2 - x_1)^2 + (y_2 - y_1)^2 = d^2.$$

By applying the Square Root Property, we obtain

$$\pm\sqrt{(x_2 - x_1)^2 + (y_2 - y_1)^2} = d.$$

However, the distance between two points cannot be negative. After getting rid of the negative sign, we obtain

$$\sqrt{(x_2 - x_1)^2 + (y_2 - y_1)^2} = d.$$

And here's our formula.

Examples. Find the distance between the given points.

1) (5, 0) and (1, 3)

We begin by labeling our numbers by variable names. It doesn't matter which ordered pair you call (x_1, y_1) or (x_2, y_2) when using the formula since the distance from (x_1, y_1) to (x_2, y_2) is the same as the distance from (x_2, y_2) to (x_1, y_1). Therefore, let $(x_1, y_1) = (5, 0)$ and $(x_2, y_2) = (1, 3)$. Then

$$\begin{aligned}
d &= \sqrt{(x_2 - x_1)^2 + (y_2 - y_1)^2} \\
&= \sqrt{(1 - 5)^2 + (3 - 0)^2} \\
&= \sqrt{(-4)^2 + (3)^2} \\
&= \sqrt{16 + 9} = \sqrt{25} = 5.
\end{aligned}$$

2) $(9, -6)$ and $(7, -6)$

Let $(x_1, y_1) = (9, -6)$ and $(x_2, y_2) = (7, -6)$. Then

$$\begin{aligned}
d &= \sqrt{(x_2 - x_1)^2 + (y_2 - y_1)^2} \\
&= \sqrt{(7-9)^2 + (-6-(-6))^2} \\
&= \sqrt{(-2)^2 + (0)^2} \\
&= \sqrt{4+0} = \sqrt{4} = 2.
\end{aligned}$$

If you plot these two points and connect them with a line segment, the line segment you'll obtain is horizontal. A horizontal line segment will always occur when the y-values of the two points are equal (in other words, whenever $y_1 = y_2$). When such a situation arises, you only need to figure out $|x_2 - x_1|$ to get the distance. This is referred to as a **horizontal distance**. In this case, notice that

$$|x_2 - x_1| = |7 - 9| = |-2| = 2,$$

which is what we've found by using the Distance Formula.

3) $(1, -4)$ and $(1, 8)$

Let $(x_1, y_1) = (1, -4)$ and $(x_2, y_2) = (1, 8)$. Then

$$\begin{aligned}
d &= \sqrt{(x_2 - x_1)^2 + (y_2 - y_1)^2} \\
&= \sqrt{(1-1)^2 + (8-(-4))^2} \\
&= \sqrt{(0)^2 + (12)^2} \\
&= \sqrt{0+144} = \sqrt{144} \doteq 12.
\end{aligned}$$

If you plot these two points and connect them with a line segment, you will notice that the line segment is vertical. A vertical line segment will always occur when the x-values of the two points are equal (in other words, whenever $x_1 = x_2$). When such a situation arises, you only need to figure out $|y_2 - y_1|$ to get the distance. This is often referred to as a **vertical distance**. In this case, we have that

$$|y_2 - y_1| = |8 - (-4)| = |12| = 12,$$

which is what we've found by using the Distance Formula.

4) $(2, -2)$ and $(-2, 6)$

Let $(x_1, y_1) = (2, -2)$ and $(x_2, y_2) = (-2, 6)$. Then

$$\begin{aligned}
d &= \sqrt{(x_2 - x_1)^2 + (y_2 - y_1)^2} \\
&= \sqrt{(-2-2)^2 + (6-(-2))^2} \\
&= \sqrt{(-2-2)^2 + (6+2)^2} \\
&= \sqrt{(-4)^2 + (8)^2} \\
&= \sqrt{16+64} \\
&= \sqrt{80} = \sqrt{16}\sqrt{5} = 4\sqrt{5}.
\end{aligned}$$

You should always simplify your answer. Be careful when working out the problem. It is very easy to slip on the arithmetic and make a mistake with the signs. You should also be careful with the algebra. For example, notice that I have **NOT** do $\sqrt{16+64} \overset{??}{=} \sqrt{16} + \sqrt{64}$. Instead, I've simply followed the order of operations.

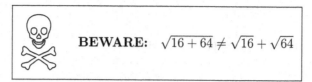

BEWARE: $\sqrt{16 + 64} \neq \sqrt{16} + \sqrt{64}$

Let's remind ourselves of the midpoint formula.

The Midpoint Formula

The **midpoint**, M, of the line segment with endpoints $A = (x_1,\ y_1)$ and $B = (x_2,\ y_2)$ is

$$\text{midpoint of } \overline{AB} = M = \left(\frac{x_1 + x_2}{2},\ \frac{y_1 + y_2}{2} \right).$$

The midpoint of a line segment is the point on the segment which divides it into two equal segments (hence, it lies in the **middle** of the segment). A simple way to remember this formula is to notice that $\frac{x_1 + x_2}{2}$ is just the average of x_1 and x_2 and $\frac{y_1 + y_2}{2}$ is the average of y_1 and y_2. Therefore, to find the midpoint, just find the average of the x's and the average of the y's and pair them up. Notice that the distance from point A to point M is **equal to** the distance from point M to point B.

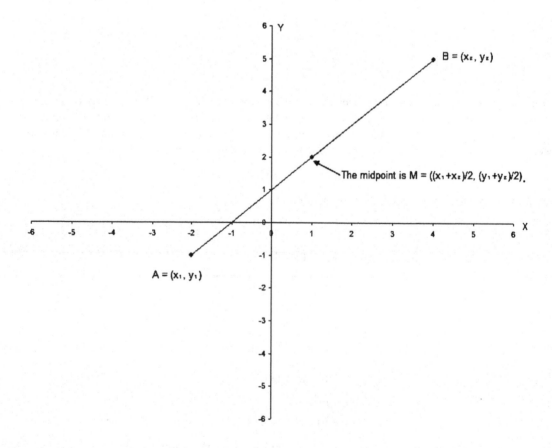

Examples. Find the midpoint of line segment $\overline{AB}$ where A and B are given.

1) $A = (4,\ 3)$ and $B = (2,\ 9)$

Let $(x_1, y_1) = (4, 3)$ and $(x_2, y_2) = (2, 9)$. Then

$$\text{the midpoint of } \overline{AB} = \left(\frac{x_1 + x_2}{2}, \ \frac{y_1 + y_2}{2} \right)$$

$$= \left(\frac{4 + 2}{2}, \ \frac{3 + 9}{2} \right)$$

$$= \left(\frac{6}{2}, \ \frac{12}{2} \right) = (3, 6).$$

Note that we could've chosen $(x_1, y_1) = (2, 9)$ and $(x_2, y_2) = (4, 3)$ instead, and the answer would've been the same.

2) $A = \left(0, \ \frac{1}{4} \right)$ and $B = \left(-\frac{2}{5}, \ -\frac{1}{8} \right)$

Let $(x_1, y_1) = \left(0, \ \frac{1}{4} \right)$ and $(x_2, y_2) = \left(-\frac{2}{5}, \ -\frac{1}{8} \right)$. Then

$$\text{the midpoint of } \overline{AB} = \left(\frac{x_1 + x_2}{2}, \ \frac{y_1 + y_2}{2} \right)$$

$$= \left(\frac{0 + \left(-\frac{2}{5} \right)}{2}, \ \frac{\frac{1}{4} + \left(-\frac{1}{8} \right)}{2} \right)$$

$$= \left(\frac{-\frac{2}{5} \times 5}{2 \times 5}, \ \frac{\left(\frac{1}{4} - \frac{1}{8} \right) \times 8}{2 \times 8} \right)$$

$$= \left(\frac{-2}{10}, \ \frac{2 - 1}{16} \right) = \left(-\frac{1}{5}, \ \frac{1}{16} \right).$$

Exercise R.1

In Exercises 1-20, plot each point in the Cartesian Plane. State the quadrant (if any) for which each point lies in.

1. $(x, y) = (2, 1)$

2. $(x, y) = (3, 4)$

3. $(x, y) = (-5, 2)$

4. $(x, y) = (-1, 1)$

5. $(x, y) = (-4, -3)$

6. $(x, y) = (-7, -2)$

7. $(x, y) = (4, -8)$

8. $(x, y) = (7, -3)$

9. $(x, y) = (3, 0)$

10. $(x, y) = (0, -9)$

11. $(x, y) = (0, 2)$

12. $(x, y) = (1, 0)$

13. $(x, y) = (0, 0)$

14. $(x, y) = (0, 6)$

15. $(x, y) = \left(5, -\frac{32}{7} \right)$

16. $(x, y) = \left(-\frac{1}{6}, \frac{8}{5} \right)$

17. $(x, y) = \left(2, -\sqrt{2} \right)$

18. $(x, y) = (-3, 4\sqrt{5})$

19. $(x, y) = (\pi, \pi)$

20. $(x, y) = (-\pi, -\pi)$

In Exercises 21-26, find the distance between the given points.

21. $(1, 0)$ and $(4, 4)$ 22. $(3, 7)$ and $(11, 13)$ 23. $(-2, 1)$ and $(4, 9)$

24. $(8, -3)$ and $(5, 1)$ 25. $(2, -6)$ and $(1, -1)$ 26. $(5, -3)$ and $(1, -2)$

In Exercises 27-32, find the midpoint of the line segment whose endpoints are given.

27. $A = (7, 0)$ and $B = (0, 6)$ 28. $A = (1, 5)$ and $B = (3, 9)$

29. $P = (1, -3)$ and $Q = (-7, 3)$ 30. $P = (-6, 2)$ and $Q = (10, -4)$

31. $G = (9, 10)$ and $H = (-1, -6)$ 32. $S = (-10, -4)$ and $T = (-7, -2)$

Section R.2 Graphs of Equations in Two Variables

In this section, we will remind ourselves of how to graph an equation in two variables. We will begin with linear equations in two variables.

Graphing Linear Equations in Two Variables

Let's graph the solutions to the equation $y = 2x + 1$. This is called a **linear equation** in x and y since both x and y are of degree one in the equation. In other words, we have $y^1 = 2x^1 + 1$. Recall that we can obtain solutions to such an equation by choosing different values for x and find the corresponding values for y. Once these two values are known, we pair them up as an ordered pair and obtain a solution. Let's find some solutions to this equation:

x	$y = 2x + 1$	Solution
0	$2(0) + 1 = 1$	$(0, 1)$
1	$2(1) + 1 = 3$	$(1, 3)$
-1	$2(-1) + 1 = -1$	$(-1, -1)$
2	$2(2) + 1 = 5$	$(2, 5)$

There are infinitely many real numbers I could have chosen for the value of x. This means that there are infinitely many solutions to this equation. I have found only four of them in the table above. If I had found **all** of the solutions, however, and plotted them in the Cartesian Plane, the graph would be a straight line (see the figure on the next page). Notice that the **slope** of this line is 2 and the y-intercept is $(0, 1)$. This information can be obtained by observing that the equation is of the form $y = mx + b$, so $m = 2$ and $b = 1$. We will not review slopes of lines in this book since it will not be needed. If you would like to review linear equations, you could refer to my 'College Algebra: A Narrative Approach' or 'Precalculus: A Narrative Approach' books.

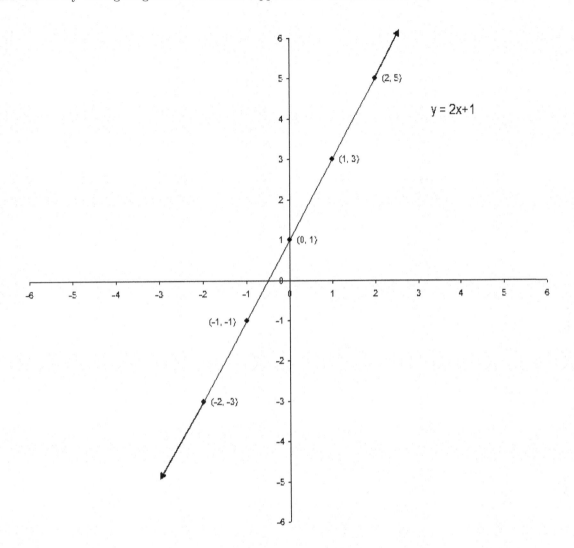

Remember that the picture of the line above is a graphical representation of all of the solutions to the equation $y = 2x+1$. In other words, if a point lies on the line, then it must satisfy the equation and vice-versa. For example, the point $(-2, 0)$ is not on the line (the geometric object) and $0 \neq 2(-2) + 1$ (the algebraic object). However, the point $(-2, -3)$ is on the line and $-3 = 2(-2) + 1$. We name the line according to its equation, in this case, $y = 2x + 1$.

Examples. Graph using the slope.

1) $y = 3x - 1$

Observe that the equation is in the form $y = mx + b$ (this is called the **slope-intercept form**). The slope m is $3 = \dfrac{+3}{+1} = \dfrac{\Delta y}{\Delta x}$ and the y-intercept is $(0, \ -1)$. Using this information, we can graph this line.

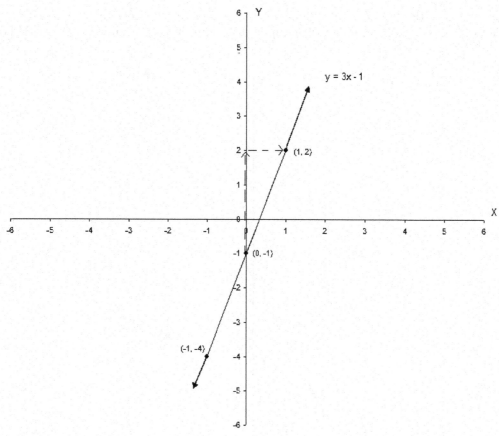

2) $y = -2x + 2$

The equation is in the form $y = mx + b$. We can see that the slope is $m = -2 = \dfrac{-2}{+1} = \dfrac{\Delta y}{\Delta x}$ and the y-intercept is $(0, 2)$. The graph is given below.

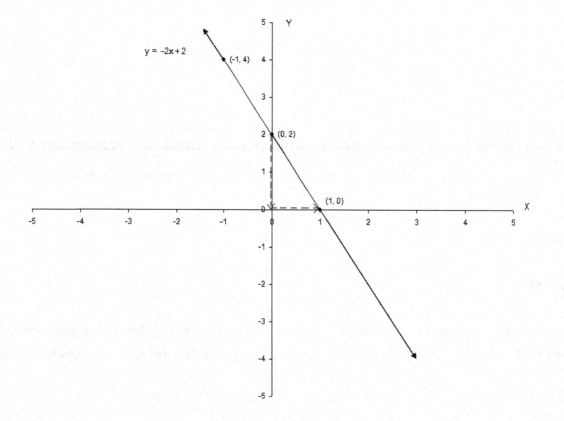

3) $y = 4$

This equation is in the form $y = b$. Such an equation has a graph which is a horizontal line whose y-intercept is $(0, b)$. Recall that every horizontal line has zero slope.

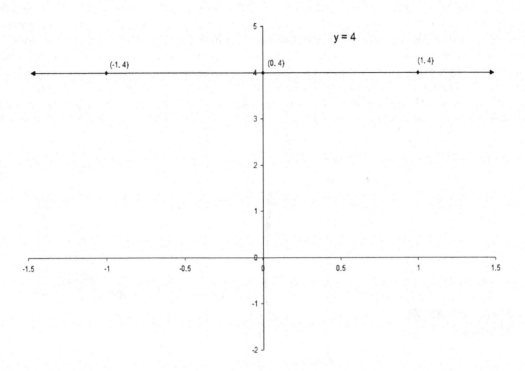

4) $x = -2$

This equation is in the form $x = a$. This type of equation has a graph which is a vertical line whose x-intercept is $(a, 0)$. Every vertical line has no slope.

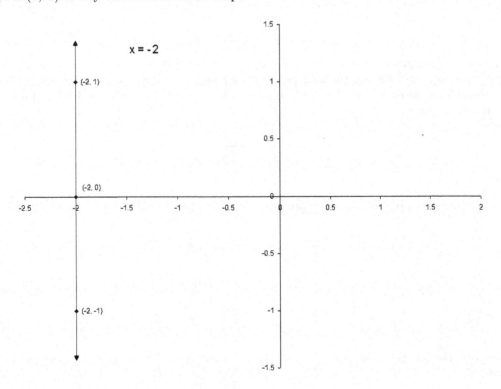

Graphs of Circles

Definition: A **circle** is a collection of points, all of whose distance from a fixed point (called the **center**) is constant.

The circle in the figure below, whose center is O, has the property that the distance from the center to any point on the circle is two inches. Recall that any line segment connecting the center to a point on the circle is called a **radius**. We say that the **radius of the circle** is 2 inches. Hence, the term 'radius' means either any line segment connecting the center of a circle to a point on the circle or the length of any such line segment. Any line segment connecting two points on a circle and going through the center is called a **diameter**, which is just two radii joined together to form a line segment. This means that the length of a diameter is twice the length of the radius. The length of any diameter of a circle is called the **diameter of the circle** (which is 4 inches in the figure below).

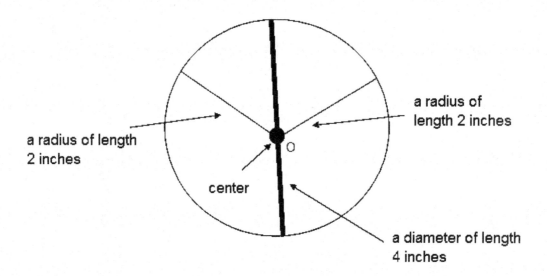

Now let's look at the graph of a circle in the Cartesian Plane. Let the center of a circle be (h, k) and let the radius be r (see the figure on the next page). If we choose any point on the circle and call it (x, y), then the distance from the center, (h, k), to the point on the circle, (x, y), will equal the radius, r. By the Distance Formula, we have

$$\sqrt{(x - h)^2 + (y - k)^2} = r.$$

After squaring each side of the equation, we will obtain

$$\boxed{(x - h)^2 + (y - k)^2 = r^2.}$$

This is an equation of the circle with center (h, k) and radius r and it is called the **standard form** for the equation.

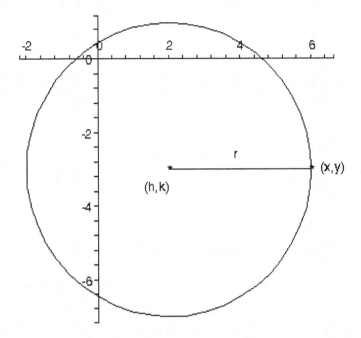

Examples. Find an equation of the circle whose center is C and radius is r. Graph the circle.

1) $C = (1, 3)$ and $r = 2$

We are given $(h, k) = (1, 3)$ and $r = 2$. After replacing h, k, and r in the equation $(x - h)^2 + (y - k)^2 = r^2$ by the given values, we'll obtain

$$(x - 1)^2 + (y - 3)^2 = 2^2 \text{ or}$$
$$(x - 1)^2 + (y - 3)^2 = 4.$$

To graph this circle, we need to first plot the center and then use the radius to locate at least three points (since three points determine a unique circle). In fact, we can easily obtain four points, by going up, down, left, and right by 2 units from the center (see the figure below).

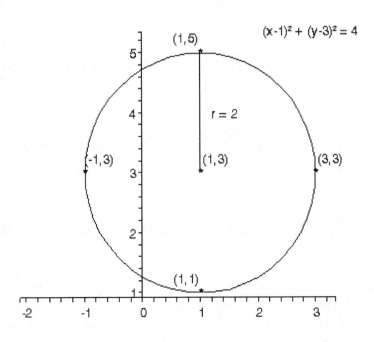

2) $C = (-2, 4)$ and $r = 4$

We are given $(h, k) = (-2, 4)$ and $r = 4$. After replacing h, k, and r in the equation $(x - h)^2 + (y - k)^2 = r^2$ by the given values, we'll obtain

$$(x - (-2))^2 + (y - 4)^2 = 4^2 \quad \text{or}$$
$$(x + 2)^2 + (y - 4)^2 = 16.$$

To graph this circle, we can find four points by going up, down, left, and right by 4 units from the center (see the figure below).

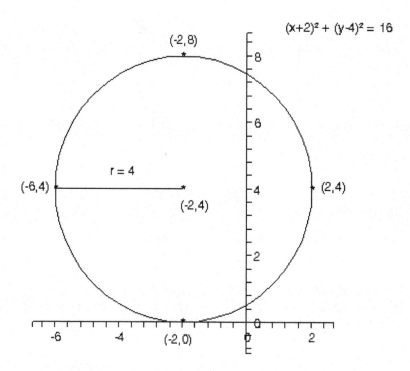

3) $C = (0, 0)$ and $r = 1$

We are given $(h, k) = (0, 0)$ and $r = 1$. The equation is

$$(x - 0)^2 + (y - 0)^2 = 1^2 \quad \text{or}$$
$$x^2 + y^2 = 1.$$

The graph is given on the next page. It is the circle whose center is $(0, 0)$ and whose radius is 1. This is called the **unit circle**. In general, a circle whose center is the origin and radius is r has the equation $x^2 + y^2 = r^2$. Circles whose center is the origin are very important to the study of trigonometry.

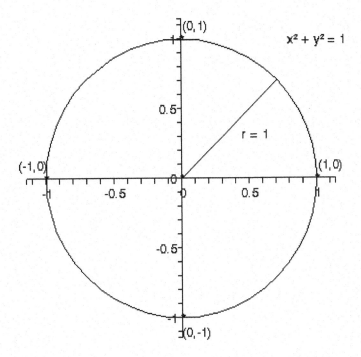

Example. Find the center and radius of the circle whose equation is $(x - 4)^2 + (y + 2)^2 = 25$.

We will compare the equation to $(x - h)^2 + (y - k)^2 = r^2$.

$$(x - h)^2 + (y - k)^2 = r^2 \text{ compared to}$$
$$(x - 4)^2 + (y + 2)^2 = 25$$

gives us $h = 4$, $k = -2$ (notice that $(y + 2)^2 = (y - (-2))^2$, and so $k = -2$) and $r^2 = 25$ (which means that $r = \sqrt{25} = 5$). Therefore, the center is $(4, -2)$, and the radius is 5.

By taking the equation of a circle in standard form and simplifying it, we obtain another form for the equation (after grouping some terms). To demonstrate it, let's write the equation $(x + 2)^2 + (y - 4)^2 = 16$ in a more simplified way. First, we will need to eliminate the parentheses by using the FOIL Method. Afterwards, we will commute some terms in order to 'group' the terms of common degrees. Here's how it looks:

$$(x + 2)^2 + (y - 4)^2 = 16$$
$$x^2 + 4x + 4 + y^2 - 8y + 16 = 16 \qquad \text{by FOIL}$$
$$x^2 + 4x + y^2 - 8y + 20 = 16 \qquad \text{by combining 4 and 16}$$
$$x^2 + y^2 + 4x - 8y + 20 = 16 \qquad \text{by grouping terms of the same degree}$$
$$x^2 + y^2 + 4x - 8y + 4 = 0 \qquad \text{by subtracting 16 from both sides}$$

Notice that the right-hand-side of the equation is 0, whereas the left-hand-side is 'descending alphabetically'. When an equation of a circle is written in this way, we say that it is in **general form**. In general, we have the following:

Any equation of a circle can be written in the form $x^2 + y^2 + Ax + By + C = 0$.

This is the **general form** for the equation of a circle.

Examples. Find the center and radius of the circle whose equation is given.

1) $x^2 + y^2 + 10x - 14y + 10 = 0$

The first thing we need to do is to write this equation in standard form. We begin by grouping the x terms and the y terms as well as carry over the constant term to the other side. Afterwards, we will **complete the square** of each group (consult with an algebra text if you don't remember how this works). This will give us the standard form. Once the equation is in this form, we can find the center and radius of the circle.

$$x^2 + y^2 + 10x - 14y + 10 = 0$$
$$\underline{ -10 \quad -10}$$
$$x^2 + y^2 + 10x - 14y = -10$$
$$x^2 + 10x + \underline{?} + y^2 - 14y + \underline{?} = -10 + \underline{?} + \underline{?}$$

$$\underbrace{x^2 + 10x + \underline{25}}_{(x+5)^2} + \underbrace{y^2 - 14y + \underline{49}}_{(y-7)^2} = -10 + \underline{25} + \underline{49}$$
$$(x+5)^2 \quad + \quad (y-7)^2 = 64$$

Now we have the standard form. By comparison, we'll get

$$(x-h)^2 + (y-k)^2 = r^2 \text{ compared to}$$
$$(x+5)^2 + (y-7)^2 = 64.$$

And so $h = -5$, $k = 7$, and $r^2 = 64$ (so $r = 8$). The circle has center $(-5, 7)$ and radius 8.

2) $x^2 + y^2 - 3x - 4 = 0$

Notice that there is no y term in the equation. This means that we don't have to complete the square of the y group (it is already completed).

$$x^2 + y^2 - 3x - 4 = 0$$
$$\underline{ +4 \quad +4}$$
$$x^2 + y^2 - 3x = 4$$
$$x^2 - 3x + \underline{?} + y^2 = 4 + \underline{?}$$

$$\underbrace{x^2 - 3x + \frac{9}{4}}_{} + y^2 = 4 + \frac{9}{4}$$

$$\left(x - \frac{3}{2}\right)^2 + y^2 = \frac{25}{4}$$

Now we have the standard form. By comparison, we'll get

$$(x-h)^2 + (y-k)^2 = r^2 \text{ compared to}$$
$$\left(x - \frac{3}{2}\right)^2 + y^2 = \frac{25}{4}.$$

So $h = \frac{3}{2}$, $k = 0$, and $r^2 = \frac{25}{4}$, giving us $r = \frac{5}{2}$. The circle has center $\left(\frac{3}{2}, 0\right)$ and radius $\frac{5}{2}$.

3) $5x^2 + 5y^2 - 10x + 2y = 0$

This equation is **not** in general form. Notice that the first two terms have coefficient 5, whereas the general form requires coefficient 1. The first thing we need to do is to divide both sides of the equation by 5.

Only then we can proceed with the method we've been using. Also, notice that the constant term is 0, which is nothing to worry about.

$$\frac{\cancel{5}x^2}{\cancel{5}} + \frac{\cancel{5}y^2}{\cancel{5}} - \frac{10x}{5} + \frac{2y}{5} = \frac{0}{5}$$

$$x^2 + y^2 - 2x + \frac{2}{5}y = 0$$

$$x^2 - 2x + \underline{?} + y^2 + \frac{2}{5}y + \underline{?} = 0 + \underline{?} + \underline{?}$$

$$\underbrace{x^2 - 2x + \underline{1}} + \underbrace{y^2 + \frac{2}{5}y + \frac{1}{25}} = 0 + \underline{1} + \frac{1}{25}$$

$$(x-1)^2 \quad + \quad \left(y + \frac{1}{5}\right)^2 = \frac{26}{25}$$

And we have the standard form. Comparing this to $(x-h)^2 + (y-k)^2 = r^2$, we obtain $h = 1$, $k = -\frac{1}{5}$, and $r^2 = \frac{26}{25}$, yielding $r = \sqrt{\frac{26}{25}} = \frac{\sqrt{26}}{5}$. The circle has center $\left(1, -\frac{1}{5}\right)$ and radius $\frac{\sqrt{26}}{5}$.

The Graphs of the Basic Equations

We will now review the graphs of the **basic equations**.

1) $y = x^2$

x	$x^2 = y$	Solutions
-2	$(-2)^2 = 4$	$(-2, 4)$
-1	$(-1)^2 = 1$	$(-1, 1)$
0	$(0)^2 = 0$	$(0, 0)$
1	$(1)^2 = 1$	$(1, 1)$
2	$(2)^2 = 4$	$(2, 4)$

This graph is called a **parabola**. Notice that the graph has a U-shape.

2) $y = x^3$

x	$x^3 = y$	Solutions
-2	$(-2)^3 = -8$	$(-2, -8)$
-1	$(-1)^3 = -1$	$(-1, -1)$
0	$(0)^3 = 0$	$(0, 0)$
1	$(1)^3 = 1$	$(1, 1)$
2	$(2)^3 = 8$	$(2, 8)$

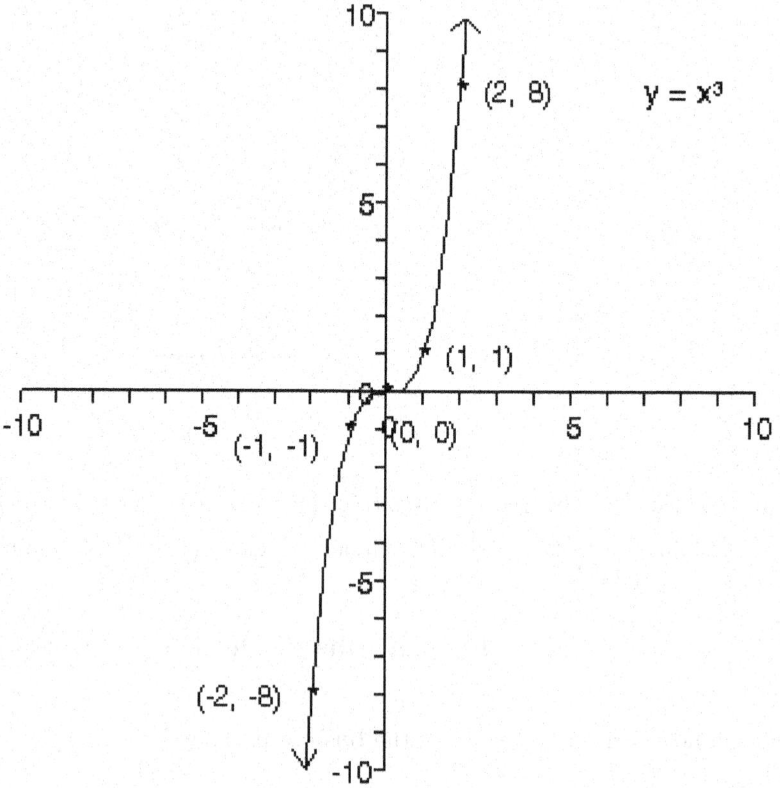

3) $y^2 = x$

Notice that $y^2 = x$, after taking the square root of each side, becomes $y = \pm\sqrt{x}$.

x	$\pm\sqrt{x} = y$	Solutions
0	$\pm\sqrt{0} = 0$	$(0, 0)$
1	$\pm\sqrt{1} = \pm 1$	$(1, -1)$ and $(1, 1)$
4	$\pm\sqrt{4} = \pm 2$	$(4, -2)$ and $(4, 2)$

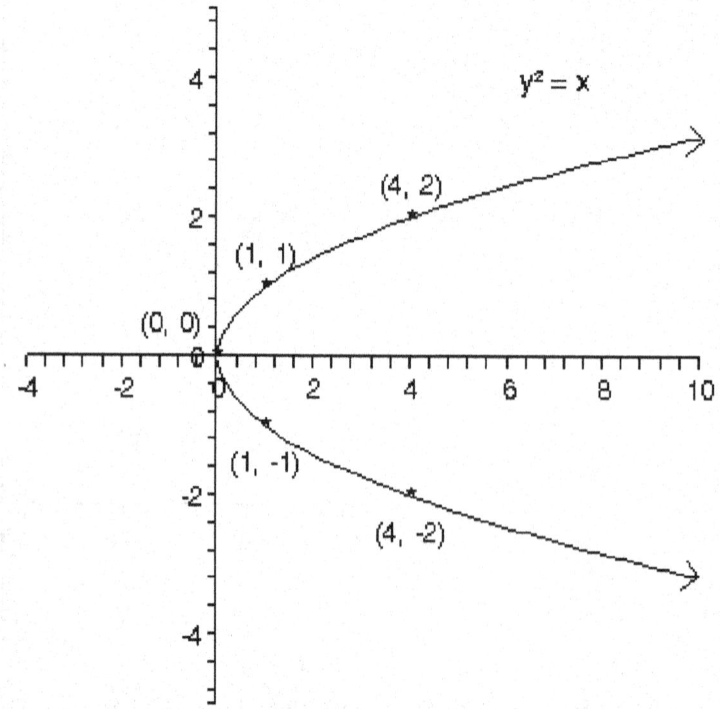

This graph is also called a **parabola**. Notice the U-shape.

4) $y = \sqrt{x}$

x	$\sqrt{x} = y$	Solutions
0	$\sqrt{0} = 0$	$(0, 0)$
1	$\sqrt{1} = 1$	$(1, 1)$
4	$\sqrt{4} = 2$	$(4, 2)$
9	$\sqrt{9} = 3$	$(9, 3)$

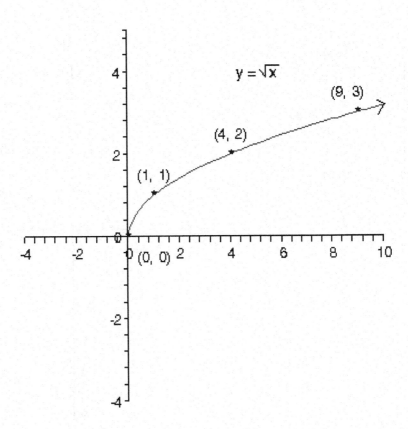

Observe that this graph is just the top piece of the graph of $y^2 = x$.

5) $y = |x|$

x	$|x| = y$	Solutions
-2	$|-2| = 2$	$(-2, 2)$
-1	$|-1| = 1$	$(-1, 1)$
0	$|0| = 0$	$(0, 0)$
1	$|1| = 1$	$(1, 1)$
2	$|2| = 2$	$(2, 2)$

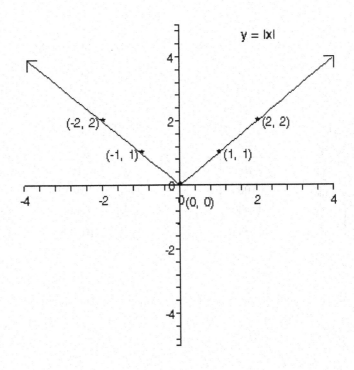

Notice that this graph has a V-shape.

6) $y = \dfrac{1}{x}$

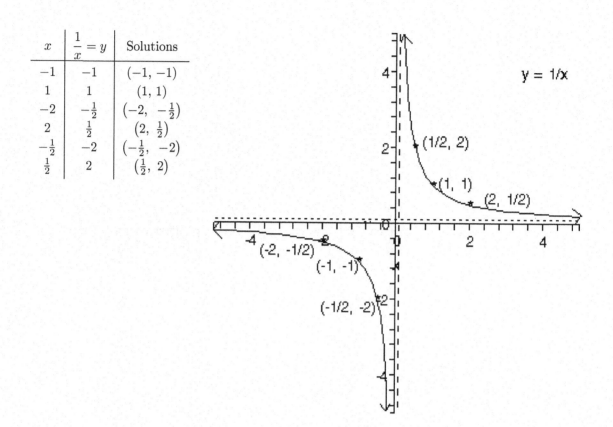

x	$\dfrac{1}{x} = y$	Solutions
-1	-1	$(-1, -1)$
1	1	$(1, 1)$
-2	$-\frac{1}{2}$	$(-2, -\frac{1}{2})$
2	$\frac{1}{2}$	$(2, \frac{1}{2})$
$-\frac{1}{2}$	-2	$(-\frac{1}{2}, -2)$
$\frac{1}{2}$	2	$(\frac{1}{2}, 2)$

We can't choose $x = 0$ since $\frac{1}{0}$ is undefined. Furthermore, there is no x-value for which $y = 0$.

Let's analyze this equation and its graph a little further. Below are some tables of values which tell us more about the equation $y = \dfrac{1}{x}$.

Table 1		Table 2		Table 3		Table 4	
x	y	x	y	x	y	x	y
10	$\frac{1}{10}$	-10	$-\frac{1}{10}$	$\frac{1}{10}$	10	$-\frac{1}{10}$	-10
100	$\frac{1}{100}$	-100	$-\frac{1}{100}$	$\frac{1}{100}$	100	$-\frac{1}{100}$	-100
$1,000$	$\frac{1}{1,000}$	$-1,000$	$-\frac{1}{1,000}$	$\frac{1}{1,000}$	$1,000$	$-\frac{1}{1,000}$	$-1,000$
$10,000$	$\frac{1}{10,000}$	$-10,000$	$-\frac{1}{10,000}$	$\frac{1}{10,000}$	$10,000$	$-\frac{1}{10,000}$	$-10,000$

Table 1 shows us that as the value of x gets larger positively, the values for $y = \frac{1}{x}$ get closer to 0. Symbolically, we write:

$$\text{As } x \to \infty, \; y = \frac{1}{x} \to 0.$$

Table 2 shows us that as the value of x gets larger negatively, the values for y again get closer to 0. Symbolically, we write:

$$\text{As } x \to -\infty, \, y = \frac{1}{x} \to 0.$$

Remember that y can never equal 0, but it will be very close to 0 for very large values of x (positive or negative). This behavior of the y-values as x gets large (positively or negatively) is seen on the graph as you go out to the right and out to the left on the graph.

Table 3 shows us that as the value of x gets closer to 0 from the positive (right-hand) side, the y-values get positively large. Symbolically, we write:

$$\text{As } x \to 0^+, \, y = \frac{1}{x} \to \infty.$$

The '+' symbol in '0^+' represents the fact that the values of x are on the right-hand side of 0 on the x-axis. On the graph of $y = \frac{1}{x}$, notice that the graph goes up as it gets closer to the y-axis on the right hand side.

Table 4 shows us that as the value of x gets closer to 0 from the negative (left-hand) side, the y-values get negatively large. Symbolically, we write:

$$\text{As } x \to 0^-, \, y = \frac{1}{x} \to -\infty.$$

The '−' symbol in '0^-' represents the fact that the values of x are on the left-hand side of 0 on the x-axis. On the graph of $y = \frac{1}{x}$, notice that the graph goes down as it gets closer to the y-axis on the left hand side.

Exercise R.2

In Exercises 1-20, graph the line whose equation is given.

1. $y = 2x + 3$ 2. $y = 4x + 1$ 3. $y = \frac{1}{5}x - 2$ 4. $y = \frac{2}{3}x - 1$

5. $y = -\frac{3}{7}x + 2$ 6. $y = -\frac{5}{6}x + 7$ 7. $y = x - 6$ 8. $y = x + 8$

9. $y = -x + 7$ 10. $y = -x - 5$ 11. $2x + 5y - 5 = 0$ 12. $-3x + 4y + 6 = 0$

13. $x - 2y + 1 = 0$ 14. $6x - y + 12 = 0$ 15. $5x + 9y = 0$ 16. $3x - 7y = 0$

17. $x = 3$ 18. $x = -1$ 19. $y = -4$ 20. $y = 5$

In Exercises 21-28, write an equation of the circle whose center is (h, k) and radius is r.

21. $(h, k) = (4, 1)$; $r = 3$ 22. $(h, k) = (7, 2)$; $r = 1$ 23. $(h, k) = (6, -3)$; $r = 5$

24. $(h, k) = (-3, 4)$; $r = 6$ 25. $(h, k) = (0, 0)$; $r = 2$ 26. $(h, k) = (0, 0)$; $r = 7$

27. $(h, k) = (-9, -8)$; $r = 2\sqrt{7}$ 28. $(h, k) = (-5, -12)$; $r = 3\sqrt{3}$

In Exercises 29-40, find the center and radius of the circle whose equation is given.

29. $x^2 + y^2 = 49$

30. $x^2 + y^2 = 36$

31. $4x^2 + 4y^2 = 16$

32. $3x^2 + 3y^2 = 27$

33. $(x - 6)^2 + (y - 5)^2 = 64$

34. $(x - 3)^2 + (y - 9)^2 = 4$

35. $(x + 8)^2 + y^2 = 9$

36. $x^2 + (y - 1)^2 = 100$

37. $x^2 + y^2 - 6x + 2y - 6 = 0$

38. $x^2 + y^2 - 4x + 4y - 1 = 0$

39. $x^2 + y^2 - 12x - 7 = 0$

40. $x^2 + y^2 - 16y - 5 = 0$

In Exercises 41-46, graph each of the given equations.

41. $y = x^2$

42. $y^2 = x$

43. $y = x^3$

44. $y = |x|$

45. $y = \sqrt{x}$

46. $y = \dfrac{1}{x}$

In Exercises 47-64, determine whether or not the given point is on the graph of the given equation.

47. $(4,\ 5)$; $y = 3x - 7$

48. $(2,\ 3)$; $y = 2x - 1$

49. $(0,\ -6)$; $y = x - 6$

50. $(-3,\ 8)$; $y = -4x - 4$

51. $(5,\ 3)$; $y = -\dfrac{3}{5}x + 2$

52. $(2,\ -5)$; $y = \dfrac{1}{4}x + 7$

53. $(5,\ 9)$; $y = x^2 - 16$

54. $(0, -2)$; $y = 2 - x^2$

55. $(64, -8)$; $y = \sqrt{x}$

56. $(-3,\ 3)$; $y = |x|$

57. $(4,\ 0)$; $y = \sqrt{x} - 2$

58. $(-1,\ 4)$; $y^2 = x^3 - 12$

59. $(-0.5,\ -2)$; $y = \dfrac{1}{x}$

60. $(3, 0.\overline{3})$; $y = \dfrac{1}{x}$

61. $(2.17,\ 13.7089)$; $y = x^2 + 9$

62. $(-1.6,\ 12.57)$; $y = 4x^2 + 3$

63. $(7.2,\ 363)$; $y = x^3 - 10.248$

64. $(5.03,\ 5.51)$; $y^2 = x^2 + 5.01$

Section R.3 Finding Intercepts and Checking for Symmetry

In this section, we will review the method of finding intercepts for the graph of an equation. We will also recall how to determine whether or not the graph of an equation has x-axis, y-axis, or origin symmetry.

I) Finding Intercepts

Definition 1: An **x-intercept** of a graph is a point where the graph crosses the x-axis. An x-intercept is of the form $(a,\ 0)$, where a is a real number.

Definition 2: A **y-intercept** of a graph is a point where the graph crosses the y-axis. A y-intercept is of the form $(0,\ b)$, where b is a real number.

The figure on the next page has three intercepts. The point $(0,\ 3)$ is a y-intercept and the points $(-1,\ 0)$, $(1,\ 0)$, and $(3.2,\ 0)$ are x-intercepts.

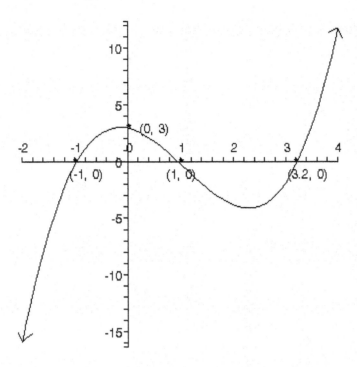

We can find the intercept(s) for the graph of an equation as follows:

> To find the y-intercept, we set $x = 0$ and solve for y.
>
> To find the x-intercept, we set $y = 0$ and solve for x.

Examples: Find the intercept(s) for the graph of each equation.

1) $y = x^2 - 4$

First, let's find the y-intercept(s) by setting $x = 0$ and solving for y :

$$y = (0)^2 - 4$$
$$y = -4$$

The y-intercept is $(0, -4)$. Now, let's find the x-intercept(s) by setting $y = 0$ and solving for x :

$$0 = x^2 - 4$$
$$\underline{+4 \qquad\quad +4}$$
$$4 = x^2$$
$$\pm\sqrt{4} = \sqrt{x^2}$$
$$\pm 2 = x$$

There are two x-intercepts, $(-2,\ 0)$ and $(2,\ 0)$. The graph of this equation is given below.

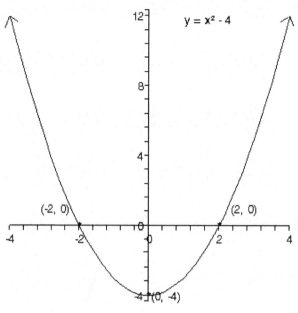

2) $y = x^3 + 3x^2$

To find the y-intercept(s), we set $x = 0$ and solve for y :

$$y = (0)^3 + 3(0)^2$$
$$y = 0$$

The y-intercept is $(0,\ 0)$. Notice that $(0,\ 0)$ is also an x-intercept. Let's see if there are any other x-intercepts. To find the x-intercept(s), we set $y = 0$ and solve for x :

$$0 = x^3 + 3x^2$$
$$0 = x^2(x + 3)$$

$$x^2 = 0 \quad \bigg| \quad x + \cancel{3} = 0$$
$$x = 0 \quad \bigg| \quad \cancel{3} \ \ -3$$
$$ \quad \bigg| \quad x = -3$$

The x-intercepts are $(0,\ 0)$ and $(-3,\ 0)$. The graph of this equation is given below.

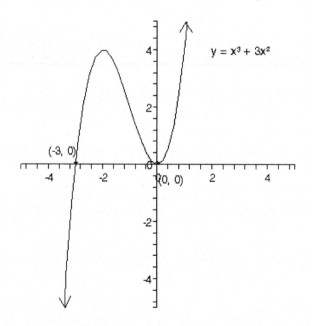

3) $y = \dfrac{2x - 12}{3 - x}$

To find the y-intercept(s), we set $x = 0$ and solve for y :

$$y = \frac{2\,(0) - 12}{3 - (0)}$$

$$y = \frac{-12}{3} = -4$$

The y-intercept is $(0, \, -4)$. To find the x-intercept(s), we set $y = 0$ and solve for x :

$$0 = \frac{2x - 12}{3 - x}$$

To solve this equation, we will use the following property:

> **Property:** If $\dfrac{a}{b} = 0$ and $\dfrac{a}{b}$ is a simplified fraction, then $a = 0$.

Since $\dfrac{2x - 12}{3 - x} = \dfrac{2\,(x - 6)}{3 - x}$ is simplified, we can apply the property and obtain:

$$
\begin{array}{r}
0 = 2x - 12 \\
\underline{+12 \qquad +12} \\
\dfrac{12}{2} = \dfrac{\cancel{2}x}{\cancel{2}} \\
6 = x
\end{array}
$$

The x-intercept is $(6, \, 0)$.

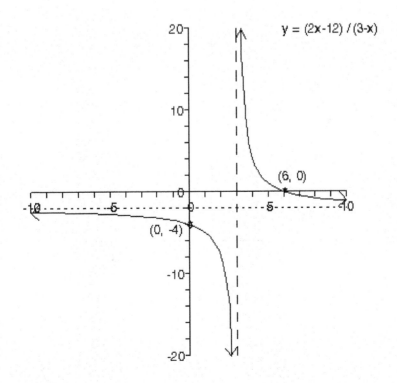

II) Symmetry

There are different types of symmetries which a graph may have. We will focus our attention on y-axis symmetry, x-axis symmetry, and origin symmetry.

1) y-Axis Symmetry

Definition: The graph of an equation has **y-axis symmetry** if the point $(-x, y)$ is on the graph whenever the point (x, y) is on the graph. We say that the graph is **symmetric about the y-axis**.

Examples. The following graphs have y-axis symmetry:

1)

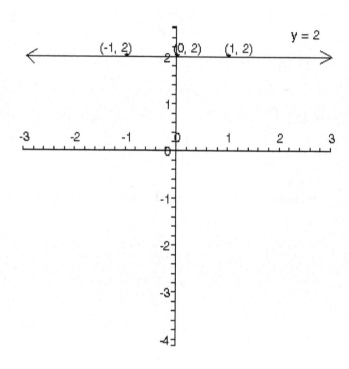

2)

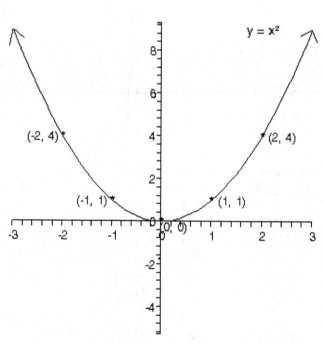

3)

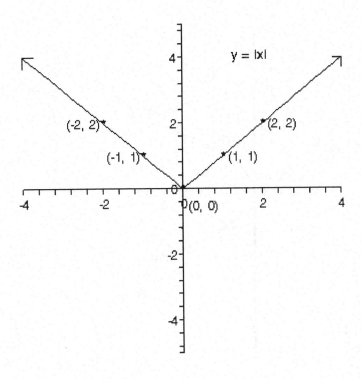

2) *x*-Axis Symmetry

Definition: The graph of an equation has *x*-**axis symmetry** if the point $(x, -y)$ is on the graph whenever the point (x, y) is on the graph. We say that the graph is **symmetric about the *x*-axis**.

Examples. The following graphs have *x*-axis symmetry:

1)

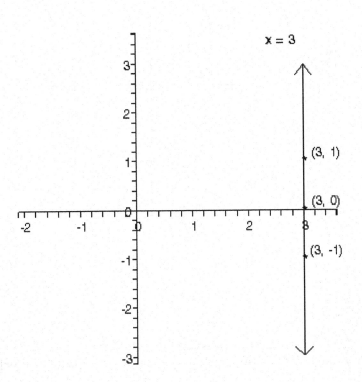

2)

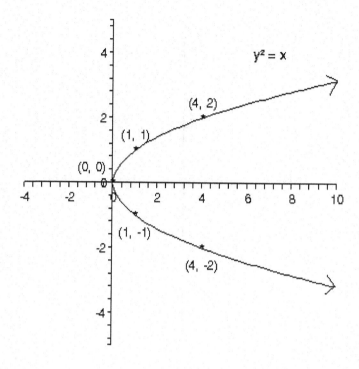

3)

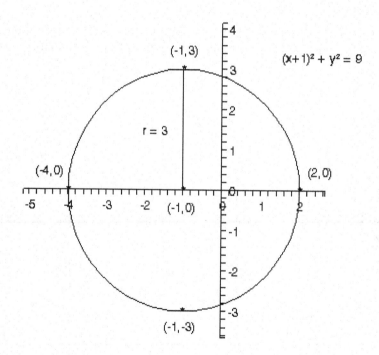

3) __Origin Symmetry__

Definition: The graph of an equation has **origin symmetry** if the point $(-x, -y)$ is on the graph whenever the point (x, y) is on the graph. We say that the graph is **symmetric about the origin**.

Examples. The following graphs have origin symmetry:

1)

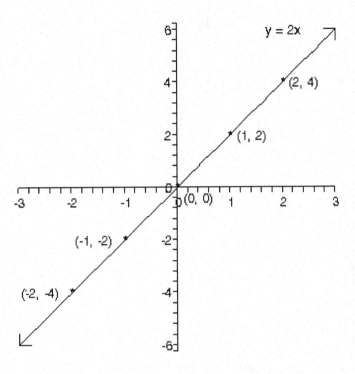

2)

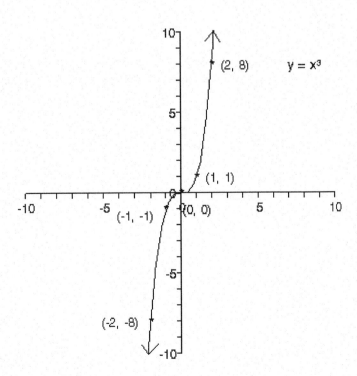

3)

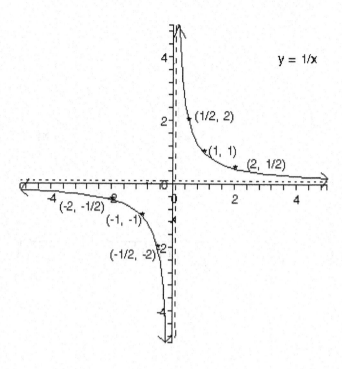

Checking for Symmetry

We now know about three different types of symmetries. By examining an equation, we can determine whether or not its graph has one or more of these symmetries. Let's learn how to do this.

Suppose we are given an equation.

1) To check for y-axis symmetry, we replace the variable x in our equation by $-x$. If the new equation we get can be algebraically manipulated to become the original equation, then its graph is symmetric about the y-axis.

2) To check for x-axis symmetry, we replace the variable y in our equation by $-y$. If the new equation we get can be algebraically manipulated to become the original equation, then its graph is symmetric about the x-axis.

3) To check for origin symmetry, we replace both x by $-x$ and y by $-y$ in our equation. If the new equation we get can be algebraically manipulated to become the original equation, then its graph is symmetric about the origin.

Examples. Check each for y-axis, x-axis, and/or origin symmetry.

1) $y = x^2$

We already know that the graph of $y = x^2$ has y-axis symmetry. Let's now verify this algebraically.

– For *y*-axis symmetry: Replace $x \rightsquigarrow -x$.

$$y = (-x)^2 \quad \text{(the new equation)} \quad \text{becomes}$$
$$y = x^2 \qquad \text{(the original equation)}.$$

Therefore, the graph has *y*-axis symmetry (as we know).

– For *x*-axis symmetry: Replace $y \rightsquigarrow -y$.

$$-y = x^2 \qquad \text{(the new equation)} \quad \text{can be written as}$$
$$y = -x^2 \qquad \text{(NOT the original equation)}.$$

– For origin symmetry: Replace $x \rightsquigarrow -x$ and $y \rightsquigarrow -y$.

$$-y = (-x)^2 \qquad \text{(the new equation)} \quad \text{can be written as}$$
$$-y = x^2 \qquad \text{(NOT the original equation)}.$$

2) $y = x^3$

We already know that the graph of $y = x^3$ has origin symmetry. Let's verify this algebraically.

– For *y*-axis symmetry: Replace $x \rightsquigarrow -x$.

$$y = (-x)^3 \qquad \text{(the new equation)} \quad \text{becomes}$$
$$y = -x^3 \qquad \text{(NOT the original equation)} \quad \text{or}$$
$$-y = x^3 \qquad \text{(NOT the original equation)}.$$

– For *x*-axis symmetry: Replace $y \rightsquigarrow -y$.

$$-y = x^3 \qquad \text{(the new equation)} \quad \text{can be written as}$$
$$y = -x^3 \qquad \text{(NOT the original equation)}.$$

– For origin symmetry: Replace $x \rightsquigarrow -x$ and $y \rightsquigarrow -y$.

$$-y = (-x)^3 \qquad \text{(the new equation)} \quad \text{can be written as}$$
$$-y = -x^3$$
$$-1(-y) = -1(-x^3)$$
$$y = x^3 \qquad \text{(the original equation)}.$$

Therefore, the new equation can be written as the original one. The graph has origin symmetry (as we know).

3) $5x - 3y^2 = 7$

- <u>For y-axis symmetry:</u>   Replace $x \rightsquigarrow -x$.

$$
\begin{aligned}
5\left(-x\right) - 3y^2 &= 7 && \text{(the new equation)} \quad \text{becomes} \\
-5x - 3y^2 &= 7 && \text{(NOT the original equation)} \quad \text{or} \\
5x + 3y^2 &= -7 && \text{(NOT the original equation)}.
\end{aligned}
$$

The graph does not have y-axis symmetry.

- <u>For x-axis symmetry:</u>   Replace $y \rightsquigarrow -y$.

$$
\begin{aligned}
5x - 3\left(-y\right)^2 &= 7 && \text{(the new equation)} \quad \text{becomes} \\
5x - 3y^2 &= 7 && \text{(the original equation)}.
\end{aligned}
$$

The graph has x-axis symmetry.

Since the graph has x-axis symmetry but not y-axis symmetry, it cannot have origin symmetry (check this for yourself).

4) $x^2 + y^2 = 4$

Notice that this is the equation of the circle of radius 2 centered at the origin. Any circle with a center at the origin has x-axis, y-axis, and origin symmetry. Let's verify this algebraically for the given equation.

- <u>For y-axis symmetry:</u>   Replace $x \rightsquigarrow -x$.

$$
\begin{aligned}
\left(-x\right)^2 + y^2 &= 4 && \text{(the new equation)} \quad \text{becomes} \\
x^2 + y^2 &= 4 && \text{(the original equation)}.
\end{aligned}
$$

The graph has y-axis symmetry.

- <u>For x-axis symmetry:</u>   Replace $y \rightsquigarrow -y$.

$$
\begin{aligned}
x^2 + \left(-y\right)^2 &= 4 && \text{(the new equation)} \quad \text{becomes} \\
x^2 + y^2 &= 4 && \text{(the original equation)}.
\end{aligned}
$$

The graph has x-axis symmetry.

- <u>For origin symmetry:</u>   Replace $x \rightsquigarrow -x$ and $y \rightsquigarrow -y$.

$$
\begin{aligned}
\left(-x\right)^2 + \left(-y\right)^2 &= 4 && \text{(the new equation)} \quad \text{can be written as} \\
x^2 + y^2 &= 4 && \text{(the original equation)}.
\end{aligned}
$$

Therefore, the graph has origin symmetry.

Exercise R.3

In Exercises 1-8, the graph of an equation is given.
  a) What is (are) the intercept(s) for the graph?
  b) Does the graph have *x*-axis symmetry, *y*-axis symmetry, origin symmetry, or none of these?

1.

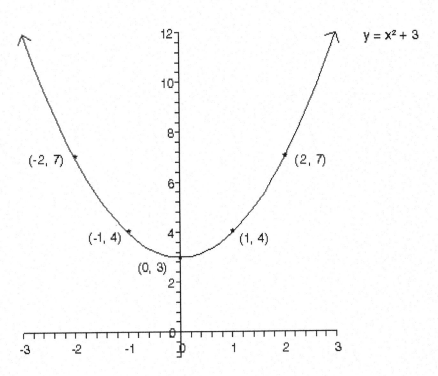

2.

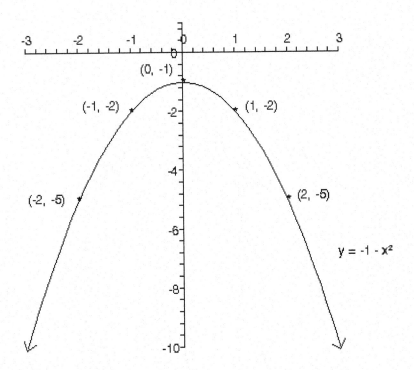

3.

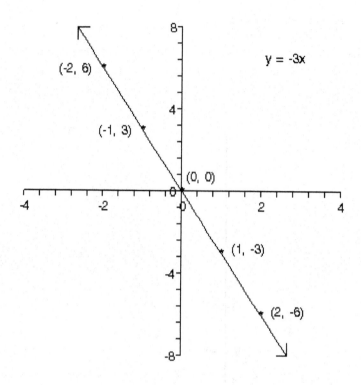

4.

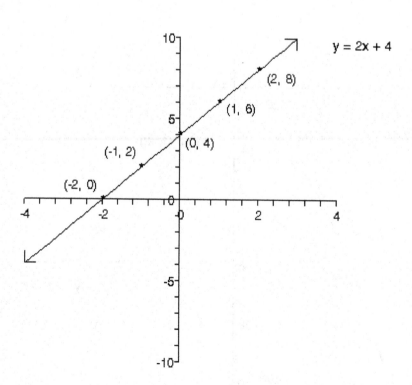

5.

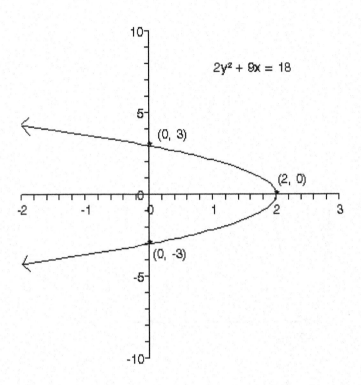

6.

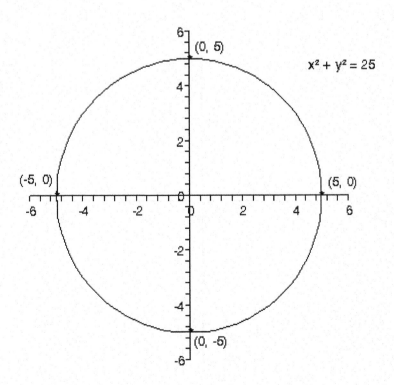

7.

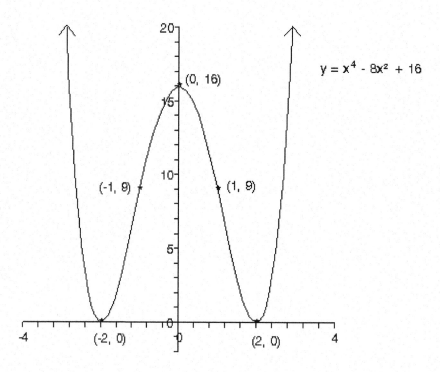

$y = x^4 - 8x^2 + 16$

(0, 16)

(-1, 9)   (1, 9)

(-2, 0)   (2, 0)

-4   0   4

8.

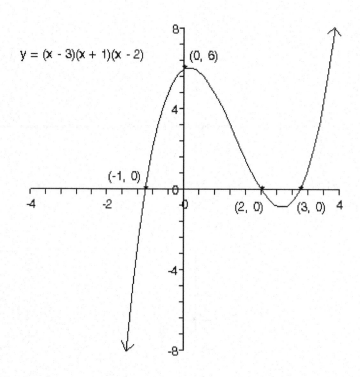

$y = (x - 3)(x + 1)(x - 2)$

(0, 6)

(-1, 0)

(2, 0)   (3, 0)

-4   -2   0   4

In Exercises 9-40, an equation is given.
   a) What is (are) the intercept(s) for the graph of the equation?
   b) Does the graph of the equation have x-axis symmetry, y-axis symmetry, origin
      symmetry, or none of these?

9. $y = 3x$ 10. $y = 7x$ 11. $y = 6x + 18$ 12. $y = -5x + 2$

13. $y = x^2 - 16$ 14. $y = x^2 - 9$ 15. $y = 2x^2 + 8$ 16. $y = 5x^2 + 25$

17. $y^2 = x - 5$ 18. $y^2 = x + 1$ 19. $x^2 + y^2 = 25$ 20. $x^2 + y^2 = 64$

21. $x^2 - 3xy + 4y^2 = 25$ 22. $x^2 + 2xy - 16y^2 = 9$ 23. $y = \dfrac{x + 8}{x - 2}$

24. $y = \dfrac{x - 9}{x - 3}$ 25. $y = \dfrac{6}{x^2 + 1}$ 26. $y = \dfrac{2}{x^2 - 1}$ 27. $y = \dfrac{x^2 - 81}{x^2 + 9}$

28. $y = \dfrac{x^2 - 64}{x^2 + 4}$ 29. $y = \dfrac{5x}{x^2 - 25}$ 30. $y = \dfrac{8x}{x^2 - 8}$ 31. $y = \sqrt{2x + 9}$

32. $y = \sqrt{5x + 4}$ 33. $y = |x + 5| - 6$ 34. $y = |x - 7| - 2$ 35. $y = |x| + 10$

36. $y = |x| + 3$ 37. $x^2 - 4y^2 = 16$ 38. $y^2 - 7x^2 = 25$ 39. $x^2y^2 + 3xy - 2 = 0$

40. $4xy - 5x^2y^2 + 11 = 0$

Section R.4   Functions

   In this section, we will review functions. We will recall how functions relate to equations in two variables and how to do computations with them. We will also review how to find the domain of a function and how to determine information about a function by looking at its graph in the Cartesian Plane.

Definition of a Function

   We begin with the definition of a function. If X is a non-empty set, then '$x \in X$' means that x is an element of X.

Definition: A **function** between two non-empty sets, X and Y, is a correspondence between the two sets in which each element of X corresponds to **exactly one** element of Y.

   We call X the **domain** of the function and the set of elements of Y which are corresponded to by elements of X the **range** (or the **image set**) of the function. If an element $x \in X$ corresponds to $y \in Y$, then we say that y is the **image** of x. The range of a function, therefore, is just the set of all images of elements of X.

   In general, the range of Y may be a subset of Y and not all of Y. In other words, not every element of Y may be the image of some element $x \in X$. If it is the case that the range of the function is the whole set Y (in other words, if every $y \in Y$ is the image of some $x \in X$), we say that the function is **onto**.

   A function between two sets is usually given a name to describe the correspondence. When an element, x, corresponds to an element, y, then we can write $x \to y$ or write a pair (x, y) to denote the correspondence. For example, consider the two sets $X = \{$John, Steve, Mike$\}$ and $Y = \{$fish, pizza, cereal$\}$. Suppose the correspondence between the two sets is named 'favorite food is'. Then

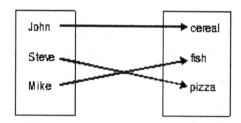

describes the function which says that John's favorite food is cereal, Steve's favorite food is pizza, and Mike's favorite food is fish. This is a function since each domain member (John, Steve, and Mike) corresponds to exactly one member of Y. The range of this function is {cereal, pizza, fish} since each of these elements is an image of a domain member. Notice that the arrow symbol '$\longrightarrow$' represents the phrase 'favorite food is'. If we write down this function as pairs, we'll obtain the set of pairs

$$\{(\text{John, cereal}), (\text{Steve, pizza}), (\text{Mike, fish})\}.$$

Not every correspondence between two non-empty sets is a function. For example, the element $2 \in X$ in the diagram below corresponds to two elements of Y, namely, a and c. Therefore, the correspondence is not a function.

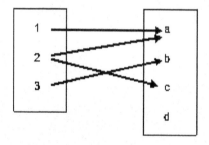

Let's look at another example, something more mathematical. Suppose that both X and Y are sets of all of the real numbers and let the correspondence between the two sets be 'multiplied by 2 equals'. Here are a few correspondences which follow from this correspondence:

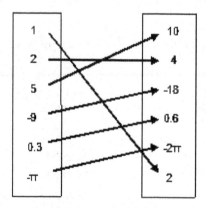

To get these correspondences, I've chosen some real numbers randomly (since X is the set containing all real numbers, I can do this) and I've found their corresponding value by multiplying each of them by 2. Notice that there are infinitely many correspondences between the elements, so I couldn't possibly write the full list obtained from this function. However, if you give me an element $x \in X$, I know that it will correspond to the element $y \in Y$ which satisfies $y = 2x$. In the midst of discussing this example, notice that the equation $y = 2x$ shows up. We see that correspondences between elements of sets are related to equations in two variables (one variable representing the domain elements, and the other representing the range elements).

Examples. Which of the correspondences are functions? State the domain and range of those which are functions.

1)

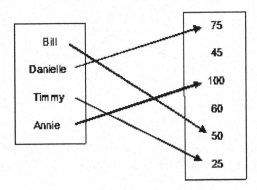

This is a function since each element on the left-hand side corresponds to exactly one element on the right-hand side. The domain is the set {Bill, Danielle, Timmy, Annie}, and the range is the set {50, 75, 25, 100}.

2)

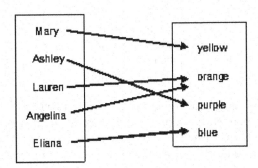

This is a function since each element on the left-hand side corresponds to exactly one element on the right-hand side. The domain is the set {Mary, Ashley, Lauren, Angelina, Eliana}, and the range is the set {yellow, purple, orange, blue}. Notice that both 'Lauren' and 'Angelina' correspond to the range member 'orange'. Two or more domain elements can certainly correspond to the same range element in a function. This function is onto, since every element in the set {yellow, purple, orange, blue} is an image of at least one element of the set {Mary, Ashley, Lauren, Angelina, Eliana}. Thus, every element of {yellow, purple, orange, blue} is in the range.

3)

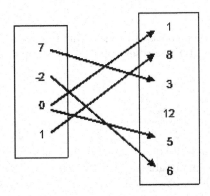

This is a not a function since the element '0' corresponds to two elements: '1' and '5'.

4)

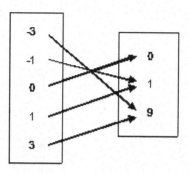

This is a function. The domain is the set $\{-3, -1, 0, 1, 3\}$, and the range is the set $\{9, 1, 0\}$. Notice that if we represent the domain elements by x and the range elements by y, then the equation $y = x^2$ describes the correspondence.

5) {(pizza, soda), (cereal, milk), (fish, water), (pasta, wine)}

Notice that this correspondence can be written as:

$$\text{pizza} \longrightarrow \text{soda}$$
$$\text{cereal} \longrightarrow \text{milk}$$
$$\text{fish} \longrightarrow \text{water}$$
$$\text{pasta} \longrightarrow \text{wine}$$

This is a function whose domain is {pizza, cereal, fish, pasta} and whose range is {soda, milk, water wine}. In order to verify that this correspondence is a function by looking at the given set of pairs, all that we need to do is to check that the first entries of the pairs appear exactly once in all of the pairs. If the first entry in a pair appears **more than once**, then the correspondence is **not** a function.

6) {(0, 3), (1, 2), (1, 4), (2, 6)}

This is not a function since '1' appears in two pairs, namely: (1, 2) and (1, 4). This means that '1' corresponds to both '2' and '4', which cannot occur for a function.

Functional Notations and Computations with Functions

A function whose domain and range consist of real numbers may be represented as an equation in two variables. For example, if both X and Y represent the set of all real numbers, then for any $x \in X$, the correspondence

$$\underbrace{x}_{\text{domain element}} \longrightarrow \underbrace{2x}_{\text{range element}} = y$$

is a function. Why is it a function? Well, if you take any real number (which we are representing by x), then multiplying it by 2 can only give us one possible answer (which we are representing by y). Hence, if X is the domain and Y is the range, then each $x \in X$ corresponds to EXACTLY ONE $y \in Y$. If we view the equation

$y = 2x$ as the correspondence which takes us from an x-value to a y-value, then this correspondence is a function. Let us put this in a more mathematical setting now:

The **domain** is a set of real numbers whose elements represent the x-**values**.
The **range** is a set of real numbers whose elements represent the y-**values**.
The **correspondence** between the domain and range is an **equation in x and y**.

Notice that the domain and range may not be the whole set of real numbers but just a subset. For example, for the function $y = 2x$, we could've defined the domain to be the set of real numbers $X = \{x \mid -4 \le x \le 6\}$. In this case, the range would be $Y = \{y \mid -8 \le y \le 12\}$ (why?). If we choose the domain to be $X = \{0,\ 8,\ 15\}$, then the range will be $Y = \{0,\ 16,\ 30\}$ (why?).

When we have an equation which describes a functional correspondence, a special notation is used. It is called the **functional notation** of the equation. A function is denoted by an alphabetical letter, like f or g or whatever you would like to name it. For example, the function $y = 2x$ can be given the name f by renaming the y variable as $f(x)$. By doing so, we obtain:

$$\underbrace{y = 2x}_{\text{equation in } x \text{ and } y} \qquad \Longrightarrow \qquad \underbrace{f(x) = 2x}_{\text{functional notation}}$$

We read '$f(x)$' as 'f of x' and call $f(x)$ the **value** of f at x. Notice that $f(x)$ is just another name for the y variable. The reason why we bother renaming the y variable is that we are stressing the fact that for each x-value in the domain, there corresponds **exactly one** y-value in the range. We write $y = f(x)$ to represent the fact that y equals a function of x and read it as 'y is a function of x'.

It is helpful to think of a function as a machine. In the figure below, the machine is named f. If you input a number from the domain into the machine, the function f computes the output according to its rule. The output is called $f(x)$. In this setting, we call x (the input variable) the **independent variable** and y (or $f(x)$, the output variable) the **dependent variable.**

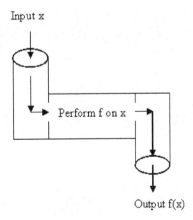

Input x

Perform f on x

Output f(x)

Let's look at some equations which are functions. We will rewrite each equation in functional notation and practice finding the values of a function.

Examples. The following equations are functions:

1) $y = -4x + 3$

This is a linear equation in x and y. Notice that for any real number we choose for x, there corresponds **exactly one** value for y. Hence, this linear equation is a function. We can, therefore, write

$$\underbrace{y = -4x + 3}_{\text{linear equation}} \Longrightarrow \underbrace{f(x) = -4x + 3}_{\text{linear function}}$$

and obtain a **linear function**. Once again, I have chosen the name of the function to be f. You can choose any name you'd like to. Let's practice doing computations with functions. Below, I've given a table with three columns. The first column contains some values for x which I have chosen at random. The second one is the linear equation, and the third one is the linear function. Keep an eye on how the answers are related for each column.

	$y = -4x + 3$	$f(x) = -4x + 3$
$x = 0$	$y = -4(0) + 3 = 3$	$f(0) = -4(0) + 3 = 3$
$x = 2$	$y = -4(2) + 3 = -5$	$f(2) = -4(2) + 3 = -5$
$x = -\frac{1}{4}$	$y = -4\left(-\frac{1}{4}\right) + 3 = 4$	$f\left(-\frac{1}{4}\right) = -4\left(-\frac{1}{4}\right) + 3 = 4$
$x = -6$	$y = -4(-6) + 3 = 27$	$f(-6) = -4(-6) + 3 = 27$

Notice how the y-value we've obtained for each of the chosen x-values is just equal to $f(x)$. For example, $f(0) = 3$ is the same as saying that when $x = 0$, $y = 3$, and $f\left(-\frac{1}{4}\right) = 4$ is the same as saying that when $x = -\frac{1}{4}$, $y = 4$.

2) $y = 7x^2 - 3x + 1$

This is a **quadratic equation** in x and y. Observe that for any real number we choose for x, there corresponds exactly one value for y. Hence, this is a function. We can, therefore, write

$$\underbrace{y = 7x^2 - 3x + 1}_{\text{quadratic equation}} \Longrightarrow \underbrace{q(x) = 7x^2 - 3x + 1}_{\text{quadratic function}}$$

and obtain a **quadratic function**. Let's practice the plugging numbers into this function. Let's compute $q(0)$, $q(-2)$, and $q(1)$. To begin with, I will put the parentheses around my x's in the function and write $q(x) = 7(x)^2 - 3(x) + 1$. This way, I won't make any mistakes with my signs when I put in the x-values. Now, I will plug the numbers into the function as we've done in the table in Example 1.

$$q(0) = 7(0)^2 - 3(0) + 1 = 1$$

$$q(-2) = 7(-2)^2 - 3(-2) + 1$$
$$= 28 + 6 + 1 = 35$$

$$q(1) = 7(1)^2 - 3(1) + 1$$
$$= 7 - 3 + 1 = 5$$

As you can see, computing the value of a function for a specified x-value is not so difficult.

3) $y = \dfrac{x + 6}{x^2 - 9}$

If $y = p(x)$ and $y = q(x)$ are two functions, then the quotient $y = \dfrac{p(x)}{q(x)}$ is also a function. In our example, both the numerator and the denominator are linear functions, making the quotient a function as well. We write

$$\underbrace{y = \frac{x + 6}{x^2 - 9}}_{\text{rational equation}} \implies \underbrace{r(x) = \frac{x + 6}{x^2 - 9}}_{\text{rational function}}$$

Let's compute $r(0)$, $r(-1)$, $r(2)$, and $r(-3)$. First, put the parentheses around the x's. Then plug in the numbers.

$$r(0) = \frac{(0) + 6}{(0)^2 - 9} = \frac{6}{-9} = -\frac{2}{3}$$

$$r(-1) = \frac{(-1) + 6}{(-1)^2 - 9} = \frac{5}{-8} = -\frac{5}{8}$$

$$r(2) = \frac{(2) + 6}{(2)^2 - 9} = \frac{8}{-5} = -\frac{8}{5}$$

$$r(-3) = \frac{(-3) + 6}{(-3)^2 - 9} = \frac{3}{0}, \text{ which is undefined.}$$

Now we have a problem! When we plug -3 into the function r, we get an undefined answer. This is not good since we need to obtain a real number for our answer. If we think of the function as a machine, then putting -3 into our machine will make the machine explode! What this tells us is that -3 cannot be in the domain of our function since it doesn't correspond to a real number. In the next section, we will learn how to find the domain of a function like this. When working with a function, it is important to know **what** numbers can be plugged into it. By the way, notice that 3 is also a bad number for this function, since

$$r(3) = \frac{(3) + 6}{(3)^2 - 9} = \frac{9}{0}, \text{ which is undefined.}$$

Thus, -3 and 3 are not in the domain of this function. These turn out to be the **only** two numbers which make the function undefined.

4) $y = \sqrt{5x - 10}$

If $y = f(x)$ is a function, then $y = \sqrt{f(x)}$ is also a function. Since $y = 5x - 10$ is a linear function, we can write

$$\underbrace{y = \sqrt{5x - 10}}_{\text{square root equation}} \implies \underbrace{s(x) = \sqrt{5x - 10}}_{\text{square root function}}$$

Let's compute $s(2)$, $s(7)$, $s(10)$, and $s(-2)$.

$$s(2) = \sqrt{5(2) - 10} = \sqrt{0} = 0$$

$$s(7) = \sqrt{5(7) - 10} = \sqrt{25} = 5$$

$$s(10) = \sqrt{5(10) - 10} = \sqrt{40} = 2\sqrt{10}$$

$$s(-2) = \sqrt{5(-2) - 10} = \sqrt{-20}, \text{ which is not a real number.}$$

Once again, we have a problem! When we plug -2 into the function s, we don't get a real number. Remember that the functions which we are concerned with have domain and range containing only real numbers. Therefore, if we put -2 into our machine, the machine will explode! This means that -2 cannot be in the domain of our function. In fact, if you plug any real number which is less than 2 into the function s, it will not yield a real number. Consequently, any real number less than 2 will not be in the domain.

Explicit and Implicit Functions

So far, we have seen that an equation in two variables is a function if for each x-value in the domain, there corresponds exactly one y-value in the range. Such an equation, as we have seen, is usually written in the form $y = \cdots$, where the right-hand side of the equation (the $\cdots$'s) is an expression with only the variable x in it. We call x (the domain variable) the **independent variable** and y (the range variable) the **dependent variable**. For example,

$$y = 4x + 1, \ y = x^2 + 8x, \ y = \frac{1}{x+3}, \text{ and } y = \sqrt{x-5}$$

are equations of the form $y =$ an expression in x only. Since the variable y is by itself on the left-hand side and no y's appear on the right-hand side, we say that y is an **explicit function** of x or that y defines x **explicitly**. Functions can also be written as equations where the y variable (the dependent variable) is **not** by itself, but mixed in with the x's (the independent variable). For example,

$$4x + 3y - 1 = 0, \ xy = 6, \ 5x^2 + 3y = 2, \text{ and } \sqrt{x+y+2} = 8$$

are equations with x's and y's mixed up together. However, in each equation, y is a function of x. To see this, we can solve each one for y explicitly (that is, solve for y by itself). For example, if we solve $4x + 3y - 1 = 0$ for y explicitly, we get:

$$4x + 3y - 1 = 0$$
$$\frac{-3y \qquad -3y}{\dfrac{4x-1}{-3} = \dfrac{-3y}{-3}}$$

$$-\frac{4}{3}x + \frac{1}{3} = y$$

$y = -\frac{4}{3}x + \frac{1}{3}$ is a linear equation (a linear function of x). Therefore, $4x + 3y - 1 = 0$ is a functional correspondence between the independent variable, x, and the dependent variable, y. If a function is written in such a way that the dependent variable (y, for example) is **not** by itself on one side of the equation, then we say that y is an **implicit function** of x or that y defines x **implicitly**. For example, for the equation $4x + 3y - 1 = 0$, we would say that y is an implicit function of x or that y defines x implicitly.

Examples. Is y an implicit function of x?

1) $xy = 6$

Let's solve for y and see if y is a function of x.

$$xy = 6$$
$$\frac{\not{x}y}{\not{x}} = \frac{6}{x}$$

Since y is a rational equation in x, it is a rational function of x. Therefore, y is an implicit function of x. In other words, y defines x implicitly in the equation $xy = 6$

2) $5x^2 + 3y = 2$

We'll solve for y and see if y is a function of x.

$$
\begin{array}{r}
5x^2 + 3y = 2 \\
\underline{-5x^2 \qquad\quad -5x^2} \\
3y = -5x^2 + 2
\end{array}
$$

$$\frac{3y}{3} = \frac{-5x^2}{3} + \frac{2}{3}$$

$$y = -\frac{5}{3}x^2 + \frac{2}{3}$$

Since y is a quadratic equation in x, it is a quadratic function of x. Therefore, y is an implicit function of x. In other words, y defines x implicitly in the equation $5x^2 + 3y = 2$.

3) $x^2 + (y-5)^2 = 9$

Solving for y, we obtain:

$$
\begin{array}{r}
x^2 + (y-5)^2 = 9 \\
\underline{-x^2 \qquad\qquad\quad -x^2} \\
(y-5)^2 = 9 - x^2
\end{array}
$$

$$\sqrt{(y-5)^2} = \pm\sqrt{9 - x^2}$$

$$
\begin{array}{r}
y - 5 = \pm\sqrt{9 - x^2} \\
\underline{+5 \qquad\qquad +5} \\
y = 5 \pm \sqrt{9 - x^2}
\end{array}
$$

Observe that if we replace x by any number between -3 and 3, there will be **two** y-values. For example, if $x = 0$, then

$$y = 5 \pm \sqrt{9 - (0)^2} = 5 \pm \sqrt{9} = 5 \pm 3 = 2 \text{ and } 8.$$

This means that y is not a function of x, so y does **not** define x implicitly in the equation $x^2 + (y-5)^2 = 9$.

Finding the Domain of a Function

We will review how to find the domain of a polynomial function, a rational function, and a square root function.

I. Polynomial Functions

A polynomial function is of the form $y = p(x)$, where $p(x)$ is a polynomial in x. The domain of p is the set of all real numbers. To see this, recall that a polynomial is just a sum of products of numbers and variables. Isn't it true that if you multiply real numbers and add real numbers, you are guaranteed to get a real number for an answer? For example, in the quadratic function $p(x) = 3x^2 - 5x + 2$, if you replace the variable x by **any** real number, say n, then you will obtain the value of $p(n)$ by working out each of the monomials $3(n)^2$ and $-5(n)$. You will then have to add up the numbers $3n^2$, $-5n$, and 2, which is definitely going to be a real number.

The domain of p is the set of all real numbers, written as $(-\infty, \infty)$ in interval notation.

Examples. The domain of each of the functions below is the set of all real numbers.

1) $f(x) = mx + b$, where m and b are real numbers.

2) $g(x) = ax^2 + bx + c$, where a, b, and c are real numbers.

3) $f(x) = 3x^4 - 2x^3 + 6x - 14$

4) $g(x) = -4x^5 + \frac{1}{3}x^3 - \frac{3}{8}x^3 - \sqrt{6}x + 2$

II. Rational Functions

A rational function is of the form $r(x) = \dfrac{p(x)}{q(x)}$, where p and q are polynomial functions polynomial in x.

The domain of r is $\{x \mid q(x) \neq 0\}$.

Examples. Find the domain of each function.

1) $r(x) = \dfrac{x + 5}{9x + 18}$

To find the domain of a rational function, you set the denominator equal to 0 and solve for x. Any solutions you get are bad values since they make the denominator equal 0. Hence, the domain is the set of all real numbers except the bad values. Following this routine, we have:

$$
\begin{aligned}
9x + 18 &= 0 \\
-18 \quad &-18 \\
\hline
\frac{9x}{9} &= \frac{-18}{9} \\
x &= -2
\end{aligned}
$$

So, $x = -2$ is a bad value for the function. This means that the domain of r is $\{x \mid x \neq -2\}$. Notice that I have **not** set $x + 5 = 0$ and solved. **It is only a zero denominator which makes a rational function undefined.**

2) $f(x) = \dfrac{3x^2 + x - 1}{x^2 - x - 42}$

We will first find the bad values.

$$
\begin{aligned}
x^2 - x - 42 &= 0 \\
(x + 6)(x - 7) &= 0 \\
x + 6 = 0 \quad &| \quad x - 7 = 0 \\
-6 \quad -6 \quad &| \quad +7 \quad +7 \\
\hline
x = -6 \quad &| \quad x = 7
\end{aligned}
$$

So, $x = -6$ and $x = 7$ are bad values for f. This means that the domain of f is $\{x \mid x \neq -6 \text{ and } x \neq 7\}$.

3) $g(x) = \dfrac{8x - 3}{x^2 + 9}$

Let's find the bad values:

$$\begin{aligned} x^2 + \cancel{9} &= 0 \\ \underline{-9 \quad -9} & \\ x^2 \qquad &= -9 \end{aligned}$$

And there are no real solutions. This means that $x^2 + 9 \neq 0$ for any real x-values. Therefore, the domain of g is the set of all real numbers.

III. Square Root Functions

A square root function is of the form $s(x) = \sqrt{f(x)}$, where $y = f(x)$ is a function of x. Recall that the only real numbers that we can take the square root of which give a real number are those which are either positive or 0. In other words, the numbers which can replace the variable x in s are those which make $f(x)$ either positive or 0.

$$\boxed{\text{The domain of } s \text{ is } \{x \mid f(x) \geq 0\}.}$$

Examples. Find the domain of each function.

1) $s(x) = \sqrt{8x - 32}$

Unlike the situation for rational functions, where we had to first find the bad values, we look for the good values right away. All we have to do is to set the radicand (the expression under the square root symbol) greater than or equal to 0 and solve for x. The solution set is the domain. By doing so, we get the following:

$$\begin{aligned} 8x - \cancel{32} &\geq 0 \\ \cancel{+32} \quad &+32 \\ \underline{\frac{\cancel{8}x}{\cancel{8}}} &\geq \frac{32}{8} \\ x &\geq 4 \end{aligned}$$

The domain of s is $\{x \mid x \geq 4\}$. In interval notation, we write $[4, \infty)$.

2) $f(x) = \sqrt{6 - 24x}$

The same method, a different function. Observe that the inequality symbol reverses (why?).

$$6 - 24x \geq 0$$
$$\frac{-6 \qquad\quad -6}{}$$
$$\frac{-24x}{-24} \leq \frac{-6}{-24}$$

$$x \leq \frac{1}{4}$$

The domain of f is $\left\{x \mid x \leq \frac{1}{4}\right\}$. In interval notation, we write $\left(-\infty, \frac{1}{4}\right]$.

Obtaining Information from the Graph of a Function

Several properties of a function can be obtained by looking at its graph. For example, suppose we are given the graph of an equation and we want to determine whether or not it is the graph of a function. To do this, we apply the **vertical line test**.

The Vertical Line Test

A set of points in the Cartesian Plane (that is, the xy plane) is the graph of y as a function of x if and only if no vertical line crosses through the graph more than once.

Examples. Determine whether or not the given graph is the graph of a function.

1)

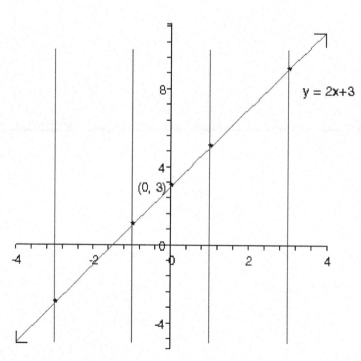

Observe that no vertical line will cross the graph more that once. Therefore, it is the graph of a function.

2)

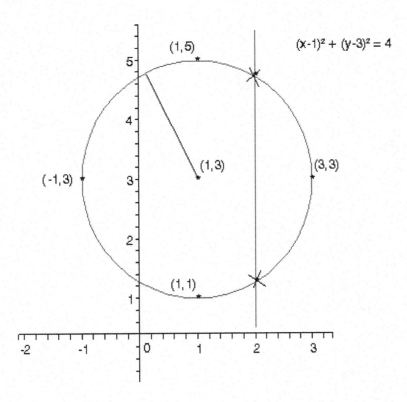

Notice that the vertical line crosses the graph at two points. Therefore, it is not the graph of a function.

3)

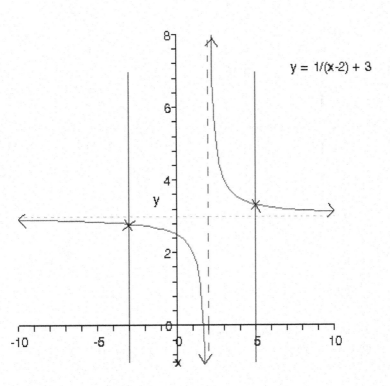

No vertical line will cross the graph more than once. Therefore, it is the graph of a function. Notice that the vertical line $x = 2$ doesn't cross the graph anywhere, which can certainly occur for the graph of a function. It just means that the number 2 is not in the domain of the function.

Let's answer some questions about a function by looking at its graph. In our first example below, the method for solving each problem will be provided.

Example. The graph of $y = f(x)$ is given below.

    1) Verify that the graph is the graph of a function.

    2) What is the domain of $y = f(x)$?

    3) What is the range of $y = f(x)$?

    4) Find the intercept(s) for the graph.

    5) Does the graph have x-axis symmetry, y-axis symmetry, origin symmetry, or none of these?

    6) Find $f(2)$.

    7) On which interval is $y = f(x)$ increasing? On which interval is $y = f(x)$ decreasing? On which interval is $y = f(x)$ constant?

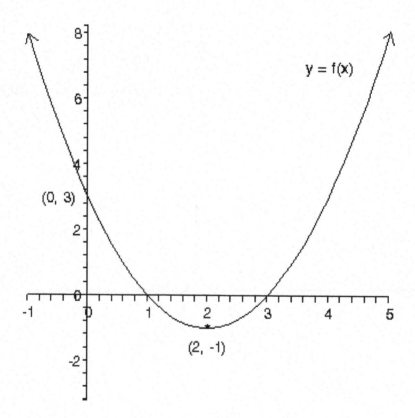

1) The graph passes the vertical line test since no vertical line crosses the graph more than once.

2) To find the domain of $y = f(x)$, you collapse the graph onto the x-axis (see the next figure). The interval which gets covered is the domain. Observe that the whole x-axis gets covered, so the domain of $y = f(x)$ is the set of all real numbers. We write this $\{x \mid -\infty < x < \infty\}$.

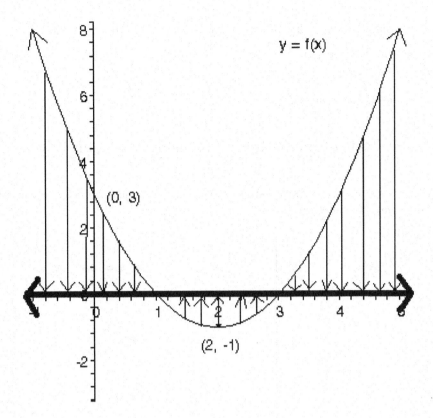

3) To find the range of $y = f(x)$, you collapse the graph onto the y-axis (see the next figure). The interval which gets covered is the range. Observe that all numbers greater than or equal to -1 get covered, so the range of $y = f(x)$ is the set $\{y \mid y \geq -1\}$.

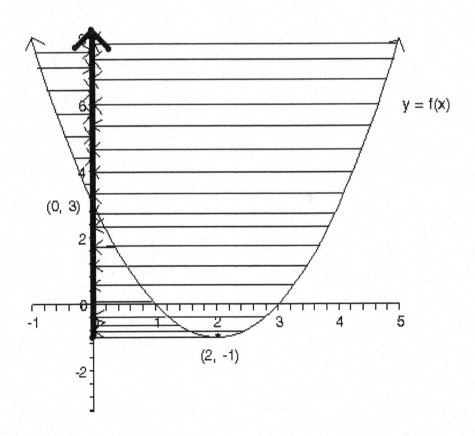

4) The y-intercept for the graph is $(0,\ 3)$, and the x-intercepts are $(1,\ 0)$ and $(3,\ 0)$.

5) The graph does not have x-axis, y-axis, or origin symmetry.

6) Since $(2,\ -1)$ is on the graph, we have that $f(2) = -1$.

7) To answer this, we need some definitions.

Intervals of Increasing, Decreasing, and Constant

Definition 1. A function $y = f(x)$ is **increasing** on an open interval $(a,\ b)$ if for any x_1 and x_2 in $(a,\ b)$ satisfying $x_1 < x_2$, we have $f(x_1) < f(x_2)$.

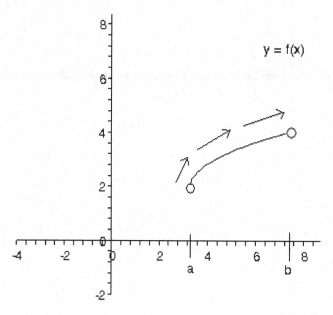

Notice that the graph of $y = f(x)$ **goes up** when you look at it from left (at $x = a$) to right (at $x = b$).

Definition 2. A function $y = f(x)$ is **decreasing** on an open interval $(a,\ b)$ if for any x_1 and x_2 in $(a,\ b)$ satisfying $x_1 < x_2$, we have $f(x_1) > f(x_2)$.

Notice that the graph of $y = f(x)$ **goes down** when you look at it from left (at $x = a$) to right (at $x = b$).

Definition 3. A function $y = f(x)$ is **constant** on an open interval (a, b) if for any x_1 and x_2 in (a, b), we have $f(x_1) = f(x_2)$.

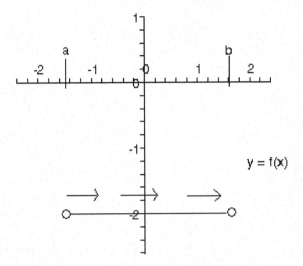

The graph of $y = f(x)$ **is a horizontal line (segment)** when you look at it from left (at $x = a$) to right (at $x = b$). All of the y-values of the points on this line (segment) are equal.

Getting back to our example, notice that the graph begins all the way out to the left (think of x as being $-\infty$) and is going downward until it reaches the point $(2, -1)$. This means that $y = f(x)$ is decreasing on $(-\infty, 2)$. Continuing to the right, the graph goes upward after $(2, -1)$ and does this all the out to the right (where x is like ∞). This means that $y = f(x)$ is increasing on $(2, \infty)$. If you have trouble with this, think of yourself as walking on the graph from left to right. You will walk downward, then turn at $(2, -1)$ and walk upward (see the next figure). There is no interval for which $y = f(x)$ is constant since there are no horizontal line segments in the graph.

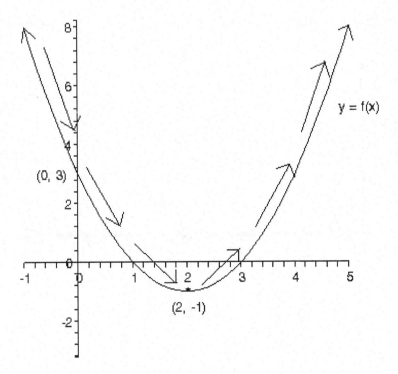

Example. The graph of $y = g(x)$ is given on the next page.
    1) Verify that the graph is the graph of a function.
    2) What is the domain of $y = g(x)$?

3) What is the range of $y = g(x)$?

4) Find the intercept(s) for the graph.

5) Does the graph have x-axis symmetry, y-axis symmetry, origin symmetry, or none of these?

6) Find $g(-1)$ and $g(-2)$.

7) On which interval is $y = g(x)$ increasing? On which interval is $y = g(x)$ decreasing? On which interval is $y = g(x)$ constant?

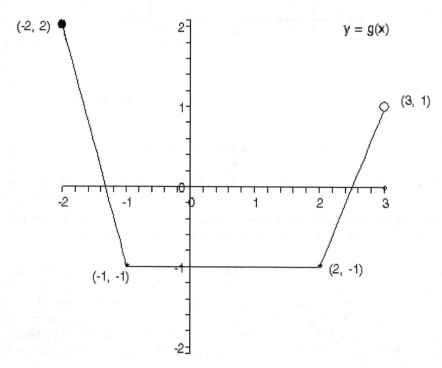

1) The graph passes the vertical line test. Therefore, it is the graph of a function.

2) After collapsing the graph onto the x-axis, notice that the interval $[-2, 3)$ is covered (see the next figure). Therefore, the domain is $\{x \mid -2 \leq x < 3\}$.

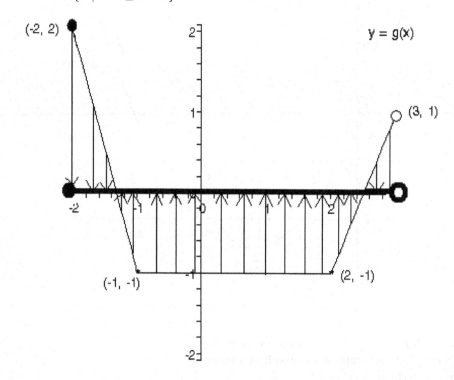

3) After collapsing the graph onto the y-axis, notice that the interval $[-1, 2]$ is covered (see the next figure). Therefore, the range is $\{y \mid -1 \leq y \leq 2\}$.

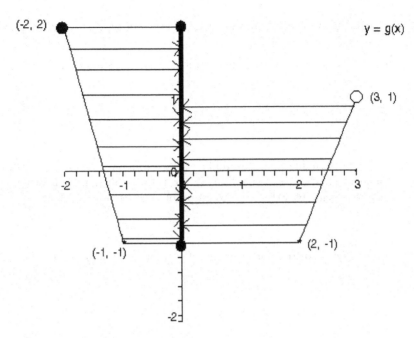

4) The y-intercept is $(0, -1)$. The x-intercepts are $\left(-\frac{4}{3}, 0\right)$ and $\left(\frac{5}{2}, 0\right)$.

5) The graph has none of the symmetries.

6) $g(-1) = -1$ and $g(-2) = 2$.

7) Beginning at the point on the left (which is $(-2, 2)$), the graph goes downward until it reaches $(-1, -1)$. Therefore, the function is decreasing on the interval $(-2, -1)$. Now, from the point $(-1, -1)$ to the point $(2, -1)$, the graph is a horizontal line segment. This means that the function is constant on the interval $(-1, 2)$. Continuing to the right of $(2, -1)$, the graph goes upward until it reaches $(3, 1)$. Therefore, the function is increasing on the interval $(2, 3)$.

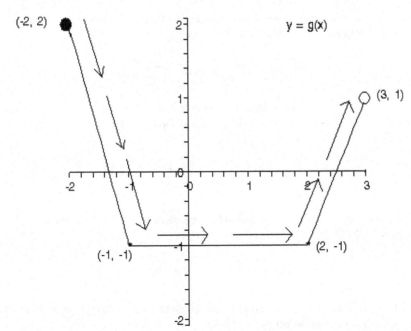

Even and Odd Functions

Let's look at even and odd functions. The graphs of these types of functions have symmetry.

Definition. A function $y = f(x)$ is **even** if for every number x in the domain of f, the number $-x$ is also in the domain and

$$f(-x) = f(x).$$

Notice that this is equivalent to saying that if we replace $x \rightsquigarrow -x$ in our function, the value of the function (in other words, the y-value) we'll stay the same. This is the type of phenomenon which occurs when the graph of an equation has y-axis symmetry. Hence, the graph of an even function has y-axis symmetry.

Definition. A function $y = f(x)$ is **odd** if for every number x in the domain of f, the number $-x$ is also in the domain and

$$f(-x) = -f(x).$$

Notice that this is equivalent to saying that if we replace $x \rightsquigarrow -x$ in our function, the value of the function (in other words, the y-value) will become negated (in other words, $y \rightsquigarrow -y$). This occurs when the graph of an equation has origin symmetry. Hence, the graph of an odd function has origin symmetry. Observe that the equation $f(-x) = -f(x)$ can also be written as $-f(-x) = f(x)$. The latter is often used.

Examples. Determine whether the given function is even, odd, or neither.

1) $f(x) = 3x^2 - 5$

We will begin by checking whether or not f is even. To do this, we replace $x \rightsquigarrow -x$ in our function and see if we'll get our original function back. Well, observe that

$$f(-x) = 3(-x)^2 - 5 = 3x^2 - 5 = f(x).$$

And so f is an even function. We don't need to check whether or not f is odd since the only function which is both even and odd is the function $f(x) = 0$ (why?). Therefore, $f(x) = 3x^2 - 5$ is only an even function.

2) $g(x) = x^3 + 6x$

Let's first check whether or not g is even. To do this, we replace $x \rightsquigarrow -x$ in our function and see if we'll get our original function back. Well, observe that

$$g(-x) = (-x)^3 + 6(-x) = -x^3 - 6x.$$

It is not the original function. Therefore, g is not even. To determine whether or not g is odd, we need to see if $-g(-x)$ gives us back our original function. Well,

$$-g\left(-x\right) = -\,\underbrace{\left(-x^3 - 6x\right)}_{g(-x) \text{ from before}} = x^3 + 6x = g\left(x\right).$$

And so g is an odd function.

3) $f\left(x\right) = 8x - 7$

Is f an even function? If we replace $x \rightsquigarrow -x$ in our function, we'll obtain

$$f\left(-x\right) = 8\left(-x\right) - 7 = -8x - 7.$$

It is not the original function. Therefore, f is not even. To determine whether or not f is odd, we need to see if $-f\left(-x\right)$ equals our original function. Well,

$$-f\left(-x\right) = -\,\underbrace{\left(-8x - 7\right)}_{f(-x) \text{ from before}} = 8x + 7,$$

which again, is not the original function. Therefore, f is neither even nor odd.

4) $g\left(x\right) = \dfrac{3x}{5x^2 - 10}$,

Is g even? We replace $x \rightsquigarrow -x$ and observe that

$$g\left(-x\right) = \frac{3\left(-x\right)}{5\left(-x\right)^2 - 10} = \frac{-3x}{5x^2 - 10} = -\frac{3x}{5x^2 - 10},$$

which is not the original function. Therefore, g is not even. Is g odd? We need to see if $-g\left(-x\right)$ is the same as $g\left(x\right)$. Well,

$$-g\left(-x\right) = -\underbrace{\left(-\frac{3x}{5x^2 - 10}\right)}_{g(-x) \text{ from before}} = \frac{3x}{5x^2 - 10} = g\left(x\right).$$

Therefore, g is an odd function.

Exercise R.4

In Exercises 1-10, determine whether or not the given correspondence is a function. State the domain and range of those which are functions.

1. Steve $\longrightarrow$ 35
   Tom $\longrightarrow$ 34
   Avi $\longrightarrow$ 36

2. Eliana $\longrightarrow$ green
   Anthony $\longrightarrow$ brown
   Angelina $\longrightarrow$ blue

3. John $\longrightarrow$ dog
   Annemarie $\longrightarrow$ cat
   John $\longrightarrow$ bird
   Nick $\longrightarrow$ turtle

4. Danielle $\longrightarrow$ drama
   Nancy $\longrightarrow$ comedy
   Kaitlyn $\longrightarrow$ horror
   JoMarie $\longrightarrow$ drama
   Nancy $\longrightarrow$ science fiction

5. 7 $\longrightarrow$ 2
   1 $\longrightarrow$ -4
   8 $\longrightarrow$ 3

6. 7 $\longrightarrow$ 0
   2 $\longrightarrow$ -3
   2 $\longrightarrow$ 1

7. $\{(1, \; -1), \; (4, \; -2), \; (9, \; -3), \; (16, \; -4)\}$ 8. $\{(3, \; 0), \; (2, \; 5), \; (9, \; -1), \; (0, \; 2)\}$

9. $\{(5, \; 0), \; (4, \; 2), \; (5, \; -2), \; (3, \; 3)\}$ 10. $\{(2, \; 10), \; (-1, \; 9), \; (0, \; 0), \; (-1, \; 2)\}$

In Exercises 11-26, find the values of the given function when $x = -2$, $x = 0$, and $x = 5$.

11. $f(x) = 3x + 1$ 12. $f(x) = 4x - 5$ 13. $g(x) = -7x + 3$ 14. $g(x) = -x + 10$

15. $f(x) = x^2 + 3x - 10$ 16. $f(x) = 2x^2 - x + 5$ 17. $f(x) = \dfrac{4}{3x - 5}$

18. $f(x) = \dfrac{9}{2x - 8}$ 19. $R(x) = \dfrac{x - 5}{x^2 - x - 3}$ 20. $R(x) = \dfrac{x + 2}{x^2 + 4x - 1}$

21. $f(x) = \sqrt{2x + 4}$ 22. $g(x) = \sqrt{8x + 25}$ 23. $f(x) = \sqrt{16 - 3x}$

24. $f(x) = \sqrt{25 - x}$ 25. $p(x) = \dfrac{\sqrt{x + 4}}{1 - x^2}$ 26. $q(x) = \dfrac{x^2 - 2}{\sqrt{x^2 + 1}}$

In Exercises 27-40, determine whether or not y is an implicit function of x.

27. $5x + 2y - 10 = 0$ 28. $3x - 6y + 2 = 0$ 29. $-4x + 9y = 0$ 30. $8x - 2y = 0$

31. $x^2 + 2x + 9 = y^2$ 32. $16 - x^2 = y^2$ 33. $x^2 + y^2 = 4$ 34. $x^2 - y^2 = 9$

35. $xy = 7$ 36. $xy + 16 = 0$ 37. $xy + 5x = 2$ 38. $xy - 6x = 7$

39. $x^2 y^2 + 5x - 10 = 0$ 40. $x^2 y^2 - 3x + 8 = 0$

In Exercises 41-66, find the domain of each function.

41. $f(x) = 3x + 8$ 42. $f(x) = 4x - 1$ 43. $g(x) = \dfrac{1}{7}x - 3$ 44. $g(x) = \dfrac{2}{5}x - \dfrac{3}{5}$

45. $g(x) = x^2 + 2x - 9$ 46. $g(x) = -x^3 + 6x^2 - 8$ 47. $g(x) = \dfrac{2}{x + 8}$ 48. $g(x) = \dfrac{-5}{x + 13}$

49. $h(x) = \dfrac{x + 2}{3x - 12}$ 50. $h(x) = \dfrac{2x - 1}{7x + 35}$ 51. $g(x) = \dfrac{6x + 1}{x^2 - 9x + 20}$ 52. $g(x) = \dfrac{-x + 5}{9x^2 - 25}$

53. $f(x) = \dfrac{3x^2 + 9}{x^2 - 16}$ 54. $f(x) = \dfrac{10x^2 + 2}{x^2 + 6x + 9}$ 55. $f(x) = \dfrac{5 - 3x}{x^2 + x + 5}$ 56. $f(x) = \dfrac{4x - 1}{x^2 - x + 3}$

57. $g(x) = \sqrt{3x - 27}$ 58. $g(x) = \sqrt{5x - 30}$ 59. $f(x) = \sqrt{x^2 - 4}$ 60. $f(x) = \sqrt{x^2 - 4}$

61. $f(x) = \sqrt{49 - x^2}$ 62. $f(x) = \sqrt{81 - x^2}$ 63. $f(x) = \sqrt{\dfrac{x + 4}{x - 3}}$ 64. $f(x) = \sqrt{\dfrac{x - 2}{x + 6}}$

65. $f(x) = \sqrt{\dfrac{4}{x^2 + 1}}$ 66. $f(x) = \sqrt{\dfrac{2}{x^2 + 3}}$

In Exercises 67-72, determine whether or not the given graph is the graph of a function.

67.

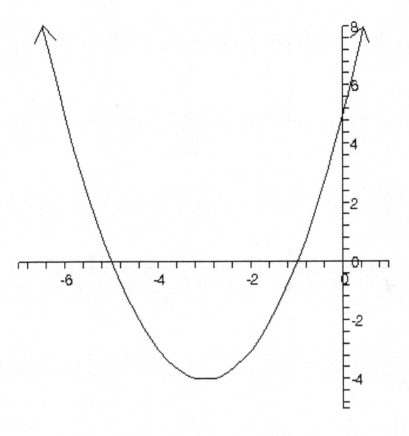

68.

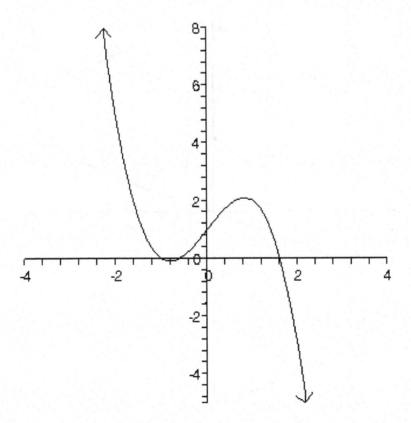

69.

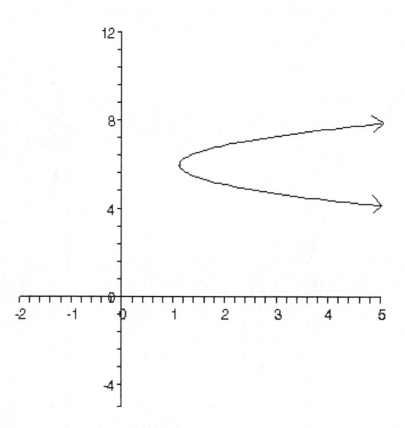

70.

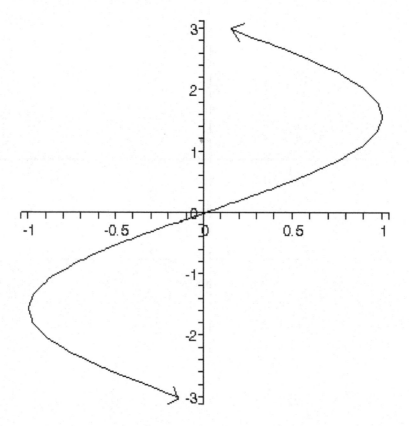

71.

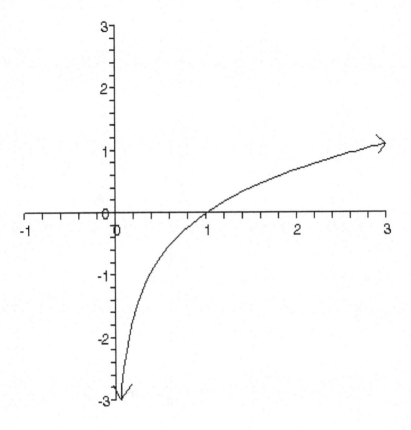

72.

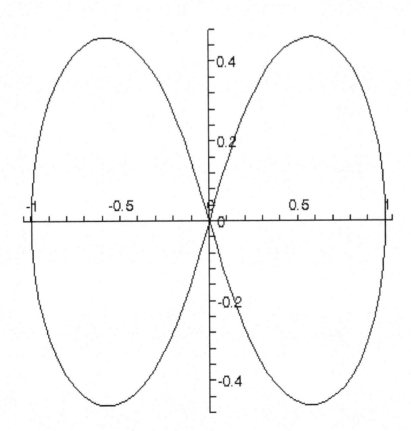

In Exercises 73-80, the graph of a function $y = f(x)$ is given. Using the graph, find
a) the domain of $y = f(x)$.
b) the range of $y = f(x)$.
c) the intercept(s) for the graph.
d) any symmetries for the graph.
e) interval(s) on which $y = f(x)$ is increasing, decreasing, or constant.

73.

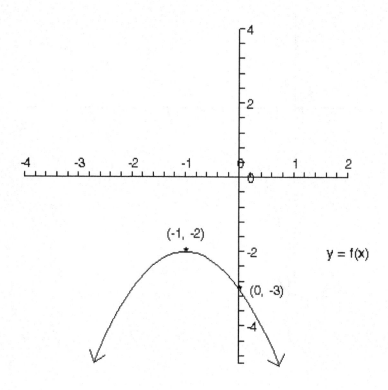

74.

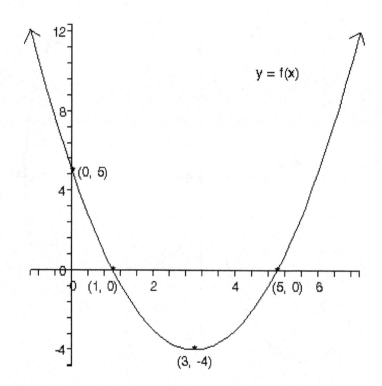

75.

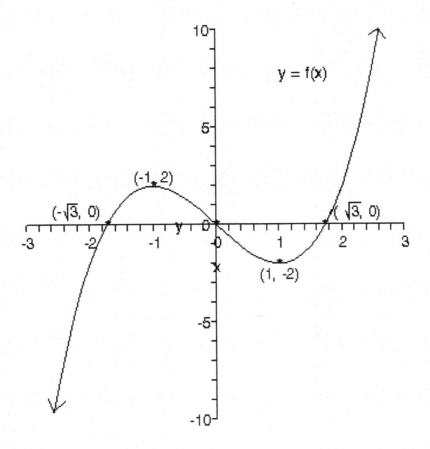

76.

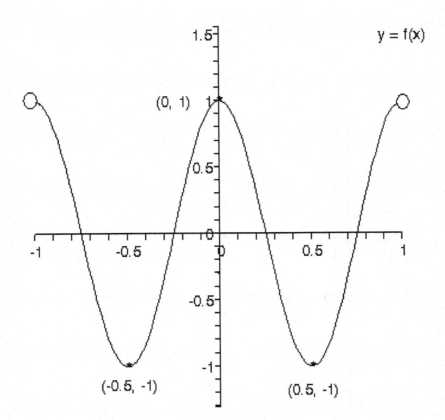

77.

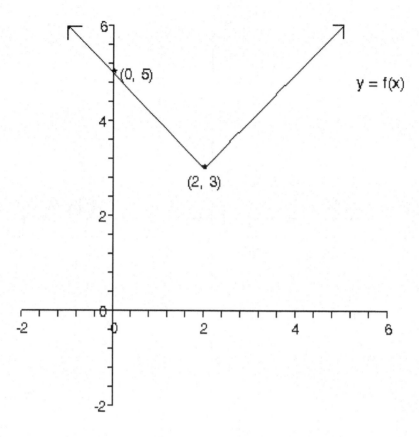

78.

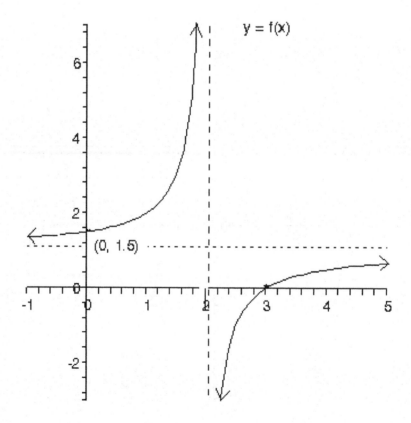

79.

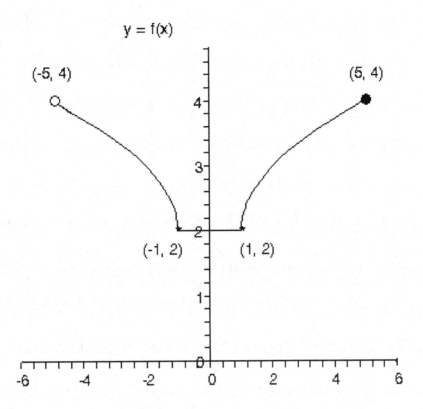

80.

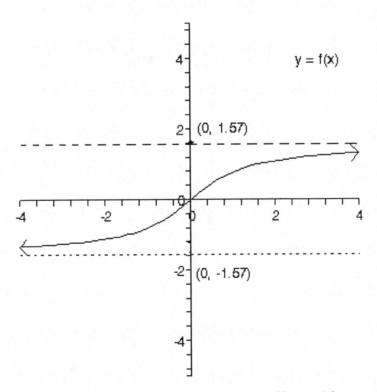

In Exercises 81-106, determine whether the given function is even, odd, or neither.

81. $f(x) = 2x^2 + 4$ 82. $f(x) = 3x^2 - 1$ 83. $f(x) = x^3 + 6x$ 84. $f(x) = x + 2x^3$

85. $f(x) = x^3 - 7x^2$ 86. $f(x) = 2x^3 - x^2$ 87. $g(x) = 8x$ 88. $g(x) = -3x$

89. $h(x) = \sqrt{x-7}$ 90. $h(x) = \sqrt{x}+5$ 91. $g(x) = \dfrac{x^2}{x^2+4}$ 92. $g(x) = \dfrac{x^2-1}{x^2}$

93. $g(x) = \dfrac{5x}{x^2-10}$ 94. $g(x) = \dfrac{9x}{x^2-18}$ 95. $g(x) = \dfrac{x+2}{2x-5}$ 96. $g(x) = \dfrac{x-8}{x+3}$

97. $h(x) = x^4 + 12x^2$ 98. $h(x) = 5x^4 + x^2$ 99. $g(x) = -x^3 + 3x^2$ 100. $g(x) = x^3 - 4x^2$

101. $f(x) = x^3 - 1$ 102. $f(x) = x^3 + 7$ 103. $f(x) = |x| - 7$ 104. $f(x) = |x| + 9$

105. $f(x) = |x - 7|$ 106. $f(x) = |x + 9|$

Section R.5 Graphs of Basic Functions and Graphing Techniques

In this section, we will review how to graph a function when it is given in explicit form (that is, in the form $y = f(x)$). We'll begin by graphing what are called the **basic functions**. We will then examine different ways of obtaining the graph of a function by using the graph of a basic function. The techniques that we will discuss are the shifting, the vertical stretch and compression, and the reflection techniques.

The Basic Functions and Piecewise-Defined Functions

In Section R.2, we've examined a library of graphs for the basic equations. If we apply the vertical line test to those graphs, we'd see that many of them are graphs of functions. We will recall these graphs, along with some new ones which come from piecewise-defined functions.

The Basic Functions

1. The Constant Function $f(x) = b$, where b is any real number.

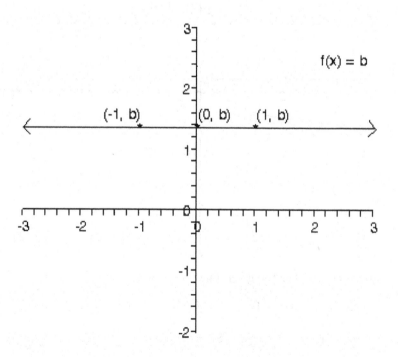

2. The Identity Function $f(x) = x$

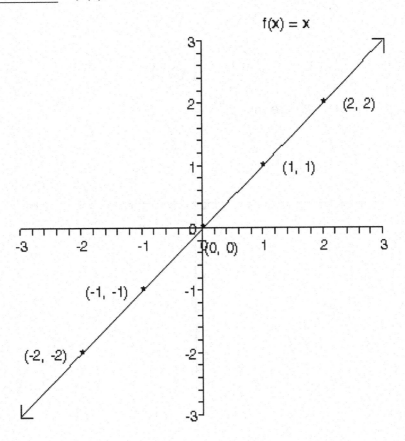

3. Linear Function $f(x) = mx + b$

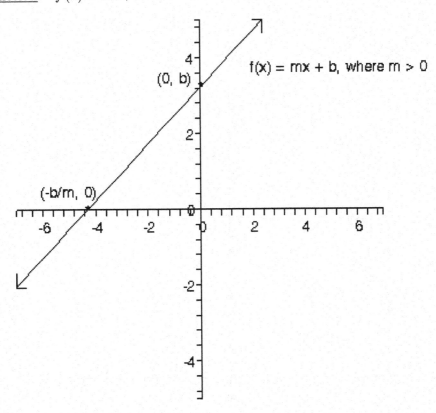

AND

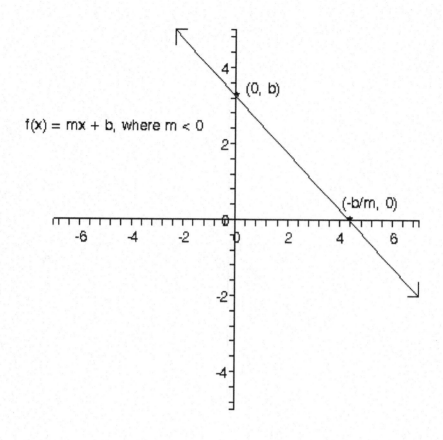

f(x) = mx + b, where m < 0

(0, b)

(-b/m, 0)

4. The Square Function $f(x) = x^2$

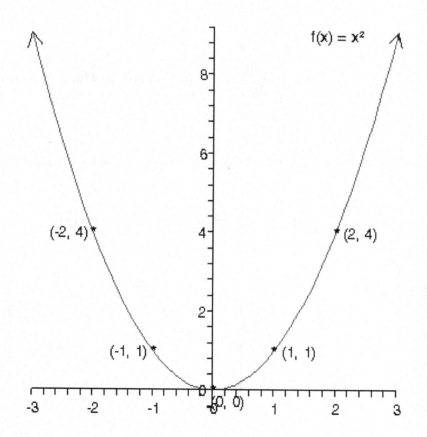

f(x) = x²

(-2, 4)   (2, 4)

(-1, 1)   (1, 1)

(0, 0)

5. The Cube Function $f(x) = x^3$

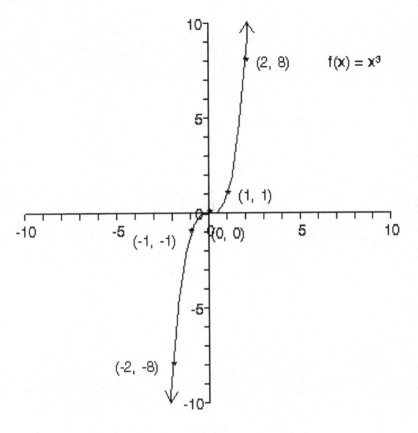

6. The Square Root Function $f(x) = \sqrt{x}$

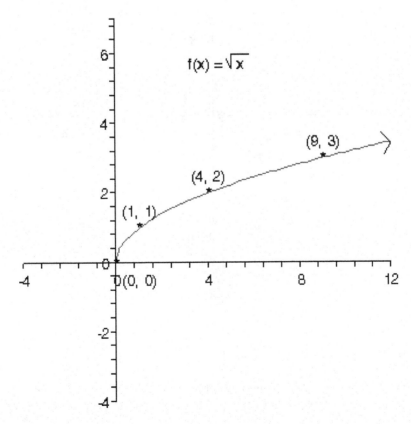

7. The Absolute Value Function $\quad f(x) = |x|$

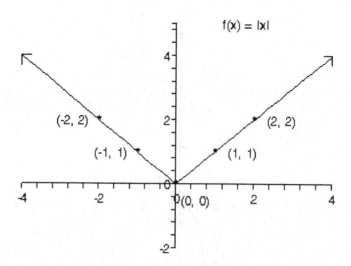

8. The Reciprocal Function $\quad f(x) = \dfrac{1}{x}$

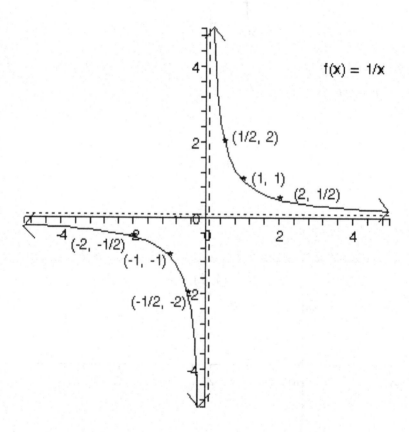

9. The Greatest Integer Function $\quad f(x) = [[x]]$

Let me explain how the greatest integer function works. By definition, $[[x]]$ represents the greatest integer which is less than or equal to x. For example, $[[3.5]] = 3$ since 3 is the greatest integer which is less than 3.5.

Similarly, $[[-7.62]] = -8$ since -8 is the greatest integer which is less than -7.62. If x is any integer, then $[[x]] = x$. For example, $[[8]] = 8$ and $[[-5]] = -5$. The graph of $f(x) = [[x]]$ on the domain $\{x \mid -2 \leq x < 4\}$ is given below.

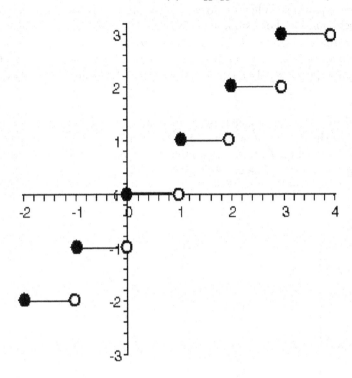

Piecewise-Defined Functions

Definition. A **piecewise-defined** function is a function which is defined by two or more equations.

One example of a piecewise-defined function is the absolute value function:

$$f(x) = |x| = \begin{cases} x & \text{if } x \geq 0 \\ -x & \text{if } x < 0 \end{cases}$$

The absolute value function has two equations which defines it as $y = x$ whenever $x \geq 0$ and $y = -x$, whenever $x < 0$. For example, $f(5) = 5$ because $5 \geq 0$ and $f(-7) = -(-7) = 7$ because $-7 < 0$.

Note: In order to guarantee that $f(x) = |x|$ is really a function, we must make sure that the domains of the definition (that is, $\{x \mid x \geq 0\}$ and $\{x \mid x < 0\}$ in the above definition) do not intersect or that where they intersect, the definitions coincide. For example, we could also define the absolute value function as:

$$g(x) = |x| = \begin{cases} x & \text{if } x \geq 0 \\ -x & \text{if } x \leq 0 \end{cases}$$

Note that 0 belongs to both domains of the definition (namely, $\{x \mid x \geq 0\}$ and $\{x \mid x \leq 0\}$). However, we have that $g(0) = 0 = -(0)$. Therefore, g is really a function.

Another example of a piecewise-defined function is:

$$f(x) = \begin{cases} x^2 & \text{if } x > 3 \\ 6 & \text{if } x = 3 \\ 5x + 2 & \text{if } -1 < x < 3 \end{cases}$$

This function is defined by three equations. When we do computations with such a function, we need to be cautious when choosing the correct equation. For example, we will use the equation $y = x^2$ to compute $f(4)$ since $4 > 3$. Hence, $f(4) = (4)^2 = 16$. To compute $f(0)$, we use the equation $y = 5x + 2$ since $-1 < 0 < 3$. Therefore, $f(0) = 5(0) + 2 = 2$. Observe that $f(3) = 6$ because the second equation states that $f(x) = 6$ if $x = 3$. The domain of this function is $\{x \mid x > -1\}$ since any x-value greater than -1 satisfies either $x > 3$, $x = 3$, or $-1 < x < 3$.

We would also like to know how to graph a piecewise-defined function. To graph a piecewise-defined function, you simply graph each of the equations which define the function for the x-values given in the definition. For example, to graph the function f above, we sketch $y = x^2$ only when $x > 3$, $y = 6$, only when $x = 3$, and $y = 5x + 2$, only when $-1 < x < 3$. The graph is given below.

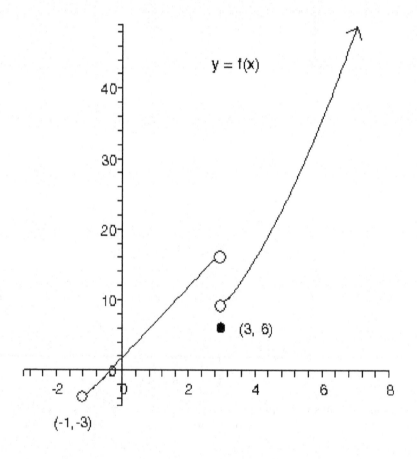

Examples. For each function, find $f(-1)$, $f(3)$, and $f(9)$. Graph each function.

1) $f(x) = \begin{cases} x + 2 & \text{if } x > 1 \\ 3x & \text{if } x \leq 1 \end{cases}$

To compute $f(-1)$, observe that $-1 \leq 1$. This means that we must use the second equation, and we get $f(-1) = 3(-1) = -3$. To compute $f(3)$, observe that $3 > 1$. This means that we will use the first equation, so $f(3) = (3) + 2 = 5$. Since $9 > 1$, we use the first equation and obtain $f(9) = (9) + 2 = 11$. The graph of f is given in the figure on the next page.

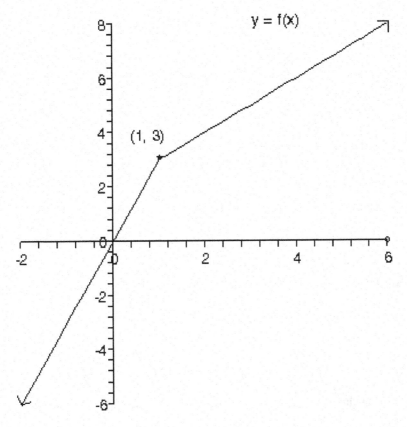

2) $f(x) = \begin{cases} \sqrt{x} & \text{if } 0 \le x \le 9 \\ -2 & \text{if } x < 0 \end{cases}$

To compute $f(-1)$, note that $-1 < 0$. This means that we will use the second equation, so $f(-1) = -2$. To compute $f(3)$, observe that $0 \le 3 \le 9$. This means that we will use the first equation, so $f(3) = \sqrt{3}$. Similarly, since $0 \le 9 \le 9$, we have that $f(9) = \sqrt{9} = 3$. The graph of f is given in the figure below.

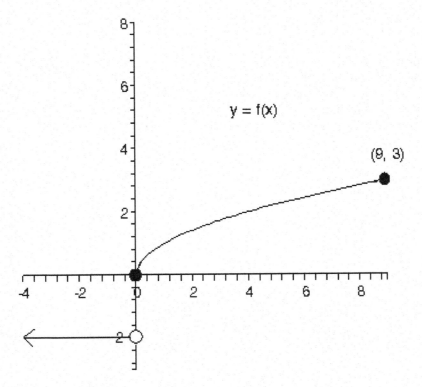

The Graphing Techniques

Now let's review how to obtain graphs of functions by using the shifting techniques. The basic idea is that we can shift the graph of a basic function to get the graph of a new function which is similar to the basic one.

1. Vertical Shifting

Suppose that we know the graph of the function $y = f(x)$, and we are interested in graphing the functions $y = f(x) + c$ and $y = f(x) - c$, where c represents any positive number.

> The graph of $y = f(x) + c$ is obtained by shifting the graph of $y = f(x)$ **upward** by c units.
>
> The graph of $y = f(x) - c$ is obtained by shifting the graph of $y = f(x)$ **downward** by c units.

The reason why we shift the graph of $y = f(x)$ up or down will become clear after a couple of examples.

Examples. Sketch each function by shifting the graph of a basic function.

1) $f(x) = x^2 + 3$

To begin with, notice that the function f has the square function built into it. In other words, if $g(x) = x^2$ is the square function, then we can write $f(x) = x^2 + 3$ as $f(x) = g(x) + 3$. This means that the graph of f can be obtained by shifting the graph of $g(x) = x^2$ **upward** by three units. Let's see why this shift occurs by looking at the tables for the solutions to $g(x) = x^2$ and $f(x) = x^2 + 3$.

x	$y = g(x) = x^2$	Solutions
-2	$(-2)^2 = 4$	$(-2, 4)$
-1	$(-1)^2 = 1$	$(-1, 1)$
0	$(0)^2 = 0$	$(0, 0)$
1	$(1)^2 = 1$	$(1, 1)$
2	$(2)^2 = 4$	$(2, 4)$

and

x	$y = f(x) = x^2 + 3$	Solutions
-2	$(-2)^2 + 3 = 4 + 3 = 7$	$(-2, 7)$
-1	$(-1)^2 + 3 = 1 + 3 = 4$	$(-1, 4)$
0	$(0)^2 + 3 = 0 + 3 = 3$	$(0, 3)$
1	$(1)^2 + 3 = 1 + 3 = 4$	$(1, 4)$
2	$(2)^2 + 3 = 4 + 3 = 7$	$(2, 7)$

Observe that the same x-values are used for each table. However, the y-values for $f(x) = x^2 + 3$ are each three more than the corresponding y-values for $g(x) = x^2$. In other words, all that we have to do to obtain the solutions for $f(x) = x^2 + 3$ is to use the same x-values for $g(x) = x^2$, but add three to each of the y-values for $g(x) = x^2$ (look at the tables). **Graphically, this means that the points for $f(x) = x^2 + 3$ can be obtained by shifting the points for $g(x) = x^2$ upward by three units.**

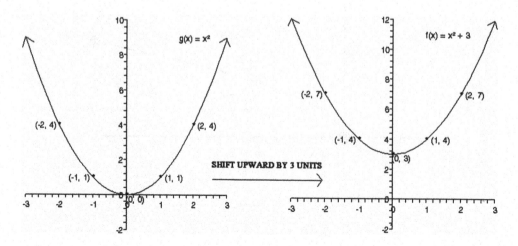

2) $f(x) = |x| - 1$

The function f has the absolute value function built into it. In other words, if $g(x) = |x|$ is the absolute value function, then we can write $f(x) = |x| - 1$ as $f(x) = g(x) - 1$. This means that **the graph of f can be obtained by shifting the graph of $g(x) = |x|$ downward by one unit**. Once again, let's see why this shift occurs by looking at the tables for the solutions to $g(x) = |x|$ and $f(x) = |x| - 1$.

<table>
<tr><td>x</td><td>$y = g(x) = |x|$</td><td>Solutions</td></tr>
<tr><td>-2</td><td>$|-2| = 2$</td><td>$(-2, 2)$</td></tr>
<tr><td>-1</td><td>$|-1| = 1$</td><td>$(-1, 1)$</td></tr>
<tr><td>0</td><td>$|0| = 0$</td><td>$(0, 0)$</td></tr>
<tr><td>1</td><td>$|1| = 1$</td><td>$(1, 1)$</td></tr>
<tr><td>2</td><td>$|2| = 2$</td><td>$(2, 2)$</td></tr>
</table>

and

<table>
<tr><td>x</td><td>$y = f(x) = |x| - 1$</td><td>Solutions</td></tr>
<tr><td>-2</td><td>$|-2| - 1 = 2 - 1 = 1$</td><td>$(-2, 1)$</td></tr>
<tr><td>-1</td><td>$|-1| - 1 = 1 - 1 = 0$</td><td>$(-1, 0)$</td></tr>
<tr><td>0</td><td>$|0| - 1 = 0 - 1 = -1$</td><td>$(0, -1)$</td></tr>
<tr><td>1</td><td>$|1| - 1 = 1 - 1 = 0$</td><td>$(1, 0)$</td></tr>
<tr><td>2</td><td>$|2| - 1 = 2 - 1 = 1$</td><td>$(2, 1)$</td></tr>
</table>

As before, notice that the same x-values are used for each table. However, the y-values for $f(x) = |x| - 1$ are each one less than the corresponding y-values for $g(x) = |x|$. In other words, all we have to do to obtain the solutions for $f(x) = |x| - 1$ is to use the same x-values for $g(x) = |x|$, but subtract one from each of the y-values for $g(x) = |x|$ (look at the tables). Graphically, this means that **the points for $f(x) = |x| - 1$ can be obtained by shifting the points for $g(x) = |x|$ downward by one unit**.

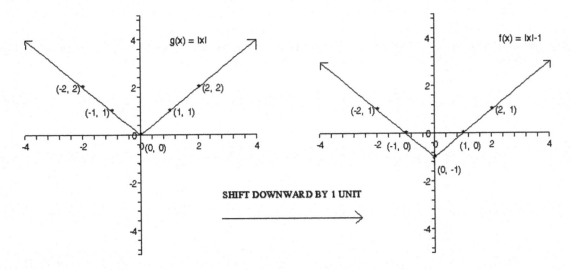

2. Horizontal Shifting

Suppose that we know the graph of the function $y = f(x)$, and we are interested in graphing the functions $y = f(x + c)$ and $y = f(x - c)$, where c represents any positive number.

The graph of $y = f(x + c)$ is obtained by shifting the graph of $y = f(x)$ **to the left** by c units.

The graph of $y = f(x - c)$ is obtained by shifting the graph of $y = f(x)$ **to the right** by c units.

At first glance, these 'rules' may seem contradictory. Why should the graph shift to the left (right) when we add (subtract) a number to (from) x? It seems that it should work the other way around. The reason why these shifts occur the way they do will become clear after looking at a couple of examples.

Examples. Sketch each function by shifting the graph of a basic function.

1) $f(x) = (x + 3)^2$

We proceed the same way we did when doing vertical shifting. Notice that the function f has the square function built into it. In other words, if $g(x) = x^2$, then we can write $f(x) = (x + 3)^2$ as $f(x) = g(x + 3)$. This means that **the graph of f can be obtained by shifting the graph of $g(x) = x^2$ to the left by three units.** We can see why this shift occurs by looking at the tables for the solutions to $g(x) = x^2$ and $f(x) = (x + 3)^2$.

x	$y = g(x) = x^2$	Solutions
-2	$(-2)^2 = 4$	$(-2, 4)$
-1	$(-1)^2 = 1$	$(-1, 1)$
0	$(0)^2 = 0$	$(0, 0)$
1	$(1)^2 = 1$	$(1, 1)$
2	$(2)^2 = 4$	$(2, 4)$

and

x	$y = f(x) = (x + 3)^2$	Solutions
-5	$(-5 + 3)^2 = (-2)^2 = 4$	$(-5, 4)$
-4	$(-4 + 3)^2 = (-1)^2 = 1$	$(-4, 1)$
-3	$(-3 + 3)^2 = (0)^2 = 0$	$(-3, 0)$
-2	$(-2 + 3)^2 = (1)^2 = 1$	$(-2, 1)$
-1	$(-1 + 3)^2 = (2)^2 = 4$	$(-1, 4)$

Notice that the y-values for $f(x) = (x + 3)^2$ are the same in each line of the table as the y-values for $g(x) = x^2$. However, the x-values in each line of the table for f are each three less than the corresponding x-values for g. In other words, all we have to do to obtain the solutions for $f(x) = (x + 3)^2$ is to use the same y-values for $g(x) = x^2$, but subtract three from each of the x-values for $g(x) = x^2$ (look at the tables). Graphically, this means that the points for $f(x) = (x + 3)^2$ can be obtained by shifting the points for $g(x) = x^2$ to the left by three units.

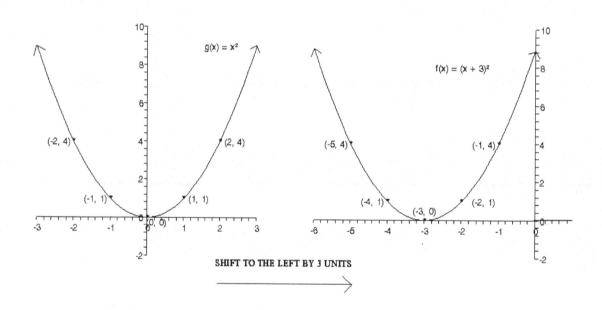

SHIFT TO THE LEFT BY 3 UNITS

2) $f(x) = |x - 2|$

The function f has the absolute value function built into it. If $g(x) = |x|$, then we can write $f(x) = |x - 2|$ as $f(x) = g(x - 2)$. This means that **the graph of f can be obtained by shifting the graph of $g(x) = |x|$ to the right by two units.** Once again, let's see why this shift occurs by looking at the tables for the solutions to $g(x) = |x|$ and $f(x) = |x - 2|$.

x	$y = g(x) = \lvert x \rvert$	Solutions
-2	$\lvert -2 \rvert = 2$	$(-2, 2)$
-1	$\lvert -1 \rvert = 1$	$(-1, 1)$
0	$\lvert 0 \rvert = 0$	$(0, 0)$
1	$\lvert 1 \rvert = 1$	$(1, 1)$
2	$\lvert 2 \rvert = 2$	$(2, 2)$

and

x	$y = f(x) = \lvert x - 2 \rvert$	Solutions
0	$\lvert 0 - 2 \rvert = \lvert -2 \rvert = 2$	$(0, 2)$
1	$\lvert 1 - 2 \rvert = \lvert -1 \rvert = 1$	$(1, 1)$
2	$\lvert 2 - 2 \rvert = \lvert 0 \rvert = 0$	$(2, 0)$
3	$\lvert 3 - 2 \rvert = \lvert 1 \rvert = 1$	$(3, 1)$
4	$\lvert 4 - 2 \rvert = \lvert 2 \rvert = 2$	$(4, 2)$

As in the previous example, the y-values for $f(x) = \lvert x - 2 \rvert$ and $g(x) = \lvert x \rvert$ are the same. However, the x-values for f are each two more than the corresponding x-values for g. In other words, all we have to do to obtain the solutions for $f(x) = \lvert x - 2 \rvert$ is to use the same y-values for $g(x) = \lvert x \rvert$, but add two to each of the x-values for $g(x) = \lvert x \rvert$ (look at the tables). Graphically, this means that **the points for $f(x) = \lvert x - 2 \rvert$ can be obtained by shifting the points for $g(x) = \lvert x \rvert$ to the right by two units**.

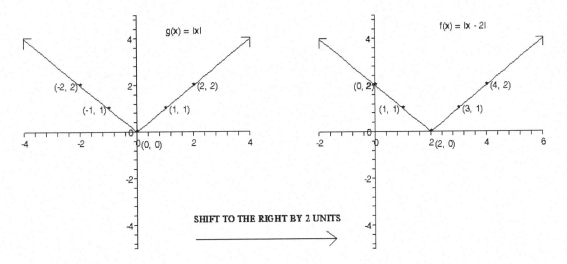

3) $f(x) = \sqrt{x + 4}$

Notice that the function $f(x) = \sqrt{x + 4}$ has the basic function $g(x) = \sqrt{x}$ in it. Moreover, since $f(x) = \sqrt{x + 4}$ can be written as $f(x) = g(x + 4)$, **the graph of f will be obtained by shifting the graph of g to the left by four units**. This means that we can get **the points for the graph of f by subtracting four from the x-value of each of the points for g**. The graphs of $g(x) = \sqrt{x}$ and $f(x) = \sqrt{x + 4}$ are shown below.

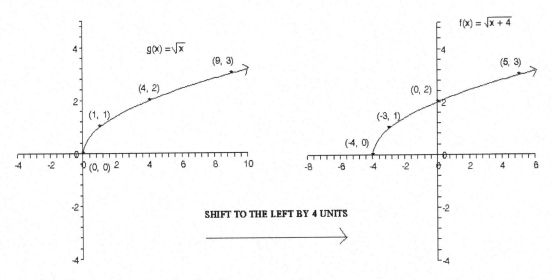

Sometimes students get confused with the shifting techniques. How did we know that $f(x) = \sqrt{x+4}$ is not the vertical shift of $g(x) = \sqrt{x}$? Well, if it were a vertical shift, then four would have to be added to the $\sqrt{x}$ and not to the variable x in the expression $\sqrt{x+4}$. In other words,

the graph of $y = \sqrt{x} + 4$ is the graph of $y = \sqrt{x}$ **shifted up** by four units, and
the graph of $y = \sqrt{x+4}$ is the graph of $y = \sqrt{x}$ **shifted to the left** by four units.

Do you see the difference? If the number is **added to** or **subtracted from the expression** in the basic function (in this case, $\sqrt{x} + 4$), then the graph results from a **vertical** shift. If the number is **added to** or **subtracted from** the variable x (as in $\sqrt{x+4}$), then the graph can be obtained from a **horizontal** shift.

4) $f(x) = \dfrac{1}{x-1}$

Notice that the function $f(x) = \dfrac{1}{x-1}$ has the basic function $g(x) = \dfrac{1}{x}$ in it. Moreover, since we are subtracting one from the variable x, **the graph of f will be obtained by shifting the graph of g to the right by one unit.** This means that we can get **the points for the graph of f by adding** one to **the x-value of each of the points for g**. The graphs of $g(x) = \dfrac{1}{x}$ and $f(x) = \dfrac{1}{x-1}$ are shown below.

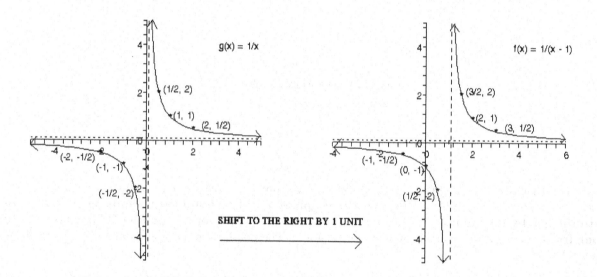

SHIFT TO THE RIGHT BY 1 UNIT

 BEWARE: $f(x) = \dfrac{1}{x-1}$ is not the graph of $g(x) = \dfrac{1}{x}$ **shifted down by one** unit.

If we were graphing $y = \dfrac{1}{x} - 1$, **then** we would shift the graph of $g(x) = \dfrac{1}{x}$ down by one unit.

3) Vertical Stretching and Compressing

Suppose we know the graph of the function $y = f(x)$, and we are interested in graphing the function $y = cf(x)$, where $c \neq 1$ is a positive number.

If $c > 1$, then the graph of $y = cf(x)$ is a **vertical stretch** of the graph of $y = f(x)$ by a factor of c.

If $0 < c < 1$, then the graph of $y = cf(x)$ is a **vertical compression** of the graph of $y = f(x)$ by a factor of c.

Examples. Sketch each function by vertically stretching or compressing the graph of a basic function.

1) $f(x) = 2\sqrt{x}$

To begin with, notice that the function f has the square root function built into it. If $g(x) = \sqrt{x}$, then we can write $f(x) = 2\sqrt{x}$ as $f(x) = 2g(x)$. This means that **the graph of f can be obtained by vertically stretching the graph of $g(x) = \sqrt{x}$ by a factor of two**. Let's see why this occurs by looking at the tables for the solutions to $g(x) = \sqrt{x}$ and $f(x) = 2\sqrt{x}$.

x	$y = g(x) = \sqrt{x}$	Solutions
0	$\sqrt{0} = 0$	$(0, 0)$
1	$\sqrt{1} = 1$	$(1, 1)$
4	$\sqrt{4} = 2$	$(4, 2)$
9	$\sqrt{9} = 3$	$(9, 3)$

and

x	$y = f(x) = 2\sqrt{x}$	Solutions
0	$2\sqrt{0} = 2(0) = 0$	$(0, 0)$
1	$2\sqrt{1} = 2(1) = 2$	$(1, 2)$
4	$2\sqrt{4} = 2(2) = 4$	$(4, 4)$
9	$2\sqrt{9} = 2(3) = 6$	$(9, 6)$

Observe that the same x-values are used for each table. However, the y-values for $f(x) = 2\sqrt{x}$ are each two times the corresponding y-values for $g(x) = \sqrt{x}$. Therefore, to obtain the solutions for $f(x) = 2\sqrt{x}$, we use the same x-values for $g(x) = \sqrt{x}$, but multiplying each of the y-values for $g(x) = \sqrt{x}$ by two (look at the tables). In the figures below, you can see that the graph of $f(x) = 2\sqrt{x}$ is similar to the graph of $g(x) = \sqrt{x}$, but 'pulled away' (or **stretched away**) from the x-axis. We say that the graph of $f(x) = 2\sqrt{x}$ is the **vertical stretch** of $g(x) = \sqrt{x}$ by a factor of two.

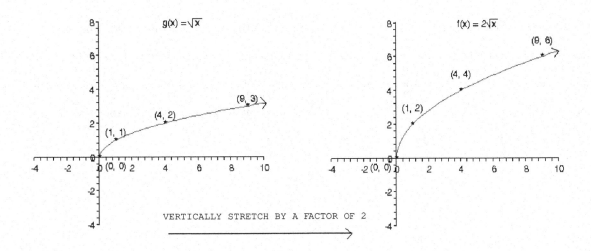

VERTICALLY STRETCH BY A FACTOR OF 2

2) $f(x) = \frac{1}{3}|x|$

The function f has the absolute value function built into it. If $g(x) = |x|$, then we can write $f(x) = \frac{1}{3}|x|$ as $f(x) = \frac{1}{3}g(x)$. This means that **the graph of f can be obtained by vertically compressing the graph of $g(x) = |x|$ by a factor of $\frac{1}{3}$**. Once again, let's see why this occurs by looking at the tables for the solutions to $g(x) = |x|$ and $f(x) = \frac{1}{3}|x|$.

x	$y = g(x) = |x|$	Solutions
-2	$|-2| = 2$	$(-2, 2)$
-1	$|-1| = 1$	$(-1, 1)$
0	$|0| = 0$	$(0, 0)$
1	$|1| = 1$	$(1, 1)$
2	$|2| = 2$	$(2, 2)$

and

x	$y = f(x) = \frac{1}{3}|x|$	Solutions
-2	$\frac{1}{3}|-2| = \frac{1}{3}(2) = \frac{2}{3}$	$(-2, \frac{2}{3})$
-1	$\frac{1}{3}|-1| = \frac{1}{3}(1) = \frac{1}{3}$	$(-1, \frac{1}{3})$
0	$\frac{1}{3}|0| = \frac{1}{3}(0) = 0$	$(0, 0)$
1	$\frac{1}{3}|1| = \frac{1}{3}(1) = \frac{1}{3}$	$(1, \frac{1}{3})$
2	$\frac{1}{3}|2| = \frac{1}{3}(2) = \frac{2}{3}$	$(2, \frac{2}{3})$

Notice that the same x-values are used for each table. However, the y-values for $f(x) = \frac{1}{3}|x|$ are each $\frac{1}{3}$ times the corresponding y-values for $g(x) = |x|$. This means that we can obtain the solutions for $f(x) = \frac{1}{3}|x|$ by using the same x-values for $g(x) = |x|$, but multiplying each of the y-values for $g(x) = |x|$ by $\frac{1}{3}$ (look at the tables). As you can see from the graphs below, the graph of $f(x) = \frac{1}{3}|x|$ is similar to the graph of $g(x) = |x|$, but 'pulled toward' (or **compressed toward**) the x-axis. We say that the graph of $f(x) = \frac{1}{3}|x|$ is the **vertical compression** of $g(x) = |x|$ by a factor of $\frac{1}{3}$.

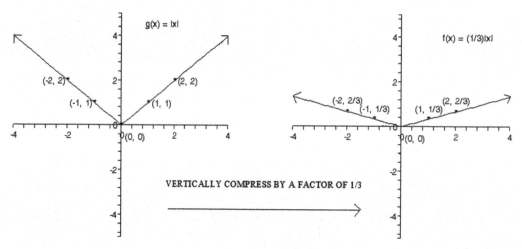

3) $f(x) = \dfrac{4}{x}$

Observe that we can rewrite f as $f(x) = \dfrac{4}{x} = 4 \cdot \dfrac{1}{x}$. By writing it in this way, we see that $f(x) = 4 \cdot \dfrac{1}{x}$ is just the reciprocal function, $g(x) = \dfrac{1}{x}$, multiplied by four. This means that we will vertically stretch the graph of the $g(x) = \dfrac{1}{x}$, by a factor of four to get the graph of f. We can obtain points on the graph of $f(x) = \dfrac{4}{x}$ by using the same x-values of $g(x) = \dfrac{1}{x}$ and multiplying each of the corresponding y-values by four. The graphs of $g(x) = \dfrac{1}{x}$ and $f(x) = \dfrac{4}{x}$ are given below.

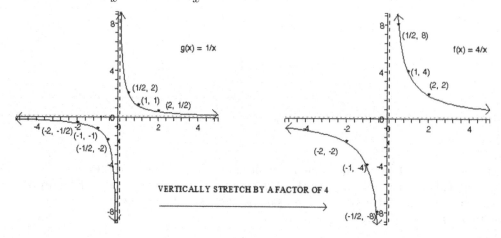

4) Horizontal Stretching and Compressing

Suppose we know the graph of the function $y = f(x)$, and we are interested in graphing the function $y = f(cx)$, where $c \neq 1$ is a positive number.

> If $c > 1$, then the graph of $y = f(cx)$ is a **horizontal compression** of the graph of $y = f(x)$ by a factor of $\dfrac{1}{c}$.
>
> If $0 < c < 1$, then the graph of $y = f(cx)$ is a **horizontal stretch** of the graph of $y = f(x)$ by a factor of $\dfrac{1}{c}$.

Examples. Sketch each function by horizontally stretching or compressing the graph of a basic function.

1) $f(x) = \sqrt{2x}$

The function f has the square root function built into it. If $g(x) = \sqrt{x}$, then we can write $f(x) = \sqrt{2x}$ as $f(x) = g(2x)$. This means that **the graph of f can be obtained by horizontally compressing the graph of $g(x) = \sqrt{x}$ by a factor of $\frac{1}{2}$**. Let's see why this occurs by looking at the tables for the solutions to $g(x) = \sqrt{x}$ and $f(x) = \sqrt{2x}$.

x	$y = g(x) = \sqrt{x}$	Solutions
0	$\sqrt{0} = 0$	$(0, 0)$
1	$\sqrt{1} = 1$	$(1, 1)$
4	$\sqrt{4} = 2$	$(4, 2)$
9	$\sqrt{9} = 3$	$(9, 3)$

and

x	$y = f(x) = \sqrt{2x}$	Solutions
0	$\sqrt{0} = (0) = 0$	$(0, 0)$
$\frac{1}{2}$	$\sqrt{2\left(\frac{1}{2}\right)} = \sqrt{1} = 1$	$\left(\frac{1}{2}, 1\right)$
2	$\sqrt{2\left(\frac{4}{2}\right)} = \sqrt{4} = 2$	$(2, 2)$
$\frac{9}{2}$	$\sqrt{2\left(\frac{9}{2}\right)} = \sqrt{9} = 3$	$\left(\frac{9}{2}, 3\right)$

Observe that the same y-values are used for each table. However, the x-values for $f(x) = \sqrt{2x}$ are each $\frac{1}{2}$ times the corresponding x-values for $g(x) = \sqrt{x}$. Therefore, to obtain the solutions for f, we use the same y-values as for g, but multiply each of the x-values for g by $\frac{1}{2}$ (look at the tables). In the figures below, you can see that the graph of $f(x) = \sqrt{2x}$ is similar to the graph of $g(x) = \sqrt{x}$, but 'pulled toward' (or **compressed toward**) the y-axis. We say that the graph of $f(x) = \sqrt{2x}$ is the **horizontal compression** of $g(x) = \sqrt{x}$ by a factor of $\frac{1}{2}$.

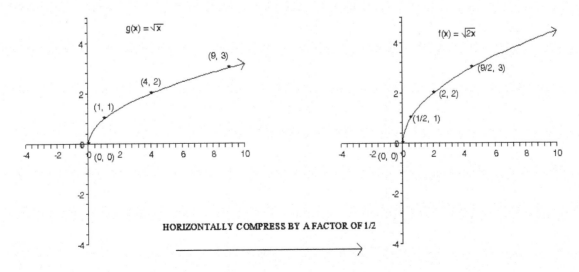

HORIZONTALLY COMPRESS BY A FACTOR OF 1/2

Notice that we can also obtain the graph by vertically stretching the graph of $g(x) = \sqrt{x}$ by a factor of $\sqrt{2}$ since

$$f(x) = \sqrt{2x} = \sqrt{2} \cdot \sqrt{x} = \sqrt{2} \cdot g(x).$$

2) $f(x) = \left|\dfrac{x}{2}\right|$

The function f has the absolute value function built into it. If $g(x) = |x|$, then we can write $f(x) = \left|\dfrac{x}{2}\right|$ as $f(x) = g\left(\dfrac{x}{2}\right) = g\left(\dfrac{1}{2}x\right)$. This means that **the graph of f can be obtained by horizontally stretching the graph of $g(x) = |x|$ by a factor of** $\dfrac{2}{1} = 2$. Once again, let's see why this occurs by looking at the tables for the solutions to $g(x) = |x|$ and $f(x) = \left|\dfrac{x}{2}\right|$.

x	$y = g(x) = |x|$	Solutions
-2	$|-2| = 2$	$(-2,\ 2)$
-1	$|-1| = 1$	$(-1,\ 1)$
0	$|0| = 0$	$(0,\ 0)$
1	$|1| = 1$	$(1,\ 1)$
2	$|2| = 2$	$(2,\ 2)$

and

x	$y = f(x) = \left|\dfrac{x}{2}\right|$	Solutions
-4	$\left|\frac{-4}{2}\right| = |-2| = 2$	$(-4,\ 2)$
-2	$\left|\frac{-2}{2}\right| = |-1| = 1$	$(-2,\ 1)$
0	$\left|\frac{0}{2}\right| = |0| = 0$	$(0,\ 0)$
2	$\left|\frac{2}{2}\right| = |1| = 1$	$(2,\ 1)$
4	$\left|\frac{4}{2}\right| = |2| = 2$	$(4,\ 2)$

Notice that the same y-values are used for each table. However, the x-values for $f(x) = \left|\dfrac{x}{2}\right|$ are each two times the corresponding x-values for $g(x) = |x|$. This means that we can obtain the solutions for f by using the same y-values for g, but multiplying each of the x-values for g by two (look at the tables). As you can see in the figures below, the graph of $f(x) = \left|\dfrac{x}{2}\right|$ is similar to the graph of $g(x) = |x|$, but 'pulled away' (or **stretched away**) from the y-axis. We say that the graph of $f(x) = \left|\dfrac{x}{2}\right|$ is the **horizontal stretch** of $g(x) = |x|$ by a factor of two.

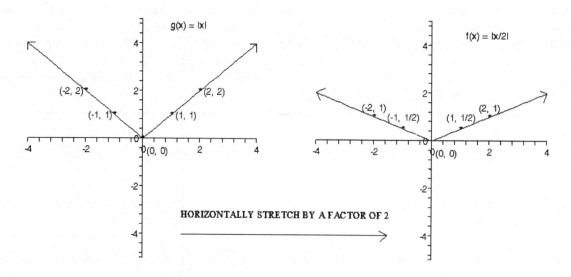

Observe that we can write $f(x) = \left|\dfrac{x}{2}\right|$ as

$$f(x) = \left|\frac{x}{2}\right| = \frac{|x|}{|2|} = \frac{|x|}{2} = \frac{1}{2}|x|.$$

So the graph is obtained by vertically compressing the graph of $g(x) = |x|$ by a factor of $\frac{1}{2}$. In general, every horizontal stretch/ compression of the graph of a basic function is the same as a vertical compression/ stretch of that basic function.

5) Reflections about the x-Axis

Suppose we know the graph of the function $y = f(x)$. The graph of $y = -f(x)$ is obtained by reflecting the graph of $y = f(x)$ about the x-axis.

Examples. Sketch.

1) $f(x) = -x^2$

Observe that $f(x) = -x^2$ is just the square function, $g(x) = x^2$, multiplied by -1. We can get the graph of f by reflecting the graph of the square function about the x-axis. To see why, let's look at the following tables:

x	$y = g(x) = x^2$	Solutions
-2	$(-2)^2 = 4$	$(-2, 4)$
-1	$(-1)^2 = 1$	$(-1, 1)$
0	$(0)^2 = 0$	$(0, 0)$
1	$(1)^2 = 1$	$(1, 1)$
2	$(2)^2 = 4$	$(2, 4)$

and

x	$y = f(x) = -x^2$	Solutions
-2	$-(-2)^2 = -4$	$(-2, -4)$
-1	$-(-1)^2 = -1$	$(-1, -1)$
0	$-(0)^2 = 0$	$(0, 0)$
1	$-(1)^2 = -1$	$(1, -1)$
2	$-(2)^2 = -4$	$(2, -4)$

Notice that the same x-values are used for each table. However, the y-values for $f(x) = -x^2$ are each -1 times the corresponding y-values for $g(x) = x^2$. Hence, we can obtain the solutions for $f(x) = -x^2$ by using the same x-values for $g(x) = x^2$, but multiplying each of the y-values for $g(x) = x^2$ by -1. The graphs of $f(x) = -x^2$ and $g(x) = x^2$ are given below.

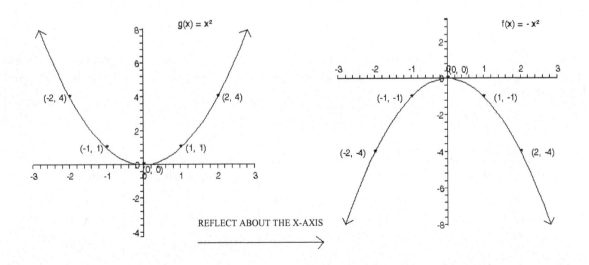

REFLECT ABOUT THE X-AXIS

2) $f(x) = -\dfrac{1}{x}$

Notice that $f(x) = -\dfrac{1}{x}$ is just the reciprocal function, $g(x) = \dfrac{1}{x}$, multiplied by -1. We can get the graph of f by reflecting the graph of the reciprocal function about the x-axis. The graphs of $f(x) = -\dfrac{1}{x}$ and $g(x) = \dfrac{1}{x}$ are given below.

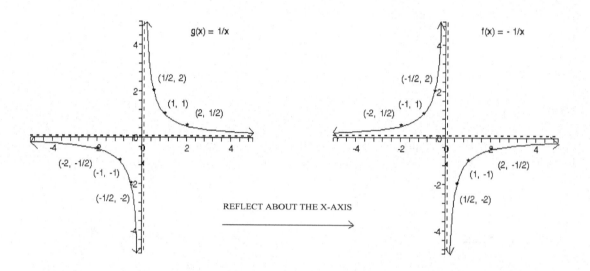

6) Reflections about the y-Axis

Suppose that we know the graph of the function $y = f(x)$. The graph of $y = f(-x)$ is obtained by reflecting the graph of $y = f(x)$ about the y-axis.

Examples. Sketch.

1) $f(x) = \sqrt{-x}$

Observe that $f(x) = \sqrt{-x}$ is just the square root function, $g(x) = \sqrt{x}$, with x multiplied by -1. We can get the graph of f by reflecting the graph of the square root function about the y-axis. To see why, let's look at the following tables:

x	$y = g(x) = \sqrt{x}$	Solutions
0	$\sqrt{0} = 0$	$(0, 0)$
1	$\sqrt{1} = 1$	$(1, 1)$
4	$\sqrt{4} = 2$	$(4, 2)$
9	$\sqrt{9} = 3$	$(9, 3)$

and

x	$y = f(x) = \sqrt{-x}$	Solutions
0	$\sqrt{-(0)} = \sqrt{0} = 0$	$(0, 0)$
-1	$\sqrt{-(-1)} = \sqrt{1} = 1$	$(-1, 1)$
-4	$\sqrt{-(-4)} = \sqrt{4} = 2$	$(-4, 2)$
-9	$\sqrt{-(-9)} = \sqrt{9} = 3$	$(-9, 3)$

Notice that the same y-values are obtained in each table. However, the x-values for $f(x) = \sqrt{-x}$ are each -1 times the corresponding x-values for $g(x) = \sqrt{x}$. Hence, we can obtain the solutions for $f(x) = \sqrt{-x}$ by using the same y-values for $g(x) = \sqrt{x}$, but multiplying each of the x-values for $g(x) = \sqrt{x}$ by -1.

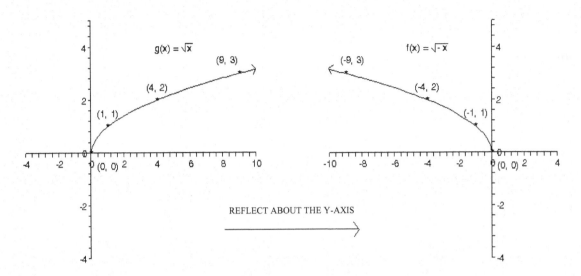

2) $h(x) = \dfrac{1}{-x}$

Notice that $h(x) = \dfrac{1}{-x}$ is just the reciprocal function $g(x) = \dfrac{1}{x}$ with x multiplied by -1. We can get the graph of h by reflecting the graph of g about the y-axis.

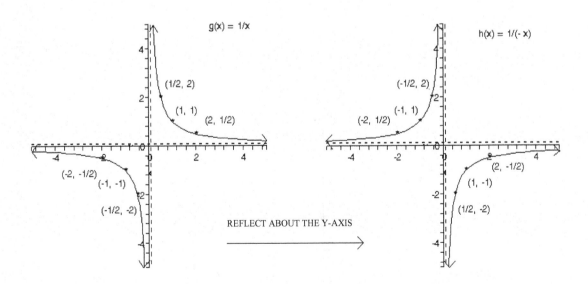

You may notice that the graph of $h(x) = \dfrac{1}{-x}$ is the same as the graph of $f(x) = -\dfrac{1}{x}$. It makes perfect sense since $\dfrac{1}{-x} = -\dfrac{1}{x}$. This means that the reflection of $y = \dfrac{1}{x}$ about the x-axis coincides with its reflection about the y-axis. What are the other basic functions with this property?

7) Combining the Graphing Techniques

Now we will graph functions which require the use of several of the graphing techniques that we have learned.

Examples. Sketch.

1) $f(x) = (x - 3)^2 + 1$

To begin with, notice that the square function is contained in the function f. Let's start by graphing $y = x^2$. Now, to graph the function $y = (x - 3)^2$, we will shift the graph of $y = x^2$ to the right by three units (since 3 is subtracted from the variable x). To get the graph of $f(x) = (x - 3)^2 + 1$, we will shift the graph of $y = (x - 3)^2$ upward by one unit (since we are adding one to the function $y = (x - 3)^2$). Each graph obtained by this procedure is given below.

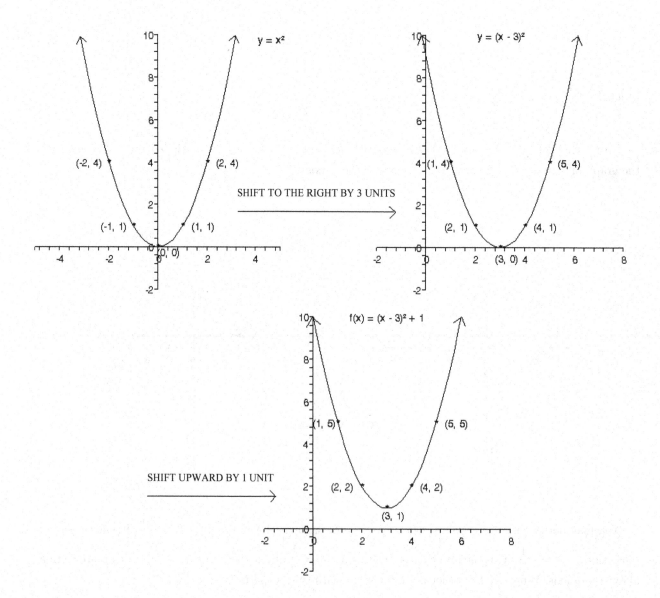

2) $g(x) = -\sqrt{x+4}$

Observe that the square root function is contained in the function g. Let's begin by graphing $y = \sqrt{x}$. Now, to graph the function $y = \sqrt{x+4}$, we will shift the graph of $y = \sqrt{x}$ to the left by four units (since 4 is added to the variable x). To graph $g(x) = -\sqrt{x+4}$, we will reflect the graph of $y = \sqrt{x+4}$ about the x-axis (since we multiply the function $y = \sqrt{x+4}$ by -1). Each graph obtained by this procedure is given below.

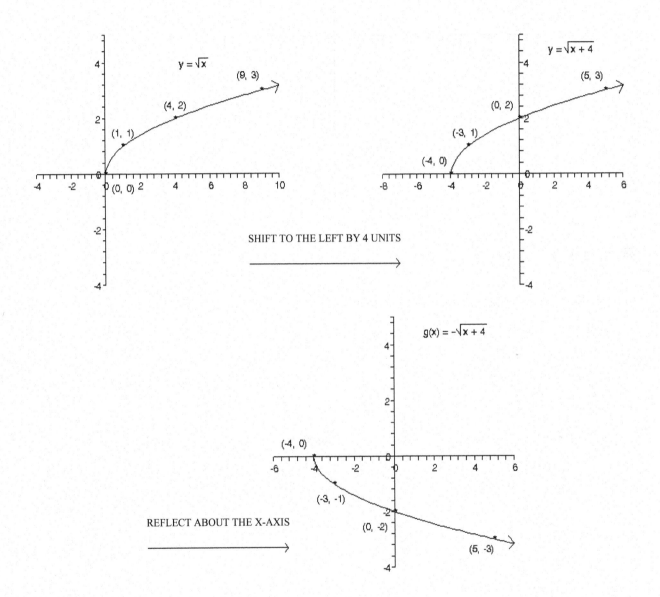

3) $g(x) = 3 - \frac{1}{2}|x+1|$

To begin with, let's rewrite our function as $g(x) = -\frac{1}{2}|x+1|+3$. The absolute value function is contained in g. Let's start by graphing $y = |x|$. Next, we will graph the function $y = |x+1|$ by shifting the graph of $y = |x|$ to the left by one unit (since 1 is added to the variable x). The graph of $y = -\frac{1}{2}|x+1|$ is then obtained by multiplying each of the y-values of the points of $y = |x+1|$ by $-\frac{1}{2}$ (this will produce a vertical compression by a factor of $\frac{1}{2}$ together with a reflection about the x-axis). The last step is to shift the graph of $y = -\frac{1}{2}|x+1|$ upward by three units (since we add 3 to the function $y = -\frac{1}{2}|x+1|$). The graph is on the next page.

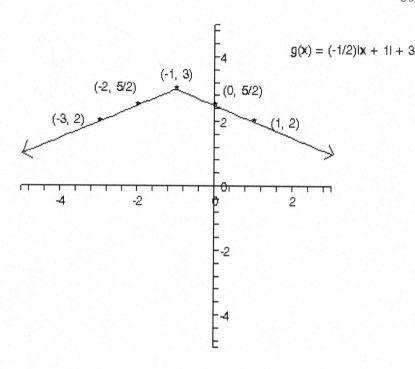

$g(x) = (-1/2)|x + 1| + 3$

(-1, 3)
(-2, 5/2)
(-3, 2)
(0, 5/2)
(1, 2)

Exercise R.5

In Exercises 1-8, sketch the graph of the given function.

1. $f(x) = x^2$ 2. $f(x) = x$ 3. $y = x^3$ 4. $y = \sqrt{x}$

5. $g(x) = |x|$ 6. $g(x) = [[x]]$ 7. $y = \dfrac{1}{x}$ 8. $f(x) = 5$

In Exercises 9-20,

   a) find $f(1)$.   b) find $f(-4)$.   c) find $f(3)$.   d) graph each function.

9. $f(x) = \begin{cases} x - 7 & \text{if } x > 2 \\ 2x & \text{if } x \le 2 \end{cases}$ 10. $f(x) = \begin{cases} 3x + 1 & \text{if } x \ge 0 \\ -4x & \text{if } x < 0 \end{cases}$ 11. $f(x) = \begin{cases} x^2 & \text{if } x \ge -2 \\ 5 & \text{if } x < -2 \end{cases}$

12. $f(x) = \begin{cases} x^2 & \text{if } x > 0 \\ -4 & \text{if } x \le 0 \end{cases}$ 13. $f(x) = \begin{cases} \sqrt{x} & \text{if } x \ge 1 \\ x^3 & \text{if } x < 1 \end{cases}$ 14. $f(x) = \begin{cases} \sqrt{x} & \text{if } x \ge 0 \\ x^2 & \text{if } x < 0 \end{cases}$

15. $f(x) = \begin{cases} x^2 & \text{if } x > 3 \\ -x + 1 & \text{if } -4 < x \le 3 \\ 2 & \text{if } x = -4 \end{cases}$ 16. $f(x) = \begin{cases} 2x - 6 & \text{if } x > -1 \\ -3 & \text{if } x = -1 \\ -x + 4 & \text{if } x < -1 \end{cases}$

17. $f(x) = \begin{cases} -1 & \text{if } x \ge 2 \\ x^3 & \text{if } -1 < x < 2 \\ x + 3 & \text{if } x \le -1 \end{cases}$ 18. $f(x) = \begin{cases} \sqrt{x} & \text{if } x \ge 4 \\ 5 - 2x & \text{if } -2 < x < 4 \\ 2 & \text{if } x \le -2 \end{cases}$

19. $f(x) = \begin{cases} 3x + 1 & \text{if } x \ge 2 \\ 4 & \text{if } 0 \le x < 2 \\ \dfrac{1}{x} & \text{if } x < 0 \end{cases}$ 20. $f(x) = \begin{cases} \dfrac{1}{x} & \text{if } x > 1 \\ -1 & \text{if } x = 1 \\ x^3 & \text{if } x < 1 \end{cases}$

In Exercises 21-56, sketch each function using the graphing techniques discussed in this section.

21. $f(x) = x^2 + 2$ 22. $f(x) = x^2 - 3$ 23. $f(x) = x^3 - 1$ 24. $f(x) = x^3 + 2$

25. $g(x) = |x| + 4$ 26. $g(x) = |x| - 4$ 27. $g(x) = \sqrt{x} - 2$ 28. $g(x) = \sqrt{x} + 1$

29. $f(x) = \dfrac{1}{x} + 5$ 30. $f(x) = \dfrac{1}{x} - 2$ 31. $h(x) = (x - 2)^2$ 32. $h(x) = (x + 1)^2$

33. $y = (x + 3)^3$ 34. $y = (x - 1)^3$ 35. $g(x) = \sqrt{x - 2}$ 36. $g(x) = \sqrt{x + 6}$

37. $f(x) = |x + 4|$ 38. $f(x) = |x - 2|$ 39. $y = \dfrac{1}{x - 3}$ 40. $y = \dfrac{1}{x + 3}$

41. $f(x) = -x^3$ 42. $f(x) = -\sqrt{x}$ 43. $f(x) = -|x|$ 44. $y = \dfrac{1}{-x}$

45. $f(x) = (x + 1)^2 + 2$ 46. $f(x) = (x - 2)^2 + 1$ 47. $h(x) = -x^2 - 3$ 48. $h(x) = -x^2 + 2$

49. $g(x) = -|x + 4| + 2$ 50. $g(x) = -|x - 3| + 1$ 51. $f(x) = \dfrac{1}{x + 3} - 1$ 52. $f(x) = \dfrac{1}{x - 2} - 3$

53. $y = \frac{1}{2}x^3 + 2$ 54. $y = \frac{1}{4}x^3 + 4$ 55. $f(x) = \dfrac{2}{x} - 3$ 56. $f(x) = \dfrac{4}{x} + 2$

Section R.6   Algebra of Functions

Recall that we can construct new functions from old ones by using algebraic techniques such as addition, subtraction, multiplication, division, and composition. We will review these techniques in this section.

Addition, Subtraction, Multiplication, and Division of Functions

Definitions: Suppose $y = f(x)$ and $y = g(x)$ are two functions.

1) The **sum** of f and g, written as $f + g$, is

$$(f + g)(x) = f(x) + g(x).$$

The domain of $f + g$ is the set of numbers which are in the domains of both f and g.

2) The **difference** of f and g, written as $f - g$, is

$$(f - g)(x) = f(x) - g(x).$$

The domain of $f - g$ is the set of numbers which are in the domains of both f and g.

3) The **product** of f and g, written as $f \cdot g$, is

$$(f \cdot g)(x) = f(x) \cdot g(x).$$

The domain of $f \cdot g$ is the set of numbers which are in the domains of both f and g.

4) The **quotient** of f and g, written as $\dfrac{f}{g}$, is

$$\left(\frac{f}{g}\right)(x) = \frac{f(x)}{g(x)}.$$

The domain of $\dfrac{f}{g}$ is the set of numbers which are in the domains of both f and g such that $g(x) \neq 0$.

Examples. Let $f(x) = x^2 - 5x - 6$ and $g(x) = 2x - 1$.

1) Find $(f+g)(x)$ and its domain.

By definition, $(f+g)(x) = f(x) + g(x) = \underbrace{(x^2 - 5x - 6)}_{f(x)} + \underbrace{(2x - 1)}_{g(x)} = x^2 - 3x - 7$. The domain of $f + g$
is the set of all real numbers since the domain of both f and g is the set of all real numbers (they are polynomial functions).

2) Find $(f-g)(x)$ and its domain.

By definition, $(f-g)(x) = f(x) - g(x) = \underbrace{(x^2 - 5x - 6)}_{f(x)} - \underbrace{(2x - 1)}_{g(x)} = x^2 - 7x - 5$. The domain of $f - g$
is the set of all real numbers since the domain of both f and g is the set of all real numbers.

3) Find $(f \cdot g)(x)$ and its domain.

By definition, $(f \cdot g)(x) = f(x) \cdot g(x) = \underbrace{(x^2 - 5x - 6)}_{f(x)} \cdot \underbrace{(2x - 1)}_{g(x)} = 2x^3 - 11x^2 - 7x + 6$. The domain of
$f \cdot g$ is the set of all real numbers.

4) Find $\left(\dfrac{f}{g}\right)(x)$ and its domain.

By definition, $\left(\dfrac{f}{g}\right)(x) = \dfrac{f(x)}{g(x)} = \dfrac{x^2 - 5x - 6}{2x - 1}$. The domain of $\dfrac{f}{g}$ is the set of all real numbers **except**
$x = \frac{1}{2}$ since $g\left(\frac{1}{2}\right) = 2\left(\frac{1}{2}\right) - 1 = 0$.

Examples. Let $f(x) = \sqrt{x - 5}$ and $g(x) = \dfrac{4}{x + 2}$.

1) Find $(f+g)(6)$.

By definition, $(f+g)(6) = f(6) + g(6) = \underbrace{\sqrt{6 - 5}}_{f(6)=1} + \underbrace{\frac{4}{6 + 2}}_{g(6)=\frac{4}{8}} = \sqrt{1} + \frac{4}{8} = 1 + \frac{1}{2} = \frac{3}{2}$. Notice that we **do**
not need to find $(f+g)(x)$ in order to solve this problem.

2) Find $(f - g)(5)$.

By definition, $(f - g)(5) = f(5) - g(5) = \underbrace{\sqrt{5-5}}_{f(5)=0} - \underbrace{\frac{4}{5+2}}_{g(5)=\frac{4}{7}} = \sqrt{0} - \frac{4}{7} = 0 - \frac{4}{7} = -\frac{4}{7}$. Notice that we **do**

not need to find $(f - g)(x)$ first.

3) Find $(f \cdot g)(x)$ and its domain.

By definition, $(f \cdot g)(x) = f(x) \cdot g(x) = \underbrace{\sqrt{x-5}}_{f(x)} \cdot \underbrace{\frac{4}{x+2}}_{g(x)} = \frac{4\sqrt{x-5}}{x+2}$. Observe that the domain of f is

$\{x \mid x \geq 5\}$ and the domain of g is $\{x \mid x \neq -2\}$. Since every value in the domain of f is contained in the domain of g, the domain of $f \cdot g$ is the same as the domain of f, $\{x \mid x \geq 5\}$.

4) Find $\left(\dfrac{f}{g}\right)(9)$.

We have that $\left(\dfrac{f}{g}\right)(9) = \dfrac{f(9)}{g(9)} = \dfrac{\sqrt{9-5}}{\frac{4}{9+2}} = \dfrac{\sqrt{4}}{\frac{4}{11}} = \dfrac{2(11)}{\frac{4}{\cancel{11}}(\cancel{11})} = \dfrac{22}{4} = \dfrac{11}{2}$.

Examples. Let $g(x) = |x + 7|$ and $h(x) = x^2 - x - 6$.

1) Find $(h - g)(-1)$.

By definition, $(h - g)(-1) = h(-1) - g(-1) = \underbrace{(-1)^2 - (-1) - 6}_{h(-1)=-4} - \underbrace{|(-1) + 7|}_{g(-1)=6} = -4 - 6 = -10$.

2) Find $(g + h)(x)$ and its domain.

By definition, $(g + h)(x) = g(x) + h(x) = |x + 7| + x^2 - x - 6$. The domain of $g + h$ is the set of all real numbers.

3) Find $\left(\dfrac{g}{h}\right)(x)$ and its domain.

By definition, $\left(\dfrac{g}{h}\right)(x) = \dfrac{g(x)}{h(x)} = \dfrac{|x + 7|}{x^2 - x - 6}$. The domain of $\dfrac{g}{h}$ is $\{x \mid x \neq 3, x \neq -2\}$ since the domain of both g and h is the set of all real numbers and $h(x) = 0$ when $x = 3$ and $x = -2$.

Examples. Let $f(x) = x + \dfrac{1}{x}$ and $g(x) = 3 - \dfrac{1}{x}$.

1) Find $(f + g)(x)$ and its domain.

By definition, $(f + g)(x) = f(x) + g(x) = \left(x + \dfrac{1}{x}\right) + \left(3 - \dfrac{1}{x}\right) = x + 3$. The domain of $f + g$ is $\{x \mid x \neq 0\}$. Observe that $x + 3$ is well-defined when we replace x by 3. However, since $(f + g)(x) = x + 3$

is created by adding two functions each of whose domain is $\{x \mid x \neq 0\}$, we cannot include 0 in the domain of $f + g$.

2) Find $(f - g)(2)$.

By definition, $(f - g)(2) = f(2) - g(2) = \left(2 + \dfrac{1}{2}\right) - \left(3 - \dfrac{1}{2}\right) = \dfrac{5}{2} - \dfrac{5}{2} = 0$.

3) Find $\left(\dfrac{f}{g}\right)(x)$ and its domain.

By definition, $\left(\dfrac{f}{g}\right)(x) = \dfrac{f(x)}{g(x)} = \dfrac{x + \frac{1}{x}}{3 - \frac{1}{x}} = \dfrac{x(x) + \frac{1}{\cancel{x}}(\cancel{x})}{3(x) - \frac{1}{\cancel{x}}(\cancel{x})} = \dfrac{x^2 + 1}{3x - 1}$. The domain of $\dfrac{f}{g}$ is $\{x \mid x \neq 0,\ x \neq \frac{1}{3}\}$.

Notice that $x \neq \frac{1}{3}$ since the denominator of $\dfrac{x^2 + 1}{3x - 1}$ equals zero when $x = \frac{1}{3}$.

The Composition of Functions

When we discussed functions, we evaluated functions for specific domain values. For example, if $f(x) = 4x - 5$, then we can compute $f(3)$ by replacing x by 3 in the function f:

$$f(3) = 4(3) - 5 = 12 - 5 = 7$$

What if we want to replace the variable x in f by a function? For example, if $g(x) = 2x$, how will we compute $f(2x)$? Well, all we would do is to replace the variable x in $f(x) = 4x - 5$ by $2x$:

$$f(2x) = 4(2x) - 5 = 8x - 5$$

If $g(x) = -x + 6$, we could compute $f(-x + 6)$ by replacing the variable x in $f(x) = 4x - 5$ by $-x + 6$:

$$f(-x + 6) = 4(-x + 6) - 5 = -4x + 19$$

We can replace the variable x in a function $y = f(x)$ by another function $y = g(x)$ as we've done above and, as a result, obtain a new function provided that the result is well-defined. When we do so, we construct the **composition** of the function f with the function g.

Definition: Suppose $y = f(x)$ and $y = g(x)$ are two functions. Then $y = (f \circ g)(x) = f(g(x))$ is called the **composition function**.

We read "$f \circ g$" as "f **composed with** g" and call "$\circ$" the **composition symbol**.

The domain of $f \circ g$ is $\{x \mid x$ is in the domain of g and $g(x)$ is in the domain of $f\}$. We will soon see how to find the domain of composition functions. The next diagram will give you an idea of how this domain is derived.

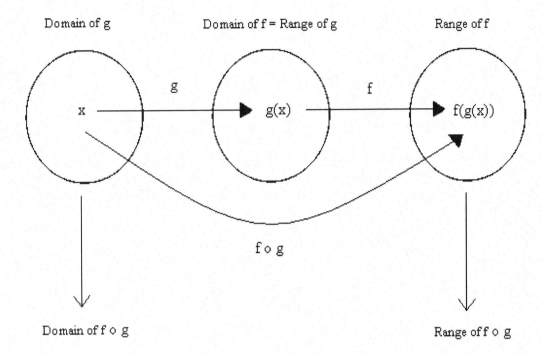

Examples. Suppose $f(x) = 2x + 5$ and $g(x) = -3x + 1$.

1) Find $(f \circ g)(x)$.

By definition,

$$(f \circ g)(x) = f(g(x)) = f(\underbrace{-3x + 1}_{g(x)}) = 2(-3x + 1) + 5 = -6x + 7.$$

2) Find $(f \circ g)(2)$.

Since $(f \circ g)(x) = -6x + 7$, we have that $(f \circ g)(2) = -6(2) + 7 = -5$.

3) Find $(g \circ f)(-1)$.

By definition,

$$(g \circ f)(-1) = g\underbrace{(f(-1))}_{2(-1)+5=3} = g(3) = -3(3) + 1 = -8.$$

Notice that we don't need to construct $(g \circ f)(x)$ to find this answer.

4) Find $(g \circ f)(x)$.

By definition,

$$(g \circ f)(x) = g(f(x)) = g(\underbrace{2x + 5}_{f(x)}) = -3(2x + 5) + 1 = -6x - 14.$$

Examples. Suppose $f(x) = \dfrac{1}{x}$ and $g(x) = x^2 + 2x + 1$.

1) Find $(f \circ g)(x)$ and its domain.

By definition,

$$(f \circ g)(x) = f(g(x)) = f(x^2 + 2x + 1) = \frac{1}{x^2 + 2x + 1}.$$

The domain of g is the set of all real numbers and the domain of f is the set of all real numbers **except** 0. By definition, the domain of $f \circ g$ is the set of numbers (the x-values) which are in the domain of g and such that $g(x)$ is in the domain of f. This means that the domain of $f \circ g$ is the set of all x-values for which $\underbrace{x^2 + 2x + 1}_{g(x)} \neq 0$. Since $x^2 + 2x + 1 = 0$ when $x = -1$, the domain of $f \circ g$ is $\{x \mid x \neq -1\}$.

2) Find $(g \circ f)(x)$ and its domain.

By definition,

$$(g \circ f)(x) = g(f(x)) = g\left(\frac{1}{x}\right) = \left(\frac{1}{x}\right)^2 + 2\left(\frac{1}{x}\right) + 1 = \frac{1}{x^2} + \frac{2}{x} + 1 = \frac{1 + 2x + x^2}{x^2}.$$

To find the domain of $g \circ f$, we look for those numbers, x, that are in the domain of f such that $f(x)$ is in the domain of g. The domain of f is the set of all real numbers **except** 0, and the domain of g is the set of all real numbers. Since the domain of g is the set of all real numbers, **every** value of $f(x)$ is in the domain of g. This implies that the domain of $g \circ f$ is the set of all x-values such that $x \neq 0$.

Examples. Suppose $f(x) = \sqrt{x+2}$ and $g(x) = \dfrac{2}{x}$.

1) Find $(f \circ g)(1)$.

By definition,

$$(f \circ g)(1) = f(\underbrace{g(1)}_{\frac{2}{1} = 2}) = f(2) = \sqrt{(2) + 2} = \sqrt{4} = 2.$$

2) Find $(f \circ g)(x)$ and its domain.

By definition,

$$(f \circ g)(x) = f(g(x)) = f\left(\frac{2}{x}\right) = \sqrt{\left(\frac{2}{x}\right) + 2} = \sqrt{\frac{2}{x} + 2} = \sqrt{\frac{2 + 2x}{x}}.$$

The domain of $f \circ g$ is the set of x-values which satisfy the inequality $\dfrac{2 + 2x}{x} \geq 0$ (why?). Let's solve this rational inequality. The critical numbers are $x = -1$ and $x = 0$. The number line is:

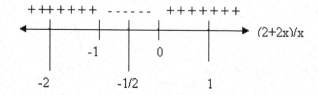

The solution set is $\{x \mid x \leq -1 \text{ or } x > 0\}$. Therefore, the domain of $f \circ g$ is $\{x \mid x \leq -1 \text{ or } x > 0\}$.

3) Find $(g \circ f)(7)$.

By definition,

$$(g \circ f)(7) = g\underbrace{(f(7))}_{\sqrt{7+2}=3} = g(3) = \frac{2}{3}.$$

4) Find $(g \circ g)(x)$ and its domain.

By definition,

$$(g \circ g)(x) = g(g(x)) = g\left(\frac{2}{x}\right) = \frac{2}{\left(\dfrac{2}{x}\right)} = \frac{2(x)}{\left(\dfrac{2}{\not x}\right)(\not x)} = \frac{2x}{2} = x.$$

Now, the domain of $g \circ g$ is $\{x \mid x \neq 0\}$ because the domain of g is $\{x \mid x \neq 0\}$. Observe that $(g \circ g)(x) = x$ is like the identity function $f(x) = x$, except that their domains are different.

Exercise R.6

In Exercises 1-16, use the functions $f(x) = -3x + 5$, $g(x) = |x| + 2$, and $h(x) = \dfrac{x+3}{x-3}$.

1. Find $(f + g)(x)$ and its domain.

2. Find $(f - g)(x)$ and its domain.

3. Find $(f - h)(x)$ and its domain.

4. Find $(g + h)(x)$ and its domain.

5. Find $(f \cdot g)(x)$ and its domain.

6. Find $(h \cdot f)(x)$ and its domain.

7. Find $\left(\dfrac{g}{f}\right)(x)$ and its domain.

8. Find $\left(\dfrac{f}{g}\right)(x)$ and its domain.

9. Find $(h + g)(6)$.

10. Find $(f - g)(2)$.

11. Find $(f - h)(9)$.

12. Find $(g + h)(-4)$.

13. Find $(f \cdot g)(-2)$.

14. Find $(h \cdot f)(0)$.

15. Find $\left(\dfrac{h}{g}\right)(0)$.

16. Find $\left(\dfrac{g}{f}\right)(-3)$.

In Exercises 17-38, use the functions $f(x) = x - 8$, $g(x) = \sqrt{x}$, and $h(x) = 5$.

17. Find $(f - g)(x)$ and its domain.

18. Find $(g + h)(x)$ and its domain.

19. Find $(f + h)(x)$ and its domain.

20. Find $(h - f)(x)$ and its domain.

21. Find $(f \cdot f)(x)$ and its domain.

22. Find $(h \cdot g)(x)$ and its domain.

23. Find $(g \cdot g)(x)$ and its domain.

24. Find $(h \cdot h)(x)$ and its domain.

25. Find $\left(\dfrac{g}{f}\right)(x)$ and its domain.

26. Find $\left(\dfrac{h}{g}\right)(x)$ and its domain.

27. Find $(f + g)(25)$.

28. Find $(f - h)(6)$.

29. Find $(h - g)(4)$.

30. Find $(g + h)(16)$.

31. Find $(g \cdot f)(1)$.

32. Find $(f \cdot h)(6)$.   33. Find $(h \cdot f)(0)$.   34. Find $(g \cdot g)(9)$.   35. Find $\left(\dfrac{f}{h}\right)(-7)$.

36. Find $\left(\dfrac{h}{g}\right)(16)$.   37. Find $\left(\dfrac{f}{f}\right)(2)$.   38. Find $\left(\dfrac{g}{g}\right)(81)$.

In Exercises 39-53, use the functions $f(x) = 4x - 1$, $g(x) = \sqrt{x}$, and $h(x) = \dfrac{x+3}{x-3}$.

39. Find $(f \circ g)(x)$ and its domain.   40. Find $(g \circ f)(x)$ and its domain.

41. Find $(h \circ f)(x)$ and its domain.   42. Find $(f \circ h)(x)$ and its domain.

43. Find $(f \circ f)(x)$ and its domain.   44. Find $(g \circ g)(x)$ and its domain.

45. Find $(h \circ h)(x)$ and its domain.   46. Find $(g \circ h)(x)$ and its domain.

47. Find $(h \circ g)(16)$.   48. Find $(f \circ h)(2)$.   49. Find $(g \circ h)(5)$.   50. Find $(f \circ g)(36)$.

51. Find $(f \circ f)(0)$.   52. Find $(g \circ g)(81)$.   53. Find $(h \circ h)(9)$.

In Exercises 54-68, use the functions $f(x) = -3$, $g(x) = |x+4|$ and $h(x) = -5x + 2$.

54. Find $(g \circ f)(x)$.   55. Find $(f \circ g)(x)$.   56. Find $(f \circ h)(x)$.   57. Find $(h \circ f)(x)$.

58. Find $(h \circ h)(x)$.   59. Find $(f \circ f)(x)$.   60. Find $(g \circ h)(2)$.   61. Find $(g \circ h)(-3)$.

62. Find $(f \circ h)(4)$.   63. Find $(f \circ h)(-6)$.   64. Find $(g \circ g)(0)$.   65. Find $(h \circ h)(0)$.

66. Find $(f \circ f)(0)$.   67. Find $(g \circ g)(-7)$.   68. Find $(h \circ h)(-1)$.

In Exercises 69-86, for the given functions f and g, find:
  a) $f \circ g$ b) $g \circ f$ c) $f \circ f$ d) $g \circ g$

69. $f(x) = 3x$; $g(x) = x - 2$ 70. $f(x) = 5x$; $g(x) = x + 1$

71. $f(x) = -x + 4$; $g(x) = 3x - 7$ 72. $f(x) = -x + 2$; $g(x) = 2x + 5$

73. $f(x) = 2$; $g(x) = 4x + 3$ 74. $f(x) = 4$; $g(x) = 7x - 2$

75. $f(x) = \sqrt{x}$; $g(x) = 5x + 7$ 76. $f(x) = \sqrt{x}$; $g(x) = 9x - 1$

77. $f(x) = \dfrac{x}{x+1}$; $g(x) = \dfrac{2}{x}$ 78. $f(x) = \dfrac{x-1}{x}$; $g(x) = \dfrac{x}{2}$

79. $f(x) = \dfrac{x+1}{3x}$; $g(x) = 3x - 2$ 80. $f(x) = \dfrac{x}{2x+1}$; $g(x) = 2x + 5$

81. $f(x) = x^2 - 4$; $g(x) = x^2 + 3$ 82. $f(x) = x^2 + 2$; $g(x) = x^2 - 6$

83. $f(x) = |x| + 4$; $g(x) = x^2$ 84. $f(x) = |x + 8|$; $g(x) = x^2$

85. $f(x) = \dfrac{1}{x+2}$; $g(x) = \dfrac{1}{4x-9}$ 86. $f(x) = \dfrac{1}{5x+7}$; $g(x) = \dfrac{1}{x+1}$

Section R.7   Inverse Functions

In this section, we will review inverse functions. From this point on, **we will assume that every function is onto** (so if the function f corresponds elements of the domain, X, to elements of the set, Y, then every element of Y is in the range of f).

The Inverse of a Function

Definition: Suppose f is a function which assigns a domain member a to a range member b (in functional notation, $f(a) = b$). The **inverse** of f is a correspondence whose first set is the range of f, and whose second set is the domain of f, which assigns $b = f(a)$ to a.

In order to understand this definition, let's look at a specific function and its inverse in detail. Suppose we are given the function f defined as

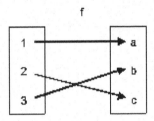

The domain of f is $\{1, 2, 3\}$, and the range of f is $\{a, b, c\}$. Recall that we can represent this function by using different notations. As a set of ordered pairs, we have

$$\{(1,\ a),\ (2,\ c),\ (3,\ b)\}.$$

In functional notation, we have $f(1) = a$, $f(2) = c$, and $f(3) = b$.

Now, let's 'go backwards' and create a correspondence between the sets $\{a, b, c\}$ and $\{1, 2, 3\}$ by reversing the arrows as follows:

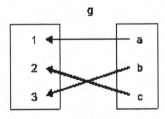

This correspondence is a new function (call it g) which is just the function f written backwards (that is, with the arrows pointing in the opposite direction). Observe that the domain of f is now the range of g, and the range of f is the domain of g. We call g the **inverse** of the function f. Let's write different notations for this inverse, g. As a set of ordered pairs, we have

$$\{(a,\ 1),\ (c,\ 2),\ (b,\ 3)\}.$$

In functional notation, we have

$$g\,(a) = 1,\ g\,(c) = 2,\ \text{and}\ g\,(b) = 3.$$

Notice that the ordered pairs for g are just the ordered pairs for f with the orders changed.

The previous example has demonstrated a function, f, whose inverse, g, is a function. However, it may not always be the case that the inverse of a function is, again, a function. For example, suppose f is defined as:

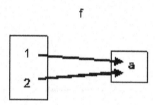

Then f is a function with domain $\{1,\ 2\}$ and range $\{a\}$. The inverse of this function, call it g, is:

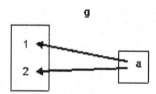

Observe that g is not a function since each member of the first set (in this case, just a) corresponds to two members of the second set: 1 and 2. This shows us that **not every function has an inverse which is also a function**.

One-to-One Functions

Suppose f is a function. What property must f have so that its inverse is also a function? Well, let's look at the two examples from before. For the function f : $\begin{array}{c} 1 \longrightarrow a \\ 2 \longrightarrow c \\ 3 \longrightarrow b \end{array}$, observe that each range member is corresponded to **exactly once** by a domain member. This means that when we 'reverse the arrows', we get a function. On the other hand, the range member, a, for f : $\begin{array}{c} 1 \longrightarrow a \\ 2 \longrightarrow a \end{array}$ is corresponded to **two times**. This means that when we 'reverse the arrows', we don't get a function. In other words, a function f has an inverse which is a function whenever each range member of f is corresponded to exactly once.

Definition: A function $y = f(x)$ is called **one-to-one** if each range member of f is corresponded to exactly once.

The definition states that once we know that an x-value, say $x = a$, corresponds to a y-value, say $y = b$, then no other x-value can correspond to b. Algebraically, the **definition** of a one-to-one function is:

A function $y = f(x)$ is called **one-to-one** if, for any members x_1 and x_2 in the domain of f, the following is true:

$$\text{Whenever } x_1 \neq x_2, \text{ we have that } f(x_1) \neq f(x_2).$$

An equivalent definition is:

$$\text{Whenever } f(x_1) = f(x_2), \text{ we have that } x_1 = x_2.$$

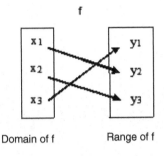

Domain of f   Range of f

f is one-to-one since each range member of f is corresponded to exactly once. In other words, each range member is the image of exactly one domain member.

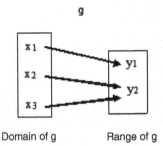

Domain of g   Range of g

g is not one-to-one since the range member y2 is corresponded to by two domain members.

It turns out that every function which is either increasing or decreasing on its domain is one-to-one. For example, $f(x) = x^3$ increases on the interval $(-\infty, \infty)$, which is its domain. This function is one-to-one. To show this algebraically, let's use the equivalent definition above. Suppose that x_1 and x_2 are any two real numbers and suppose that $f(x_1) = f(x_2)$. We want to show that $x_1 = x_2$. Well, $f(x_1) = f(x_2)$ means $(x_1)^3 = (x_2)^3$. If we cube root both sides of this equation, we will get $x_1 = x_2$. This is what we wanted to show.

We will learn how to determine whether or not a given function is one-to-one. To do this, we will use a graphical technique in which we apply the horizontal line test. An algebraic technique is also available, but we will not be concerned with it here.

The Horizontal Line Test

The horizontal line test states that a function $y = f(x)$ is one-to-one if no horizontal line crosses through the graph of f more than once. In Figure (a) (see the next page), any horizontal line which goes through the graph of f crosses at exactly one point. This means that f is one-to-one. Figure (b) on the next page shows the graph of a function, g, which fails the horizontal line test since the horizontal line drawn crosses the graph of g at four points. Therefore, g is not one-to-one.

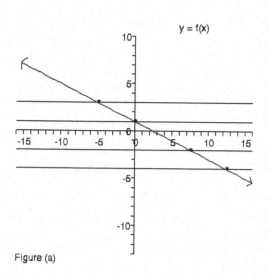

Figure (a)

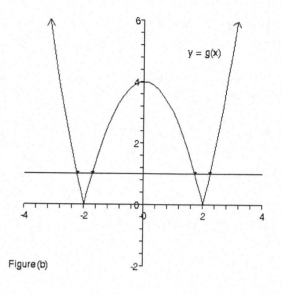

Figure (b)

Examples. Which functions are one-to-one?

1) $f(x) = x - 3$

   f is a one-to-one function since it passes the horizontal line test.

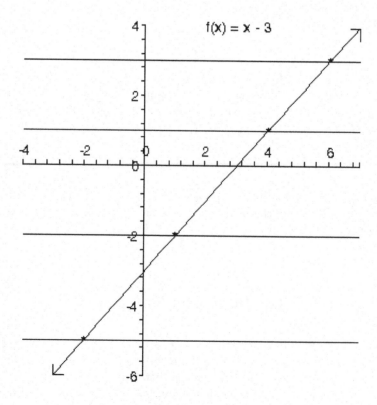

2) $g(x) = (x + 2)^3$

   g is a one-to-one function since it passes the horizontal line test.

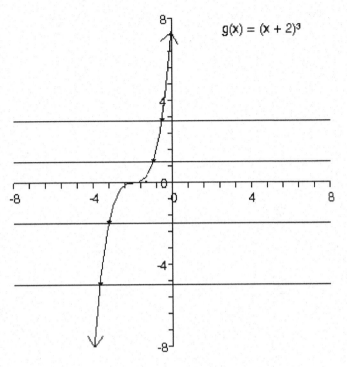

3) $f(x) = x^2$

   f is not a one-to-one function since it fails the horizontal line test.

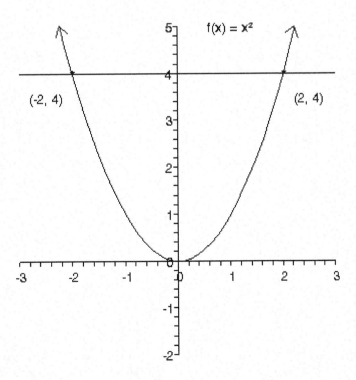

Observe that the horizontal line $y = 4$ crosses the graph twice, at $(-2, 4)$ and at $(-2, 4)$. This means that the y-value of 4 is corresponded to by **two** x-values, -2 and 2.

Inverse Functions and their Properties

We have seen that if $y = f(x)$ is a one-to-one function, then its inverse is also a function.

Definition: If $y = f(x)$ is a one-to-one function, then the inverse of f, written as $y = f^{-1}(x)$, is called the **inverse function** of f.

We read '$y = f^{-1}(x)$' as 'y equals f inverse of x'.

The notation for $f^{-1}(x)$ is sometimes confused with exponentiation. Be careful not to make this mistake!

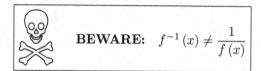

BEWARE: $f^{-1}(x) \neq \dfrac{1}{f(x)}$

Notice that

> the domain of f is the same as the range of f^{-1} and
> the range of f is the same as the domain of f^{-1}.

For example:

$$f: \begin{array}{ccc} \text{domain} & & \text{range} \\ 1 & \longrightarrow & a \\ 2 & \longrightarrow & c \\ 3 & \longrightarrow & b \end{array} \qquad\qquad f^{-1}: \begin{array}{ccc} \text{domain} & & \text{range} \\ a & \longrightarrow & 1 \\ c & \longrightarrow & 2 \\ b & \longrightarrow & 3 \end{array}$$

There is an important relationship that exists between $y = f(x)$ and $y = f^{-1}(x)$ which is true for any one-to-one function and its inverse function.

> $\left(f^{-1} \circ f\right)(x) = f^{-1}(f(x)) = x$ for any x in the domain of f and
> $\left(f \circ f^{-1}\right)(x) = f(f^{-1}(x)) = x$ for any x in the domain of f^{-1}.

Notice that in the Example above, we have that

$$\left(f^{-1} \circ f\right)(1) = f^{-1}(\underbrace{f(1)}_{a}) = f^{-1}(a) = 1.$$

When we compute $\left(f \circ f^{-1}\right)(b)$, we obtain

$$\left(f \circ f^{-1}\right)(b) = f(\underbrace{f^{-1}(b)}_{3}) = f(3) = b.$$

It turns out that if $y = f(x)$ is a one-to-one function and $y = g(x)$ is a function for which both $(g \circ f)(x) = g(f(x)) = x$ (x is in the domain of f) and $(f \circ g)(x) = f(g(x)) = x$ (x is in the domain of f), then $y = g(x)$ is the inverse function of $y = f(x)$.

Examples. Show that $y = f(x)$ and $y = g(x)$ are inverse functions of each other.

1) $f(x) = 5x + 2$ and $g(x) = \frac{1}{5}x - \frac{2}{5}$

To verify that $y = f(x)$ and $y = g(x)$ are inverses of each other, we need to show that $(g \circ f)(x) = x$ and $(f \circ g)(x) = x$. Notice that the domain of both $y = f(x)$ and $y = g(x)$ is the set of all real numbers.

$$(f \circ g)(x) = f(g(x)) = f\left(\frac{1}{5}x - \frac{2}{5}\right) = 5\left(\frac{1}{5}x - \frac{2}{5}\right) + 2 = x - 2 + 2 = x$$

and

$$(g \circ f)(x) = g(f(x)) = g(5x + 2) = \frac{1}{5}(5x + 2) - \frac{2}{5} = x + \frac{2}{5} - \frac{2}{5} = x.$$

Since both compositions work out to equal x, $y = f(x)$ and $y = g(x)$ are inverses of each other.

2) $f(x) = x^3 - 4$ and $g(x) = \sqrt[3]{x + 4}$

Again, we need to verify that $(g \circ f)(x) = x$ and $(f \circ g)(x) = x$. Notice that the domain of both $y = f(x)$ and $y = g(x)$ is the set of all real numbers.

$$(f \circ g)(x) = f(g(x)) = f\left(\sqrt[3]{x + 4}\right) = \left(\sqrt[3]{x + 4}\right)^3 - 4 = x + 4 - 4 = x$$

and

$$(g \circ f)(x) = g(f(x)) = g(x^3 - 4) = \sqrt[3]{(x^3 - 4) + 4} = \sqrt[3]{x^3} = x.$$

Therefore, $y = f(x)$ and $y = g(x)$ are inverses of each other.

3) $f(x) = x^2$, $x \geq 0$ and $g(x) = \sqrt{x}$

Note: $f(x) = x^2$ is **not** a one-to-one function on $(-\infty, \infty)$ since its graph fails the horizontal line test (right?). However, it **is** one-to one on the restricted domain $\{x \mid x \geq 0\}$. This is why the domain for f is given in this way. It turns out that if we restrict the domain in a different way, we will obtain a different inverse.

We need to verify that $(g \circ f)(x) = x$ and $(f \circ g)(x) = x$.

$$(f \circ g)(x) = \underbrace{f(g(x)) = f(\sqrt{x})}_{\sqrt{x} \geq 0, \text{ so this can be 'put into } f\text{'}.} = (\sqrt{x})^2 = x$$

and

$$(g \circ f)(x) = \underbrace{g(f(x)) = g(x^2)}_{x^2 \geq 0, \text{ so this can be 'put into } g\text{'}.} = \sqrt{x^2} = \underbrace{|x| = x}_{\text{since } x \geq 0 \text{ (why?)}}.$$

Therefore, $y = f(x)$ and $y = g(x)$ are inverses of each other.

4) $f(x) = \dfrac{3}{x - 1}$ and $g(x) = \dfrac{x + 3}{x}$

We need to verify that $(g \circ f)(x) = x$ and $(f \circ g)(x) = x$. Notice that the domain of f is $\{x \mid x \neq 1\}$ and the domain of g is $\{x \mid x \neq 0\}$.

$$(f \circ g)(x) = f(g(x)) = f\left(\frac{x + 3}{x}\right) = \frac{3}{\frac{x + 3}{x} - 1} = \frac{3(x)}{(x)\left(\frac{x + 3}{x}\right) - (x)(1)} = \frac{3x}{x + 3 - x} = \frac{3x}{3} = x$$

and

$$(g \circ f)(x) = g(f(x)) = g\left(\frac{3}{x-1}\right) = \frac{\frac{3}{x-1} + 3}{\frac{3}{x-1}} = \frac{(x-1)\left(\frac{3}{x-1}\right) + 3(x-1)}{(x-1)\left(\frac{3}{x-1}\right)} = \frac{3 + 3x - 3}{3} = \frac{3x}{3} = x.$$

Therefore, $y = f(x)$ and $y = g(x)$ are inverses of each other.

Finding the Inverse of a One-to-One Function

We will recall how to find the inverse of a one-to-one function. The key thing to remember is that the domain of a one-to-one function, f, is the range of its inverse function f^{-1} and the range of f is the domain of f^{-1}. In other words, if a is in the domain of $y = f(x)$, and $b = f(a)$ is in the range of $y = f(x)$, then b is in the domain of $y = f^{-1}(x)$, and $a = f^{-1}(b)$ is in the range of $y = f^{-1}(x)$ (see the figure below).

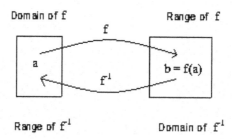

Examples. Find the inverse of the given function. Determine the domain and range of both functions.

1) $f(x) = 4x - 2$

To find the inverse of a function, we use the following procedure:

Step I: Replace the function name (in this example, $f(x)$) by the variable y.

By doing this, we obtain $y = 4x - 2$.

Step II: Interchange the variables x and y.

$$y = 4x - 2 \text{ becomes } x = 4y - 2.$$

In the equation $x = 4y - 2$, y implicitly defines x. We would like to write it in explicit form. To do so, we need to solve for y. This is done in the next step.

Step III: Solve for y.

$$x = 4y \cancel{-2}$$
$$\underline{+2 \qquad \cancel{+2}}$$
$$\frac{x+2}{4} = \frac{\cancel{4}y}{\cancel{4}}$$

Therefore, $y = \dfrac{x+2}{4} = \dfrac{x}{4} + \dfrac{2}{4} = \dfrac{1}{4}x + \dfrac{1}{2}$.

Step IV: Replace the variable y by the inverse name (in this case, $f^{-1}(x)$).

We obtain $f^{-1}(x) = \frac{1}{4}x + \frac{1}{2}$.

Now, since $f(x) = 4x - 2$ is a linear function whose graph is a line with a positive slope, the domain and, the range are $(-\infty, \infty)$. This means that the domain and the range of $f^{-1}(x) = \frac{1}{4}x + \frac{1}{2}$ are $(-\infty, \infty)$ also.

2) $g(x) = x^3 - 4$

Let's follow the steps. First, we will write our equation as $y = x^3 - 4$. Next, we will interchange x and y in the equation and obtain the new equation $x = y^3 - 4$. In this equation, y is an implicit function of x. Let's solve for y and write the equation in explicit form.

$$x = y^3 \cancel{-4}$$
$$\underline{+4 \qquad \cancel{+4}}$$
$$x + 4 = y^3$$

$$\sqrt[3]{x+4} = \sqrt[3]{y^3}$$

$$\sqrt[3]{x+4} = y$$

Replacing y by $g^{-1}(x)$, we get $g^{-1}(x) = \sqrt[3]{x+4}$.

The domain of $g(x) = x^3 - 4$ is $(-\infty, \infty)$ since g is a polynomial function. Furthermore, if you graph g and collapse the graph onto the y-axis, you will see that the range of g is also $(-\infty, \infty)$. This means that the domain and range of $g^{-1}(x) = \sqrt[3]{x+4}$ are $(-\infty, \infty)$.

3) $f(x) = \dfrac{1}{x-5}$

Let's write the function as $y = \dfrac{1}{x-5}$. After interchanging x with y, we obtain the equation $x = \dfrac{1}{y-5}$. Now let's solve for y to obtain the inverse function in explicit form.

$$x = \frac{1}{y-5}$$

$$\frac{x}{1} = \frac{1}{y-5}$$

$$x(y-5) = 1$$

$$xy - 5\cancel{x} = 1$$
$$\underline{+\cancel{5}x \qquad +5x}$$
$$\frac{\cancel{x}y}{\cancel{x}} = \frac{1+5x}{x}$$

$$y = \frac{1+5x}{x}$$

Therefore, we have $f^{-1}(x) = \dfrac{1 + 5x}{x}$.

The domain of $f(x) = \dfrac{1}{x - 5}$ is $\{x \mid x \neq 5\}$ and the range of f is $\{y \mid y \neq 0\}$. By interchanging the roles of the domain and range of f for f^{-1}, we find that the domain of $f^{-1}(x) = \dfrac{1 + 5x}{x}$ is $\{x \mid x \neq 0\}$ and the range of f^{-1} is $\{y \mid y \neq 5\}$.

4) $h(x) = x^2$, $x \leq 0$

Let's write the function as $y = x^2$. After interchanging x with y, we obtain the equation $x = y^2$. Now let's solve for y to obtain the inverse function in explicit form.

$$x = y^2$$
$$\pm\sqrt{x} = \sqrt{y^2}$$
$$\pm\sqrt{x} = y$$

This is a problem since $y = \pm\sqrt{x}$ is **not** a function. Do we want $y = -\sqrt{x}$ or $y = \sqrt{x}$? Well, to answer this question, we need to look at the domain of h. We know that the domain of $h(x) = x^2$ is $\{x \mid x \leq 0\}$. This means that the range of h^{-1} **must be** $\{y \mid y \leq 0\}$. If $y = -\sqrt{x}$, then the range is $\{y \mid y \leq 0\}$, which is what we want. Observe that the range of $y = \sqrt{x}$ is $\{y \mid y \geq 0\}$ and this is not what we want. Therefore, $h^{-1}(x) = -\sqrt{x}$.

Now, the domain of $h(x) = x^2$ is $\{x \mid x \leq 0\}$ and the range of h is $\{y \mid y \geq 0\}$. Therefore, the domain of $h^{-1}(x) = -\sqrt{x}$ is $\{x \mid x \geq 0\}$ and the range of h^{-1} is $\{y \mid y \leq 0\}$.

The Graph of a One-to-One Function and its Inverse

When we graph a one-to-one function and its inverse on the same set of axes, the graphs are symmetric to each other about the line $y = x$. This means that we could obtain the graph of f^{-1} by reflecting the graph of f about the line $y = x$.

Examples. Graph the functions $y = f(x)$ and $y = f^{-1}(x)$ on the same set of axes.

1) $f(x) = 2x + 4$ and $f^{-1}(x) = \frac{1}{2}x - 2$

Both f and f^{-1} are linear functions. The intercepts of the line for $f(x) = 2x + 4$ are $(0, 4)$ and $(-2, 0)$. The intercepts of the line for $f^{-1}(x) = \frac{1}{2}x - 2$ are $(0, -2)$ and $(4, 0)$. Observe the relationship (look familiar?):

$f(x) = 2x + 4$	$f^{-1}(x) = \frac{1}{2}x - 2$
$(0, 4)$	$(4, 0)$
$(-2, 0)$	$(0, -2)$
(a, b)	(b, a)

The graphs of both f and f^{-1} are given on the next page. Notice that they are symmetric to each other about the line $y = x$. This will always occur for the graph of a one-to-one function and its inverse.

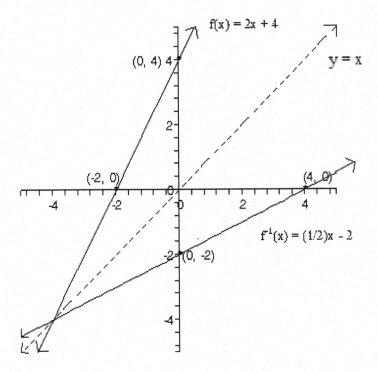

2) $g(x) = \sqrt{x-3}$ and $g^{-1}(x) = x^2 + 3$, $x \geq 0$

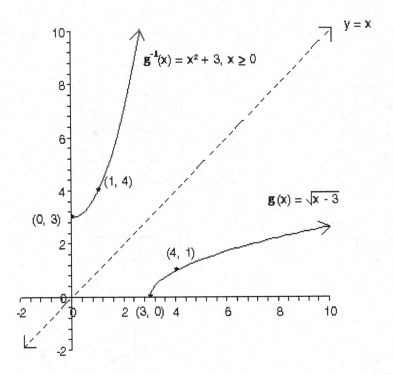

3) $f(x) = x^3$ and $f^{-1}(x) = \sqrt[3]{x}$

We know what the graph of $f(x) = x^3$ looks like, but we have never seen the graph of $f^{-1}(x) = \sqrt[3]{x}$ before. To graph f^{-1}, we use the fact that we can obtain points on its graph by interchanging the x and y coordinates of the points for f. Then we will reflect the graph of f about the line $y = x$. The graphs are given on the next page.

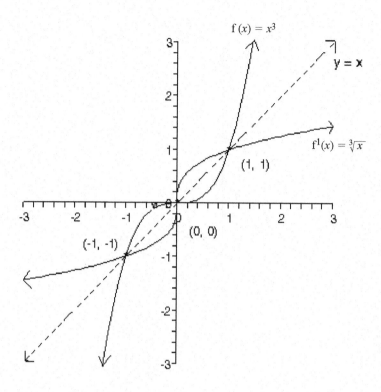

$f(x) = x^3$

$y = x$

$f^1(x) = \sqrt[3]{x}$

(1, 1)

(0, 0)

(-1, -1)

Exercise R.7

In Exercises 1-14, write the inverse of each function in ordered pair notation. Determine whether or not the inverse is a function.

1.

f

1	-6
-2	0
0	3

2.

g

0	4
3	0
-2	1

3.

f

| 1 | 9 |
| 2 | 3 |

4.

f

| -3 | 5 |
| 1 | 2 |

5.

g

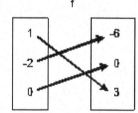
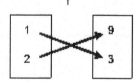

-1	
1	1
	15
4	
-3	9

6.

g

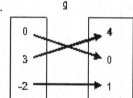
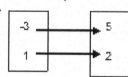

0	
4	0
-2	
8	7

7.

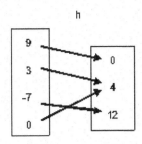

8.   f

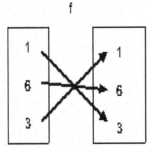

9. f: $\{(1, 1), (2, -3), (3, -7)\}$ 10. f: $\{(0, 0), (4, -4), (-1, 1)\}$

11. h: $\{(0, 4), (12, 0)\}$ 12. g: $\{(3, 3), (2, 2)\}$ 13. f: $\{(0, -1), (2, 5), (4, -1)\}$

14. h: $\{(6, 2), (9, 3), (-8, 3)\}$

In Exercises 15-36, determine whether or not the given function is one-to-one.

15. $f(x) = x - 3$ 16. $f(x) = x + 2$ 17. $h(x) = -3x + 3$ 18. $g(x) = -5x$

19. $f(x) = x^2 + 1$ 20. $f(x) = x^2 - 2$ 21. $f(x) = (x - 3)^2$, $x \geq 3$

22. $f(x) = (x + 2)^2$, $x \geq -2$ 23. $f(x) = x^2 + 2$, $x \geq -1$ 24. $f(x) = x^2 - 4$, $x \leq 2$

25. $f(x) = 5$ 26. $h(x) = -2$ 27. $f(x) = \sqrt{x} + 4$ 28. $f(x) = \sqrt{x} - 3$

29. $h(x) = \sqrt{x - 6}$ 30. $f(x) = \sqrt{x + 2}$ 31. $g(x) = \dfrac{1}{x - 2}$ 32. $h(x) = \dfrac{1}{x} - 2$

33. $g(x) = \dfrac{1}{x} + 5$ 34. $f(x) = \dfrac{1}{x + 5}$ 35. $g(x) = |x - 3|$ 36. $f(x) = |x| - 3$

In Exercises 37-56, show that the given functions are inverses of each other.

37. $f(x) = x - 5$ and $g(x) = x + 5$ 38. $f(x) = x + 4$ and $g(x) = x - 4$

39. $f(x) = 4x$ and $g(x) = \dfrac{x}{4}$ 40. $f(x) = -6x$ and $g(x) = -\dfrac{x}{6}$

41. $f(x) = 3x + 3$ and $g(x) = \dfrac{1}{3}x - 1$ 42. $f(x) = 2x + 6$ and $g(x) = \dfrac{1}{2}x - 3$

43. $f(x) = 9x - 2$ and $g(x) = \dfrac{1}{9}x + \dfrac{2}{9}$ 44. $f(x) = 3x - 4$ and $g(x) = \dfrac{1}{3}x + \dfrac{4}{3}$

45. $f(x) = \dfrac{5}{6}x + \dfrac{1}{3}$ and $g(x) = \dfrac{6}{5}x - \dfrac{2}{5}$ 46. $f(x) = \dfrac{9}{7}x - \dfrac{3}{4}$ and $g(x) = \dfrac{7}{9}x + \dfrac{7}{12}$

47. $f(x) = x^2 + 1$, $x \geq 0$ and $g(x) = \sqrt{x - 1}$ 48. $f(x) = x^2 - 3$, $x \geq 0$ and $g(x) = \sqrt{x + 3}$

49. $f(x) = (x - 4)^2$, $x \geq 4$ and $g(x) = \sqrt{x} + 4$ 50. $f(x) = (x + 1)^2$, $x \geq -1$ and $g(x) = \sqrt{x} - 1$

51. $f(x) = x^2 - 6$, $x \leq 0$ and $g(x) = -\sqrt{x + 6}$ 52. $f(x) = x^2 + 2$, $x \leq 0$ and $g(x) = -\sqrt{x - 2}$

53. $f(x) = (x-9)^3$ and $g(x) = \sqrt[3]{x} + 9$ 54. $f(x) = (x+7)^3$ and $g(x) = \sqrt[3]{x} - 7$

55. $f(x) = \dfrac{3}{x}$ and $g(x) = \dfrac{3}{x}$ 56. $f(x) = -\dfrac{5}{x}$ and $g(x) = -\dfrac{5}{x}$

In Exercises 57-84, find the inverse of the given function. State the domain and range of the inverse function.

57. $f(x) = 2x + 8$ 58. $f(x) = 3x + 9$ 59. $g(x) = -7x$ 60. $g(x) = 8x$

61. $h(x) = \dfrac{2}{3}x - 5$ 62. $h(x) = \dfrac{7}{5}x + 2$ 63. $g(x) = x^3 + 8$ 64. $g(x) = x^3 - 6$

65. $f(x) = \dfrac{1}{x+3}$ 66. $f(x) = \dfrac{1}{x-4}$ 67. $g(x) = \dfrac{1}{x} - 6$ 68. $g(x) = \dfrac{1}{x} + 5$

69. $f(x) = \dfrac{x+4}{x-2}$ 70. $f(x) = \dfrac{x}{x+5}$ 71. $f(x) = \dfrac{-2x+3}{3x+1}$ 72. $f(x) = \dfrac{5x+2}{4x-3}$

73. $f(x) = \sqrt{x+3}$ 74. $f(x) = \sqrt{x-1}$ 75. $f(x) = \sqrt{x} + 3$ 76. $f(x) = \sqrt{x} - 1$

77. $f(x) = x^2 - 9$, $x \geq 0$ 78. $f(x) = x^2 + 5$, $x \geq 0$ 79. $f(x) = x^2 + 3$, $x \leq 0$

80. $f(x) = x^2 - 1$, $x \leq 0$ 81. $f(x) = (x-5)^2$, $x \geq 5$ 82. $f(x) = (x-2)^2$, $x \geq 2$

83. $f(x) = (x+8)^2$, $x \leq -8$ 84. $f(x) = (x+10)^2$, $x \leq -10$

In Exercises 85-89, sketch the graph of $y = f^{-1}(x)$.

85.

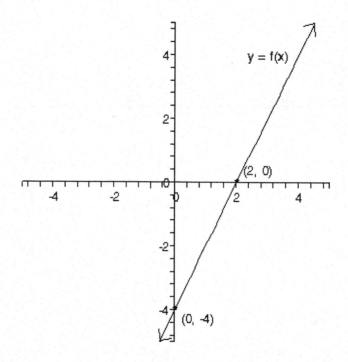

86.

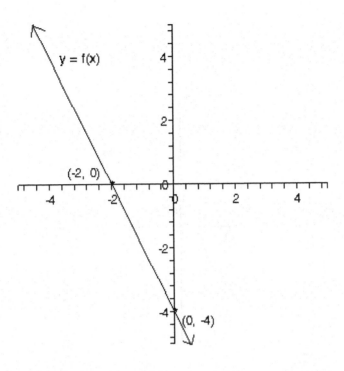

87.

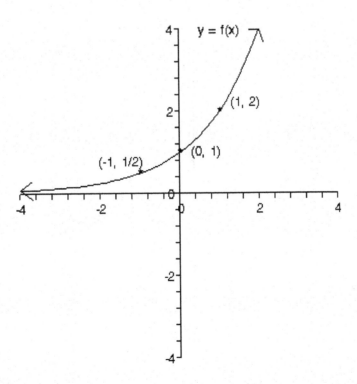

88.

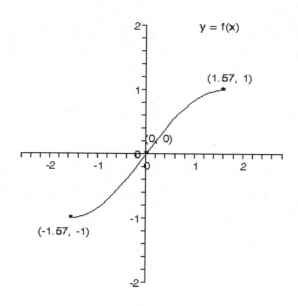

89.

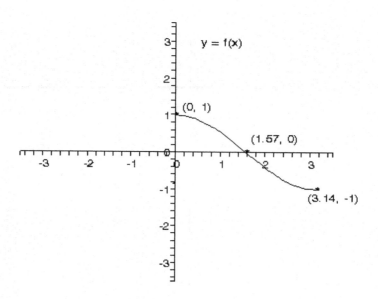

90.

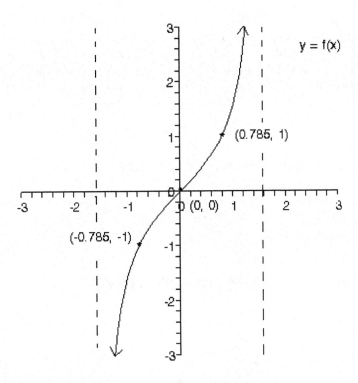

Chapter 1:   Angles and their Measures

In this chapter, we will study angles and their measures. There are two types of measurements that we will learn about: degree measurement and radian measurement. Section 1.1 contains material on degree measure of angles. In Sections 1.2 and 1.3, we will discuss radian measure and measuring the length of an arc of a circle, as well as the relationship between degree measure and radian measure. Applications of radian measure such as the area of a sector of a circle and circular motion will be studied in Section 1.4.

Section 1.1   Angles and Degree Measure

Definition: A **ray** (or **half-line**) is a portion of a line which starts at a point P (called the **vertex** of the ray) and continues indefinitely in exactly one direction.

Three rays with vertex P

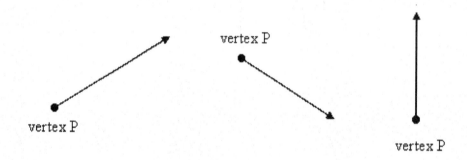

Definition: An **angle** is a figure formed by two rays with a common vertex. We call the rays the **sides** of the angle.

We form an angle by rotating a ray either clockwise or counterclockwise. The side from which we start rotating to form the angle is called the **initial side** and the side at which we stop rotating is called the **terminal side**.

If the angle is formed by rotating the initial side clockwise, it is called a **negative angle**. If the angle is formed by rotating the initial side counterclockwise, it is called a **positive angle**.

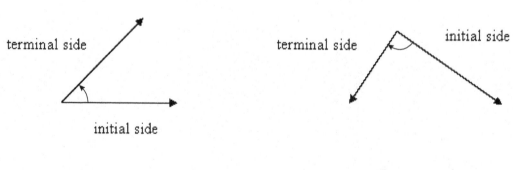

A **positive** angle   A **negative** angle

114

It is common to name an angle by an uppercase letter from the English alphabet or by a lowercase Greek letter. The Greek letters which are frequently used are

$$\theta \text{ (theta)}, \quad \alpha \text{ (alpha)}, \quad \beta \text{ (beta)}, \quad \omega \text{ (omega)}, \quad \text{and} \quad \gamma \text{ (gamma)}.$$

When we study trigonometry, we will need to use the Cartesian plane in order to visualize an angle. The following definition describes how this may be done.

Definition: An angle θ in the Cartesian plane is in **standard position** if its vertex is at the origin and its initial side coincides with the positive x-axis.

An angle in standard position will always have the terminal side which either lies in a quadrant or on an axis. If the terminal side of θ lies in a quadrant, we say that θ **lies in that quadrant**. If the terminal side of θ lies on an axis, we call θ a **quadrantal angle**.

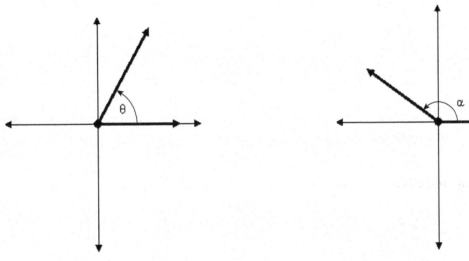

Angle θ is in standard position.   Angle α is in standard position.

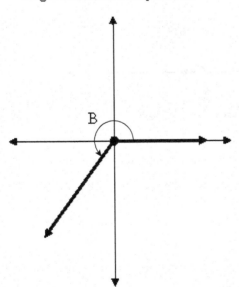

Angle B is in standard position.

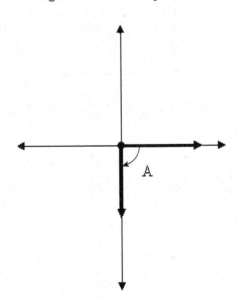

Angle A is a quadrantal angle in
standard position.

Degree Measure

I'm sure that you have seen angles and degree measure before, whether it was when you learned about the Pythagorean theorem for right triangles or when you studied any other topic in geometry. Nevertheless, it is a good idea to take a look at some examples.

Definition: The angle formed by rotating a ray one full turn in the **counterclockwise direction** until it coincides with its initial position is called one **revolution** (or one **full counterclockwise rotation**).

Definition: The measure of 1 revolution is 360 **degrees** (written as 360°).

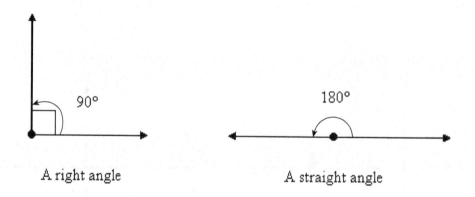

It follows that $1° = \frac{1}{360}$ revolution. In other words, an angle which has a measure of 1° can be formed by rotating a ray $\frac{1}{360}^{th}$ of a revolution.

Definitions: A **right angle** is an angle that measures 90°. A **straight angle** is an angle that measures 180°.

90°	180°
A right angle	A straight angle

The pictures above show us that a right angle is $\frac{90}{360} = \frac{1}{4}$ revolution and a straight angle is $\frac{180}{360} = \frac{1}{2}$ revolution.

Examples. Draw an angle whose measure is given and determine the number of revolutions.

1) $30° = \frac{30}{360} = \frac{1}{12}$ revolution

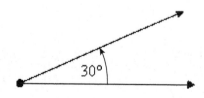

2) $270° = \frac{270}{360} = \frac{3}{4}$ revolution

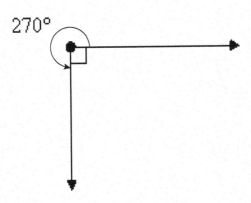

3) $315° = \frac{315}{360} = \frac{7}{8}$ revolution

4) $720° = \frac{720}{360} = 2$ revolutions

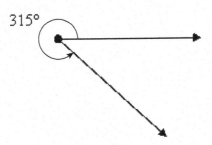

5) $-180° = \frac{-180}{360} = -\frac{1}{2}$, which means that we have $\frac{1}{2}$ revolution in the **clockwise direction**.

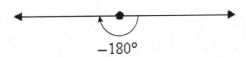

When we have an angle whose measure contains a fraction of a degree, we can write this measure in decimal form. For example, if angle θ has measure $42\frac{3}{4}$ degrees, then we can write this measure as 42.75 degrees. However, there is another way of dealing with fractions and decimals using the notion of **minutes** and **seconds**.

Definitions: One **minute**, written as 1', equals $\frac{1}{60}$ degree and one **second**, written as 1", equals $\frac{1}{60}$ minute.

By definition, we have that $1° = 60'$ and $1' = 60"$. Observe that

$$1" = \frac{1}{60} \text{ minute} = \frac{1}{60}(1') = \frac{1}{60}\left(\frac{1}{60} \text{ degree}\right) = \frac{1}{3,600} \text{ degree}.$$

Examples. Convert each of the measures to a decimal in degrees. Round off your answer to five decimal places.

1) $45°24'6"$

We begin by writing $45°24'6" = 45° + 24' + 6"$. Now, since $1' = \frac{1}{60}$ degree and $1" = \frac{1}{3,600}$ degree, we have

$$\begin{aligned}
45° + 24' + 6" &= 45° + 24\,(1') + 6\,(1") \\
&= 45° + 24\left(\frac{1}{60}\right)° + 6\left(\frac{1}{3,600}\right)° \\
&\approx 45° + 0.4° + 0.00167° = 45.40167°.
\end{aligned}$$

2) $248°53'30"$

$$\begin{aligned}
248°53'30" &= 248° + 53' + 30" \\
&= 248° + 53\,(1') + 30\,(1") \\
&= 248° + 53\left(\frac{1}{60}\right)° + 30\left(\frac{1}{3,600}\right)° \\
&\approx 248° + 0.883333° + 0.008333° = 248.89167°
\end{aligned}$$

Examples. Convert into a measure containing degrees, minutes, and seconds.

1) $39.561°$

Observe that $0.561° = 0.561\,(1°) = 0.561\,(60') = 33.66'$. Now notice that

$$0.66' = 0.66\,(1') = 0.66\,(60") = 39.6" \approx 40".$$

Therefore, we have

$$\begin{aligned}
39.561° &= 39° + 0.561° \\
&= 39° + 33.66' \\
&= 39° + 33' + 0.66' \\
&= 39° + 33' + 40" \\
&= 39°33'40"
\end{aligned}$$

2) $350.81°$

We have that $0.81° = 0.81\,(1°) = 0.81\,(60') = 48.6'$. Notice that $0.6' = 0.6\,(1') = 0.6\,(60") = 36"$.

Therefore,

$$350.81° = 350° + 0.81°$$
$$= 350° + 48.6'$$
$$= 350° + 48' + 0.6'$$
$$= 350° + 48' + 36"$$
$$= 350°48'36"$$

Try These (Set 1):

I) Draw an angle whose measure is given and determine the number of revolutions.
   1) 45°   2) 210°   3) 1, 125°

II) Convert each of the measures to a decimal in degrees. Round off your answer to 4 decimal places.
   1) 88°7'25"   2) 180°59'2"   3) 0°39'1"

III) Convert into a measure containing degrees, minutes, and seconds.
   1) 103.675°   2) 11.402°   3) 450.018°

Section 1.2   Radian Measure and Arc Length

We will learn about another measure for an angle called radian measure.

Definition: If C is a circle with center O, then angle θ is called a **central angle** if its vertex is O. The arc of the circle which is intercepted by θ is called the **arc subtended by** θ.

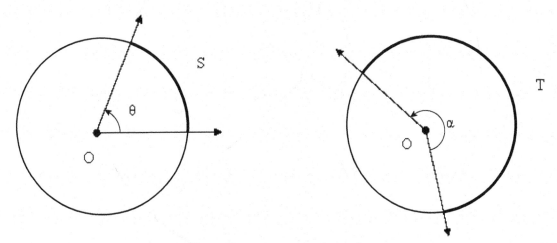

Angles θ and α are central angles.
Arc S is subtended by θ and arc T
is subtended by α.

Suppose that we have a circle C with radius r and let angle θ be a central angle which subtends an arc of length r. Then we define the measure of θ to equal 1 **radian**. Hence, 1 radian is the measure of the angle for which the length of the arc subtended by θ equals the radius of the circle.

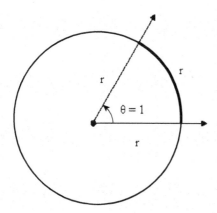

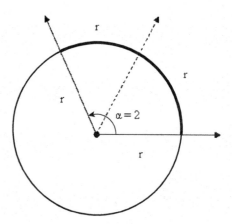

The measure of θ is defined to be
1 radian. The measure of the arc
subtended by θ equals the radius
of the circle.

The measure of α is 2 radians,
since two arcs of length r are
subtended by α.

We will now derive the arc length theorem. Suppose that C is a circle with center O and let θ and α be two central angles of C (see the figure below).

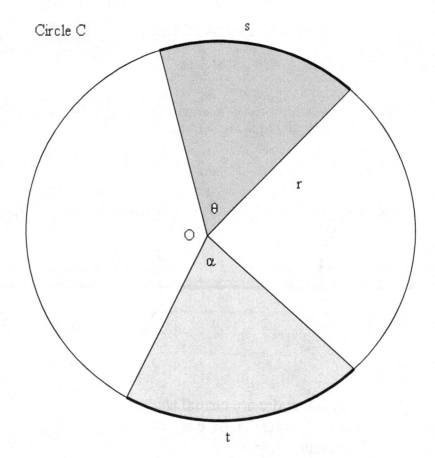

A theorem from plane geometry states that the ratio of the measures of any two central angles equals the ratio of the corresponding lengths of the arcs which these angles subtend. Referring to the figure above, we have

$$\frac{s}{t} = \frac{\theta}{\alpha}.$$

Now, if $\alpha = 1$ radian, then $t = r$ (the radius of the circle) by definition of a radian. Substituting this into the equation above yields

$$\frac{s}{r} = \frac{\theta}{1}, \quad \text{which becomes} \quad s = r\theta.$$

So, we have a relationship between the radius of a circle, the measure of a central angle of the circle (in radians), and the length of the arc that it subtends.

The Arc Length Theorem

If an arc of a circle of radius r which is subtended by a central angle θ has length s, then

$$s = r\theta.$$

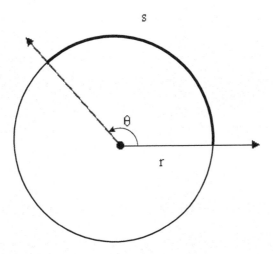

We call the length of the arc subtended by a central angle θ its **arc length**. Note that the measure of θ is in radians and the units of r and s are the same. Hence, if r is in feet, then s is in feet. Furthermore, if $\theta = 1$ radian, then the theorem gives us $s = r$, which is just our definition of 1 radian.

Examples.

1) Find the length of the arc of a circle of radius 12 inches subtended by a central angle of 0.25 radians.

We are given that $r = 12$ and $\theta = 0.25$. We can find s by using the formula $s = r\theta$.

$$s = 12\,(0.25) = 3.0 \text{ inches}$$

2) Circle C has a central angle of $2\frac{1}{3}$ radians which subtends an arc whose length is 21 feet. Find the radius of C.

We know that $\theta = 2\frac{1}{3} = \frac{7}{3}$ and $s = 21$. We want to find r.

$$s = r\theta$$

$$21 = r\left(\frac{7}{3}\right)$$

$$\frac{3}{7}(21) = \frac{3}{7}\left(\frac{7r}{3}\right)$$

$$r = 9 \text{ feet}$$

3) How many radians must a central angle of a circle of radius 10 meters be in order to subtend an arc of length 18 meters long?

Set $r = 10$ and $s = 18$. We need to determine θ.

$$18 = 10\theta$$

$$\frac{18}{10} = \frac{10\theta}{10}$$

$$\theta = \frac{9}{5} \text{ radians}$$

Try These (Set 2):

1) Find the length of the arc of a circle of radius 8 yards subtended by a central angle of $\frac{3\pi}{4}$ radians.

2) A circle has a central angle of 4.35 radians which subtends an arc whose length is 17 feet. Find the radius of the circle to the nearest tenth of a foot.

3) How many radians must a central angle of a circle of radius 8 yards be in order to subtend an arc 44 yards long?

Section 1.3 The Relationship between Degrees and Radians

Suppose that we have a circle of radius r and that θ is a central angle which subtends an arc that equals the circumference of the circle.

Then $\theta = 1$ revolution. By using the arc length theorem and the fact that the circumference of the circle is $C = 2\pi r$, we obtain:

$$s = r\theta$$
$$2\pi r = r\theta$$
$$\theta = 2\pi \text{ radians}$$

This means that

$$\boxed{1 \text{ revolution} = 2\pi \text{ radians.}}$$

However, 1 revolution = 360° by definition. Therefore,

$$\boxed{360° = 2\pi \text{ radians}}$$

or, equivalently,

$$\boxed{180° = \pi \text{ radians.}}$$

Now let's find out how many degrees are in 1 radian.

$$\pi \text{ radians} = 180°$$
$$\left(\frac{\pi}{\pi}\right) \text{ radians} = \left(\frac{180}{\pi}\right)°$$
$$1 \text{ radian} = \left(\frac{180}{\pi}\right)° \approx 57.2958°$$

We can also find out how many radians are in 1°.

$$180° = \pi \text{ radians}$$
$$\left(\frac{180}{180}\right)° = \left(\frac{\pi}{180}\right) \text{ radians}$$
$$1° = \left(\frac{\pi}{180}\right) \text{ radians} \approx 0.01745 \text{ radians}$$

To summarize, we have the following conversion formulas:

$$\boxed{1 \text{ radian} = \left(\frac{180}{\pi}\right)° \quad \text{ and } \quad 1° = \left(\frac{\pi}{180}\right) \text{ radians}}$$

Let's see some examples on converting from one type of measure to the other.

Examples. Convert each measure to radians. Leave each answer in terms of π.

1) $60° = \frac{60}{1}\left(\frac{\pi}{180}\right) = \frac{\pi}{3}$ radians

2) $0° = 0\left(\frac{\pi}{180}\right) = 0$ radians

3) $135° = \frac{135}{1}\left(\frac{\pi}{180}\right) = \frac{3\pi}{4}$ radians

4) $330° = \frac{330}{1}\left(\frac{\pi}{180}\right) = \frac{11\pi}{6}$ radians

5) $-90° = \frac{-90}{1}\left(\frac{\pi}{180}\right) = -\frac{\pi}{2}$ radians

6) $3{,}000° = \frac{3{,}000}{1}\left(\frac{\pi}{180}\right) = \frac{50\pi}{3}$ radians

Examples. Convert each measure to degrees.

1) $\frac{\pi}{6} = \frac{\pi}{6}\left(\frac{180}{\pi}\right) = 30°$

2) $\frac{7\pi}{6} = \frac{7\pi}{6}\left(\frac{180}{\pi}\right) = 210°$

3) $\frac{3\pi}{2} = \frac{3\pi}{2}\left(\frac{180}{\pi}\right) = 270°$

4) $\frac{10\pi}{3} = \frac{10\pi}{3}\left(\frac{180}{\pi}\right) = 600°$

5) $-\frac{8\pi}{9} = -\frac{8\pi}{9}\left(\frac{180}{\pi}\right) = -160°$

6) $-\frac{\pi}{4} = -\frac{\pi}{4}\left(\frac{180}{\pi}\right) = -45°$

Try These (Set 3):

I) Convert each measure to radians. Leave each answer in terms of π.

1) $180°$ 2) $585°$ 3) $-240°$ 4) $-6°$

II) Convert each measure to degrees.

1) $\frac{2\pi}{3}$ 2) $\frac{23\pi}{4}$ 3) $-\frac{5\pi}{6}$ 4) 0

Section 1.4 Applications of Radian Measure

We will now see several examples of radian measure being used to solve geometric and physical problems.

Area of a Sector

Let C be a circle of radius r and suppose that θ, measured in radians, is a central angle of C. The **sector of C formed by** θ is the piece of the interior of C which is intercepted by θ (see the figure below).

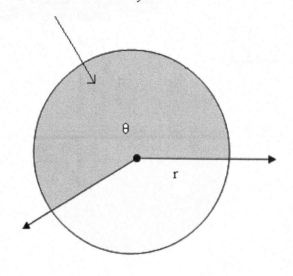

Sector of circle C formed by θ

Circle C

Suppose we want to find the area, A, of sector S which is formed by θ. Recall that the area of a circle of radius r is the quantity obtained by computing πr^2. We can think of this as the area of the sector (which is the whole interior of circle C) formed by 1 full revolution, which equals 2π radians (see the next figure).

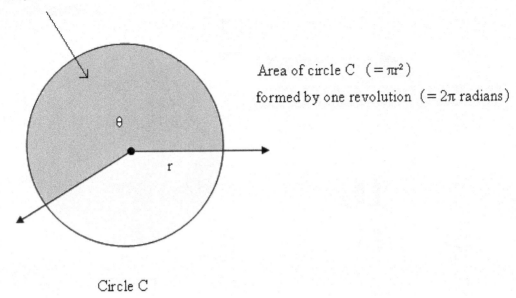

Circle C

If we set up a proportion between these quantities, we obtain:

$$\frac{\text{area of sector } S}{\text{area of sector } C} = \frac{\text{angle which forms sector } S}{\text{angle which forms sector } C}$$

$$\frac{A}{\pi r^2} = \frac{\theta}{2\pi}$$

$$\frac{A\,(2\pi)}{2\pi} = \frac{\theta\,(\pi r^2)}{2\pi}$$

$$A = \frac{r^2\theta}{2}$$

The Area of a Sector

The area of the sector of C formed by θ, where θ is in radians, is given by

$$A = \tfrac{1}{2}r^2\theta.$$

Examples. Solve each problem and round off the answer to four decimal places.

1) Find the area of the sector of a circle of radius 5 inches formed by an angle of 45°.

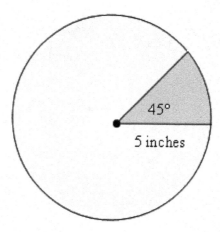

We are given that $r = 5$ inches and $\theta = 45° = 45\left(\frac{\pi}{180}\right) = \frac{\pi}{4}$ radians.

$$A = \tfrac{1}{2}r^2\theta = \tfrac{1}{2}\left(5 \text{ inches}\right)^2\left(\tfrac{\pi}{4}\right) = \tfrac{25\pi}{8} \text{ square inches} \approx 9.8175 \text{ square inches}$$

2) What measure must the angle α of a circle of radius 9 miles be (in radians and degrees) to form a sector of area 175 square miles?

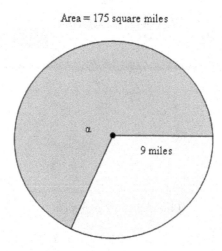

According to the figure above, we are given that $r = 9$ miles and $A = 175$ square miles. We want to find α in radians and in degrees.

$$A = \frac{1}{2}r^2\alpha$$

$$175 \text{ square miles} = \frac{1}{2}(9 \text{ miles})^2 \alpha$$

$$175 \text{ square miles} = (40.5 \text{ square miles})\alpha$$

$$\frac{175 \text{ square miles}}{40.5 \text{ square miles}} = \frac{(40.5 \text{ square miles})\alpha}{40.5 \text{ square miles}}$$

$$4.32099 \text{ radians} \approx \alpha$$

To find the degree measure of α, we compute

$$\alpha \approx 4.32099 \text{ radians} = 4.32099\left(\frac{180}{\pi}\right) \approx 247.5745°.$$

Circular Motion

One aspect of the study of circular motion deals with finding the speed of an object which is traveling in a circular path. There are two types of speeds which arise naturally: **linear speed** and **angular speed**. We will learn how to determine these two speeds and see how they are related to each other.

One way of measuring the speed of an object in circular motion is by calculating the distance traveled around the circle and dividing it by the time elapsed (see the figure below). We will always assume that the speed of the object is constant, meaning that it never changes as time goes on. This is referred to as **uniform circular motion**.

Definition: Suppose that an object is traveling with uniform circular motion around a circle C of radius r. Let s represent the distance traveled in time t around circle C. The **linear speed**, v, of the object is given by the formula:

$$\boxed{v = \frac{s}{t}}$$

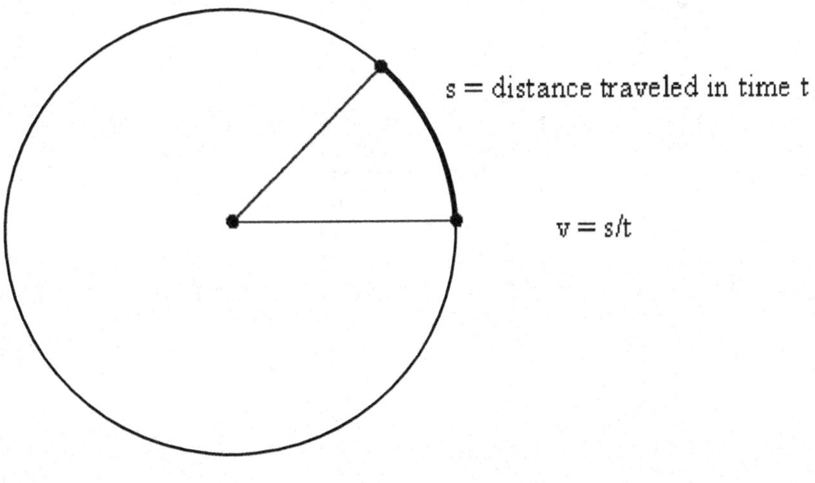

$s = $ distance traveled in time t

$v = s/t$

Examples.

1) An object is traveling along a circular path at a constant speed. If it travels 24 inches in 3 seconds, what is the linear speed of the object?

We are given that $s = 24$ feet when $t = 3$ seconds and we are asked to find v.

$$v = \frac{24 \text{ inches}}{3 \text{ seconds}}$$

$$= \frac{8 \text{ inches}}{1 \text{ second}} \quad \text{or} \quad 8 \text{ inches per second} \quad \text{or} \quad 8 \text{ in/sec}$$

2) A ball is moving with uniform circular motion. How long does it take for the ball to move 18 feet if its linear speed is 4 feet per second?

Remember that 'uniform circular motion' just means that the ball is moving along a circular path at a constant speed. We are given that $s = 18$ feet and $v = 4$ feet per second (which can be written as $\frac{4 \text{ feet}}{1 \text{ second}}$). We want to find t.

$$\frac{4 \text{ feet}}{1 \text{ second}} = \frac{18 \text{ feet}}{t}$$

$$\frac{(\cancel{4 \text{ feet}})(t)}{\cancel{4 \text{ feet}}} = \frac{(18 \text{ feet})(1 \text{ second})}{4 \text{ feet}}$$

$$t = 4.5 \text{ seconds}$$

Definition: Suppose that an object is traveling with uniform circular motion around a circle C of radius r. Let θ (in radians) represent the central angle which is swept out in time t by the object. The **angular speed**, ω, of the object is given by the formula:

$$\boxed{\omega = \frac{\theta}{t}}$$

$\theta =$ angle swept out in time t

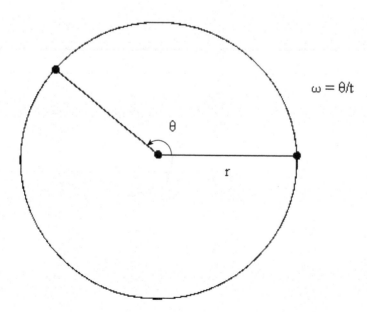

Examples.

1) An object is traveling with uniform circular motion around a circle. If it rotates through an angle of measure $\frac{5\pi}{6}$ radians in 4 seconds, find the angular speed of the object.

We want to find ω when $\theta = \frac{5\pi}{6}$ radians and $t = 4$ seconds.

$$\omega = \frac{\frac{5\pi}{6} \text{ radians}}{4 \text{ seconds}} = \frac{5\pi \text{ radians}}{24 \text{ seconds}} \quad \text{or} \quad \frac{5\pi}{24} \text{ radians per second} \quad \text{or} \quad \frac{5\pi}{24} \text{ rad/sec}$$

2) A wheel has a radius of 1.2 feet and turns with an angular speed of 2.25 radians per second. Determine the distance traveled by a point on the wheel in 2 minutes.

We are given that $r = 1.2$ feet and $\omega = 2.25$ radians per second. We want to find s, the distance traveled when $t = 2$ minutes. Well, we can find s by using the arc length formula $s = r\theta$. However, we need to find θ first. Observe that

$$\omega = \frac{\theta}{t} \quad \text{becomes} \quad \theta = \omega t.$$

And so

$$\begin{aligned} \theta &= (2.25 \text{ radians per second}) (2 \text{ minutes}) \\ &= (2.25 \text{ radians per second}) (120 \text{ seconds}) \\ &= 270 \text{ radians.} \end{aligned}$$

Therefore,

$$s = r\theta = (1.2 \text{ feet}) (270 \text{ radians}) = 324 \text{ feet.}$$

3) Timothy is swinging a ball attached to the end of a string which is 6 feet long (see the next figure). How far does the ball travel in 4 minutes if he swings the ball at 55 rpm (revolutions per minute)? Round off your answer to the nearest foot.

6 feet

This example is similar to the one we have just done, with one slight difference. We are given that $r = 6$ feet and $\omega = 55$ revolutions per minute. We want to find the distance traveled, s, when $t = 4$ minutes. Notice that ω (the angular speed) is not in radians per minute but in revolutions per minute. Let's convert it into the proper units. Using the fact that 1 revolution equals 2π radians, we have

$$\omega = 55 \text{ rpm} = \frac{55 \text{ revolutions}}{1 \text{ minute}} = \frac{55 \text{ revolutions}}{1 \text{ minute}} \left(\frac{2\pi \text{ radians}}{1 \text{ revolution}} \right) = \frac{110\pi \text{ radians}}{1 \text{ minute}} = 110\pi \text{ rad/min.}$$

We can find s by using the arc length formula $s = r\theta$. However, we need to find θ first. As before, notice that

$$\omega = \frac{\theta}{t} \quad \text{becomes} \quad \theta = \omega t.$$

And so

$$\theta = (110\pi \text{ radians per minute}) \, (4 \text{ minutes})$$
$$= 440\pi \text{ radians.}$$

Therefore,

$$s = r\theta = (6 \text{ feet}) \, (440\pi \text{ radians}) \approx 8{,}294 \text{ feet.}$$

Let's determine the relationship between the two types of speeds. Let s be the length of an arc of a circle of radius r subtended by angle θ. By the arc length theorem, we know that $s = r\theta$. If we divide both sides of this equation by t, both of the speed formulas will appear.

$$s = r\theta$$
$$\frac{s}{t} = \frac{r\theta}{t}$$
$$\frac{s}{t} = r\frac{\theta}{t}$$
$$v = r\omega$$

Therefore, the linear speed of an object with uniform circular motion equals the product of the radius and the angular speed.

Examples.

1) A physics teacher is doing an experiment in class which demonstrates a concept known as centripetal force. He ties a pail of water to one end of a 3 foot piece of rope and rotates the pail of water in a vertical manner at a constant speed. If the angular speed of the pail of water is 40 rpm, what is the linear speed?

We need to find v when $r = 3$ feet and $\omega = 40$ revolutions per minute. Notice that

$$\omega = 40 \text{ rpm} = \frac{40 \text{ revolutions}}{1 \text{ minute}} = \frac{40 \text{ revolutions}}{1 \text{ minute}} \left(\frac{2\pi \text{ radians}}{1 \text{ revolution}} \right) = \frac{80\pi \text{ radians}}{1 \text{ minute}} = 80\pi \text{ rad/min.}$$

Therefore,

$$v = r\omega$$
$$= (3 \text{ ft}) (80\pi \text{ rad/min})$$
$$= 240\pi \text{ ft/min}$$
$$\approx 754 \text{ ft/min.}$$

2) A 3.5 inch diskette rotates at 275 rpm when placed in the disk drive of a computer. Find the linear speed of a point which is 1.75 inches from the center of the diskette.

We are given that $\omega = 275$ revolutions per minute. We want to find v when $r = 1.75$ inches. Observe that

$$\omega = 275 \text{ rpm} = \frac{275 \text{ revolutions}}{1 \text{ minute}} = \frac{275 \text{ revolutions}}{1 \text{ minute}} \left(\frac{2\pi \text{ radians}}{1 \text{ revolution}} \right) = \frac{550\pi \text{ radians}}{1 \text{ minute}} = 550\pi \text{ rad/min.}$$

Therefore,

$$v = r\omega$$
$$= (1.75 \text{ inches}) (550\pi \text{ rad/min})$$
$$= 962.5\pi \text{ in/min}$$
$$\approx 3,024 \text{ in/min.}$$

We can express this answer in the units feet per minute by using the fact that 12 inches equal 1 foot. Observe that

$$\frac{3,024 \text{ inches}}{1 \text{ minute}} = \frac{3,024 \text{ inches}}{1 \text{ minute}} \left(\frac{1 \text{ foot}}{12 \text{ inches}} \right) = \frac{3,024 \text{ feet}}{12 \text{ minutes}} = 252 \text{ feet/minute.}$$

More Examples

1) A pendulum swings through an angle of 60° each second. If the pendulum is 27 inches long, how far does its tip move each second? Round off your answer to the nearest hundredth of an inch.

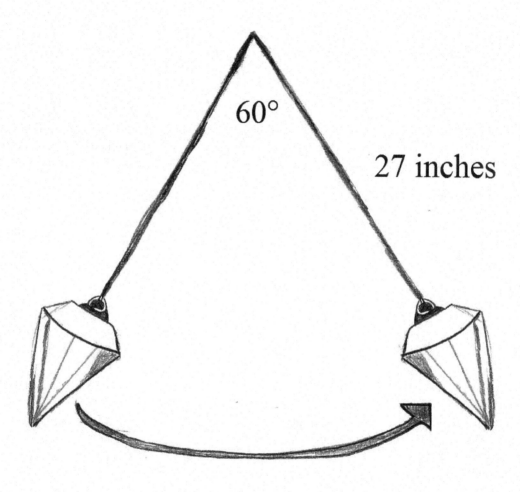

We are given that $r = 27$ inches and $\theta = 60° = \frac{\pi}{3}$ radians. We want to find s. By the arc length theorem, we have

$$
\begin{aligned}
s &= r\theta \\
&= (27 \text{ inches}) \left(\frac{\pi}{3} \text{ radians} \right) \\
&= 9\pi \text{ inches} \\
&\approx 28.27 \text{ inches.}
\end{aligned}
$$

2) The minute hand of a clock is 15 inches long. How far does the tip of the minute hand move in 20 minutes? Round off your answer to the nearest inch.

We are given that $r = 15$ inches and we want to find the value of s after 20 minutes have elapsed. In order to use the arc length theorem, we need to know the value for θ, the angle which subtends the arc after 20 minutes have gone by. Well, we know that 60 minutes equals 1 hour, so we have that

$$20 \text{ minutes} = \frac{1}{3} (60 \text{ minutes}) = \frac{1}{3} \text{ hour}.$$

Now, since the tip of the minute hand moves 1 revolution (or 2π radians) in 1 hour, we have

$$\frac{1}{3} \text{ hour} = \frac{1}{3} (2\pi \text{ radians}) = \frac{2\pi}{3} \text{ radians}.$$

Therefore, $\theta = \frac{2\pi}{3}$ radians and so

$$\begin{aligned}
s &= r\theta \\
&= (15 \text{ inches}) \left(\frac{2\pi}{3} \text{ radians} \right) \\
&= 10\pi \text{ inches} \\
&\approx 31 \text{ inches}.
\end{aligned}$$

3) The windshield wiper of a car is 18 inches long. Find the linear speed of the tip of the wiper if it takes 1.5 seconds to trace out $\frac{1}{3}$ revolution.

We want to find the linear speed, v, when $r = 18$ inches, $t = 1.5$ seconds, and $\theta = \frac{1}{3}$ revolution. Let's begin by finding a formula which relates these quantities. This is not too difficult. Notice that

$$v = \frac{s}{t} = \frac{r\theta}{t}.$$

Now, since 1 revolution equals 2π radians, we obtain

$$\theta = \frac{1}{3} \text{ revolution} = \frac{1}{3} (2\pi \text{ radians}) = \frac{2\pi}{3} \text{ radians}.$$

Therefore,

$$v = \frac{r\theta}{t} = \frac{(18 \text{ inches}) \left(\frac{2\pi}{3} \text{ radians}\right)}{1.5 \text{ seconds}}$$
$$\approx 25.13 \text{ in/sec.}$$

Try These (Set 4):

1) Find the area of the sector of a circle of radius 10 inches formed by an angle of 120°.

2) An object is moving along a circular path at a constant speed. If it travels 42 feet in 2.75 minutes, what is the linear speed of the object?

3) A wheel has a radius of 1.4 feet and turns with an angular speed of 2.85 radians per second. Determine the distance traveled by a point on the wheel in $1\frac{1}{2}$ minutes.

For the next problem, use the following conversion factors:

$$1 \text{ mile} = 5,280 \text{ feet} \quad \text{and} \quad 1 \text{ foot} = 12 \text{ inches}$$

4) Pete rides his bike at a constant rate for 1 hour and travels 8 miles. If the radius of each wheel is 10.56 inches, find the angular speed of each wheel.

Exercise 1

In Exercises 1-30, draw an angle whose measure is given and determine the number of revolutions.

1. 0°	2. 30°	3. 60°	4. 45°	5. 90°	6. 150°
7. 120°	8. 225°	9. 210°	10. 240°	11. 300°	12. 315°
13. −90°	14. −180°	15. −150°	16. −210°	17. −315°	18. −360°
19. $\frac{\pi}{4}$	20. $\frac{\pi}{6}$	21. $\frac{3\pi}{2}$	22. $\frac{\pi}{2}$	23. $\frac{5\pi}{6}$	24. $\frac{4\pi}{3}$
25. 3π	26. 4π	27. $-\frac{9\pi}{4}$	28. $-\frac{7\pi}{3}$	29. $-\frac{13\pi}{6}$	30. -5π

In Exercises 31-38, convert each of the measures to a decimal in degrees. Round off your answer to four decimal places.

31. 70°30'15"   32. 84°41'10"   33. 154°28'7"   34. 127°55'11"

35. 53°9'44"   36. 21°4'59"   37. 179°0'14"   38. 165°40'2"

In Exercises 39-46, convert each into a measure containing degrees, minutes, and seconds.

39. 16.14°   40. 23.47°   41. 76.831°   42. 50.116°

43. 35.991°   44. 79.168°   45. 0.368°   46. 0.095°

In Exercises 47-58, s represents the arc length of the arc of a circle of radius r subtended by the central angle θ. Solve for the unknown quantity. Round off the answers to three decimal places.

47. $r = 6$ inches, $\theta = \frac{1}{3}$ radian, $s = ?$

48. $r = 10$ feet, $\theta = \frac{1}{2}$ radian, $s = ?$

49. $r = 15$ meters, $\theta = \frac{2\pi}{5}$ radians, $s = ?$

50. $r = 21$ miles, $\theta = \frac{8\pi}{7}$ radians, $s = ?$

51. $r = 18$ yards, $s = 54$ yards, $\theta = ?$

52. $r = 14$ meters, $s = 56$ meters, $\theta = ?$

53. $r = 2$ miles, $s = \frac{8\pi}{3}$ miles, $\theta = ?$

54. $r = 5$ inches, $s = \frac{3\pi}{10}$ inches, $\theta = ?$

55. $r = 0.65$ feet, $\theta = 60°$, $s = ?$

56. $r = 19.86$ miles, $\theta = 135°$, $s = ?$

57. $s = 72.15$ meters, $\theta = 330°$, $r = ?$

58. $s = 45.33$ centimeters, $\theta = 225°$, $r = ?$

In Exercises 59-76, convert each measure to radians. Leave each answer in terms of π.

59. $30°$

60. $60°$

61. $135°$

62. $210°$

63. $330°$

64. $150°$

65. $120°$

66. $225°$

67. $-90°$

68. $-270°$

69. $-360°$

70. $-180°$

71. $720°$

72. $1{,}080°$

73. $1{,}125°$

74. $3{,}600°$

75. $2{,}100°$

76. $2{,}385°$

In Exercises 77-94, convert each measure to degrees.

77. $\frac{\pi}{4}$

78. $\frac{\pi}{3}$

79. $\frac{3\pi}{4}$

80. $\frac{7\pi}{4}$

81. $\frac{5\pi}{12}$

82. $\frac{4\pi}{5}$

83. $\frac{7\pi}{18}$

84. $\frac{8\pi}{9}$

85. $\frac{3\pi}{10}$

86. $-\frac{\pi}{2}$

87. $-\pi$

88. -2π

89. $\frac{13\pi}{6}$

90. $\frac{7\pi}{3}$

91. 5π

92. 3π

93. 11π

94. 15π

In Exercises 95-98, find s (the arc subtended by the given angle) and A (the area of the labeled region).

95.

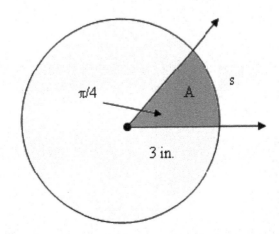

96.

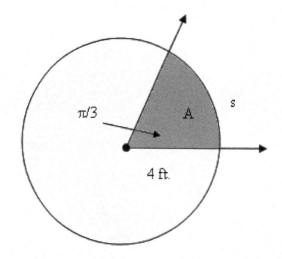

97.

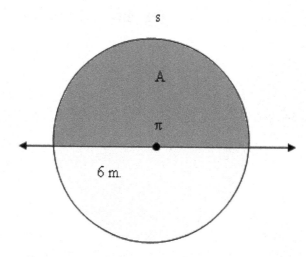

98.

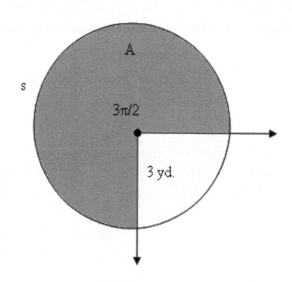

99. A pendulum swings through an angle of 30° each second. If the pendulum is 50 inches long, how far does its tip move each second?

100. A pendulum swings through an angle of 45° each second. If the pendulum is 2 feet long, how far does its tip move each second?

101. The minute hand of a clock is 9 inches long. How far does the tip of the minute hand move in 20 minutes?

102. The minute hand of a clock is 7 inches long. How far does the tip of the minute hand move in 50 minutes?

103. Annemarie makes a round lemon pie and cuts it into 12 equal slices. If the outer edge of one slice of pie measures $3\frac{5}{6}$ inches, what is the radius of the pie? Round off your answer to the nearest hundredth of an inch.

104. John purchases a large circular pizza that is divided into eight equal slices. He measures along the outer edge of the crust of one slice and finds that it is $4\frac{3}{4}$ inches. What is the diameter of the pizza?

105. A dog has a 25 foot leash attached to the corner where two fences meet. When the dog pulls the leash tight and walks from one fence to the other, the distance traveled is 62.3 feet. Find the measure of the angle, in radians and degrees, between the two fences.

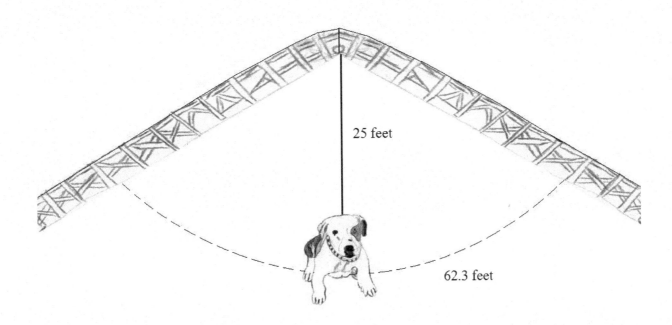

106. A windshield wiper of a car is 18 inches long. How many inches does the tip of the wiper trace out in $\frac{2}{3}$ revolution?

107. An object is traveling along a circle at a constant speed. Find the linear speed of the object if it moves 40 inches in 8 seconds.

108. Find the linear speed of an object which is in circular uniform motion if it moves 3 feet in 18 seconds.

109. A ball is traveling with uniform circular motion around a circle. If it rotates through an angle of measure $\frac{\pi}{3}$ radians in 2 seconds, find the angular speed of the object.

110. An object is traveling around a circle with constant speed. If it rotates through an angle of measure $\frac{5\pi}{18}$ radians in 6 seconds, find the angular speed of the object.

111. A wheel has a radius of 1.4 feet and turns with an angular speed of 2.65 radians per second. Determine the distance traveled by a point on the wheel in 3 minutes.

112. Nicky is twirling a model airplane that is attached to the end of a string which is 7 feet long. If he twirls the plane at 62 rpm, how far does the plane travel in 7 minutes?

113. An 3.25 inch floppy disk rotates at 320 rpm when placed in the disk drive of a computer. Find the linear speed, in feet per minute, of a point which is 2.25 inches from the center of the disk.

114. A 4.75 inch diskette rotates at 335 rpm when placed in the disk drive of a computer. Find the linear speed, in feet per minute, of a point which is 3 inches from the center of the diskette.

For Exercises 115 and 116, use the following conversion factor:

$$1 \text{ mile} = 63{,}360 \text{ inches}$$

115. The diameter of each wheel of Tony's bicycle is 11.5 inches. If Tony is riding his bicycle at a constant rate of 32 miles per hour, through how many revolutions per minute is each wheel turning?

116. The radius of each wheel of Michael's bicycle is 5.9 inches. How many revolutions per minute is each wheel turning if Michael rides his bicycle at a constant rate of 28 miles per hour?

Chapter 2: Right Triangle Trigonometry

In this chapter, we will learn about the trigonometry of a right triangle. Right triangle trigonometry can be regarded as the study of the relationship between an acute angle of a right triangle and the ratio of any two sides of the triangle. Since any triangle has three sides, there are six possible ratios of sides. We relate an acute angle to one of the six ratios by defining a function which corresponds the angle measure to the ratio value of interest. These functions are defined as the **trigonometric functions of acute angles**.

Section 2.1 begins with a review of some elementary definitions and properties of right triangles. The definitions of the trigonometric functions of acute angles will be given in this section as well. As we will see, the trigonometric functions are related in various ways. We will discuss this in Section 2.2 and list the set of fundamental identities which these functions satisfy. Section 2.3 contains properties of complementary angles and cofunctions. Two special triangles, the $30° - 60° - 90°$ triangle and the $45° - 45° - 90°$ triangle, are mentioned in Section 2.4. The measures of the sides of these triangles are easy to figure out once one side is known. Consequently, we can find the trigonometric values of the angles $30°$, $60°$, and $45°$. These measures often appear in the study of trigonometry. In Section 2.5, we will learn how the calculator can be used to do computations with the trigonometric functions. Section 2.6 ends the chapter with a look at some applications of the trigonometric functions.

Section 2.1 Trigonometric Functions of Acute Angles

Definition 1: A **right angle** is an angle whose measure is $90°$.

Recall that $90° = 90 \left(\frac{\pi}{180} \text{ radians} \right) = \frac{\pi}{2}$ radians. Therefore, we say that a right angle has radian measure $\frac{\pi}{2}$.

Definition 2: A **right triangle** is a triangle which contains a right angle. The side opposite the right angle is called the **hypotenuse** and the remaining two sides are called the **legs** of the right triangle.

Recall that the sum of the angles of every triangle is $180°$. In a right triangle, one angle must be $90°$. Therefore, the other two angles must add up to $90°$ (such angles are called **complementary angles**). This means that θ must measure between $0°$ and $90°$ (see the figure below). We write $0° < \theta < 90°$ and call θ an **acute angle**. In radians, we write $0 < \theta < \frac{\pi}{2}$.

Definition 3: Side $\overline{BC}$ is the **opposite side** of θ. Side $\overline{AC}$ is the **adjacent side** to θ.

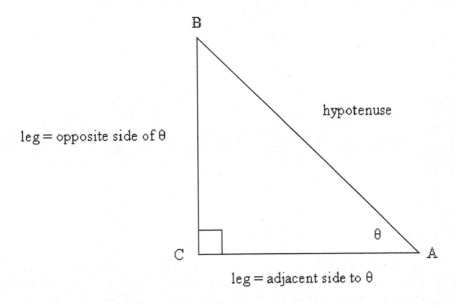

Let's recall some basic facts about right triangles. Refer to the previous figure.

1. **The Pythagorean Theorem** states that $a^2 + b^2 = c^2$ for every right triangle whose hypotenuse has length c and whose legs measure a and b.

2. The hypotenuse is the longest side of a right triangle. Algebraically, we write

$$c > a \quad \text{and} \quad c > b.$$

3. The sum of the lengths of any two sides of **any** triangle is always more than the length of the third side. Algebraically, we write

$$a + b > c,\, a + c > b,\quad \text{and}\quad b + c > a.$$

4. Two right triangles are **similar** if their angles have the same measures. If two right triangles are similar, then their corresponding sides have equal ratios. In the figure below, $\triangle A_1 B_1 C_1$ is similar to $\triangle A_2 B_2 C_2$. The following equalities hold:

$$\frac{a_1}{c_1} = \frac{a_2}{c_2},\quad \frac{b_1}{c_1} = \frac{b_2}{c_2},\quad \frac{a_1}{b_1} = \frac{a_2}{b_2} \quad \text{and} \quad \frac{c_1}{a_1} = \frac{c_2}{a_2},\quad \frac{c_1}{b_1} = \frac{c_2}{b_2},\quad \frac{b_1}{a_1} = \frac{b_2}{a_2}.$$

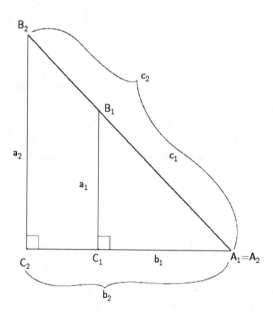

As you can see, these ratios don't depend on the size of the triangle. Instead, they depend only on the size of the angle measures in the triangle. Consequently, we can give a name to each ratio which corresponds to θ without worrying about how large or small the triangle containing θ is.

Definition of the Six Trigonometric Functions of Acute Angles

1. sine of $\theta = \dfrac{\text{opposite side of } \theta}{\text{hypotenuse}}$, abbreviated as $\sin\theta = \dfrac{a}{c}$.

2. cosine of $\theta = \dfrac{\text{adjacent side to } \theta}{\text{hypotenuse}}$, abbreviated as $\cos\theta = \dfrac{b}{c}$.

3. tangent of $\theta = \dfrac{\text{opposite side of } \theta}{\text{adjacent side to } \theta}$, abbreviated as $\tan\theta = \dfrac{a}{b}$.

4. cosecant of $\theta = \dfrac{\text{hypotenuse}}{\text{opposite side of } \theta}$, abbreviated as $\csc\theta = \dfrac{c}{a}$.

5. secant of $\theta = \dfrac{\text{hypotenuse}}{\text{adjacent side to } \theta}$, abbreviated as $\sec\theta = \dfrac{c}{b}$.

6. cotangent of $\theta = \dfrac{\text{adjacent side to } \theta}{\text{opposite side of } \theta}$, abbreviated as $\cot\theta = \dfrac{b}{a}$.

An easy way to remember the definitions for $\sin\theta$, $\cos\theta$, and $\tan\theta$ is given in the following 'phrase' consisting of the first letters of each of the definitions:

SOH CAH TOA

Notice that '**SOH**' stands for '$\sin\theta = \dfrac{\textbf{O}\text{pposite}}{\textbf{H}\text{ypotenuse}}$', '**CAH**' stands for '$\cos\theta = \dfrac{\textbf{A}\text{djacent}}{\textbf{H}\text{ypotenuse}}$', and '**TOA**' stands for '$\tan\theta = \dfrac{\textbf{O}\text{pposite}}{\textbf{A}\text{djacent}}$'. We will soon see an easy way to remember the definitions of the $\csc\theta$, $\sec\theta$, and $\cot\theta$.

Examples. Find the value of each of the six trigonometric functions of the labeled acute angle.

1)

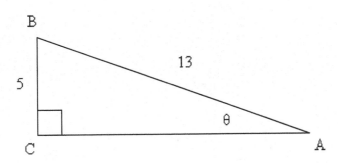

In order to find the trigonometric values of θ, we first need to find the length of the side adjacent to θ. To do this, we use the Pythagorean Theorem.

$$a^2 + b^2 = c^2$$
$$5^2 + b^2 = 13^2$$
$$2\!\!\!/5 + b^2 = 169$$
$$\underline{-2\!\!\!/5 \qquad\qquad -25}$$
$$b^2 = 144$$
$$b = \pm\sqrt{144} = \pm 12$$

We reject the answer $b = -12$ since the length of a side of a triangle must be positive. Therefore, $b = 12$ and the lengths of the sides of our triangle are all known. So, we can find the trigonometric values of θ.

$$\sin\theta = \frac{\text{opposite}}{\text{hypotenuse}} = \frac{5}{13} \qquad\qquad \csc\theta = \frac{\text{hypotenuse}}{\text{opposite}} = \frac{13}{5}$$

$$\cos\theta = \frac{\text{adjacent}}{\text{hypotenuse}} = \frac{12}{13} \qquad\qquad \sec\theta = \frac{\text{hypotenuse}}{\text{adjacent}} = \frac{13}{12}$$

$$\tan\theta = \frac{\text{opposite}}{\text{adjacent}} = \frac{5}{12} \qquad\qquad \cot\theta = \frac{\text{adjacent}}{\text{opposite}} = \frac{12}{15}$$

2)

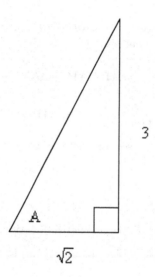

Let's first find the length of the hypotenuse by using the Pythagorean Theorem.

$$a^2 + b^2 = c^2$$
$$\left(\sqrt{2}\right)^2 + 3^2 = c^2$$
$$2 + 9 = c^2$$
$$11 = c^2$$
$$c = \pm\sqrt{11}$$

Again, we reject the negative answer $c = -\sqrt{11}$. Therefore, $c = \sqrt{11}$ and the lengths of the sides of our triangle are all known. We can now find the trigonometric values of A. Notice that the denominator of each answer is rationalized (the square root has been removed).

$$\sin A = \frac{\text{opp.}}{\text{hyp.}} = \frac{3}{\sqrt{11}} = \frac{3}{\sqrt{11}} \left(\frac{\sqrt{11}}{\sqrt{11}} \right) = \frac{3\sqrt{11}}{11} \qquad\qquad \csc A = \frac{\text{hyp.}}{\text{opp.}} = \frac{\sqrt{11}}{3}$$

$$\cos A = \frac{\text{adj.}}{\text{hyp.}} = \frac{\sqrt{2}}{\sqrt{11}} = \frac{\sqrt{2}}{\sqrt{11}} \left(\frac{\sqrt{11}}{\sqrt{11}} \right) = \frac{\sqrt{22}}{11} \qquad\qquad \sec A = \frac{\text{hyp.}}{\text{adj.}} = \frac{\sqrt{11}}{\sqrt{2}} = \frac{\sqrt{11}}{\sqrt{2}} \left(\frac{\sqrt{2}}{\sqrt{2}} \right) = \frac{\sqrt{22}}{2}$$

$$\tan A = \frac{\text{opp.}}{\text{adj.}} = \frac{3}{\sqrt{2}} = \frac{3}{\sqrt{2}} \left(\frac{\sqrt{2}}{\sqrt{2}} \right) = \frac{3\sqrt{2}}{2} \qquad\qquad \cot A = \frac{\text{adj.}}{\text{opp.}} = \frac{\sqrt{2}}{3}$$

Try These (Set 1): Find the value of each of the six trigonometric functions of the labeled angle.

1)

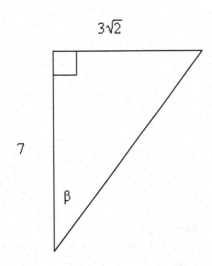

2)

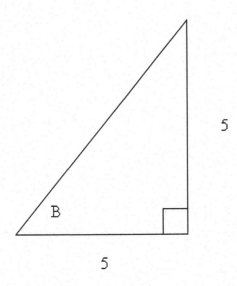

Section 2.2 The Fundamental Trigonometric Identities

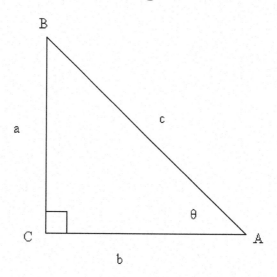

Referring to the figure above, we have:

$$\sin\theta = \frac{a}{c} \qquad\qquad \csc\theta = \frac{c}{a}$$

$$\cos\theta = \frac{b}{c} \qquad\qquad \sec\theta = \frac{c}{b}$$

$$\tan\theta = \frac{a}{b} \qquad\qquad \cot\theta = \frac{b}{a}$$

Using these definitions, along with the Pythagorean theorem, we can establish some identities which are satisfied by the trigonometric functions.

I) The Reciprocal Identities

1. $\sin\theta = \dfrac{1}{\csc\theta}$ $\qquad$ 2. $\cos\theta = \dfrac{1}{\sec\theta}$ $\qquad$ 3. $\tan\theta = \dfrac{1}{\cot\theta}$

4. $\csc\theta = \dfrac{1}{\sin\theta}$ $\qquad$ 5. $\sec\theta = \dfrac{1}{\cos\theta}$ $\qquad$ 6. $\cot\theta = \dfrac{1}{\tan\theta}$

These identities show that $\sin\theta$ is the reciprocal of $\csc\theta$, $\cos\theta$ is the reciprocal of $\sec\theta$, and $\tan\theta$ is the reciprocal of $\cot\theta$. This is easily seen to be true by just looking at the definitions above. For example, $\sin\theta = \dfrac{a}{c}$ and $\csc\theta = \dfrac{c}{a}$, so $\sin\theta$ is the reciprocal of $\csc\theta$. Another way of writing these identities is:

$$1'. \ \sin\theta\csc\theta = 1 \qquad\qquad 2'. \ \cos\theta\sec\theta = 1 \qquad\qquad 3'. \ \tan\theta\cot\theta = 1$$

II) The Quotient Identities

1. $\dfrac{\sin\theta}{\cos\theta} = \tan\theta$
2. $\dfrac{\cos\theta}{\sin\theta} = \cot\theta$

To verify that these identities are true, we use the definitions of $\sin\theta$, $\cos\theta$, $\tan\theta$ and $\cot\theta$. Observe that

$$\frac{\sin\theta}{\cos\theta} = \frac{\frac{a}{c}}{\frac{b}{c}} = \frac{a}{c}\left(\frac{c}{b}\right) = \frac{a}{b} = \tan\theta$$

and

$$\frac{\cos\theta}{\sin\theta} = \frac{\frac{b}{c}}{\frac{a}{c}} = \frac{b}{c}\left(\frac{c}{a}\right) = \frac{b}{a} = \cot\theta.$$

Another way of verifying the identity $\dfrac{\cos\theta}{\sin\theta} = \cot\theta$ is by taking the reciprocal of both sides of the equation $\dfrac{\sin\theta}{\cos\theta} = \tan\theta$.

III) The Pythagorean Identities

1. $\underbrace{\sin^2\theta + \cos^2\theta = 1}_{\text{same as }(\sin\theta)^2+(\cos\theta)^2=1}$

2. $\underbrace{\tan^2\theta + 1 = \sec^2\theta}_{\text{same as }(\tan\theta)^2+1=(\sec\theta)^2}$

3. $\underbrace{1 + \cot^2\theta = \csc^2\theta}_{\text{same as }1+(\cot\theta)^2=(\csc\theta)^2}$

Notice that I've written $(\sin\theta)^2 = \sin^2\theta$, $(\cos\theta)^2 = \cos^2\theta$, etc. It is customary to put a positive exponent before the angle when we raise a trigonometric function to that exponent. For example, $(\sin\theta)^6$ means $\sin^6\theta$ and $\cot^3\theta$ means $(\cot\theta)^3$. If the exponent is negative, then we do not use this convention. For example, $(\cos\theta)^{-1}$ does not mean $\cos^{-1}\theta$ and $(\tan\beta)^{-4}$ does not mean $\tan^{-4}\beta$.

Let's verify that these identities are true. Recall that the Pythagorean theorem states that $a^2 + b^2 = c^2$. To verify the first identity, we divide both sides of the equation $a^2 + b^2 = c^2$ by c^2:

$$\frac{a^2}{c^2} + \frac{b^2}{c^2} = \frac{c^2}{c^2}$$

$$\underbrace{\left(\frac{a}{c}\right)^2} + \underbrace{\left(\frac{b}{c}\right)^2} = 1$$

$$(\sin\theta)^2 + (\cos\theta)^2 = 1$$

$$\sin^2\theta + \cos^2\theta = 1$$

To verify the second identity, we divide both sides of the equation $a^2 + b^2 = c^2$ by b^2:

$$\frac{a^2}{b^2} + \frac{b^2}{b^2} = \frac{c^2}{b^2}$$

$$\left(\frac{a}{b}\right)^2 + 1 = \left(\frac{c}{b}\right)^2$$

$$\underbrace{\left(\tan\theta\right)^2}_{} + 1 = \underbrace{\left(\sec\theta\right)^2}_{}$$

$$\tan^2\theta + 1 = \sec^2\theta$$

The third identity comes from dividing both sides of $a^2 + b^2 = c^2$ by a^2:

$$\frac{a^2}{a^2} + \frac{b^2}{a^2} = \frac{c^2}{a^2}$$

$$1 + \left(\frac{b}{a}\right)^2 = \left(\frac{c}{a}\right)^2$$

$$1 + \underbrace{\left(\cot\theta\right)^2}_{} = \underbrace{\left(\csc\theta\right)^2}_{}$$

$$1 + \cot^2\theta = \csc^2\theta$$

Examples. Find the exact values of each expression by using the identities.

1) $\sin 40° \csc 40° = 1$

2) $\underbrace{\dfrac{\sin 82°}{\cos 82°}}_{\tan 82°} - \tan 82° = \tan 82° - \tan 82° = 0$

3) $2\sin^2 \frac{\pi}{8} + 2\cos^2 \frac{\pi}{8} = 2\underbrace{\left(\sin^2 \frac{\pi}{8} + \cos^2 \frac{\pi}{8}\right)}_{1} = 2\,(1) = 2$

4) $5\tan^2 \frac{2\pi}{11} - 5\sec^2 \frac{2\pi}{11} = \underbrace{5\left(\tan^2 \frac{2\pi}{11} - \sec^2 \frac{2\pi}{11}\right) = 5\,(-1)}_{\tan^2 \frac{2\pi}{11} + 1 = \sec^2 \frac{2\pi}{11},\ \text{so}\ \tan^2 \frac{2\pi}{11} - \sec^2 \frac{2\pi}{11} = -1.} = -5$

5) $\dfrac{3\cos 24°}{5\sin 24°} - \dfrac{3}{5}\cot 24° = \dfrac{3}{5}\underbrace{\left(\dfrac{\cos 24°}{\sin 24°}\right)}_{\cot 24°} - \dfrac{3}{5}\cot 24° = \dfrac{3}{5}\cot 24° - \dfrac{3}{5}\cot 24° = 0$

Examples.

1) Suppose that $\sin\alpha = \frac{2}{5}$ and α is an acute angle. Find the exact value of each of the remaining five trigonometric functions of α.

There are two methods for solving this problem. The first method makes use of our identities. The second method uses a right triangle and the definitions of the trigonometric functions.

<u>**Method I.**</u> Using the Identities.

1. $\csc\alpha = \frac{5}{2}$ since $\csc\alpha$ is the reciprocal of $\sin\alpha$.

2. We can find $\cos\alpha$ by using the identity $\sin^2\alpha + \cos^2\alpha = 1$.

$$\sin^2\alpha + \cos^2\alpha = 1$$

$$\left(\tfrac{2}{5}\right)^2 + \cos^2\alpha = 1$$

$$\tfrac{4}{25} + \cos^2\alpha = 1$$

$$\cos^2\alpha = \tfrac{21}{25}$$

$$\cos\alpha = \sqrt{\tfrac{21}{25}}$$

$$\cos\alpha = \tfrac{\sqrt{21}}{5}$$

Notice that the answer $\cos\alpha = -\sqrt{\tfrac{21}{25}}$ has been rejected.

3. $\sec\alpha = \dfrac{5}{\sqrt{21}} = \dfrac{5}{\sqrt{21}}\left(\dfrac{\sqrt{21}}{\sqrt{21}}\right) = \dfrac{5\sqrt{21}}{21}$ since $\sec\alpha$ is the reciprocal of $\cos\alpha$.

4. We can find $\tan\alpha$ by using the identity $\dfrac{\sin\alpha}{\cos\alpha} = \tan\alpha$.

$$\tan\alpha = \frac{\sin\alpha}{\cos\alpha} = \frac{\frac{2}{5}}{\frac{\sqrt{21}}{5}} = \frac{\frac{2}{\cancel{5}}}{\frac{\sqrt{21}}{\cancel{5}}}\left(\frac{\frac{\cancel{5}}{1}}{\frac{\cancel{5}}{1}}\right) = \frac{2}{\sqrt{21}} = \frac{2}{\sqrt{21}}\left(\frac{\sqrt{21}}{\sqrt{21}}\right) = \frac{2\sqrt{21}}{21}$$

5. $\cot\alpha = \dfrac{\sqrt{21}}{2}$ since $\cot\alpha$ is the reciprocal of $\tan\alpha$.

Method II. Using a right triangle.

We are given that $\sin\alpha = \tfrac{2}{5}$ and α is an acute angle. We can draw a right triangle which contains α and satisfies the given condition.

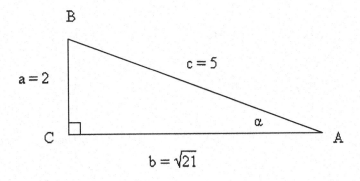

Note that $b = \sqrt{21}$ was found by using the Pythagorean Theorem:

$$a^2 + b^2 = c^2$$
$$2^2 + b^2 = 5^2$$
$$\cancel{4} + b^2 = 25$$
$$\underline{-\cancel{4} \qquad\qquad -4}$$
$$b^2 = 21$$
$$b = \sqrt{21}$$

We can use the triangle to find the values of the remaining five trigonometric functions of α. We will get the same answers as we did using Method I.

2) Suppose that $\cot B = 7$ and $0 < B < \frac{\pi}{2}$. Find the exact value of each of the remaining five trigonometric functions of B.

Let's construct a right triangle which contains angle B and satisfies the equality $\cot B = 7 = \frac{7}{1}$.

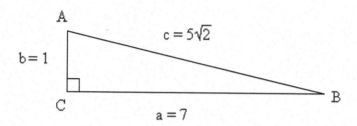

The value of C was obtained by using the Pythagorean Theorem:

$$a^2 + b^2 = c^2$$
$$7^2 + 1^2 = c^2$$
$$49 + 1 = c^2$$
$$50 = c^2$$
$$c = \sqrt{50} = \sqrt{25}\sqrt{2} = 5\sqrt{2}$$

We can now use the triangle to find the values of the remaining five trigonometric functions of B.

$$\sin B = \frac{1}{5\sqrt{2}} = \frac{1}{5\sqrt{2}}\left(\frac{\sqrt{2}}{\sqrt{2}}\right) = \frac{\sqrt{2}}{10} \qquad \cos B = \frac{7}{5\sqrt{2}} = \frac{7}{5\sqrt{2}}\left(\frac{\sqrt{2}}{\sqrt{2}}\right) = \frac{7\sqrt{2}}{10}$$

$$\tan B = \frac{1}{7} \qquad \csc B = \frac{5\sqrt{2}}{1} = 5\sqrt{2} \qquad \sec B = \frac{5\sqrt{2}}{7}$$

If you try this problem using the identities instead, you will obtain the same answers. Why don't you give it a try?

Try These (Set 2):

I) Find the exact values of each expression by using the identities.

1) $\dfrac{\sin 49°}{\cos 49°} - \tan 49°$ 2) $3\sin^2 68° + 3\cos^2 68°$ 3) $7\sec^2 \frac{2\pi}{5} - 7\tan^2 \frac{2\pi}{5}$

II) Suppose that $\tan \beta = \frac{\sqrt{6}}{4}$ and β is an acute angle. Find the exact value of each of the remaining five trigonometric functions of β.

Section 2.3 Complementary Angles and Cofunctions

Definition: Two acute angles, β and α, are called **complementary** if their measures add up to 90°.

In a right triangle, the right angle measures 90°. Since the measures of all three angles add up to 180°, the two remaining angle measures must add up to 90°. This means that the two angles (neither of which is the right angle) are complementary.

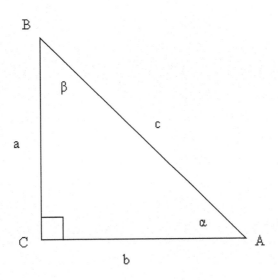

$$\beta + \alpha = 90°$$

Let's take a look at the figure above. Notice that $\sin \alpha = \frac{a}{c} = \cos \beta$, $\tan \alpha = \frac{a}{b} = \cot \beta$, and $\sec \alpha = \frac{c}{b} = \csc \beta$. Similarly, we have $\cos \alpha = \frac{b}{c} = \sin \beta$, $\cot \alpha = \frac{b}{a} = \tan \beta$, and $\csc \alpha = \frac{c}{a} = \sec \beta$. These relationships will always hold whenever β and α are complementary angles.

The Complementary Angle Theorem

Suppose that β and α are complementary angles. Then:

$$\sin \beta = \cos \alpha \qquad \sin \alpha = \cos \beta$$
$$\tan \beta = \cot \alpha \qquad \tan \alpha = \cot \beta$$
$$\sec \beta = \csc \alpha \qquad \sec \alpha = \csc \beta$$

Notice how the prefix 'co' appears once in each equation above:

$$\text{sine } \beta = \underline{\text{co}}\text{sine } \alpha, \quad \text{tangent } \beta = \underline{\text{co}}\text{tangent } \alpha, \quad \text{secant } \beta = \underline{\text{co}}\text{secant } \alpha, \text{ etc.}$$

We say that sine and cosine, tangent and cotangent, and secant and cosecant are **cofunctions** of each other. Since $\beta + \alpha = 90°$, we can write $\alpha = 90° - \beta$. And so, the complementary angle theorem can be written as:

$$
\begin{array}{ll}
\sin \beta = \cos (90° - \beta) & \cos \beta = \sin (90° - \beta) \\
\tan \beta = \cot (90° - \beta) & \cot \beta = \tan (90° - \beta) \\
\sec \beta = \csc (90° - \beta) & \csc \beta = \sec (90° - \beta)
\end{array}
$$

In radian measure, we write (since $90° = \frac{\pi}{2}$ radians):

$$
\begin{array}{ll}
\sin \beta = \cos \left(\frac{\pi}{2} - \beta\right) & \cos \beta = \sin \left(\frac{\pi}{2} - \beta\right) \\
\tan \beta = \cot \left(\frac{\pi}{2} - \beta\right) & \cot \beta = \tan \left(\frac{\pi}{2} - \beta\right) \\
\sec \beta = \csc \left(\frac{\pi}{2} - \beta\right) & \csc \beta = \sec \left(\frac{\pi}{2} - \beta\right)
\end{array}
$$

Examples. Write each expression in terms of its cofunction.

1) $\sin 53° = \cos (90° - 53°) = \cos 37°$

2) $\cot \frac{\pi}{3} = \tan \left(\frac{\pi}{2} - \frac{\pi}{3}\right) = \tan \left(\frac{3\pi}{6} - \frac{2\pi}{6}\right) = \tan \frac{\pi}{6}$

3) $\sec 28° = \csc (90° - 28°) = \csc 62°$

4) $\cos \frac{2\pi}{7} = \sin \left(\frac{\pi}{2} - \frac{2\pi}{7}\right) = \sin \left(\frac{7\pi}{14} - \frac{4\pi}{14}\right) = \sin \frac{3\pi}{14}$

Examples. Find the exact value of each expression.

1) $\sin 50° - \underbrace{\cos 40°}_{\sin(90° - 40°)} = \sin 50° - \sin 50° = 0$

2) $\underbrace{\tan^2 \frac{\pi}{8} - \csc^2 \frac{3\pi}{8} = \tan^2 \frac{\pi}{8} - \sec^2 \frac{\pi}{8} = -1}$

$\csc^2 \frac{3\pi}{8} = \sec^2 \left(\frac{\pi}{2} - \frac{3\pi}{8}\right) = \sec^2 \frac{\pi}{8}$ and $\tan^2 \frac{\pi}{8} + 1 = \sec^2 \frac{\pi}{8}$.

3) $\underbrace{\dfrac{\cot 27°}{\tan 63°}}_{\tan 63° = \cot(90° - 63°) = \cot 27°} = \dfrac{\cot 27°}{\cot 27°} = 1$

4) $\underbrace{\cos 30° \cdot \tan 30° \cdot \sec 60° = \dfrac{\cos 30°}{1} \cdot \dfrac{\sin 30°}{\cos 30°} \cdot \dfrac{1}{\sin 30°} = 1}_{\sec 60° = \csc(90° - 60°) = \csc 30° = \frac{1}{\sin 30°}}$

Try These (Set 3):

I) Write each expression in terms of its cofunction.

   1) $\sec 41°$ 2) $\sin 12°$ 3) $\tan \frac{\pi}{5}$ 4) $\csc \frac{2\pi}{13}$

II) Find the exact value of each expression.

   1) $\tan 20° - \cot 70°$ 2) $\dfrac{\sec 9°}{\csc 81°} + 3$ 3) $\sin^2 \frac{\pi}{3} + \sin^2 \frac{\pi}{6}$

Section 2.4 Trigonometric Functions of $30° = \dfrac{\pi}{6}$, $45° = \dfrac{\pi}{4}$, and $60° = \dfrac{\pi}{3}$

The $45° - 45° - 90°$ (or $\dfrac{\pi}{4} - \dfrac{\pi}{4} - \dfrac{\pi}{2}$) Right Triangle

An angle measurement which often appears is 45°. We can find the values of the trigonometric functions of 45° by using the following right triangle:

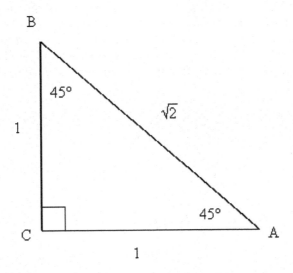

Notice that the two sides which are opposite the 45° angles have the same length, 1. We call a triangle with two sides of equal length an **isosceles triangle**. Using this triangle, we find that:

$$\sin 45° = \frac{1}{\sqrt{2}} = \frac{\sqrt{2}}{2} \qquad \csc 45° = \frac{\sqrt{2}}{1} = \sqrt{2}$$

$$\cos 45° = \frac{1}{\sqrt{2}} = \frac{\sqrt{2}}{2} \qquad \sec 45° = \frac{\sqrt{2}}{1} = \sqrt{2}$$

$$\tan 45° = \frac{1}{1} = 1 \qquad \cot 45° = \frac{1}{1} = 1$$

The $30° - 60° - 90°$ (or $\dfrac{\pi}{6} - \dfrac{\pi}{3} - \dfrac{\pi}{2}$) Right Triangle

One right triangle whose angles measure 30°, 60°, and 90° looks like this:

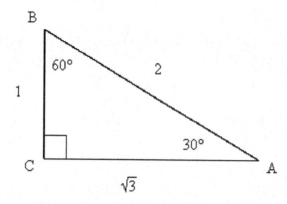

How do we get the lengths of the sides of this triangle? Well, we begin with an **equilateral triangle** (a triangle whose three sides have equal length) whose sides measure 2 units. We draw a line segment from one of the vertices of the triangle to the opposite side of the vertex in such a way that the line segment is perpendicular to the opposite side. This perpendicular line divides the equilateral triangle into two congruent right triangles, each having angles which measure 30°, 60°, and 90°, and sides which measure 1, $\sqrt{3}$, and 2 (see the figure below).

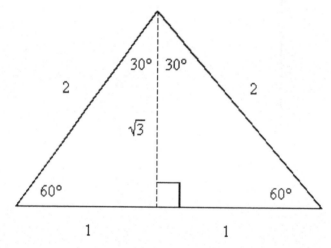

Using this triangle, we find that:

$$\sin 30° = \frac{1}{2} \qquad\qquad\qquad \sin 60° = \frac{\sqrt{3}}{2}$$

$$\cos 30° = \frac{\sqrt{3}}{2} \qquad\qquad\qquad \cos 60° = \frac{1}{2}$$

$$\tan 30° = \frac{1}{\sqrt{3}} = \frac{\sqrt{3}}{3} \qquad\qquad \tan 60° = \frac{\sqrt{3}}{1} = \sqrt{3}$$

$$\csc 30° = \frac{2}{1} = 2 \qquad\qquad\qquad \csc 60° = \frac{2}{\sqrt{3}} = \frac{2\sqrt{3}}{3}$$

$$\sec 30° = \frac{2}{\sqrt{3}} = \frac{2\sqrt{3}}{3} \qquad\qquad \sec 60° = \frac{2}{1} = 2$$

$$\cot 30° = \frac{\sqrt{3}}{1} = \sqrt{3} \qquad\qquad \cot 60° = \frac{1}{\sqrt{3}} = \frac{\sqrt{3}}{3}$$

Examples. Find the exact value of each expression.

1) $\sin 45° + \cos 60° = \frac{\sqrt{2}}{2} + \frac{1}{2} = \frac{\sqrt{2}+1}{2}$

2) $\tan 30° \csc 45° = \frac{\sqrt{3}}{3} \left(\frac{\sqrt{2}}{1} \right) = \frac{\sqrt{6}}{3}$

3) $\cos^2 30° - \cot 45° = \left(\frac{\sqrt{3}}{2} \right)^2 - 1 = \frac{3}{4} - 1 = -\frac{1}{4}$

4) $\underbrace{\cos^2 \frac{\pi}{4} + \tan \frac{\pi}{3} = \left(\frac{\sqrt{2}}{2} \right)^2 + \sqrt{3}}\ = \frac{2}{4} + \sqrt{3} = \frac{1}{2} + \frac{2\sqrt{3}}{2} = \frac{1+2\sqrt{3}}{2}$

$\cos \frac{\pi}{4} = \cos 45° = \frac{\sqrt{2}}{2}$ and $\tan \frac{\pi}{3} = \tan 60° = \sqrt{3}.$

Try These (Set 4): Find the exact value of each expression.

1) $\tan 45° + \cos 30°$ 2) $\sin^2 60° - \sec^2 45°$ 3) $\dfrac{\tan \frac{\pi}{6}}{\csc \frac{\pi}{4}}$

Section 2.5   Using the Calculator

We've seen how to determine the values of the trigonometric functions for $30°$, $60°$, and $45°$. What if an angle has a measure different from any of these? Well, if you take a look at your calculator, you will notice that there are three buttons which correspond to the trigonometric functions. They are

$$\boxed{\text{SIN}}, \quad \boxed{\text{COS}}, \quad \text{and} \quad \boxed{\text{TAN}}.$$

There are no buttons for the other three functions, but we can still compute values for these functions by using the reciprocal identities:

$$\csc \theta = \frac{1}{\sin \theta} \qquad \sec \theta = \frac{1}{\cos \theta} \qquad \cot \theta = \frac{1}{\tan \theta}$$

When you use the TI-30XII calculator to compute the value of a trigonometric function, you must make sure that you are in the right mode (degree or radian). To go into degree or radian mode, press the $\boxed{\text{DRG}}$ button and use the arrow keys to move the underline to the mode which you want (either DEG or RAD). After choosing the mode, press $\boxed{=}$ to set this mode.

Note: The $\boxed{\text{SIN}}$, $\boxed{\text{COS}}$, and $\boxed{\text{TAN}}$ keys automatically follow the trigonometric with a ' ('. You must type in a ') ' to show where the angle expression ends. The next examples demonstrate this.

Examples. Evaluate each expression and round off to three decimal places.

1) $\cos 56° = 0.559$, found by typing in: $\boxed{\text{COS}}\ 56\ \boxed{)}\ \boxed{=}$ (Are you in degree mode?)

2) $\tan 20° = 0.364$, found by typing in: $\boxed{\text{TAN}}\ 20\ \boxed{)}\ \boxed{=}$ (Are you in degree mode?)

3) $\sin \frac{\pi}{7} = 0.434$, found by typing in: $\boxed{\text{SIN}}\ \boxed{\pi}\ \boxed{\div}\ \boxed{7}\ \boxed{)}\ \boxed{=}$ (Are you in radian mode?)

4) $\sec \frac{2\pi}{9} = 1.305$, found by typing in: $\underbrace{1\ \boxed{\div}\ \boxed{\text{COS}}\ \boxed{2}\ \boxed{\pi}\ \boxed{\div}\ \boxed{9}\ \boxed{)}\ \boxed{=}}_{\sec \frac{2\pi}{9} = \frac{1}{\cos \frac{2\pi}{9}} = 1 \div \cos \frac{2\pi}{9}}$ (Are you in radian mode?)

Alternatively, $\underbrace{\boxed{\text{COS}}\ \boxed{2}\ \boxed{\pi}\ \boxed{\div}\ \boxed{9}\ \boxed{)}\ \boxed{x^{-1}}\ \boxed{=}}_{\sec \frac{2\pi}{9} = \frac{1}{\cos \frac{2\pi}{9}} = \left(\cos \frac{2\pi}{9}\right)^{-1}}$ gives the same answer.

5) $\csc 1 = 1.188$, found by typing in: $\underbrace{1\ \boxed{\div}\ \boxed{\text{SIN}}\ \boxed{1}\ \boxed{)}\ \boxed{=}}_{\csc 1 = \frac{1}{\sin 1} = 1 \div \sin 1}$ (Are you in radian mode?)

Alternatively, $\underbrace{\boxed{\text{SIN}}\ \boxed{1}\ \boxed{)}\ \boxed{x^{-1}}\ \boxed{=}}_{\csc 1 = \frac{1}{\sin 1} = (\sin 1)^{-1}}$ gives the same answer.

6) $\csc 1° = 57.299$, found by typing in: $\underbrace{1\ \boxed{\div}\ \boxed{\text{SIN}}\ \boxed{1}\ \boxed{)}\ \boxed{=}}_{\csc 1° = \frac{1}{\sin 1°} = 1 \div \sin 1°}$ (Are you in degree mode?)

Alternatively, $\underbrace{\boxed{\text{SIN}}\ \boxed{1}\ \boxed{)}\ \boxed{x^{-1}}\ \boxed{=}}_{\csc 1° = \frac{1}{\sin 1°} = (\sin 1°)^{-1}}$ gives the same answer.

7) $7 \sin^2 23° = 1.069$ Type in: $7\ \boxed{\times}\ \boxed{\text{SIN}}\ 23\ \boxed{)}\ \boxed{x^2}\ \boxed{=}$ (Are you in degree mode?)

Try These (Set 5): Evaluate and round off to three decimal places.

1) $\sin 72°$ 2) $\cos \frac{\pi}{9}$ 3) $\cot \frac{2\pi}{7}$ 4) $\csc^2 19° - 3 \cos^2 62°$

Section 2.6 Solving Right Triangles; Applications

We will apply our knowledge of the trigonometric functions to solve right triangle problems. If we are given one angle and one side of a right triangle, we can determine the remaining two sides by using trigonometry. The first set of examples deal with such problems.

Examples. Solve each right triangle. Round off your answers to three decimal places.

1)

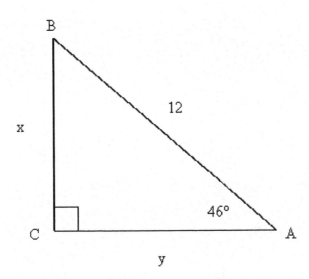

We want to find the values of x, y, and B. From the definitions of sine and cosine, we have that

$$\sin 46° = \frac{x}{12} \quad \text{and} \quad \cos 46° = \frac{y}{12}.$$

Therefore, if we cross multiply in each equation, we obtain:

$$12\sin 46° = x \quad \text{and} \quad 12\cos 46° = y$$
$$x \approx 8.632 \quad \text{and} \quad y \approx 8.336$$

Let's find B. We have that $90° + 46° + B = 180°$. Solving for B, we get:

$$90° + 46° + B = 180°$$
$$13\!\!\!/6° + B \quad = 180°$$
$$\underline{-1\!\!\!/36° \qquad\quad -136°}$$
$$B = 44°$$

2)

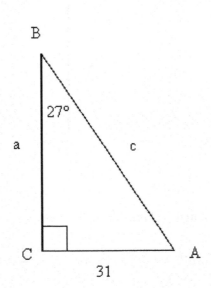

We want to find the values of a, c, and A. From the definitions of sine and tangent, we have that

$$\sin 27° = \frac{31}{c} \quad \text{and} \quad \tan 27° = \frac{31}{a}.$$

We solve each equation.

$$\sin 27° = \frac{31}{c} \quad \text{and} \quad \tan 27° = \frac{31}{a}$$

$$\frac{c\,\cancel{\sin 27°}}{\cancel{\sin 27°}} = \frac{31}{\sin 27°} \quad \text{and} \quad \frac{a\,\cancel{\tan 27°}}{\cancel{\tan 27°}} = \frac{31}{\tan 27°}$$

$$c \approx 68.283 \quad \text{and} \quad a \approx 60.841$$

Observe that $90° + 27° + A = 180°$. Solving for A, we obtain:

$$90° + 27° + A = 180°$$
$$117° + A \quad = 180°$$
$$\underline{-117° \qquad\qquad -117°}$$
$$A = 63°$$

3)

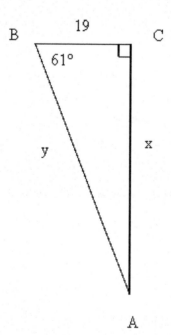

We want to find the values of x, y, and A. From the definitions of tangent and cosine, we have that

$$\tan 61° = \frac{x}{19} \quad \text{and} \quad \cos 61° = \frac{19}{y}.$$

Let's solve each equation:

$$\tan 61° = \frac{x}{19} \quad \text{and} \quad \cos 61° = \frac{19}{y}$$

$$19 \tan 61° = x \quad \text{and} \quad \frac{y \cancel{\cos 61°}}{\cancel{\cos 61°}} = \frac{19}{\cos 61°}$$

$$x \approx 9.211 \quad \text{and} \quad y \approx 39.191$$

Since $90° + 61° + A = 180°$, we have that $A = 29°$.

Trigonometry is used in many different areas of study and is applicable in real life problems. The next set of examples illustrate the different types of situations where trigonometry comes in handy. Before we consider these examples, let's take a look at two commonly used concepts called the angle of elevation and the angle of depression.

Suppose that a bird watcher wants to see a blue jay sitting in a tree that is some horizontal distance away. If he is using a telescope, he would need to elevate his telescope from a horizontal position to view the blue jay (see the figure below). The line segment joining the eye of the bird watcher to the blue jay is called the **line of sight**. The angle determined by the horizontal line segment and the line of sight is called the **angle of elevation** of the blue jay from the bird watcher. In the figure below, θ represents the angle of elevation. Note that the horizontal line and the line of sight must lie in the same vertical plane.

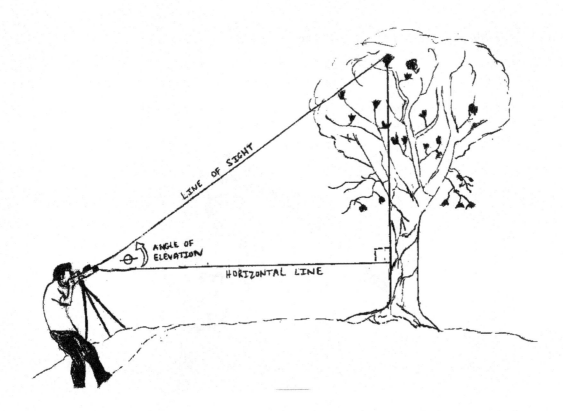

Now suppose that the bird watcher is on a cliff and he sees a robin some distance away and below him. If he uses his telescope to view the robin, he would look downward by depressing his telescope from the horizontal position (see the figure on next page). As before, the line segment joining the eye of the bird watcher to the robin is called the **line of sight**. The angle determined by the horizontal line segment and the line of sight is called the **angle of depression** of the robin from the bird watcher. In the figure below, θ represents the angle of depression. Once again, the horizontal line must lie in the same vertical plane as the line of sight.

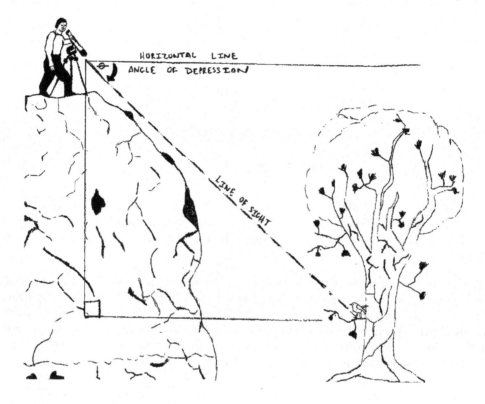

Examples. Solve. Round off your answers to the nearest foot.

1) A 24 foot ladder is leaning against a wall. The foot of the ladder makes an angle of 57° with the ground. Find the vertical distance from the top of the ladder to the ground.

The first step in this type of example is to draw a picture which contains the given information. Here, we are given a ladder leaning against a wall. A sketch of this is given below.

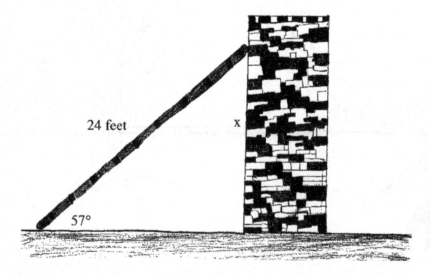

We want to solve for x in the figure above. What trigonometric function relates the opposite of an angle to the hypotenuse? Well, sine does. We will, therefore, use sine to solve the problem. By the definition of sine, we have:

$$\sin 57° = \frac{x}{24}$$

$$x = 24 \sin 57° \approx 20 \text{ feet}$$

2) If the sun is 20° above the horizon, find the length of a shadow cast by a building that is 600 feet tall.

Let's begin by sketching a figure which describes our situation.

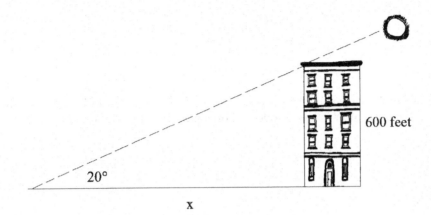

We want to solve for x in the accompanying diagram. By the definition of tangent, we have:

$$\tan 20° = \frac{600}{x}$$

$$\frac{x\,\tan 20°}{\tan 20°} = \frac{600}{\tan 20°} \approx 1,648 \text{ feet}$$

3) From the top of a lighthouse 245 feet above sea level, the angle of depression of a buoy at sea is 41° (see the figure below). Find the length of the line of sight.

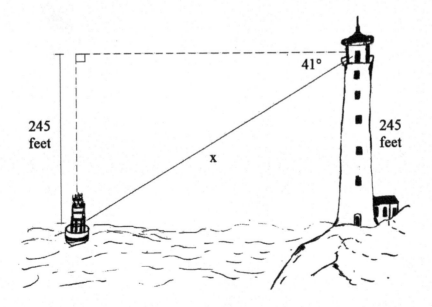

The diagram shows that:

$$\sin 41° = \frac{245}{x}$$

$$\frac{x \cancel{\sin 41°}}{\cancel{\sin 41°}} = \frac{245}{\sin 41°} \approx 373 \text{ feet}$$

4) A plane takes off from a runway and rises at an angle of 12° with the horizontal (see the figure below). Find the height of the plane after it has traveled a horizontal distance of 990 feet.

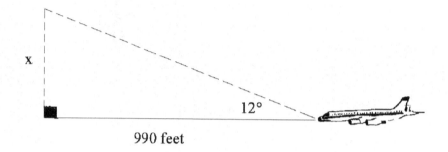

We have

$$\tan 12° = \frac{x}{990}, \quad \text{so} \quad x = 990 \tan 12° \approx 210 \text{ feet.}$$

5) Marcos is flying a kite. The straight string of the kite makes an angle of elevation of 55° with the horizontal (see the figure below). If the kite is 168 feet above the ground and Marcos is holding the string 5 feet above the ground, find the horizontal distance from the kite to Marcos.

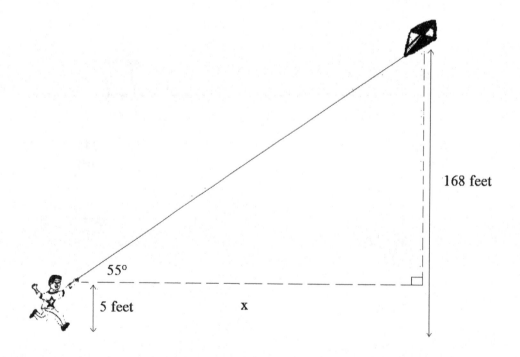

Using the Figure on the previous page, we find that

$$\tan 55° = \frac{168 - 5}{x} = \frac{163}{x}$$

$$\frac{x \tan 55°}{\tan 55°} = \frac{163}{\tan 55°} \approx 114 \text{ feet.}$$

Try These (Set 6):

1) Find x.

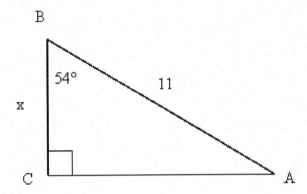

2) A road is inclined at an angle of 11° with the horizontal. Find the distance, to the nearest hundredth of a foot, that a car must drive on this road in order for it to be elevated 12 feet above the horizontal.

Exercise 2

In Exercises 1-10, find the exact value of the six trigonometric functions of the labeled angle in each triangle.

1.

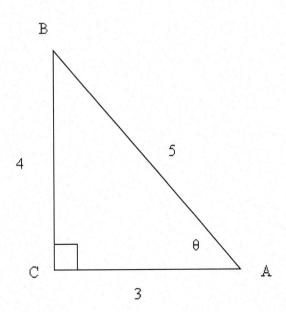

2.

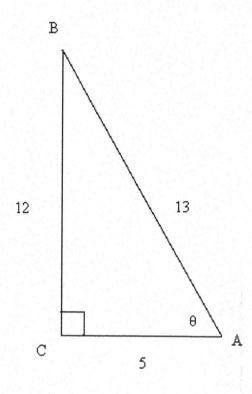

3.

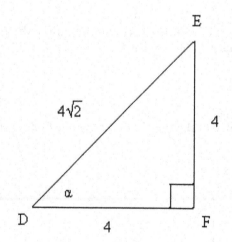

4.

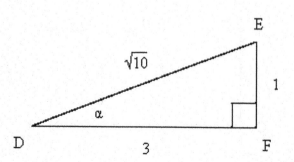

5.

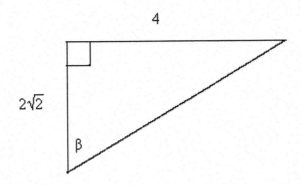

6.

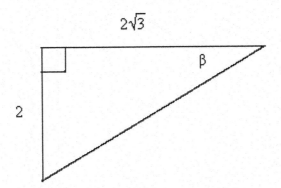

7.

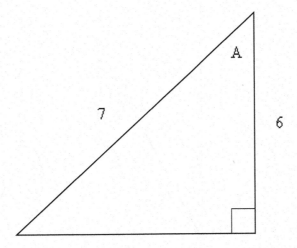

8.

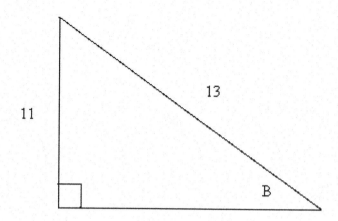

9.

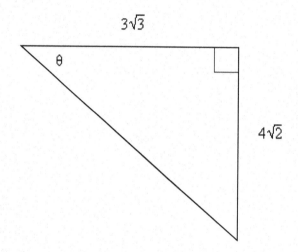

10.

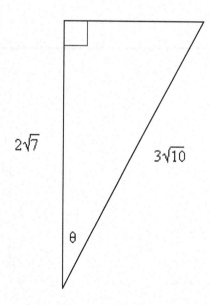

In Exercises 11-50, find the exact value of the given expression.

11. $\sin 10° \csc 10°$

12. $\cot 72° \tan 72°$

13. $\sec \frac{\pi}{5} \cos \frac{\pi}{5}$

14. $\csc \frac{3\pi}{10} \sin \frac{3\pi}{10}$

15. $\dfrac{\sin 49°}{\cos 49°} (\cot 49°)$

16. $\dfrac{\cos 76°}{\sin 76°} (\tan 76°)$

17. $\tan 15° - \dfrac{\sin 15°}{\cos 15°}$

18. $\cot 80° - \dfrac{\cos 80°}{\sin 80°}$

19. $\sin^2 56° + \cos^2 56°$

20. $\cos^2 3° + \sin^2 3°$

21. $\tan^2 \frac{2\pi}{7} - \sec^2 \frac{2\pi}{7}$

22. $\sec^2 \frac{5\pi}{12} - \tan^2 \frac{5\pi}{12}$

23. $\cot^2 25° - \csc^2 25°$

24. $\csc^2 33° - \cot^2 33°$

25. $3 \sin^2 \frac{\pi}{9} + 3 \cos^2 \frac{\pi}{9}$

26. $-5 \sin^2 \frac{\pi}{3} - 5 \cos^2 \frac{\pi}{3}$

27. $1 - \cos^2 88° - \sin^2 88°$

28. $1 - \sin^2 9° - \cos^2 9°$

29. $1 - \sec^2 \frac{\pi}{4} + \tan^2 \frac{\pi}{4}$

30. $\tan^2 \frac{\pi}{6} - \sec^2 \frac{\pi}{6} + 1$

31. $\dfrac{\sin 10°}{\cos 80°}$

32. $\dfrac{\cos 24°}{\sin 66°}$

33. $\tan 55° - \dfrac{\sin 55°}{\sin 35°}$

34. $\cot 82° - \dfrac{\cos 82°}{\cos 8°}$

35. $\sin 40° - \cos 50°$

36. $\cot 37° - \tan 53°$

37. $2 \sec \frac{2\pi}{9} - 2 \csc \frac{5\pi}{18}$

38. $7 \tan \frac{\pi}{4} - 7 \cot \frac{\pi}{4}$

39. $\sin 21° \cot 21° \csc 69°$

40. $\tan 57° \cos 57° \sec 33°$

41. $\sin 36° \cos 54° + \cos 36° \sin 54°$

42. $\cos 13° \sin 77° + \sin 77° \cos 13°$

43. $\tan 45° \cot 45° - \csc 45° \sec 45°$

44. $\csc 28° \sec 62° - \tan 62° \cot 28°$

45. $\dfrac{\sin^2 16° + \cos^2 16°}{4 \sin^2 54° + 4 \cos^2 54°}$

46. $\dfrac{8 \sin^2 62° + 8 \cos^2 62°}{2 \sin^2 19° + 2 \cos^2 19°}$

47. $\dfrac{6 \sec \frac{\pi}{3} \cos \frac{\pi}{3}}{9 \cot \frac{2\pi}{9} \tan \frac{2\pi}{9}}$

48. $\dfrac{-2 \csc \frac{\pi}{11} \sin \frac{\pi}{11}}{12 \tan \frac{2\pi}{13} \cot \frac{2\pi}{13}}$

49. $\dfrac{1 - \sec^2 33° + \tan^2 33°}{\sin 26° \cos 54° + \cos 26° \sin 54°}$

50. $\dfrac{1 - \sin^2 18° - \cos^2 18°}{7 \csc^2 56° - 7 \cot^2 56°}$

In Exercises 51-64, use the trigonometric identities to find the exact value of the expression(s). All angles are acute angles.

51. If $\sin \theta = \frac{2}{3}$, find $\csc \theta$.

52. If $\tan \theta = \frac{8}{5}$, find $\cot \theta$.

53. If $\sec A = 7$, find $\cos A$.

54. If $\csc B = \frac{19}{2}$, find $\sin B$.

55. If $\sin \alpha = \frac{\sqrt{3}}{2}$, find $\cos \alpha$.

56. If $\cos \alpha = \frac{\sqrt{2}}{2}$, find $\sin \alpha$.

57. If $\tan \beta = \frac{\sqrt{5}}{6}$, find $\sec \beta$.

58. If $\sec \beta = \frac{9}{5}$, find $\tan \beta$.

59. If $\csc \alpha = \frac{10}{3}$, find $\cot \alpha$.

60. If $\cot C = \frac{\sqrt{3}}{7}$, find $\csc C$.

61. If $\sin \theta = \frac{1}{6}$, find $\cos \theta$ and $\tan \theta$.

62. If $\cos \theta = \frac{7}{8}$, find $\sin \theta$ and $\tan \theta$.

63. If $\cos \gamma = \frac{\sqrt{6}}{3}$, find $\sin \gamma$ and $\cot \gamma$.

64. If $\sin \gamma = \frac{\sqrt{10}}{4}$, find $\cos \gamma$ and $\cot \gamma$.

In Exercises 65-76, use a right triangle to find the exact value of each expression. All angles are acute angles.

65. If $\sin A = \frac{1}{3}$, find $\cos A$.

66. If $\tan B = \frac{9}{5}$, find $\csc B$.

67. If $\sec \theta = 5$, find $\sin \theta$.

68. If $\csc \theta = \frac{13}{3}$, find $\cot \theta$.

69. If $\sin \alpha = \frac{1}{2}$, find $\cos \alpha$.

70. If $\sin \alpha = \frac{\sqrt{2}}{2}$, find $\cos \alpha$.

71. If $\tan \beta = \frac{\sqrt{11}}{4}$, find $\sec \beta$.   72. If $\sec \beta = \frac{15}{8}$, find $\sin \beta$.   73. If $\csc \alpha = 8$, find $\cos \alpha$.

74. If $\cot \alpha = 13$, find $\sec \alpha$.   75. If $\cos A = \frac{\sqrt{5}}{7}$, find $\sin A$.   76. If $\csc \theta = 2$, find $\tan \theta$.

77. Given $\sin 60° = \frac{\sqrt{3}}{2}$, use the trigonometric identities to find the exact value of each expression.

   (a) $\csc 60°$ (c) $\cos^2 60°$ (e) $\tan^2 60°$

   (b) $\cos 30°$ (d) $\sec 60°$ (f) $\cot^2 60°$

78. Given $\tan 30° = \frac{\sqrt{3}}{3}$, use the trigonometric identities to find the exact value of each expression.

   (a) $\sec^2 30°$ (c) $\tan^2 60°$ (e) $\sin 60°$

   (b) $\cot 30°$ (d) $\cos 60°$ (f) $\csc 60°$

79. If $\cos \frac{\pi}{9} = x$, use the trigonometric identities to express each expression in terms of x.

   (a) $\sec \frac{\pi}{9}$ (b) $\sin \frac{7\pi}{18}$ (c) $\sin^2 \frac{\pi}{9}$ (d) $\tan^2 \frac{\pi}{9}$ (e) $\tan \frac{\pi}{9}$ (f) $\csc \frac{7\pi}{18}$

80. If $\csc \frac{2\pi}{15} = y$, use the trigonometric identities to express each expression in terms of y.

   (a) $\sin \frac{2\pi}{15}$ (b) $\cos \frac{2\pi}{15}$ (c) $\csc \frac{11\pi}{30}$ (d) $\cos \frac{11\pi}{30}$ (e) $\tan \frac{2\pi}{15}$ (f) $\cot \frac{11\pi}{30}$

In Exercises 81-94, evaluate **without** using a calculator.

81. $\cos 45° \sin 45°$ 82. $\tan 45° \sec 45°$ 83. $\sec 30° + \cot 45°$ 84. $\csc 30° + \sin 60°$

85. $\cos^2 60° - \tan^2 30°$ 86. $\sin^2 45° - \csc^2 30°$ 87. $\csc^2 \frac{\pi}{3} - \tan^2 \frac{\pi}{4}$ 88. $\cot^2 \frac{\pi}{6} - \sec^2 \frac{\pi}{3}$

89. $\sin^2 \frac{\pi}{4} - 2\cos \frac{\pi}{4}$ 90. $3\cos^2 \frac{\pi}{3} - \csc \frac{\pi}{3}$ 91. $\dfrac{\sin^2 \frac{\pi}{6}}{\cos^2 \frac{\pi}{6}}$ 92. $\dfrac{\cos^2 \frac{\pi}{3}}{\sin^2 \frac{\pi}{3}}$

93. $1 + \dfrac{\tan 45°}{\sec 45°}$ 94. $\dfrac{\csc 30°}{\sec 30°} - 6$

In Exercises 95-110, use a calculator to compute each expression to three decimal places.

95. $\tan 29°$ 96. $\sin 44°$ 97. $\cos 71°$ 98. $\tan 26°$

99. $\csc 68°$ 100. $\sec 39°$ 101. $\cot 9°$ 102. $\csc 80°$

103. $\cos \frac{\pi}{5}$ 104. $\tan \frac{\pi}{10}$ 105. $\sin 1$ 106. $\cos 1$

107. $\sec \frac{2\pi}{11}$ 108. $\cot \frac{2\pi}{7}$ 109. $\cot 4.15$ 110. $\csc 8.08$

In Exercises 111-116, solve for x to two decimal places.

111.

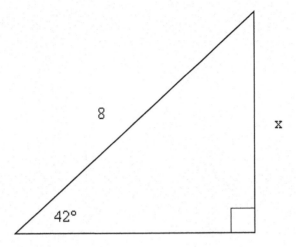

112.

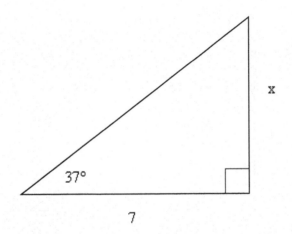

113.

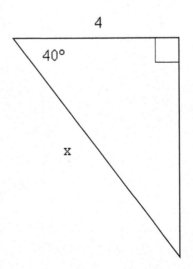

114.

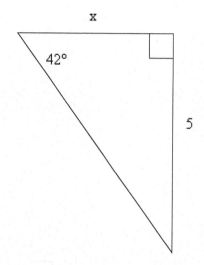

115.

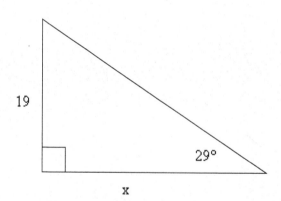

116.

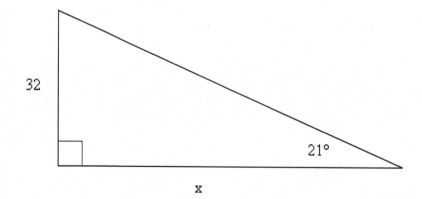

In Exercises 117-125, round off all answers to the nearest hundredth of a unit.

117. A 34 foot extension ladder leaning against a building makes a 62° angle with the ground. How high above the ground is the top of the ladder?

118. A 21 foot ladder is leaning against a house and makes a 59° angle with the ground. How high on the house does the ladder reach?

119. The angle of elevation from a point 105.35 feet from the base of a telephone pole to the top of the pole is 37°. What is the height of the pole?

120. The angle of elevation from a point 79.6 feet from the base of a flag pole to the top of the pole is 34°. What is the height of the pole?

121. Suppose that the angle of elevation of the sun is 24.7°. Find the length of the shadow cast by a building that is 73 feet tall.

122. When the angle of elevation of the sun is 33.38°, the shadow of a vertical tower is 41.3 meters long. Find the height of the tower.

123. A candy store owner wants to install a security camera in the back of the store which will face the cash register. How high on a wall must the security camera be mounted so that it is horizontally 34 feet from the cash register and makes an angle of depression of 29.5° from the wall to the register?

124. A lighthouse built at sea level is 180 feet high. From the top of the lighthouse, the angle of depression of a row boat measures 26°. Find the distance from the row boat to the foot of the lighthouse.

125. A bird watcher is on a cliff and sees a rare bird some distance away and below himself. He sets his telescope so that the angle of depression of the bird measures 34°. What is the horizontal distance from the birdwatcher to the bird if the length of his line of sight is 102 feet?

Chapter 3:   Trigonometric Functions of Any Angle

In this chapter, we will define the trigonometric functions of any angle. Recall that if the angle θ is an acute angle, then we have defined the trigonometric functions as the ratios of the sides of a right triangle which contains θ. Our new definitions do not involve right triangles, but instead use the Cartesian plane. Nevertheless, we will see that right triangle trigonometry is incorporated into the new definitions.

Section 3.1 Definitions of the Trigonometric Functions for Any Angle

Recall that angle θ is in **standard position** if its vertex is the origin and its initial side coincides with the positive x-axis.

Definition: Let θ be an angle in standard position. Suppose that (a, b) is any point on the terminal side of θ (with the exception of the origin). If we set $r = \sqrt{a^2 + b^2}$ (which is the distance from (a, b) to the origin), then the trigonometric functions are defined as follows (provided that no zero denominator appears):

1. sine of θ equals $\dfrac{b}{r}$.

2. cosine of θ equals $\dfrac{a}{r}$.

3. tangent of θ equals $\dfrac{b}{a}$.

4. cosecant of θ equals $\dfrac{r}{b}$.

5. secant of θ equals $\dfrac{r}{a}$.

6. cotangent of θ equals $\dfrac{a}{b}$.

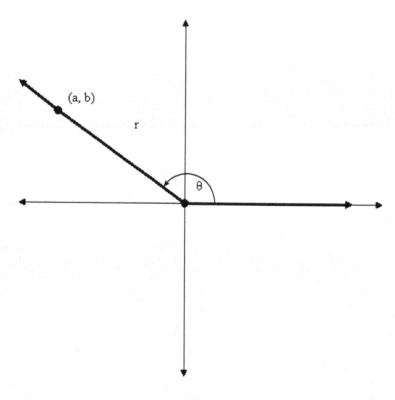

We abbreviate each function the same way as before:

$$\sin\theta = \frac{b}{r} \qquad\qquad \csc\theta = \frac{r}{b},\ b \neq 0$$

$$\cos\theta = \frac{a}{r} \qquad\qquad \sec\theta = \frac{r}{a},\ a \neq 0$$

$$\tan\theta = \frac{b}{a},\ a \neq 0 \qquad \cot\theta = \frac{a}{b},\ b \neq 0$$

Unlike the case when θ is an acute angle, our new trigonometric functions can have negative values and even equal 0. Furthermore, there are angles for which some of the trigonometric functions are undefined. We will see each of these occurrences in the next set of examples.

Examples.

1) Find the exact value of each of the six trigonometric functions of θ, where $0° < \theta < 360°$, if $(-5,\ 12)$ is a point on its terminal side.

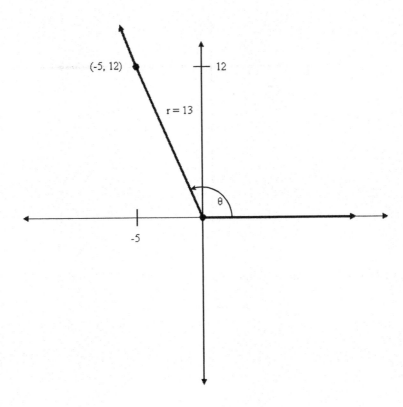

Since $(-5,\ 12)$ is a point on the terminal side of θ, we set $a = -5$ and $b = 12$. We can find r by using the formula given in the definition.

$$r = \sqrt{a^2 + b^2} = \sqrt{(-5)^2 + 12^2} = \sqrt{25 + 144} = \sqrt{169} = 13$$

And so:

$$\sin \theta = \frac{b}{r} = \frac{12}{13} \qquad\qquad \csc \theta = \frac{r}{b} = \frac{13}{12}$$

$$\cos \theta = \frac{a}{r} = \frac{-5}{13} \qquad\qquad \sec \theta = \frac{r}{a} = \frac{13}{-5}$$

$$\tan \theta = \frac{b}{a} = \frac{12}{-5} \qquad\qquad \cot \theta = \frac{a}{b} = \frac{-5}{12}$$

2) Find the exact value of each of the six trigonometric functions of A, where $0 < A < 2\pi$, if $\left(-7, \ -\sqrt{6}\right)$ is a point on its terminal side.

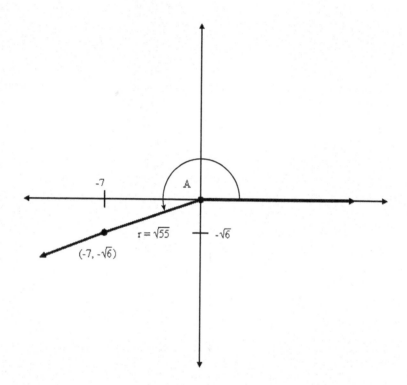

Since $\left(-7, \ -\sqrt{6}\right)$ is a point on the terminal side of θ, we set $a = -7$ and $b = -\sqrt{6}$. We can find r by using the formula.

$$r = \sqrt{a^2 + b^2} = \sqrt{(-7)^2 + \left(-\sqrt{6}\right)^2} = \sqrt{49 + 6} = \sqrt{55}$$

Therefore:

$$\sin A = \frac{b}{r} = \frac{-\sqrt{6}}{\sqrt{55}} = -\frac{\sqrt{6}}{\sqrt{55}} \left(\frac{\sqrt{55}}{\sqrt{55}}\right) = -\frac{\sqrt{330}}{55} \qquad\qquad \csc A = \frac{r}{b} = \frac{\sqrt{55}}{-\sqrt{6}} = -\frac{\sqrt{55}}{\sqrt{6}} \left(\frac{\sqrt{6}}{\sqrt{6}}\right) = -\frac{\sqrt{330}}{6}$$

$$\cos A = \frac{a}{r} = \frac{-7}{\sqrt{55}} = -\frac{7}{\sqrt{55}} \left(\frac{\sqrt{55}}{\sqrt{55}}\right) = -\frac{7\sqrt{55}}{55} \qquad\qquad \sec A = \frac{r}{a} = \frac{\sqrt{55}}{-7}$$

$$\tan A = \frac{b}{a} = \frac{-\sqrt{6}}{-7} = \frac{\sqrt{6}}{7} \qquad\qquad \cot A = \frac{a}{b} = \frac{-7}{-\sqrt{6}} = \frac{7}{\sqrt{6}} \left(\frac{\sqrt{6}}{\sqrt{6}}\right) = \frac{7\sqrt{6}}{6}$$

3) Find the exact value of each of the six trigonometric functions of β when $\beta = 0°$, $90°$, $180°$, and $270°$.

Recall that an angle in standard position is called a **quadrantal angle** if its terminal side lies on either the x-axis or the y-axis). The measure of such an angle is always an integer multiple of $90°$ (or $\frac{\pi}{2}$ radians). Notice that $0° = 0$ radians, $90° = \frac{\pi}{2}$ radians, $180° = \pi$ radians, and $270° = \frac{3\pi}{2}$ radians.

(a) If $\beta = 0°$, then $(1, 0)$ is a point on its terminal side. We set $a = 1$ and $b = 0$. Then

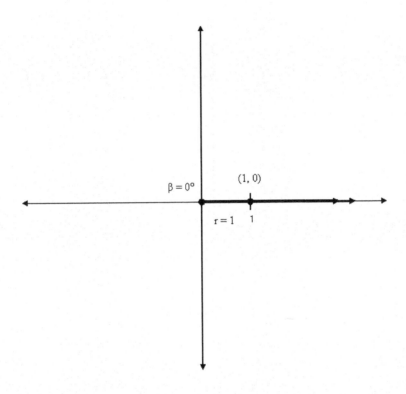

$$r = \sqrt{a^2 + b^2} = \sqrt{1^2 + 0^2} = \sqrt{1 + 0} = \sqrt{1} = 1.$$

We obtain:

$$\sin 0° = \frac{b}{r} = \frac{0}{1} = 0 \qquad\qquad \csc 0° = \frac{r}{b} = \frac{1}{0} \text{ is undefined.}$$

$$\cos 0° = \frac{a}{r} = \frac{1}{1} = 1 \qquad\qquad \sec 0° = \frac{r}{a} = \frac{1}{1} = 1$$

$$\tan 0° = \frac{b}{a} = \frac{0}{1} = 0 \qquad\qquad \cot 0° = \frac{a}{b} = \frac{1}{0} \text{ is undefined.}$$

(b) If $\beta = 90°$, then (0, 1) is a point on its terminal side (see the figure below). We set $a = 0$ and $b = 1$. Then

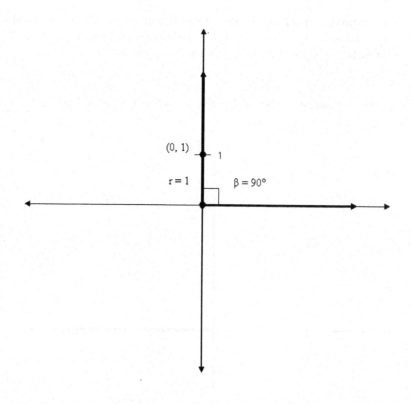

$$r = \sqrt{a^2 + b^2} = \sqrt{0^2 + 1^2} = \sqrt{0 + 1} = \sqrt{1} = 1.$$

Therefore:

$$\sin 90° = \frac{b}{r} = \frac{1}{1} = 1 \qquad\qquad \csc 90° = \frac{r}{b} = \frac{1}{1} = 1$$

$$\cos 90° = \frac{a}{r} = \frac{0}{1} = 0 \qquad\qquad \sec 90° = \frac{r}{a} = \frac{1}{0} \text{ is undefined.}$$

$$\tan 90° = \frac{b}{a} = \frac{1}{0} \text{ is undefined.} \qquad\qquad \cot 90° = \frac{a}{b} = \frac{0}{1} = 0$$

(c) If $\beta = 180°$, then $(-1, 0)$ is a point on its terminal side (see the figure on the next page). We set $a = -1$ and $b = 0$. Then

$$r = \sqrt{a^2 + b^2} = \sqrt{(-1)^2 + 0^2} = \sqrt{1 + 0} = \sqrt{1} = 1.$$

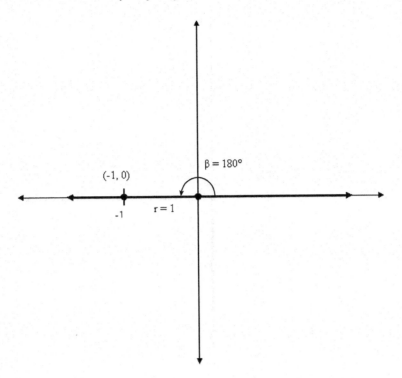

Therefore:

$$\sin 180° = \frac{b}{r} = \frac{0}{1} = 0 \qquad\qquad \csc 180° = \frac{r}{b} = \frac{1}{0} \text{ is undefined.}$$

$$\cos 180° = \frac{a}{r} = \frac{-1}{1} = -1 \qquad\qquad \sec 180° = \frac{r}{a} = \frac{1}{-1} = -1$$

$$\tan 180° = \frac{b}{a} = \frac{0}{-1} = 0 \qquad\qquad \cot 180° = \frac{a}{b} = \frac{-1}{0} \text{ is undefined.}$$

(d) If $\beta = 270°$, then $(0, -1)$ is a point on its terminal side (see the figure on the next page). We set $a = 0$ and $b = -1$. Then

$$r = \sqrt{a^2 + b^2} = \sqrt{0^2 + (-1)^2} = \sqrt{0 + 1} = \sqrt{1} = 1.$$

we get:

$$\sin 270° = \frac{b}{r} = \frac{-1}{1} = -1 \qquad\qquad \csc 270° = \frac{r}{b} = \frac{1}{-1} = -1$$

$$\cos 270° = \frac{a}{r} = \frac{0}{1} = 0 \qquad\qquad \sec 270° = \frac{r}{a} = \frac{1}{0} \text{ is undefined.}$$

$$\tan 270° = \frac{b}{a} = \frac{-1}{0} \text{ is undefined.} \qquad\qquad \cot 270° = \frac{a}{b} = \frac{0}{-1} = 0$$

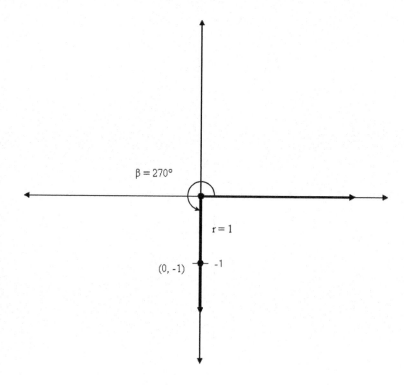

Observe that a trigonometric function of an angle α equals 0 if and only if the reciprocal trigonometric function of the same angle is undefined; that is,

$\csc \alpha$ is undefined when $\sin \alpha = 0$.

$\sec \alpha$ is undefined when $\cos \alpha = 0$.

$\tan \alpha$ is undefined when $\cot \alpha = 0$.

$\cot \alpha$ is undefined when $\tan \alpha = 0$.

Try These (Set 1): Find the exact value of each of the six trigonometric functions of θ (if it exists), where $0° < \theta < 360°$, if the given point P is on its terminal side.

1) $P = (4, \ -3)$ 2) $P = \left(-5, \ -\sqrt{2}\right)$ 3) $P = (7, \ 0)$

Section 3.2 The Fundamental Trigonometric Identities for Any Angle

If θ is any angle and $(a, \ b)$ is a point on its terminal side, then we defined the trigonometric values of θ as:

$$\sin \theta = \frac{b}{r} \qquad\qquad \csc \theta = \frac{r}{b}, \; b \neq 0$$

$$\cos \theta = \frac{a}{r} \qquad\qquad \sec \theta = \frac{r}{a}, \; a \neq 0$$

$$\tan \theta = \frac{b}{a}, \; a \neq 0 \qquad\qquad \cot \theta = \frac{a}{b}, \; b \neq 0$$

Recall that $r = \sqrt{a^2 + b^2}$ is the distance between $(a, \, b)$ and $(0, \, 0)$. The trigonometric identities which hold for the case when θ is an acute angle also hold when θ is any angle.

I) The Reciprocal Identities

1. $\sin \theta = \dfrac{1}{\csc \theta}$ 2. $\cos \theta = \dfrac{1}{\sec \theta}$ 3. $\tan \theta = \dfrac{1}{\cot \theta}$

4. $\csc \theta = \dfrac{1}{\sin \theta}$ 5. $\sec \theta = \dfrac{1}{\cos \theta}$ 6. $\cot \theta = \dfrac{1}{\tan \theta}$

Each of these identities is true, provided that no zero denominator appears.

Proof: 1. $\sin \theta = \dfrac{b}{r}$ and $\dfrac{1}{\csc \theta} = \dfrac{1}{\frac{r}{b}} = \dfrac{1\left(\frac{b}{1}\right)}{\frac{r}{b}\left(\frac{b}{1}\right)} = \dfrac{b}{r}$, so $\sin \theta = \dfrac{1}{\csc \theta}$.

2. $\cos \theta = \dfrac{a}{r}$ and $\dfrac{1}{\sec \theta} = \dfrac{1}{\frac{r}{a}} = \dfrac{1\left(\frac{a}{1}\right)}{\frac{r}{a}\left(\frac{a}{1}\right)} = \dfrac{a}{r}$, so $\cos \theta = \dfrac{1}{\sec \theta}$.

3. $\tan \theta = \dfrac{b}{a}$ and $\dfrac{1}{\cot \theta} = \dfrac{1}{\frac{a}{b}} = \dfrac{1\left(\frac{b}{1}\right)}{\frac{a}{b}\left(\frac{b}{1}\right)} = \dfrac{b}{a}$, so $\tan \theta = \dfrac{1}{\cot \theta}$.

I'll leave the proofs of the remaining identities for you to try.

II) The Quotient Identities

1. $\dfrac{\sin \theta}{\cos \theta} = \tan \theta$ 2. $\dfrac{\cos \theta}{\sin \theta} = \cot \theta$

Each of these identities is true, provided that no zero denominator appears.

Proof: 1. $\dfrac{\sin \theta}{\cos \theta} = \dfrac{\frac{b}{r}}{\frac{a}{r}} = \dfrac{\frac{b}{r}}{\frac{a}{r}}\left(\dfrac{\frac{r}{1}}{\frac{r}{1}}\right) = \dfrac{b}{a} = \tan \theta$ 2. $\dfrac{\cos \theta}{\sin \theta} = \dfrac{\frac{a}{r}}{\frac{b}{r}} = \dfrac{\frac{a}{r}}{\frac{b}{r}}\left(\dfrac{\frac{r}{1}}{\frac{r}{1}}\right) = \dfrac{a}{b} = \cot \theta$

III) The Pythagorean Identities

1. $\sin^2\theta + \cos^2\theta = 1$ 2. $\tan^2\theta + 1 = \sec^2\theta$ 3. $1 + \cot^2\theta = \csc^2\theta$

Each of these identities is true, provided that the trigonometric function exists for the angle θ.

Proof: 1. $\sin^2\theta + \cos^2\theta = \left(\dfrac{b}{r}\right)^2 + \left(\dfrac{a}{r}\right)^2 = \dfrac{b^2}{r^2} + \dfrac{a^2}{r^2} = \underbrace{\dfrac{b^2+a^2}{r^2} = \dfrac{r^2}{r^2}}_{r=\sqrt{a^2+b^2},\ \text{so } r^2=a^2+b^2.} = 1$

2. $\tan^2\theta + 1 = \left(\dfrac{b}{a}\right)^2 + 1 = \dfrac{b^2}{a^2} + 1 = \dfrac{b^2}{a^2} + \dfrac{a^2}{a^2} = \dfrac{b^2+a^2}{a^2} = \dfrac{r^2}{a^2} = \left(\dfrac{r}{a}\right)^2 = \sec^2\theta$

3. $1 + \cot^2\theta = 1 + \left(\dfrac{a}{b}\right)^2 = 1 + \dfrac{a^2}{b^2} = \dfrac{b^2}{b^2} + \dfrac{a^2}{b^2} = \dfrac{b^2+a^2}{b^2} = \dfrac{r^2}{b^2} = \left(\dfrac{r}{b}\right)^2 = \csc^2\theta$

Examples. Simplify. Your answers should each contain at most one trigonometric function. Assume that all expressions are well-defined.

1) $\underbrace{\dfrac{\sin\theta}{\cos\theta}}_{\frac{\sin\theta}{\cos\theta}=\tan\theta} \cdot \tan\theta = \tan\theta \cdot \tan\theta = \tan^2\theta$

2) $\underbrace{\dfrac{1}{\csc A} \cdot \cot A = \overset{1}{\cancel{\sin A}} \cdot \cot A = \overset{}{\cancel{\sin A}} \cdot \dfrac{\cos A}{\underset{1}{\cancel{\sin A}}}\ .}_{\frac{1}{\csc A}=\sin A \text{ and } \cot A=\frac{\cos A}{\sin A}.} = \cos A$

3) $\sec^2\alpha - \tan^2\alpha = 1$ (since $\tan^2\alpha + 1 = \sec^2\alpha$)

4) $\dfrac{\tan B}{\sin B} = \dfrac{\frac{\sin B}{\cos B}}{\sin B} = \left(\dfrac{\frac{\sin B}{\cos B}}{1}\right)\left(\dfrac{\frac{\cos B}{1}}{\sin B}\right) = \dfrac{\frac{\sin B}{\cos B}\left(\frac{\cancel{\cos B}}{1}\right)}{\sin B\left(\frac{\cos B}{1}\right)} = \dfrac{\overset{1}{\cancel{\sin B}}}{\underset{1}{\cancel{\sin B}}\cos B} = \dfrac{1}{\cos B} = \sec B$

5) $\underbrace{\sqrt{1 - \cos^2\theta} = \sqrt{\sin^2\theta}}_{\sin^2\theta+\cos^2\theta=1} = |\sin\theta|$ (Recall from algebra that $\sqrt{a^2} = |a|$ for any real number a.)

6) $\underbrace{\dfrac{\sqrt{\sec^2 x - 1}}{\tan x} = \dfrac{\sqrt{\tan^2 x}}{\tan x}}_{\tan^2 x+1=\sec^2 x} = \dfrac{|\tan x|}{\tan x}$ (Again, recall that $\sqrt{a^2} = |a|$ for any real number a.)

We can simplify this even further by using a property about absolute value. Recall:

$$|a| = \begin{cases} a & \text{if } a \geq 0 \\ -a & \text{if } a < 0 \end{cases}$$

If we replace a by $\tan x$, we get:

$$|\tan x| = \begin{cases} \tan x & \text{if } \tan x \geq 0 \\ -\tan x & \text{if } \tan x < 0 \end{cases}$$

Therefore, we can write our answer as:

$$\frac{|\tan x|}{\tan x} = \begin{cases} \dfrac{\tan x}{\tan x} = 1 & \text{if } \tan x \geq 0 \\ \\ \dfrac{-\tan x}{\tan x} = -1 & \text{if } \tan x < 0 \end{cases}$$

which becomes

$$\frac{|\tan x|}{\tan x} = \begin{cases} 1 & \text{if } \tan x \geq 0 \\ -1 & \text{if } \tan x < 0 \end{cases}$$

Try These (Set 2): Simplify. Your answers should each contain at most one trigonometric function. Assume that all expressions are well-defined.

1) $\dfrac{\sin x \cos x}{\sin^2 x}$

2) $\dfrac{\cot \theta}{\sin \theta} \cdot \sec \theta$

3) $\sqrt{1 - \sin^2 \beta}$

Section 3.3   The Relationship between Right Triangle Trigonometry and Trigonometry of Any Angle

The next thing that we would like to do is to somehow incorporate our knowledge of right triangle trigonometry into these new definitions of the trigonometric functions for any angle. If the point (a, b) lies on the terminal side of an angle θ, where θ is **not** a quadrantal angle (so its terminal side lies in a quadrant), then we can construct a right triangle whose base is $|a|$ and whose height is $|b|$. The hypotenuse of this triangle is $r = \sqrt{a^2 + b^2}$. The angle which we will focus our attention on is the angle in the right triangle which is the **acute** angle whose rays are the positive or negative x-axis and the hypotenuse. We call such an angle a **reference angle**.

There are four cases to consider, each case depending on which quadrant angle θ lies in. We will assume, for the moment, that $0° < \theta < 360°$ and $\theta \neq 90°$, $180°$, or $270°$.

Case I: θ lies in **Quadrant I**.

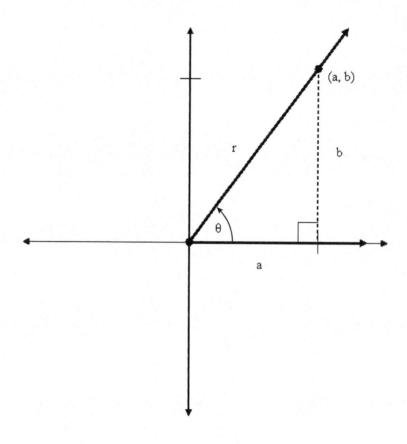

Notice that $a > 0$ and $b > 0$. The base of the triangle is a, the height is b and the hypotenuse is r. The reference angle is θ itself. As you can see, our new definitions for the trigonometric functions coincide with the definitions we learned about when using the right triangle. We have:

$$\underbrace{\sin \theta = \frac{b}{r}}_{\text{new definition}} \quad \text{and} \quad \underbrace{\sin \theta = \frac{b}{r}}_{\sin \theta = \frac{\text{opp}}{\text{hyp}}} \qquad\qquad \underbrace{\csc \theta = \frac{r}{b}}_{\text{new definition}} \quad \text{and} \quad \underbrace{\csc \theta = \frac{r}{b}}_{\csc \theta = \frac{\text{hyp}}{\text{opp}}}$$

$$\underbrace{\cos \theta = \frac{a}{r}}_{\text{new definition}} \quad \text{and} \quad \underbrace{\cos \theta = \frac{a}{r}}_{\cos \theta = \frac{\text{adj}}{\text{hyp}}} \qquad\qquad \underbrace{\sec \theta = \frac{r}{a}}_{\text{new definition}} \quad \text{and} \quad \underbrace{\sec \theta = \frac{r}{a}}_{\sec \theta = \frac{\text{hyp}}{\text{adj}}}$$

$$\underbrace{\tan \theta = \frac{b}{a}}_{\text{new definition}} \quad \text{and} \quad \underbrace{\tan \theta = \frac{b}{a}}_{\tan \theta = \frac{\text{opp}}{\text{adj}}} \qquad\qquad \underbrace{\cot \theta = \frac{a}{b}}_{\text{new definition}} \quad \text{and} \quad \underbrace{\cot \theta = \frac{a}{b}}_{\cot \theta = \frac{\text{adj}}{\text{opp}}}$$

Note that when θ lies in **quadrant I, all of the trigonometric functions are positive.**

Case II: θ lies in **Quadrant II**.

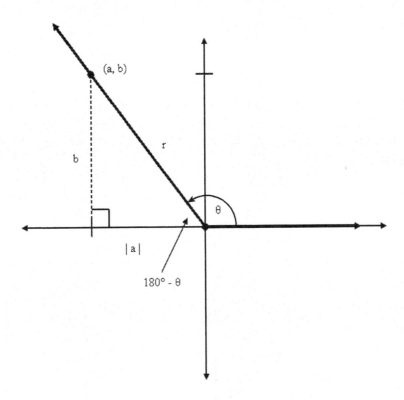

In this case, $a < 0$ and $b > 0$. The base of the triangle is $|a|$, the height is b and the hypotenuse is r. The reference angle is $180° - \theta$. Observe that the trigonometric values of θ, using our new definitions, are closely related to the trigonometric values of $180° - \theta$, using the right triangle. The only difference are the signs of the answers. Let's see why:

$$\underbrace{\sin\theta = \frac{b}{r} > 0}_{\text{new definition}} \text{ and } \underbrace{\sin(180° - \theta) = \frac{b}{r} > 0}_{\sin(180° - \theta) = \frac{\text{opp}}{\text{hyp}}} \qquad \underbrace{\csc\theta = \frac{r}{b} > 0}_{\text{new definition}} \text{ and } \underbrace{\csc(180° - \theta) = \frac{r}{b} > 0}_{\csc(180° - \theta) = \frac{\text{hyp}}{\text{opp}}}$$

$$\underbrace{\cos\theta = \frac{a}{r} < 0}_{\text{new definition}} \text{ and } \underbrace{\cos(180° - \theta) = \frac{|a|}{r} > 0}_{\cos(180° - \theta) = \frac{\text{adj}}{\text{hyp}}} \qquad \underbrace{\sec\theta = \frac{r}{a} < 0}_{\text{new definition}} \text{ and } \underbrace{\sec(180° - \theta) = \frac{r}{|a|} > 0}_{\sec(180° - \theta) = \frac{\text{hyp}}{\text{adj}}}$$

$$\underbrace{\tan\theta = \frac{b}{a} < 0}_{\text{new definition}} \text{ and } \underbrace{\tan(180° - \theta) = \frac{b}{|a|} > 0}_{\tan(180° - \theta) = \frac{\text{opp}}{\text{adj}}} \qquad \underbrace{\cot\theta = \frac{a}{b} < 0}_{\text{new definition}} \text{ and } \underbrace{\cot(180° - \theta) = \frac{|a|}{b} > 0}_{\cot(180° - \theta) = \frac{\text{adj}}{\text{opp}}}$$

From this, we see (using the fact that $|a| = -a$ when $a < 0$):

$$\sin \theta = \frac{b}{r} = \sin(180° - \theta) \qquad\qquad \csc \theta = \frac{r}{b} = \csc(180° - \theta)$$

$$\cos \theta = \frac{a}{r} = -\frac{|a|}{r} = -\cos(180° - \theta) \qquad \sec \theta = \frac{r}{a} = -\frac{r}{|a|} = -\sec(180° - \theta)$$

$$\tan \theta = \frac{b}{a} = -\frac{b}{|a|} = -\tan(180° - \theta) \qquad \cot \theta = \frac{a}{b} = -\frac{|a|}{b} = -\cot(180° - \theta)$$

Notice that when θ lies in **quadrant II**, only $\sin \theta$ and $\csc \theta$ **are positive**; the other trigonometric functions are negative.

Case III: θ lies in **Quadrant III**.

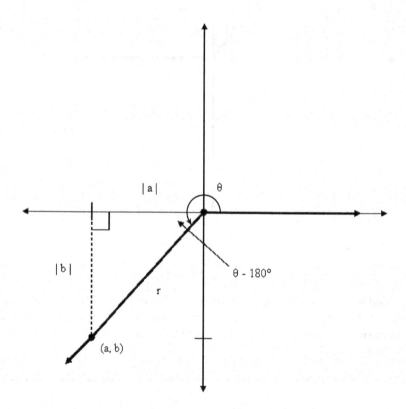

In this case, $a < 0$ and $b < 0$. The base of the triangle is $|a|$, the height is $|b|$ and the hypotenuse is r. The reference angle is $\theta - 180°$ (**not** $270° - \theta$, which is what many students think it is). Let's see the relationships between the trigonometric values of θ and the trigonometric values of $\theta - 180°$.

$$\underbrace{\sin \theta = \frac{b}{r} < 0}_{\text{new definition}} \text{ and } \underbrace{\sin(\theta - 180°) = \frac{|b|}{r} > 0}_{\sin(\theta-180°)=\frac{\text{opp}}{\text{hyp}}} \qquad \underbrace{\csc \theta = \frac{r}{b} < 0}_{\text{new definition}} \text{ and } \underbrace{\csc(180° - \theta) = \frac{r}{|b|} > 0}_{\csc(\theta-180°)=\frac{\text{hyp}}{\text{opp}}}$$

$$\underbrace{\cos \theta = \frac{a}{r} < 0}_{\text{new definition}} \text{ and } \underbrace{\cos(180° - \theta) = \frac{|a|}{r} > 0}_{\cos(\theta-180°)=\frac{\text{adj}}{\text{hyp}}} \qquad \underbrace{\sec \theta = \frac{r}{a} < 0}_{\text{new definition}} \text{ and } \underbrace{\sec(180° - \theta) = \frac{r}{|a|} > 0}_{\sec(\theta-180°)=\frac{\text{hyp}}{\text{adj}}}$$

$$\underbrace{\tan\theta = \frac{b}{a} > 0}_{\text{new definition}} \text{ and } \underbrace{\tan(180° - \theta) = \frac{|b|}{|a|} > 0}_{\tan(\theta-180°)=\frac{\text{opp}}{\text{adj}}} \qquad \underbrace{\cot\theta = \frac{a}{b} > 0}_{\text{new definition}} \text{ and } \underbrace{\cot(180° - \theta) = \frac{|a|}{|b|} > 0}_{\cot(\theta-180°)=\frac{\text{adj}}{\text{opp}}}$$

From this, we see that (using the fact that $\frac{|b|}{|a|} = \left|\frac{b}{a}\right| = \frac{b}{a}$ when $\frac{b}{a} > 0$ and $\frac{|a|}{|b|} = \left|\frac{a}{b}\right| = \frac{a}{b}$ when $\frac{a}{b} > 0$)

$$\sin\theta = \frac{b}{r} = -\frac{|b|}{r} = -\sin(\theta - 180°) \qquad \csc\theta = \frac{r}{b} = -\frac{r}{|b|} = -\csc(\theta - 180°)$$

$$\cos\theta = \frac{a}{r} = -\frac{|a|}{r} = -\cos(\theta - 180°) \qquad \sec\theta = \frac{r}{a} = -\frac{r}{|a|} = -\sec(\theta - 180°)$$

$$\tan\theta = \frac{b}{a} = \frac{|b|}{|a|} = \tan(\theta - 180°) \qquad \cot\theta = \frac{a}{b} = \frac{|a|}{|b|} = \cot(\theta - 180°)$$

Notice that when θ lies in **quadrant III**, only $\tan\theta$ **and** $\cot\theta$ **are positive**; the other trigonometric functions are negative.

Case IV: θ lies in **Quadrant IV**.

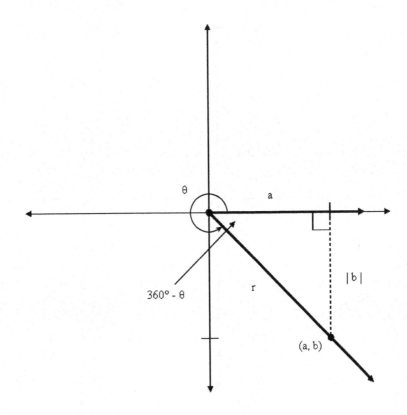

In this case, $a > 0$ and $b < 0$. The base of the triangle is a, the height is $|b|$ and the hypotenuse is r. The reference angle is $360° - \theta$. Let's see the relationships between the trigonometric values of θ and the trigonometric values of $360° - \theta$.

$$\underbrace{\sin\theta = \frac{b}{r} < 0}_{\text{new definition}} \text{ and } \underbrace{\sin\left(360° - \theta\right) = \frac{|b|}{r} > 0}_{\sin(360°-\theta)=\frac{\text{opp}}{\text{hyp}}} \qquad \underbrace{\csc\theta = \frac{r}{b} < 0}_{\text{new definition}} \text{ and } \underbrace{\csc\left(360° - \theta\right) = \frac{r}{|b|} > 0}_{\csc(360°-\theta)=\frac{\text{hyp}}{\text{opp}}}$$

$$\underbrace{\cos\theta = \frac{a}{r} > 0}_{\text{new definition}} \text{ and } \underbrace{\cos\left(360° - \theta\right) = \frac{a}{r} > 0}_{\cos(360°-\theta)=\frac{\text{adj}}{\text{hyp}}} \qquad \underbrace{\sec\theta = \frac{r}{a} > 0}_{\text{new definition}} \text{ and } \underbrace{\sec\left(360° - \theta\right) = \frac{r}{a} > 0}_{\sec(360°-\theta)=\frac{\text{hyp}}{\text{adj}}}$$

$$\underbrace{\tan\theta = \frac{b}{a} < 0}_{\text{new definition}} \text{ and } \underbrace{\tan\left(360° - \theta\right) = \frac{|b|}{a} > 0}_{\tan(360°-\theta)=\frac{\text{opp}}{\text{adj}}} \qquad \underbrace{\cot\theta = \frac{a}{b} < 0}_{\text{new definition}} \text{ and } \underbrace{\cot\left(360° - \theta\right) = \frac{a}{|b|} > 0}_{\cot(360°-\theta)=\frac{\text{adj}}{\text{opp}}}$$

From this, we see that (using the fact that $|b| = -b$ when $b < 0$):

$$\sin\theta = \frac{b}{r} = -\frac{|b|}{r} = -\sin\left(360° - \theta\right) \qquad \csc\theta = \frac{r}{b} = -\frac{r}{|b|} = -\csc\left(360° - \theta\right)$$

$$\cos\theta = \frac{a}{r} = \cos\left(360° - \theta\right) \qquad\qquad \sec\theta = \frac{r}{a} = \sec\left(360° - \theta\right)$$

$$\tan\theta = \frac{b}{a} = -\frac{|b|}{a} = -\tan\left(360° - \theta\right) \qquad \cot\theta = \frac{a}{b} = -\frac{a}{|b|} = -\cot\left(360° - \theta\right)$$

Notice that when θ lies in **quadrant IV**, only $\cos\theta$ **and** $\sec\theta$ **are positive**; the other trigonometric functions are negative.

The information that we found is summarized below.

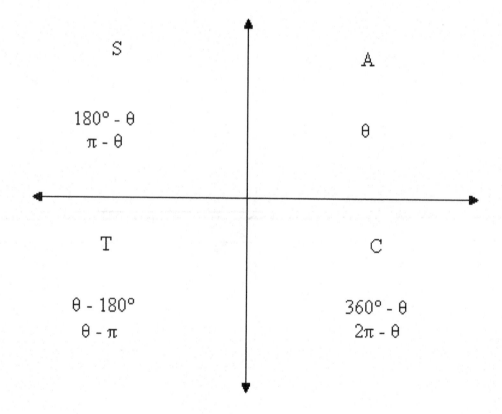

Each quadrant contains the formula for obtaining the reference angle when θ (or any angle) lies in that particular. The letters '**ASTC**' are the initials of the trigonometric functions which are positive valued in that quadrant.

1) If θ lies in quadrant I, then **A**ll trigonometric values are positive.

2) If θ lies in quadrant II, then only **S**ine (and cosecant) have positive values.

3) If θ lies in quadrant III, then only **T**angent (and cotangent) have positive values.

4) If θ lies in quadrant IV, then only **C**osine (and secant) have positive values.

Examples.

1) If $\sin\theta > 0$ and $\cos\theta < 0$, what quadrant does angle θ lie in?

Well, $\sin\theta$ is positive in quadrants I and II and $\cos\theta$ is negative in quadrants II and III. Therefore, the only quadrant where $\sin\theta$ is positive and $\cos\theta$ is negative is quadrant II.

2) If $\cot\beta < 0$ and $\sec\beta < 0$, what quadrant does angle β lie in?

We know that $\cot\beta$ is negative in quadrants II and IV and $\sec\beta$ is negative in quadrants II and III. This means that β lies in quadrant II.

3) If $\cos x > 0$ and $\tan x > 0$, what quadrant does angle x lie in?

Since $\cos x$ is positive in quadrants I and IV and $\tan x$ is positive in quadrants I and III, x must lie in quadrant I.

Examples. Evaluate using reference angles.

1) $\underbrace{\sin 120° = +\sin(180° - 120°)}_{\theta=120° \text{ lies in quadrant II and } \sin\theta>0 \text{ here.}}$ $= \sin 60° = \frac{\sqrt{3}}{2}$

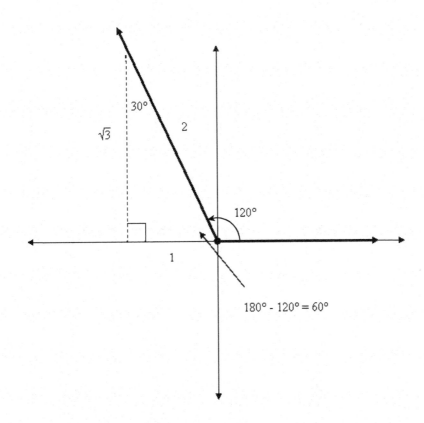

2) $\underbrace{\cos 225° = -\cos(225° - 180°)}_{\theta = 225° \text{ lies in quadrant III and } \cos\theta < 0 \text{ here.}} = -\cos 45° = -\frac{\sqrt{2}}{2}$

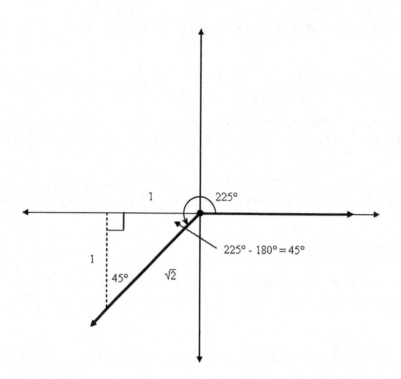

3) $\underbrace{\cot \frac{4\pi}{3} = +\cot\left(\frac{4\pi}{3} - \pi\right) = \cot \frac{\pi}{3}}_{\theta = \frac{4\pi}{3} \text{ lies in quadrant III and } \cot\theta > 0 \text{ here.}} = \frac{\sqrt{3}}{3}$

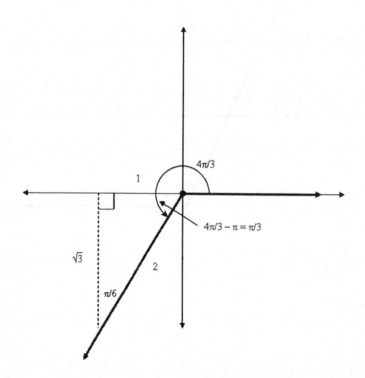

4) $\underbrace{\csc \frac{7\pi}{4} = -\csc\left(2\pi - \frac{7\pi}{4}\right) = -\csc \frac{\pi}{4}}$ $= -\sqrt{2}$

$\theta = \frac{7\pi}{4}$ lies in quadrant IV and $\csc \theta < 0$ here.

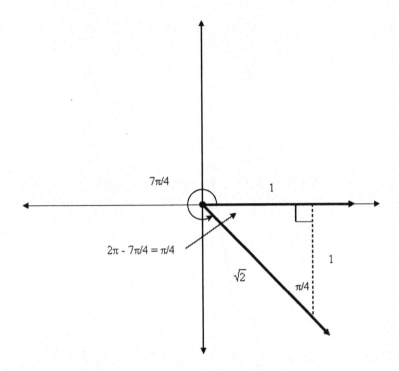

What would happen if θ were a negative angle or an angle whose measure exceeded 360°? Well, to answer these questions, we need the definition of coterminal angles.

Definition: Two angles θ and α are **coterminal** if they have the same terminal side.

Examples. The given pairs of angles are coterminal.

1) $\theta = 20°$ and $\alpha = 380°$

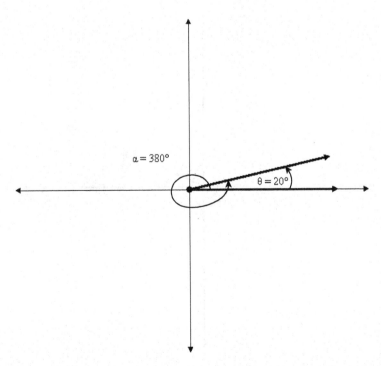

2) $A = -100°$ and $B = 260°$

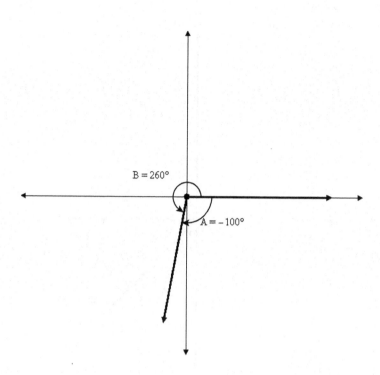

3) $\beta = 30°$ and $\alpha = -690°$

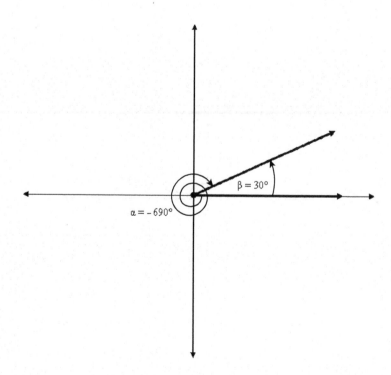

By definition, two coterminal angles always have the same terminal side. This means that they both contain the same point, $(a,\ b)$, on their terminal sides. Since the trigonometric values of an angle depend on a point on the terminal side, we have the following theorem:

Theorem: If angles θ and α are coterminal, then:

$$\sin\theta = \sin\alpha \qquad\qquad \csc\theta = \csc\alpha$$

$$\cos\theta = \cos\alpha \qquad\qquad \sec\theta = \sec\alpha$$

$$\tan\theta = \tan\alpha \qquad\qquad \cot\theta = \cot\alpha$$

Examples. Evaluate using reference angles.

1) $\underbrace{\sec\left(-60°\right) = \sec 300° = \sec\left(360° - 300°\right) = \sec 60°}_{\theta = -60°\ \text{and}\ \alpha = 300°\ \text{are coterminal.}} = 2$

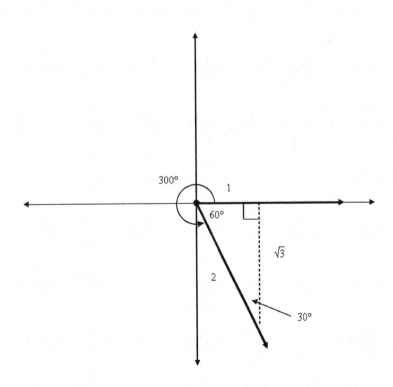

2) $\underbrace{\sin(-135°) = \sin 225° = -\sin(225° - 180°)}$ $\quad = -\sin 45° = -\dfrac{\sqrt{2}}{2}$

$\theta = -135°$ and $\alpha = 225°$ are coterminal and lie in quadrant III.

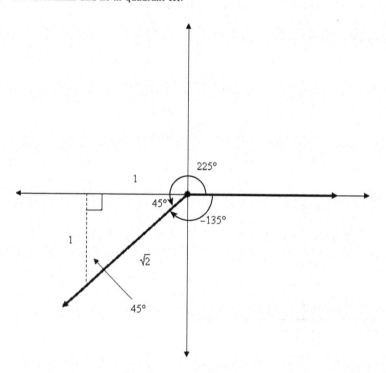

3) $\underbrace{\tan 495° = \tan 135° = -\tan(180° - 135°)}$ $\quad = -\tan 45° = -1$

$\theta = 495°$ and $\alpha = 135°$ are coterminal and lie in quadrant II.

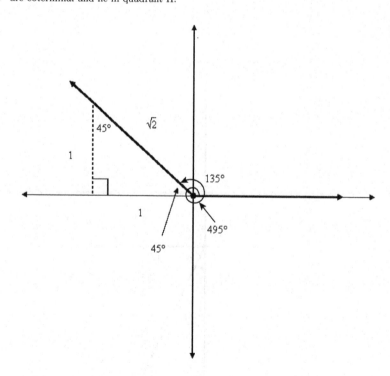

In the figure above, notice that $\theta = 495°$ contains one revolution plus an additional 135°, which is the measure of α. This means that we can write

$$\theta = 495° = 135° + 360° = \alpha + 360°$$

and, as we've seen in Example 3, $\theta = 495°$ and $\alpha = 135°$ are coterminal. In other words, the addition of one revolution ($= 360°$) to α gives us the same terminal side as α itself. This should be of no surprise since adding $360°$ to an angle α simply takes us around one revolution and ends up on the same terminal side as α. Let's look at another example of an angle which contains more than one revolution.

4) $\underbrace{\csc 1,140° = \csc 60° = \frac{2\sqrt{3}}{3}}_{\theta = 1,140° \text{ and } \alpha = 60° \text{ are coterminal.}}$

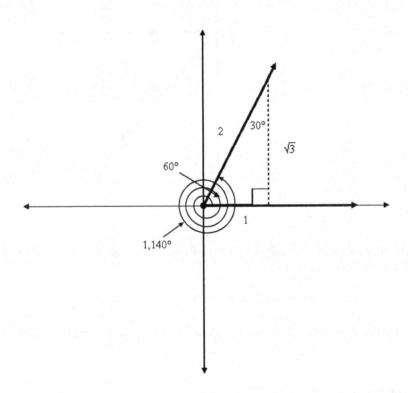

As you can see in the figure above, the angle $\theta = 1,140°$ is just three revolutions plus an additional $60°$, which is the measure of α. We can, therefore, write

$$\theta = 1,140° = 60° + 3\,(360°) = \alpha + 3\,(360°).$$

Again, notice that adding three revolutions ($= 3\,(360°) = 1,080°$) to α gives us the same terminal side as α itself. Hence, the addition of these three revolutions will give us a coterminal angle (in this case, $\theta = \alpha + 3\,(360°)$).

5) $\underbrace{\cos{(-765^\circ)} = \cos{(-45^\circ)} = \cos{315^\circ}}_{\theta=-765^\circ,\ \alpha=-45^\circ,\ \text{and}\ \beta=315^\circ\ \text{are coterminal.}} = \cos{(360^\circ - 315^\circ)} = \cos{45^\circ} = \frac{\sqrt{2}}{2}$

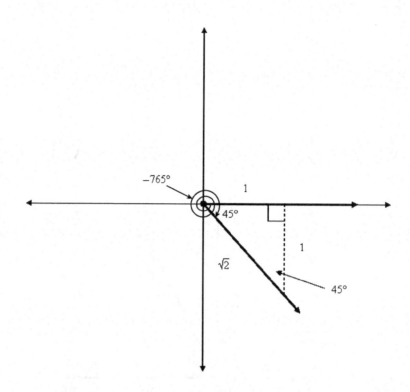

Notice in the figure above that the angle $\theta = -765^\circ$ contains two **clockwise** revolutions plus an additional **clockwise** angle of $\alpha = 45^\circ$. We can write

$$\theta = -765^\circ = -45^\circ + 2\,(-360^\circ) = \alpha + (-2)\,(360^\circ).$$

Therefore, since θ and α determine the same terminal side, they are coterminal.

In general, suppose that k is any integer. Then

$\sin\theta = \sin{(\theta + 360^\circ k)}$	$\csc\theta = \csc{(\theta + 360^\circ k)}$
$\cos\theta = \cos{(\theta + 360^\circ k)}$	$\sec\theta = \sec{(\theta + 360^\circ k)}$
$\tan\theta = \tan{(\theta + 360^\circ k)}$	$\cot\theta = \cot{(\theta + 360^\circ k)}$

(provided that the trigonometric value of θ is well-defined). For example,

$$\sin 25^\circ = \sin{(25^\circ + 360^\circ\,(8))} = \sin 2{,}905^\circ.$$

However,

$$\tan 90^\circ \neq \tan{(90^\circ + 360^\circ k)}$$

for any k since $\tan 90°$ is undefined.

In radian measure, we write these equalities as:

$$
\begin{array}{ll}
\sin\theta = \sin\left(\theta + 2\pi k\right) & \csc\theta = \csc\left(\theta + 2\pi k\right) \\
\cos\theta = \cos\left(\theta + 2\pi k\right) & \sec\theta = \sec\left(\theta + 2\pi k\right) \\
\tan\theta = \tan\left(\theta + 2\pi k\right) & \cot\theta = \cot\left(\theta + 2\pi k\right)
\end{array}
$$

When $\theta > 360°$, there is a simple way to determine an angle α which is coterminal with θ and satisfies $0° < \alpha < 360°$. What we do is to divide $\theta \div 360$. The quotient tells us how many revolutions θ contains. The remainder tells us the measure of an angle α which is coterminal to θ. It is α that we are interested in. This is illustrated in the next two examples.

6) $\underbrace{\sin 1,230° = \sin 150°}_{1,230 \div 360 = 3 \text{ R } 150} = \sin\left(180° - 150°\right) = \sin 30° = \frac{1}{2}$

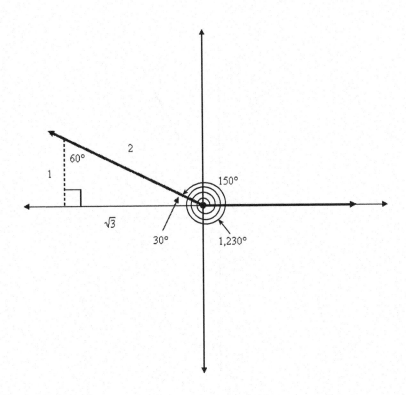

7) $\cot \frac{35\pi}{3} = \underbrace{\cot 2,100° = \cot 300°}_{2,100 \div 360 = 5 \text{ R } 300} = -\cot(360° - 300°) = -\cot 60° = -\frac{\sqrt{3}}{3}$

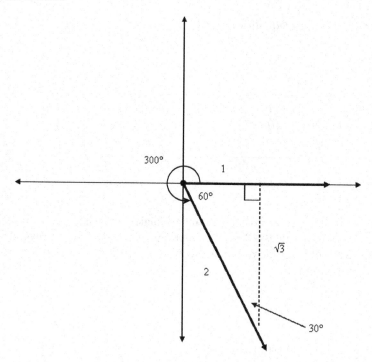

When $\theta < -360°$, we can find an angle α which is coterminal with θ and satisfies $-360° < \alpha < 0°$ in a similar way: we divide $\theta \div 360$. The quotient tells us how many **clockwise** revolutions θ contains. The remainder (**with the negative sign included**) tells us the measure of an angle α which is coterminal to θ. As before, α is the angle that we care about.

8) $\tan\left(-\frac{11\pi}{3}\right) = \underbrace{\tan(-660°) = \tan(-300°)}_{(-660) \div 360 = -1 \text{ R } -300} = \tan 60° = \frac{\sqrt{3}}{1} = \sqrt{3}$

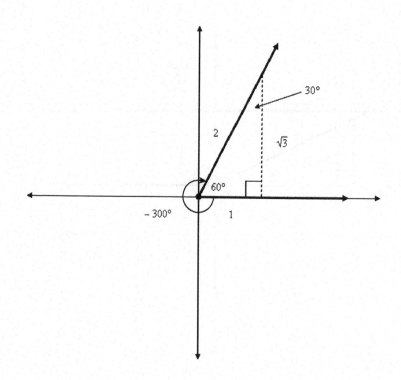

9) $\sec\left(-\frac{53\pi}{4}\right) = \underbrace{\sec\left(-2,385°\right) = \sec\left(-225°\right)}_{(-2,385)\div360=-6\text{ R }-225} = \underbrace{\sec 135° = -\sec 45°}_{180°-135°=45°} = -\sqrt{2}$

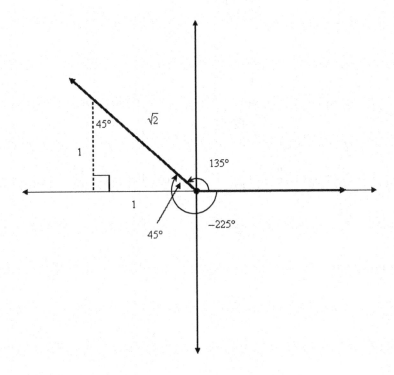

Here is another set of examples that you should know how to work out.

Examples. Find the exact value of each of the remaining trigonometric functions of A.

1) $\sin A = \frac{5}{13}$ and $90° < A < 180°$.

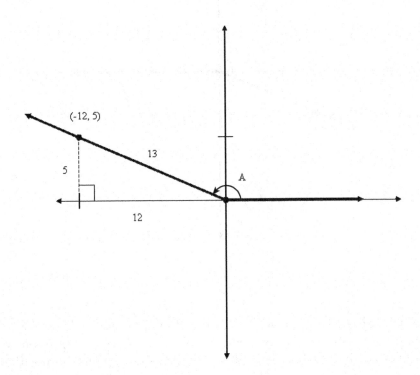

We are given that angle A is in quadrant II. Furthermore, $\sin A = \frac{b}{r} = \frac{5}{13}$, so we may choose $b = 5$ and $r = 13$. By using the Pythagorean Theorem and the fact that $a < 0$ for any point (a, b) in quadrant II, we see that $a = -12$ (see the figure on the previous page). Therefore:

$$\sin A = \frac{b}{r} = \frac{5}{13} \qquad\qquad \csc A = \frac{r}{b} = \frac{13}{5}$$

$$\cos A = \frac{a}{r} = \frac{-12}{13} \qquad\qquad \sec A = \frac{r}{a} = \frac{13}{-12}$$

$$\tan A = \frac{b}{a} = \frac{5}{-12} \qquad\qquad \cot A = \frac{a}{b} = \frac{-12}{5}$$

2) $\sec A = -\frac{\sqrt{5}}{2}$ and $\tan A > 0$.

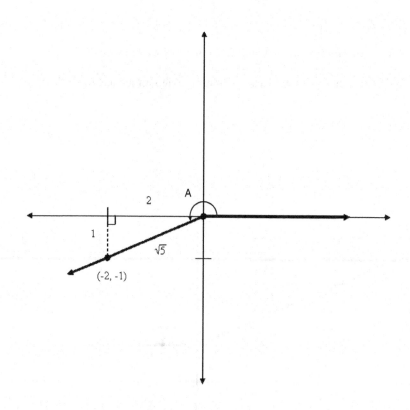

Notice that $\sec A$ is negative in quadrants II and III and $\tan A$ is positive in quadrants I and III. This means that A is in quadrant III (see the figure above). Since $\sec A = \frac{r}{a} = -\frac{\sqrt{5}}{2}$, we may choose $a = -2$ and $r = \sqrt{5}$ (remember that a and b may be positive or negative, but r **must be positive**). By using the formula $a^2 + b^2 = r^2$ and the fact that $b < 0$ for any point (a, b) in quadrant III, we see that $b = -1$. We obtain:

$$\sin A = \frac{b}{r} = \frac{-1}{\sqrt{5}} = -\frac{\sqrt{5}}{5} \qquad\qquad \csc A = \frac{r}{b} = \frac{\sqrt{5}}{-1} = -\sqrt{5}$$

$$\cos A = \frac{a}{r} = \frac{-2}{\sqrt{5}} = \frac{-2\sqrt{5}}{5} \qquad\qquad \sec A = \frac{r}{a} = -\frac{\sqrt{5}}{2}$$

$$\tan A = \frac{b}{a} = \frac{-1}{-2} = \frac{1}{2} \qquad\qquad \cot A = \frac{a}{b} = \frac{-2}{-1} = 2$$

3) If $\tan A = -\sqrt{17}$ and $\csc A < 0$, find the exact value of each of the remaining trigonometric functions of A.

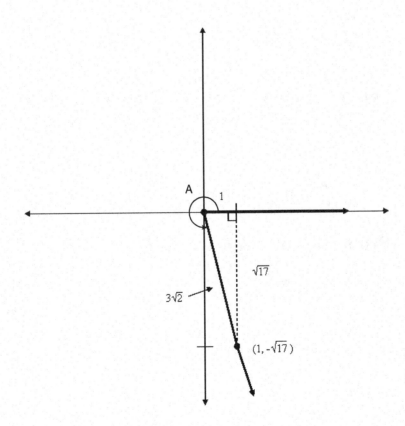

We know that $\tan A$ is negative in quadrants II and IV and $\csc A$ is negative in quadrants III and IV. This implies that A is in quadrant IV (see the figure above). Since $\tan A = \frac{b}{a} = \frac{-\sqrt{17}}{1}$, we may choose $a = 1$

and $b = -\sqrt{17}$ and obtain the point $\left(1, \ -\sqrt{17}\right)$ on the terminal side of A (notice that we **cannot** choose $a = -1$ and $b = \sqrt{17}$ since this would mean that $(a, \ b) = \left(-1, \ \sqrt{17}\right)$, which is in quadrant II and **not** quadrant IV). By using the formula $a^2 + b^2 = r^2$, we obtain $r = \sqrt{18} = 3\sqrt{2}$. Therefore:

$$\sin A = \frac{b}{r} = \frac{-\sqrt{17}}{3\sqrt{2}} = -\frac{\sqrt{34}}{6} \qquad \csc A = \frac{r}{b} = \frac{3\sqrt{2}}{-\sqrt{17}} = -\frac{3\sqrt{34}}{17}$$

$$\cos A = \frac{a}{r} = \frac{1}{3\sqrt{2}} = \frac{\sqrt{2}}{6} \qquad \sec A = \frac{r}{a} = \frac{3\sqrt{2}}{1} = 3\sqrt{2}$$

$$\tan A = \frac{b}{a} = \frac{-\sqrt{17}}{1} = -\sqrt{17} \qquad \cot A = \frac{a}{b} = \frac{1}{-\sqrt{17}} = -\frac{\sqrt{17}}{17}$$

Try These (Set 3):

I) If $\sin \alpha < 0$ and $\cot \alpha > 0$, in which quadrant does angle α lie in?

II) Evaluate using reference angles.

1) $\cos 150°$ 2) $\tan 225°$ 3) $\sin \frac{3\pi}{4}$ 4) $\cot \frac{5\pi}{3}$

5) $\cos 780°$ 6) $\csc \frac{29\pi}{4}$ 7) $\tan(-300°)$ 8) $\sec\left(-\frac{\pi}{4}\right)$

III) If $\cos \alpha = \frac{\sqrt{17}}{5}$ and $\tan \alpha < 0$, find the exact value of each of the remaining trigonometric functions of α.

Section 3.4   Properties of Negative Angles

Trigonometric values of negative angles can be dealt with by converting the negative angle into a positive one. The next theorem describes how this is done.

Theorem: Suppose that θ is any positive angle. Then

$$\begin{array}{ll} \cos(-\theta) = \cos\theta & \sec(-\theta) = \sec\theta \\ \sin(-\theta) = -\sin\theta & \csc(-\theta) = -\csc\theta \\ \tan(-\theta) = -\tan\theta & \cot(-\theta) = -\cot\theta \end{array}$$

(provided that the expression is well-defined).

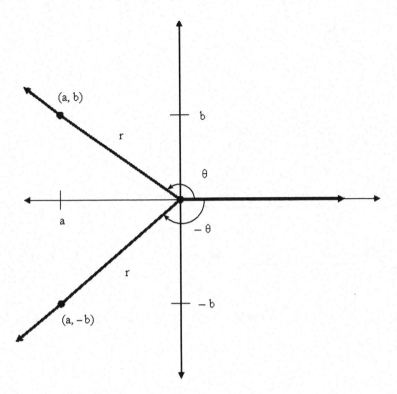

Proof: The figure above shows us that the terminal side of $-\theta$ is the reflection of the terminal side of θ about the x-axis. If (a, b) is on the terminal side of θ, then $(a, -b)$ is on the terminal side of $-\theta$. Notice that the distance, r, from (a, b) to $(0, 0)$ is the same as the distance from $(a, -b)$ to $(0, 0)$. Therefore, by using our definitions, we have:

$$\cos\left(-\theta\right) = \frac{a}{r} = \cos\theta \qquad \sin\left(-\theta\right) = \frac{-b}{r} = -\left(\frac{b}{r}\right) = -\sin\theta \qquad \tan\left(-\theta\right) = \frac{-b}{a} = -\left(\frac{b}{a}\right) = -\tan\theta$$

$$\sec\left(-\theta\right) = \frac{r}{a} = \sec\theta \qquad \csc\left(-\theta\right) = \frac{r}{-b} = -\left(\frac{r}{b}\right) = -\csc\theta \qquad \cot\left(-\theta\right) = \frac{a}{-b} = -\left(\frac{a}{b}\right) = -\cot\theta$$

These are also true when $\theta > 360°$ (why?).

Notice that we can derive some of these properties by using our identities as well. For example, since $\cos\left(-\theta\right) = \cos\theta$ and $\sin\left(-\theta\right) = -\sin\theta$, we have

$$\tan\left(-\theta\right) = \frac{\sin\left(-\theta\right)}{\cos\left(-\theta\right)} = \frac{-\sin\theta}{\cos\theta} = -\frac{\sin\theta}{\cos\theta} = -\tan\theta$$

which is what we found using the definitions.

Examples. Find the exact value.

1) $\underbrace{\cos(-30°) = \cos 30°}_{\cos(-\theta)=\cos\theta} = \frac{\sqrt{3}}{2}$

2) $\underbrace{\sin(-135°) = -\sin 135°}_{\sin(-\theta)=-\sin\theta} = -\sin(180° - 135°) = -\sin 45° = -\frac{\sqrt{2}}{2}$

3) $\underbrace{\tan(-300°) = -\tan 300°}_{\tan(-\theta)=-\tan\theta} = \underbrace{-(-\tan(360° - 300°))}_{\tan 300°} = \tan 60° = \frac{\sqrt{3}}{1} = \sqrt{3}$

4) $\underbrace{\sec\left(-\frac{21\pi}{4}\right) = \sec\frac{21\pi}{4}}_{\sec(-\theta)=\sec\theta} = \underbrace{\sec 945° = \sec 225°}_{945÷360=2\text{ R }225} = -\sec(225° - 180°) = -\sec 45° = -\sqrt{2}$

5) $\underbrace{\cot\left(-\frac{3\pi}{2}\right) = -\cot\frac{3\pi}{2}}_{\cot(-\theta)=-\cot\theta} = -\cot 270° = 0$ (Recall that $\theta = 270°$ is a quadrantal angle.)

Try These (Set 4): Find the exact value.

1) $\cos(-45°)$　　　　2) $\sin(-1,380°)$　　　　3) $\cot\left(-\frac{7\pi}{6}\right)$　　　　4) $\sec(-14\pi)$

Exercise 3

In Exercises 1-8, find the exact value of each of the six trigonometric functions of θ if the given point P is on its terminal side.

1. $P = (3,\ 4)$　　　　2. $P = (12,\ 5)$　　　　3. $P = (4,\ -\sqrt{2})$　　　　4. $P = (-\sqrt{3},\ \sqrt{3})$

5. $P = (-12,\ 0)$　　　6. $P = (0,\ 6)$　　　7. $P = \left(-\frac{\sqrt{2}}{2},\ -\frac{\sqrt{2}}{2}\right)$　　　8. $P = \left(\frac{\sqrt{3}}{2},\ -\frac{1}{2}\right)$

In Exercises 9-26, simplify each expression. Your answers should each contain at most one trigonometric function. Assume that all expressions are well-defined.

9. $\dfrac{\tan x \cot x}{\sin x}$　　　　10. $\dfrac{\sin y \csc y}{\cos y}$　　　　11. $\dfrac{\sin\theta}{\tan\theta} \cdot \cos\theta$　　　　12. $\dfrac{\cot\theta}{\sin\theta} \cdot \csc\theta$

13. $\sqrt{\sin^2 A + \cos^2 A}$　　　　14. $\sqrt{\tan^2\alpha + 1}$　　　　15. $\dfrac{\sqrt{1 - \cos^2 x}}{2\sin x}$, where $0 < x < \frac{\pi}{2}$

16. $\dfrac{\sqrt{\sec^2 y - \tan^2 y}}{\cot x}$　　　　17. $\sin^4\beta + 2\sin^2\beta\cos^2\beta + \cos^4\beta$　　　　18. $\sec^4 B - 2\sec^2 B \tan^2 B + \tan^4 B$

19. $\dfrac{5\sin\theta}{\cos\theta}\left(2\tan^2\theta - 2\sec^2\theta\right)$

20. $\left(3\sin^2\theta + 3\cos^2\theta\right)\left(\dfrac{3\cos\theta}{4\tan\theta}\right)$

21. $\sqrt{1 - \sin^2\theta}$, where $\frac{3\pi}{2} < \theta < 2\pi$

22. $\sqrt{1 - \cos^2 A}$, where $\frac{\pi}{2} < A < \pi$

23. $\dfrac{\sqrt{1 - \sin^2\theta}}{\cos\theta}$, where $\pi < \theta < \frac{3\pi}{2}$

24. $\dfrac{\sqrt{1 - \cos^2 A}}{\sin A}$, where $\frac{3\pi}{2} < A < 2\pi$

25. $\dfrac{\sqrt{\sec^2 x - 1}}{\tan x}$, where $-\frac{\pi}{2} < x < 0$

26. $\dfrac{\sqrt{1 + \cot^2 y}}{\csc y}$, where $-\pi < y < -\frac{\pi}{2}$

In Exercises 27-50, find the reference angle of each angle.

27. $135°$ 28. $150°$ 29. $330°$ 30. $315°$ 31. $210°$

32. $240°$ 33. $405°$ 34. $480°$ 35. $1,020°$ 36. $855°$

37. $-60°$ 38. $-45°$ 39. $-120°$ 40. $-210°$ 41. $-315°$

42. $-240°$ 43. $\dfrac{5\pi}{4}$ 44. $\dfrac{4\pi}{3}$ 45. $\dfrac{11\pi}{6}$ 46. $\dfrac{7\pi}{4}$

47. $-\dfrac{3\pi}{4}$ 48. $-\dfrac{5\pi}{3}$ 49. $-\dfrac{10\pi}{3}$ 50. $-\dfrac{15\pi}{6}$

In Examples 51-136, find the exact value of each expression **without** using a calculator.

51. $\sin 150°$ 52. $\tan 225°$ 53. $\cos 315°$ 54. $\sin 135°$ 55. $\tan 300°$

56. $\cos 120°$ 57. $\csc 330°$ 58. $\sec 135°$ 59. $\cot 240°$ 60. $\csc 300°$

61. $\sec 210°$ 62. $\cot 150°$ 63. $\cos\dfrac{11\pi}{6}$ 64. $\sin\dfrac{3\pi}{4}$ 65. $\tan\dfrac{7\pi}{6}$

66. $\sec\dfrac{5\pi}{3}$ 67. $\csc\dfrac{3\pi}{4}$ 68. $\cot\dfrac{2\pi}{3}$ 69. $\tan\dfrac{7\pi}{4}$ 70. $\cos\dfrac{5\pi}{6}$

71. $\sin\dfrac{5\pi}{3}$ 72. $\csc\dfrac{7\pi}{4}$ 73. $\cot\dfrac{3\pi}{4}$ 74. $\sec\dfrac{7\pi}{6}$ 75. $\sec 780°$

76. $\sin 480°$ 77. $\tan 1,020°$ 78. $\cos 750°$ 79. $\csc 405°$ 80. $\cot 450°$

81. $\sin 1,290°$ 82. $\sec 1,320°$ 83. $\cos\dfrac{9\pi}{4}$ 84. $\csc\dfrac{11\pi}{3}$ 85. $\tan\dfrac{13\pi}{6}$

86. $\cos\dfrac{13\pi}{4}$ 87. $\cot\dfrac{11\pi}{4}$ 88. $\csc\dfrac{8\pi}{3}$ 89. $\sin(-45°)$ 90. $\tan(-30°)$

91. $\cos(-60°)$ 92. $\sin(-135°)$ 93. $\tan(-210°)$ 94. $\cos(-330°)$ 95. $\csc(-120°)$

96. $\sec(-240°)$ 97. $\cot(-150°)$ 98. $\csc(-300°)$ 99. $\cos\left(-\dfrac{\pi}{6}\right)$ 100. $\sin\left(-\dfrac{\pi}{4}\right)$

101. $\tan\left(-\dfrac{5\pi}{6}\right)$ 102. $\cos\left(-\dfrac{5\pi}{4}\right)$ 103. $\sin\left(-\dfrac{4\pi}{3}\right)$ 104. $\tan\left(-\dfrac{3\pi}{4}\right)$ 105. $\csc\left(-\dfrac{\pi}{3}\right)$

106. $\sec\left(-\dfrac{\pi}{4}\right)$ 107. $\cot\left(-\dfrac{7\pi}{6}\right)$ 108. $\csc\left(-\dfrac{11\pi}{6}\right)$ 109. $\cos 90°$ 110. $\tan 360°$

111. $\sin 0°$ 112. $\cos 180°$ 113. $\tan 0°$ 114. $\cos 270°$ 115. $\csc 90°$

116. $\cot 90°$ 117. $\sec 180°$ 118. $\csc 270°$ 119. $\tan \pi$ 120. $\cos 2\pi$

121. $\sin\dfrac{3\pi}{2}$ 122. $\csc\dfrac{\pi}{2}$ 123. $\sec 2\pi$ 124. $\cot\dfrac{\pi}{2}$ 125. $\sin 4\pi$

126. $\tan 3\pi$ 127. $\cos 5\pi$ 128. $\sec 4\pi$ 129. $\cot\dfrac{5\pi}{2}$ 130. $\csc\dfrac{7\pi}{2}$

131. $\sin(-3\pi)$ 132. $\cos(-4\pi)$ 133. $\cot\left(-\dfrac{3\pi}{2}\right)$ 134. $\csc\left(-\dfrac{5\pi}{2}\right)$ 135. $\sec(-8\pi)$

136. $\sec(-5\pi)$

In Exercises 137–144, state the quadrant in which angle α lies.

137. $\sin\alpha > 0$, $\tan\alpha > 0$ 138. $\tan\alpha < 0$, $\cos\alpha > 0$ 139. $\cos\alpha < 0$, $\cot\alpha > 0$

140. $\sec\alpha < 0$, $\sin\alpha < 0$ 141. $\csc\alpha > 0$, $\tan\alpha < 0$ 142. $\cot\alpha > 0$, $\sec\alpha > 0$

143. $\cos\alpha > 0$, $\sin\alpha < 0$ 144. $\tan\alpha < 0$, $\cos\alpha < 0$

In Exercises 145–158, find the exact value of each of the remaining trigonometric functions of A.

145. $\tan A = \dfrac{4}{3}$, A is in quadrant I   146. $\sin A = \dfrac{5}{13}$, A is in quadrant II

147. $\cos A = -\dfrac{2}{5}$, A is in quadrant III   148. $\tan A = -\dfrac{7}{4}$, A is in quadrant II

149. $\tan A = -\dfrac{\sqrt{2}}{3}$, $\dfrac{\pi}{2} < A < \pi$ 150. $\cos A = \dfrac{\sqrt{13}}{2}$, $\dfrac{3\pi}{2} < A < 2\pi$

151. $\sin A = -\dfrac{\sqrt{5}}{4}$, $\dfrac{3\pi}{2} < A < 2\pi$ 152. $\csc A = -6$, $\pi < A < \dfrac{3\pi}{2}$

153. $\sec A = -5$, $180° < A < 270°$ 154. $\cot A = -\dfrac{9}{2}$, $90° < A < 180°$

155. $\cos A = \dfrac{\sqrt{10}}{4}$, $\cot A > 0$ 156. $\sin A = \dfrac{\sqrt{6}}{8}$, $\cos A < 0$

157. $\tan A = -3$, $\sin A < 0$ 158. $\csc A = -\dfrac{4\sqrt{6}}{5}$, $\sec A < 0$

Chapter 4: The Unit Circle Approach; Functional Properties

In Section 3.1, we defined each of the trigonometric functions as a function of an angle θ. Recall that if (a, b) is a point on the terminal side of θ which is r units from the origin, then all of the trigonometric functions are defined in terms of a, b, and r.

Another approach to the trigonometric functions uses the unit circle (the circle of radius 1 centered at the origin). Instead of defining the six trigonometric functions as functions of an angle θ, we define them as functions of a real number, t.

If the two definitions are equivalent, why study both? The reason is that some important properties of the trigonometric functions can be more easily proved by using the unit circle approach. This is because the equation of the unit circle is $x^2 + y^2 = 1$. Therefore, for any point (a, b) on the unit circle, $a^2 + b^2 = 1$. So, $r = \sqrt{a^2 + b^2} = \sqrt{1} = 1$. Using the fact that $r = 1$ simplifies the trigonometric function definitions.

Section 4.1 The Unit Circle; The Definitions of the Trigonometric Functions of Real Numbers

Definition: The **unit circle** is the circle whose center is $(0, 0)$ and radius is 1.

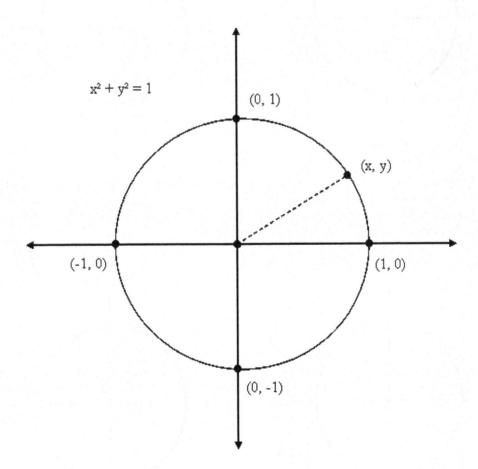

As you can see from the figure above, every point on the unit circle satisfies the equation $x^2 + y^2 = 1$, has an x-value between -1 and 1, and has a y-value between -1 and 1. Writing this in terms of inequalities, we have

$$-1 \le x \le 1 \quad \text{and} \quad -1 \le y \le 1$$

for any point (x, y) on the unit circle. In fact, given any x-value which satisfies $-1 \leq x \leq 1$, there exists a y-value satisfying $-1 \leq y \leq 1$ for which $x^2 + y^2 = 1$. Similarly, given any y-value which satisfies $-1 \leq y \leq 1$, there exists an x-value satisfying $-1 \leq x \leq 1$ for which $x^2 + y^2 = 1$.

Definitions of the Trigonometric Functions of Real Numbers

Let's discuss how the trigonometric functions are defined. Suppose that $t \geq 0$ is any non-negative number. Let's imagine that we are walking on the unit circle in the counterclockwise direction, starting our walk at the point $(1, 0)$. If we walk exactly t units in this direction, then we will end up at a point (a, b) on the unit circle (see the next figure). The length of the arc which we have walked along is t units.

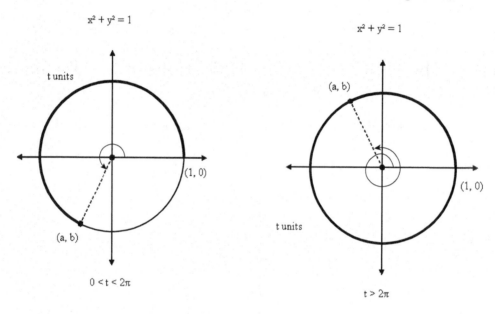

If $t < 0$ is any negative number, then we imagine ourselves walking on the unit circle, starting at the point $(1, 0)$, in the clockwise direction. If we walk exactly $|t|$ units in this direction, then we will end up at a point (a, b) on the unit circle (see the next figure). The length of the arc which we have walked along this time is $|t|$ units because the length of an arc cannot be negative.

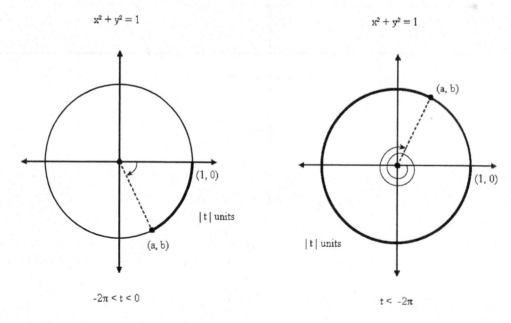

Thus, for any real number, t, we start at $(1, 0)$ and walk $|t|$ units (counterclockwise or clockwise) along the unit circle to reach a unique finishing point (a, b). Our walk may actually go all the way around the circle one or more times before ending at (a, b), as the previous figures show. We call this point (a, b) the **point on the unit circle corresponding to** t.

Definitions: Let t be any real number and let (a, b) be the point on the unit circle corresponding to t. The six trigonometric functions of t are defined as follows:

1. sine of t equals b.

2. cosecant of t equals $\dfrac{1}{b}$, provided that $b \neq 0$.

3. cosine of t equals a.

4. secant of t equals $\dfrac{1}{a}$, provided that $a \neq 0$.

5. tangent of t equals $\dfrac{b}{a}$, provided that $a \neq 0$.

6. cotangent of t equals $\dfrac{a}{b}$, provided that $b \neq 0$.

We will abbreviate these functions as:

$$
\begin{array}{lll}
\sin t = b & \cos t = a & \tan t = \dfrac{b}{a},\ a \neq 0 \\[2em]
\csc t = \dfrac{1}{b},\ b \neq 0 & \sec t = \dfrac{1}{a},\ a \neq 0 & \cot t = \dfrac{a}{b},\ b \neq 0
\end{array}
$$

Notice that $\cos t$ is the x-coordinate of the point (a, b) and $\sin t$ is the y-coordinate of the point (a, b). Since $-1 \leq a \leq 1$ and $-1 \leq b \leq 1$, we have that for any value of t,

$$-1 \leq \cos t \leq 1 \quad \text{and} \quad -1 \leq \sin t \leq 1.$$

This means that the cosine and sine functions are well-defined for any value of t. On the other hand, notice that $\tan t$ is not always well-defined. For example, if $(a, b) = (0, 1)$ is the point corresponding to t, then

$$\tan t = \frac{b}{a} = \frac{1}{0}$$

is undefined. The other three functions also have values of t which don't give well-defined values. We will explore this further when we discuss the domain and range of these functions.

Examples. Find the values of the six trigonometric functions of t if the given point, P, is the point on the unit circle corresponding to t.

1) $P = \left(\frac{\sqrt{2}}{2}, -\frac{\sqrt{2}}{2} \right)$ has x-coordinate $a = \frac{\sqrt{2}}{2}$ and y-coordinate $b = -\frac{\sqrt{2}}{2}$. Therefore:

$$\sin t = b = -\frac{\sqrt{2}}{2} \qquad\qquad \cos t = a = \frac{\sqrt{2}}{2} \qquad\qquad \tan t = \frac{b}{a} = \frac{-\frac{\sqrt{2}}{2}}{\frac{\sqrt{2}}{2}} = -1$$

$$\csc t = \frac{1}{b} = \frac{1}{-\frac{\sqrt{2}}{2}} = -\frac{2}{\sqrt{2}} = -\sqrt{2} \qquad \sec t = \frac{1}{a} = \frac{1}{\frac{\sqrt{2}}{2}} = \frac{2}{\sqrt{2}} = \sqrt{2} \qquad \cot t = \frac{a}{b} = \frac{\frac{\sqrt{2}}{2}}{-\frac{\sqrt{2}}{2}} = -1$$

2) $P = \left(-\frac{\sqrt{3}}{2}, -\frac{1}{2}\right)$ has x-coordinate $a = -\frac{\sqrt{3}}{2}$ and y-coordinate $b = -\frac{1}{2}$. Therefore:

$$\sin t = b = -\frac{1}{2} \qquad\qquad \cos t = a = -\frac{\sqrt{3}}{2} \qquad\qquad \tan t = \frac{b}{a} = \frac{-\frac{1}{2}}{-\frac{\sqrt{3}}{2}} = \frac{1}{\sqrt{3}} = \frac{\sqrt{3}}{3}$$

$$\csc t = \frac{1}{b} = \frac{1}{-\frac{1}{2}} = -2 \qquad \sec t = \frac{1}{a} = \frac{1}{-\frac{\sqrt{3}}{2}} = -\frac{2}{\sqrt{3}} = -\frac{2\sqrt{3}}{3} \qquad \cot t = \frac{a}{b} = \frac{-\frac{\sqrt{3}}{2}}{-\frac{1}{2}} = \sqrt{3}$$

3) $P = (-1,\ 0)$ has x-coordinate $a = -1$ and y-coordinate $b = 0$. Therefore,

$$\sin t = b = 0 \qquad\qquad \cos t = a = -1 \qquad\qquad \tan t = \frac{b}{a} = \frac{0}{-1} = 0$$

$$\csc t = \frac{1}{b} = \frac{1}{0} \text{ is undefined.} \qquad \sec t = \frac{1}{a} = \frac{1}{-1} = -1 \qquad \cot t = \frac{a}{b} = \frac{-1}{0} \text{ is undefined.}$$

Try These (Set 1): Find the value of each of the six trigonometric functions of t (if it exists) if the given point, P, corresponds to t.

1) $P = \left(-\frac{\sqrt{2}}{2}, -\frac{\sqrt{2}}{2}\right)$ 2) $P = \left(\frac{1}{4}, \frac{\sqrt{15}}{4}\right)$ 3) $P = (0,\ 1)$

Section 4.2 Trigonometric Functions of Angles

Suppose that $(a,\ b)$ is the point on the unit circle which corresponds to the real number t. Let θ denote the angle (in standard position and measured in radians) whose terminal side is the ray which contains $(a,\ b)$ and subtends an arc of length $|t|$. Recall that the arc length theorem states that if an arc of a circle of radius r is subtended by a central angle θ has length s, then $s = r\theta$. Since the unit circle has radius 1, we obtain

$$s = r\theta = 1\,(\theta) = \theta.$$

Therefore, if $s = |t|$, then $\theta = t$ radians (see the figure on the next page).

The point $(a,\ b)$ on the unit circle which corresponds to t is precisely the point on the terminal side of the angle $\theta = t$ radians. Consequently, we have

$$\boxed{\begin{array}{lll} \sin t = \sin\theta & \cos t = \cos\theta & \tan t = \tan\theta \\[2mm] \csc t = \csc\theta & \sec t = \sec\theta & \cot t = \cot\theta \end{array}}$$

We define these as the **trigonometric functions of angle** θ. Notice that t is a real number, whereas $\theta = t$ is a radian measure. Since the trigonometric functions of t correspond to the trigonometric functions of θ in this way, we simply call sine, cosine, etc. the **trigonometric functions.**

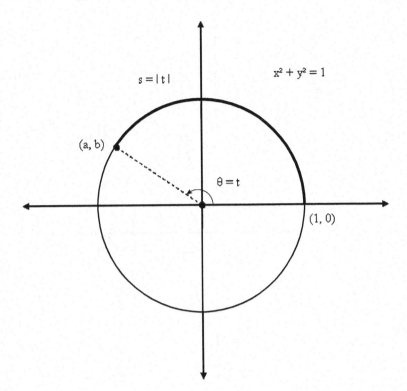

The values of the trigonometric functions of an angle θ are determined by the coordinates of the point (a, b) on the unit circle corresponding to θ. What if we want to find the trigonometric values of an angle θ if the point (a, b) lies on the terminal side of θ and (a, b) is not on the unit circle? Well, let's take a look at the figure on the next page. If the point (a, b) is r units from $(0, 0)$, then it lies on the circle whose center is $(0, 0)$ and whose radius is r. Notice that $\triangle OAB$ is similar to $\triangle OA'B'$. This means that the ratios of the corresponding sides are equal. We have:

$$\frac{b'}{1} = \frac{b}{r} \qquad \frac{a'}{1} = \frac{a}{r} \qquad \frac{b'}{a'} = \frac{b}{a}$$

$$\frac{1}{b'} = \frac{r}{b} \qquad \frac{1}{a'} = \frac{r}{a} \qquad \frac{a'}{b'} = \frac{a}{b}$$

As a result of these equal ratios and the definitions of the trigonometric functions, we have the next theorem.

Theorem: If angle θ is in standard position and (a, b) is any point on the terminal side of θ which lies on the circle whose equation is $x^2 + y^2 = r^2$, then:

$$\sin\theta = \frac{b}{r} \qquad\qquad \cos\theta = \frac{a}{r} \qquad\qquad \tan\theta = \frac{b}{a}, \, a \neq 0$$

$$\csc\theta = \frac{r}{b}, \, b \neq 0 \qquad \sec\theta = \frac{r}{a}, \, a \neq 0 \qquad \cot\theta = \frac{a}{b}, \, b \neq 0$$

By comparing these results to the definitions that we have learned about in Section 3.1, we see that they are identical. Observe that when we solve the equation

$$a^2 + b^2 = r^2 \quad \text{(since } (a, b) \text{ is a point on the circle whose equation is } x^2 + y^2 = r^2\text{)}$$

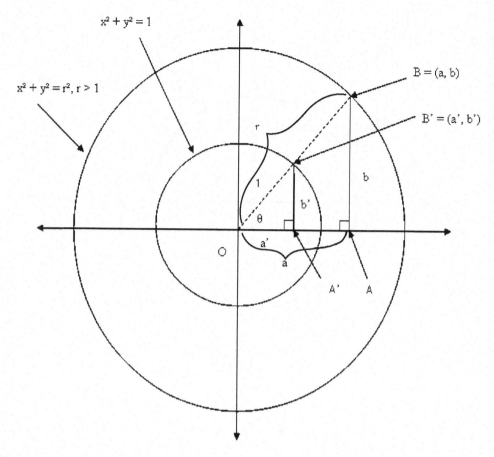

for r, we obtain $r = \sqrt{a^2 + b^2}$ (remember that $r > 0$ since it is the radius of a circle). Again, this is the same formula for r that we have used in our definitions in Section 3.1.

The examples below are solved in the same way as we have discussed in the previous chapter. We'll just do a couple for review.

Examples.

1) The point $(4, \; -3)$, which lies on the circle whose equation is $x^2 + y^2 = 25$, is a point on the terminal side of θ. Find the exact value of each of the six trigonometric functions of θ.

Since $(4, \; -3)$ is a point on the terminal side of θ, we set $a = 4$ and $b = -3$. Let's find r.

$$r = \underbrace{\sqrt{x^2 + y^2} = \sqrt{25}}_{\text{We are given that } x^2 + y^2 = 25.} = 5$$

Therefore:

$$\sin\theta = \frac{b}{r} = \frac{-3}{5} \qquad \csc\theta = \frac{r}{b} = \frac{5}{-3}$$

$$\cos\theta = \frac{a}{r} = \frac{4}{5} \qquad \sec\theta = \frac{r}{a} = \frac{5}{4}$$

$$\tan\theta = \frac{b}{a} = \frac{-3}{4} \qquad \cot\theta = \frac{a}{b} = \frac{4}{-3}$$

2) Find the exact value of each of the six trigonometric functions of A, where $0 < A < 2\pi$, if $\left(-2\sqrt{5}, -7\right)$ is a point on its terminal side.

Since $\left(-2\sqrt{5}, \; -7\right)$ is a point on the terminal side of A, we set $a = -2\sqrt{5}$ and $b = -7$. We can find r by using the formula.

$$r = \sqrt{a^2 + b^2} = \sqrt{\left(-2\sqrt{5}\right)^2 + (-7)^2} = \sqrt{20 + 49} = \sqrt{69}.$$

We obtain:

$$\sin A = \frac{b}{r} = \frac{-7}{\sqrt{69}} = -\frac{7}{\sqrt{69}}\left(\frac{\sqrt{69}}{\sqrt{69}}\right) = -\frac{7\sqrt{69}}{69} \qquad\qquad \csc A = \frac{r}{b} = \frac{\sqrt{69}}{-7} = -\frac{\sqrt{69}}{7}$$

$$\cos A = \frac{a}{r} = \frac{-2\sqrt{5}}{\sqrt{69}} = -\frac{2\sqrt{5}}{\sqrt{69}}\left(\frac{\sqrt{69}}{\sqrt{69}}\right) = -\frac{2\sqrt{345}}{69} \qquad\qquad \sec A = \frac{r}{a} = \frac{\sqrt{69}}{-2\sqrt{5}} = -\frac{\sqrt{69}}{2\sqrt{5}}\left(\frac{\sqrt{5}}{\sqrt{5}}\right) = -\frac{\sqrt{345}}{10}$$

$$\tan A = \frac{b}{a} = \frac{-7}{-2\sqrt{5}} = \frac{7}{2\sqrt{5}}\left(\frac{\sqrt{5}}{\sqrt{5}}\right) = \frac{7\sqrt{5}}{10} \qquad\qquad \cot A = \frac{a}{b} = \frac{-2\sqrt{5}}{-7} = \frac{2\sqrt{5}}{7}$$

Try These (Set 2):

1) Find the exact value of each of the six trigonometric functions of A, where $0 < A < 2\pi$, if $\left(3, \; -\sqrt{6}\right)$ is a point on its terminal side.

2) The point $(-11, 0)$, which lies on the circle whose equation is $x^2 + y^2 = 121$, is a point on its terminal side of α. Find the exact value of each of the six trigonometric functions of α (if it exists).

Section 4.3 The Domain and Range of the Trigonometric Functions

Now we will determine the domain and the range of each trigonometric function. As a reminder, let's write the definitions of the trigonometric functions.

Suppose that θ is an angle in standard position, and let (a, b) be the point on its terminal side which lies on the unit circle (see the next figure). Then:

$\sin\theta = b$	$\cos\theta = a$	$\tan\theta = \dfrac{b}{a}, a \neq 0$
$\csc\theta = \dfrac{1}{b}, b \neq 0$	$\sec\theta = \dfrac{1}{a}, a \neq 0$	$\cot\theta = \dfrac{a}{b}, b \neq 0$

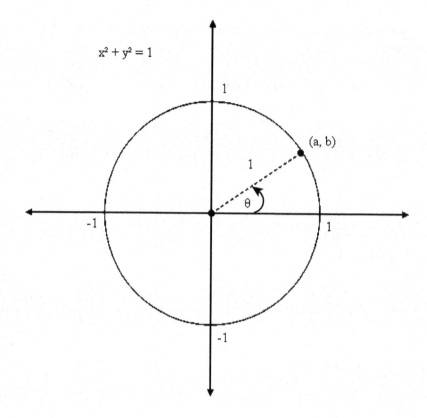

$$x^2 + y^2 = 1$$

I) The Domain and Range of $f(\theta) = \cos\theta$ and $g(\theta) = \sin\theta$

From the definitions of sine θ and cosine θ, we see that $\sin\theta$ is the y coordinate of (a, b) and $\cos\theta$ is the x coordinate of (a, b). Every angle θ has a terminal side which contains **exactly one** point on the unit circle. This means that every angle θ uniquely determines the value of $a = \cos\theta$ and $b = \sin\theta$. In other words, for each angle θ, there corresponds **exactly one** value for $\cos\theta$ and **exactly one** value for $\sin\theta$. Therefore, we have the following:

*** **The domain of $f(\theta) = \cos\theta$ is the set of all real numbers.** ***

*** **The domain of $g(\theta) = \sin\theta$ is the set of all real numbers.** ***

Now, suppose we are given **any** real number, a, such that $-1 \leq a \leq 1$. Notice that the point $\left(a, \sqrt{1-a^2}\right)$ lies on the unit circle since

$$(a)^2 + \left(\sqrt{1-a^2}\right)^2 = a^2 + 1 - a^2 = 1.$$

If θ denotes an angle whose terminal side contains $\left(a, \sqrt{1-a^2}\right)$, then we have that $\cos\theta = a$. This shows us that every number, a, satisfying the inequality $-1 \leq a \leq 1$ is in the range of $f(\theta) = \cos\theta$.

Observe that if $a < -1$ or $a > 1$, then $a^2 > 1$. This implies that $1 - a^2 < 0$, so $\sqrt{1-a^2}$ is not a real number. Consequently, if $a < -1$ or $a > 1$, then a cannot be the x-value of a point on the unit circle. In other words, there is no angle θ for which $\cos\theta = a$ when $a < -1$ or $a > 1$. Hence, the range of $f(\theta) = \cos\theta$ does not contain numbers which are less than -1 or more than 1.

Similarly, if we are given **any** real number, b, such that $-1 \le b \le 1$, then the point $\left(\sqrt{1-b^2},\, b\right)$ lies on the unit circle. Repeating the above argument shows that every number, b, satisfying the inequality $-1 \le b \le 1$ is in the range of $g(\theta) = \sin\theta$. Moreover, there is no angle θ for which $\sin\theta = b$ when $b < -1$ or $b > 1$. Hence, the range of $g(\theta) = \sin\theta$ does not contain numbers which are less than -1 or more than 1.

*** **The range of $f(\theta) = \cos\theta$ is $\{y \mid -1 \le y \le 1\}$.** ***

*** **The range of $g(\theta) = \sin\theta$ is $\{y \mid -1 \le y \le 1\}$.** ***

II) The Domain and Range of $f(\theta) = \tan\theta$

By definition, we know that $\tan\theta = \frac{b}{a}$. The domain of $f(\theta) = \tan\theta$ will consist of those values of θ for which $\frac{b}{a}$ is well-defined. In other words, any values of θ for which $a = 0$ will not be in the domain since $\tan\theta = \frac{b}{a} = \frac{b}{0}$ is undefined. Well, notice that $a = 0$ when $(a,\, b) = (0,\, 1)$ and when $(a,\, b) = (0,\, -1)$. These points correspond to the angles $\theta = 90° = \frac{\pi}{2}$ and $\theta = 270° = \frac{3\pi}{2}$.

The angles which are coterminal to $\theta = 90°$ and $\theta = 270°$ will also contain either $(0,\, 1)$ or $(0,\, -1)$ on the terminal sides, respectively. Notice that $\theta = 90°$ is coterminal to $\underbrace{\alpha = 90° + 360°k}_{\text{in radians, } \frac{\pi}{2} + 2\pi k}$, where k is any integer,

and $\theta = 270°$ is coterminal to $\underbrace{\alpha = 270° + 360°k}_{\text{in radians, } \frac{3\pi}{2} + 2\pi k}$, where k is any integer. This gives us the domain of f.

*** **The domain of $f(\theta) = \tan\theta$ is $\left\{\theta \mid \theta \ne \dfrac{\pi}{2} + 2\pi k \text{ and } \theta \ne \dfrac{3\pi}{2} + 2\pi k, \text{ where } k \text{ is any integer}\right\}$** ***

Observe the following: 1) If $k = 0$, then $\theta \ne \frac{\pi}{2} + 2\pi(0) = \frac{\pi}{2}$ and $\theta \ne \frac{3\pi}{2} + 2\pi(0) = \frac{3\pi}{2}$.

2) If $k = 1$, then $\theta \ne \frac{\pi}{2} + 2\pi = \frac{5\pi}{2}$ and $\theta \ne \frac{3\pi}{2} + 2\pi = \frac{7\pi}{2}$.

3) If $k = 2$, then $\theta \ne \frac{\pi}{2} + 4\pi = \frac{9\pi}{2}$ and $\theta \ne \frac{3\pi}{2} + 4\pi = \frac{11\pi}{2}$.

4) If $k = -1$, then $\theta \ne \frac{\pi}{2} - 2\pi = -\frac{3\pi}{2}$ and $\theta \ne \frac{3\pi}{2} - 2\pi = -\frac{\pi}{2}$.

5) If $k = -2$, then $\theta \ne \frac{\pi}{2} - 4\pi = -\frac{7\pi}{2}$ and $\theta \ne \frac{3\pi}{2} - 4\pi = -\frac{5\pi}{2}$.

Notice that all of the numbers above are of the form $\frac{n\pi}{2}$, where n is an **odd integer**. This type of number will always occur when we replace k by an integer in the expressions $\frac{\pi}{2} + 2\pi k$ and $\frac{3\pi}{2} + 2\pi k$. As you can see,

$$\frac{\pi}{2} + 2\pi k = \frac{\pi}{2} + \frac{2\pi k}{1}\left(\frac{2}{2}\right) = \frac{\pi + 4\pi k}{2} = \frac{\overbrace{(1 + 4k)}^{\text{always odd}}\pi}{2} \quad \text{and} \quad \frac{3\pi}{2} + 2\pi k = \frac{3\pi}{2} + \frac{2\pi k}{1}\left(\frac{2}{2}\right) = \frac{3\pi + 4\pi k}{2} = \frac{\overbrace{(3 + 4k)}^{\text{always odd}}\pi}{2}.$$

Therefore, we can write the domain of $f(\theta) = \tan\theta$ in a more compact way.

*** **The domain of** $f(\theta) = \tan\theta$ **is** $\left\{\theta \mid \theta \neq \dfrac{n\pi}{2}, \text{ where } n \text{ is any odd integer}\right\}$. ***

Let's now determine the range of $f(\theta) = \tan\theta$. Suppose that y is **any real number**. Notice that the point $P = (a,\ b) = \left(\dfrac{1}{\sqrt{1+y^2}},\ \dfrac{y}{\sqrt{1+y^2}}\right)$ is on the unit circle since

$$\left(\frac{1}{\sqrt{1+y^2}}\right)^2 + \left(\frac{y}{\sqrt{1+y^2}}\right)^2 = \frac{1}{1+y^2} + \frac{y^2}{1+y^2} = \frac{1+y^2}{1+y^2} = 1.$$

If we let x be an angle whose terminal side contains the point P, then

$$\tan x = \frac{b}{a} = \frac{\dfrac{y}{\sqrt{1+y^2}}}{\dfrac{1}{\sqrt{1+y^2}}} = \frac{y}{1} = y.$$

And so y is in the range. Since y represented any real number, we have the following:

*** **The range of** $f(\theta) = \tan\theta$ **is the set of all real numbers.** ***

III) The Domain and Range of $f(\theta) = \sec\theta$ and $g(\theta) = \csc\theta$

To find the domain of $f(\theta) = \sec\theta$, we use the definition. Recall that $\sec\theta = \frac{1}{a}$ whenever $(a,\ b)$ lies on the terminal side of θ and is on the unit circle. If $a \neq 0$, then $\sec\theta$ is well-defined. However, if $a = 0$, then $\sec\theta$ is undefined. This happens at the points $(0,\ 1)$ and $(0,\ -1)$ on the unit circle. These points correspond to $\theta = 90° = \frac{\pi}{2}$ and $\theta = 270° = \frac{3\pi}{2}$, respectively. The domain of $f(\theta) = \sec\theta$ will not contain these values. Furthermore, any angle which is coterminal to these angles will not be in the domain. Therefore, we have the following:

*** **The domain of** $f(\theta) = \sec\theta$ **is** $\left\{\theta \mid \theta \neq \dfrac{\pi}{2} + 2\pi k \text{ and } \theta \neq \dfrac{3\pi}{2} + 2\pi k, \text{ where } k \text{ is any integer}\right\}$. ***

*** **Equivalently, the domain of** $f(\theta) = \sec\theta$ **is** $\left\{\theta \mid \theta \neq \dfrac{n\pi}{2}, \text{ where } n \text{ is any odd integer}\right\}$. ***

To find the domain of $g(\theta) = \csc\theta$, recall that $\csc\theta = \frac{1}{b}$ whenever $(a,\ b)$ lies on the terminal side of θ and is on the unit circle. If $b \neq 0$, then $\csc\theta$ is well-defined. However, if $b = 0$, then $\csc\theta$ is undefined. This occurs at the points $(1,\ 0)$ and $(-1,\ 0)$ on the unit circle. These points correspond to $\theta = 0° = 0$ and $\theta = 180° = \pi$, respectively. The domain of $g(\theta) = \csc\theta$, therefore, will not contain these values. Moreover, any angle which is coterminal to these will not be in the domain. Therefore, we have the following:

$$\boxed{\text{*** \textbf{The domain of} } g\left(\theta\right) = \csc\theta \text{ \textbf{is} } \{\theta \mid \theta \neq 2\pi k \text{ and } \theta \neq \pi + 2\pi k, \text{ where } k \text{ is any integer}\}. \text{ ***}}$$

Observe the following: 1) If $k = 0$, then $\theta \neq 0$ and $\theta \neq \pi$.

2) If $k = 1$, then $\theta \neq 2\pi$ and $\theta \neq \pi + 2\pi = 3\pi$.

3) If $k = 2$, then $\theta \neq 4\pi$ and $\theta \neq \pi + 4\pi = 5\pi$.

4) If $k = -1$, then $\theta \neq -2\pi$ and $\theta \neq \pi - 2\pi = -\pi$.

5) If $k = -2$, then $\theta \neq -4\pi$ and $\theta \neq \pi - 4\pi = -3\pi$.

All of the numbers above are of the form $n\pi$, where n is an integer. This type of number will always occur when we replace k by an integer in the expressions $2\pi k$ and $\pi + 2\pi k$. Therefore, we can write the domain of $g\left(\theta\right) = \csc\theta$ in a more simplified way.

$$\boxed{\text{*** \textbf{The domain of} } g\left(\theta\right) = \csc\theta \text{ \textbf{is} } \{\theta \mid \theta \neq n\pi, \text{ where } n \text{ is any integer}\}. \text{ ***}}$$

To find the range of both $f\left(\theta\right) = \sec\theta$ and $g\left(\theta\right) = \csc\theta$, we will use the following algebraic property:

$$\boxed{\text{If } -1 \leq t \leq 1 \text{ and } t \neq 0, \text{ then either } \frac{1}{t} \leq -1 \text{ or } \frac{1}{t} \geq 1.}$$

This property simply states that the reciprocal of a number between -1 and 1 (excluding 0) will always be either less than -1 or larger than 1. If $t = -1$, then $\frac{1}{t} = -1$. If $t = 1$, then $\frac{1}{t} = 1$. Using absolute value inequalities we write this property as follows:

$$\text{If } |t| \leq 1 \text{ and } t \neq 0, \text{ then } \left|\frac{1}{t}\right| \geq 1.$$

Now, since $-1 \leq a \leq 1$ for any point (a, b) on the unit circle and $\sec\theta = \frac{1}{a}$, the property above tells us that if $a \neq 0$, then either $\frac{1}{a} \leq -1$ or $\frac{1}{a} \geq 1$. This means that either $\sec\theta \leq -1$ or $\sec\theta \geq 1$ for any θ in the domain of $f\left(\theta\right) = \sec\theta$. Similarly, since $-1 \leq b \leq 1$ for any point (a, b) on the unit circle and $\csc\theta = \frac{1}{b}$, we have that either $\frac{1}{b} \leq -1$ or $\frac{1}{b} \geq 1$, provided that $b \neq 0$. This means that either $\csc\theta \leq -1$ or $\csc\theta \geq 1$ for any θ in the domain of $g\left(\theta\right) = \csc\theta$.

$$\boxed{\begin{array}{l} \text{*** \textbf{The range of} } f\left(\theta\right) = \sec\theta \text{ \textbf{is} } \{y \mid y \leq -1 \text{ or } y \geq 1\} = \{y \mid |y| \geq 1\}. \text{ ***} \\[2mm] \text{*** \textbf{The range of} } g\left(\theta\right) = \csc\theta \text{ \textbf{is} } \{y \mid y \leq -1 \text{ or } y \geq 1\} = \{y \mid |y| \geq 1\}. \text{ ***} \end{array}}$$

IV) The Domain and Range of $f(\theta) = \cot\theta$

By definition, we have that $\cot\theta = \frac{a}{b}$. The domain of $f(\theta) = \cot\theta$ will consist of those values of θ for which $\frac{a}{b}$ is well-defined. Any values of θ for which $b = 0$ will not be in the domain since $\cot\theta = \frac{a}{b} = \frac{a}{0}$ is undefined. Well, observe that $b = 0$ when $(a,\ b) = (1,\ 0)$ and when $(a,\ b) = (-1,\ 0)$. These points correspond to the angles $\theta = 0° = 0$ and $\theta = 180° = \pi$, respectively.

The angles which are coterminal to $\theta = 0°$ and $\theta = 180°$ will also contain either $(1,\ 0)$ or $(-1,\ 0)$ on their terminal sides. Notice $\theta = 0$ is coterminal to $\alpha = 2\pi k$, where k is any integer, and $\theta = \pi$ is coterminal to $\alpha = \pi + 2\pi k$, where k is any integer. This gives us the domain of f.

*** **The domain of $f(\theta) = \cot\theta$ is $\{\theta \mid \theta \neq 2\pi k$ and $\theta \neq \pi + 2\pi k$, where k is any integer$\}$**. ***

*** **Equivalently, the domain of $f(\theta) = \cot\theta$ is $\{\theta \mid \theta \neq n\pi$, where n is any integer$\}$**. ***

To find the range of $f(\theta) = \cot\theta$, notice that if y is **any real number**, then the point $P = (a,\ b) = \left(\frac{y}{\sqrt{1+y^2}},\ \frac{1}{\sqrt{1+y^2}}\right)$ is on the unit circle since

$$\left(\frac{y}{\sqrt{1+y^2}}\right)^2 + \left(\frac{1}{\sqrt{1+y^2}}\right)^2 = \frac{y^2}{1+y^2} + \frac{1}{1+y^2} = \frac{y^2+1}{1+y^2} = 1.$$

If we let x be an angle whose terminal side contains the point P, then

$$\cot x = \frac{a}{b} = \frac{\frac{y}{\sqrt{1+y^2}}}{\frac{1}{\sqrt{1+y^2}}} = \frac{y}{1} = y.$$

And so y is in the range. Since y represented any real number, we have the following:

*** **The range of $f(\theta) = \cot\theta$ is the set of all real numbers.** ***

Let's now summarize all of the information regarding the domain and range of each trigonometric function.

Function	Domain	Range
$y = f(\theta) = \sin\theta$	All real numbers.	$\{y \mid -1 \leq y \leq 1\}$
$y = f(\theta) = \cos\theta$	All real numbers.	$\{y \mid -1 \leq y \leq 1\}$
$y = f(\theta) = \tan\theta$	$\left\{\theta \mid \theta \neq \frac{n\pi}{2}, \text{ where } n \text{ is any odd integer}\right\}$	All real numbers.
$y = f(\theta) = \csc\theta$	$\{\theta \mid \theta \neq n\pi, \text{ where } n \text{ is any odd integer}\}$	$\{y \mid y \leq -1 \text{ or } y \geq 1\}$
$y = f(\theta) = \sec\theta$	$\left\{\theta \mid \theta \neq \frac{n\pi}{2}, \text{ where } n \text{ is any odd integer}\right\}$	$\{y \mid y \leq -1 \text{ or } y \geq 1\}$
$y = f(\theta) = \cot\theta$	$\{\theta \mid \theta \neq n\pi, \text{ where } n \text{ is any odd integer}\}$	All real numbers.

Try These (Set 3):

1) Is $\frac{6\pi}{7}$ in the domain of $f(x) = \sin x$?   2) Is $\frac{3\pi}{2}$ in the domain of $g(\theta) = \tan\theta$?

3) Is 1.542 in the range of $h(t) = \cos t$?   4) Is -0.992 in the range of $f(\alpha) = \sin\alpha$?

5) Is 13.45 in the range of $g(x) = \cot x$?   6) Is 0.441 in the range of $h(\beta) = \csc\beta$?

7) Is -4π in the domain of $g(\alpha) = \cot\alpha$?   8) Is 5π in the domain of $f(\theta) = \sec\theta$?

Section 4.4   Periodicity of the Trigonometric Functions

In Section 3.3, we have discussed the notion of coterminal angles. We saw that if k represents any integer, then θ is coterminal to $\theta + 2\pi k$. Consequently, for those values of θ which provide a well-defined trigonometric value, we have the following identities:

$$\sin\theta = \sin(\theta + 2\pi k) \qquad \csc\theta = \csc(\theta + 2\pi k)$$
$$\cos\theta = \cos(\theta + 2\pi k) \qquad \sec\theta = \sec(\theta + 2\pi k)$$
$$\tan\theta = \tan(\theta + 2\pi k) \qquad \cot\theta = \cot(\theta + 2\pi k)$$

These equalities state that the trigonometric values of $\theta + 2\pi k$ are the same as trigonometric values of θ, provided that such a value exists. In other words, if we change the value of θ by an integer multiple of 2π, the trigonometric value won't change. This property of the trigonometric functions is very important.

Definition: A function f is called **periodic** if there is a positive real number p such that, whenever x is the domain of f, so is $x + p$, and

$$f(x + p) = f(x).$$

The smallest value of p (if it exists) which satisfies this equality is called the **period of** f.

Returning to our identities, notice that if $k = 1$, then:

$$\sin\theta = \sin(\theta + 2\pi) \qquad \csc\theta = \csc(\theta + 2\pi)$$
$$\cos\theta = \cos(\theta + 2\pi) \qquad \sec\theta = \sec(\theta + 2\pi)$$
$$\tan\theta = \tan(\theta + 2\pi) \qquad \cot\theta = \cot(\theta + 2\pi)$$

And so each of the trigonometric functions is periodic. In fact, each of them has period 2π except the tangent and cotangent functions. It turns out that for those values of θ which are in the domain of tangent or cotangent, we have

$$\tan\theta = \tan(\theta + \pi) \quad \text{and} \quad (\theta + \pi).$$

Consequently, the tangent and cotangent functions have period π. To see why this is the case, let's take a look at the figure on the next page.

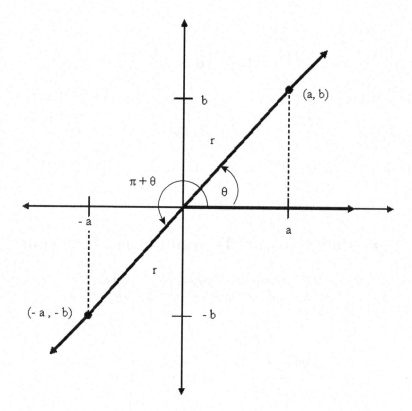

Let θ be any angle **which is not** of the form $\theta = \frac{n\pi}{2}$, where n is any odd integer. Notice that the point (a, b) lies on the terminal side of θ and $(-a, -b)$ lies on the terminal side of $\theta + \pi$ (since the two terminal sides form a line through the origin and such a line has origin symmetry). Now, by definition,

$$\tan\theta = \frac{b}{a} \quad \text{and} \quad \tan(\theta + \pi) = \frac{-b}{-a} = \frac{b}{a}.$$

And so $\tan\theta = \tan(\theta + \pi)$. Similarly, if $\theta \neq n\pi$ (n is any integer) and (a, b) is on the terminal side of θ, then $(-a, -b)$ lies on the terminal side of $\theta + \pi$. Therefore,

$$\cot\theta = \frac{a}{b} \quad \text{and} \quad \cot(\theta + \pi) = \frac{-a}{-b} = \frac{a}{b}.$$

And we're done. Let's summarize our results:

For those values of θ which provide a well-defined trigonometric value and for any integer, k, we have:

$$\sin\theta = \sin(\theta + 2\pi k) \qquad \csc\theta = \csc(\theta + 2\pi k)$$
$$\cos\theta = \cos(\theta + 2\pi k) \qquad \sec\theta = \sec(\theta + 2\pi k)$$
$$\tan\theta = \tan(\theta + \pi k) \qquad \cot\theta = \cot(\theta + \pi k)$$

Examples.

1) If $\sin\theta = \frac{1}{5}$, find the value of $\sin(\theta + 2\pi)$.

By the periodicity of the sine function, we know that $\sin(\theta + 2\pi) = \sin\theta$. Therefore,

$$\sin(\theta + 2\pi) = \sin\theta = \frac{1}{5}.$$

2) If $\sec x = -\frac{8}{3}$, find the value of $\sec (x - 2\pi)$.

We know that $\sec (x + 2\pi k) = \sec x$ for any integer k. In particular, if we replace k by -1, we have $\sec (x - 2\pi) = \sec x$. Therefore,

$$\sec (x - 2\pi) = \sec x = -\frac{8}{3}.$$

3) If $\tan \alpha = 2$, find the value of $\tan (\alpha + 5\pi)$.
Since the tangent function has period π, we have that $\tan (\alpha + \pi k) = \tan \alpha$ for any integer k. In particular, if $k = 5$, we have $\tan (\alpha + 5\pi) = \tan \alpha$. Therefore,

$$\tan (\alpha + 5\pi) = \tan \alpha = 2.$$

Try These (Set 4):

1) If $\cos \alpha = -\frac{3}{4}$, find the value of $\cos (\alpha - 4\pi)$.   2) If $\cot B = 19.135$, find the value of $\cot (B + 9\pi)$.

3) If $\csc (\theta + 2\pi) = 5.13$, find the value of $\csc \theta$.   4) If $\tan (x - 12\pi) = 2.07$, find the value of $\tan x$.

Exercise 4

In Exercises 1-8, find the values of the six trigonometric functions of t if the given point, P, on the unit circle corresponds to t.

1. $P = \left(\frac{1}{2}, -\frac{\sqrt{3}}{2} \right)$ 2. $P = \left(-\frac{\sqrt{2}}{2}, \frac{\sqrt{2}}{2} \right)$ 3. $P = (-1, 0)$ 4. $P = (0, 1)$

5. $P = \left(\frac{1}{6}, \frac{\sqrt{35}}{6} \right)$ 6. $P = \left(-\frac{1}{4}, -\frac{\sqrt{15}}{4} \right)$ 7. $P = \left(-\frac{\sqrt{3}}{3}, -\frac{\sqrt{6}}{3} \right)$ 8. $P = \left(\frac{\sqrt{5}}{6}, \frac{\sqrt{31}}{6} \right)$

In Exercises 9-16, find the exact values of the six trigonometric functions of θ if the given point, P, lies on its terminal side.

9. $P = (2, -4)$ 10. $P = (-3, 3)$ 11. $P = (-5, 1)$ 12. $P = (1, 3)$

13. $P = (9, 3)$ 14. $P = (-1, -6)$ 15. $P = (-\sqrt{3}, -\sqrt{6})$ 16. $P = (\sqrt{5}, \sqrt{31})$

17. What is the domain of $f(x) = \cos x$?   18. What is the domain of $f(t) = \sin t$?

19. What is the domain of $g(\theta) = \cot \theta$?   20. What is the domain of $h(x) = \sec x$?

21. What is the range of the tangent function?   22. What is the range of the secant function?

23. What is the range of the sine function?   24. What is the range of the cosine function?

25. For which values of x is $\tan x$ undefined?   26. For which values of x is $\csc x$ undefined?

27. Is $\frac{2\pi}{9}$ in the domain of $f(x) = \sin x$?   28. Is 2π in the domain of $g(x) = \cos x$?

29. Is -0.841 in the range of $h(\alpha) = \sec \alpha$?   30. Is 0.777 in the range of $f(\beta) = \tan \beta$?

31. What is the period of $f(x) = \cos x$?   32. What is the period of $f(x) = \sin x$?

33. What is the period of $y = \tan x$?   34. What is the period of $y = \sec x$?

35. If $\sin A = \dfrac{2}{3}$, find the value of $\sin(A + 2\pi)$.   36. If $\cos B = \dfrac{1}{7}$, find the value of $\cos(B + 2\pi)$.

37. If $\tan \beta = -3$, find the value of $\tan(\beta - \pi)$.   38. If $\cot x = -\dfrac{3}{4}$, find the value of $\cot(x - 3\pi)$.

39. If $\sin \alpha = -0.76$, find the value of $\sin(\alpha + 6\pi)$.   40. If $\sec \alpha = 1.82$, find the value of $\sec(\alpha + 4\pi)$.

Chapter 5:   Graphing Trigonometric Functions

Section 5.1   The Graphs of the Six Trigonometric Functions

We are prepared to graph each of the trigonometric functions. The properties which lead to the graphs of the sine, cosine, and tangent functions will be thoroughly discussed now.

I) The Graph of $y = \sin x$

We will begin by reviewing some of the properties of the sine function. They will assist us in graphing the function.

1) $y = \sin x$ has period 2π.

2) The domain of $y = \sin x$ is the set of all real numbers, $\{x \mid -\infty < x < \infty\}$.

3) The range of $y = \sin x$ is the set $\{y \mid -1 \le y \le 1\}$.

4) The graph will contain the points $(0, 0)$, $\left(\frac{\pi}{2}, 1\right)$, $(\pi, 0)$, $\left(\frac{3\pi}{2}, -1\right)$, and $(2\pi, 0)$.

This is due to the fact that:

$$\sin 0° = \sin 0 = 0 \qquad\qquad \sin 270° = \sin \tfrac{3\pi}{2} = -1$$
$$\sin 90° = \sin \tfrac{\pi}{2} = 1 \qquad\qquad \sin 360° = \sin 2\pi = 0$$
$$\sin 180° = \sin \pi = 0$$

5) $\sin(-x) = -\sin x$

This property concerning negative angles shows us that the graph will have origin symmetry. Notice that if $f(x) = \sin x$, then

$$f(-x) = \sin(-x) = -\sin x = -f(x).$$

And so f is an odd function. The graph of every odd function has origin symmetry.

6) Every x-intercept for the graph has an x-value of the form $x = n\pi$, where n is an integer.

We know that $(0, 0)$, $(\pi, 0)$, and $(2\pi, 0)$ are x-intercepts and their x-values have the form $n\pi$, where $n = 0$, 1, and 2, respectively. By periodicity, we can obtain every x-intercept by adding integer multiples of 2π to these x-values. In fact, for negative angles, we can use the property that $\sin(-x) = -\sin x$ and work with positive angles instead. For example, notice that:

$$\sin 3\pi = \sin(\pi + 2\pi) = \sin \pi = 0 \qquad\qquad \sin(-\pi) = -\sin \pi = 0$$
$$\sin 4\pi = \sin(2\pi + 2\pi) = \sin 2\pi = 0 \qquad\qquad \sin(-2\pi) = -\sin 2\pi = 0$$
$$\sin 5\pi = \sin(3\pi + 2\pi) = \sin 3\pi = 0 \qquad\qquad \sin(-3\pi) = -\sin 3\pi = 0$$
$$\vdots \qquad\qquad\qquad\qquad\qquad \vdots$$

Notice that every angle measure is an integer multiple of π and such an expression may be written as $x = n\pi$, where n is any integer.

7) The graph will increase from $x = 0$ to $x = \frac{\pi}{2}$, then decrease from $x = \frac{\pi}{2}$ to $x = \frac{3\pi}{2}$, and increase again from $x = \frac{3\pi}{2}$ to $x = 2\pi$.

Recall that $\sin x = b$, where (a, b) is the point on the unit circle which corresponds to angle x. As x increases from 0 to $\frac{\pi}{2}$, the corresponding point moves upward on the unit circle from $(1, 0)$ to $(0, 1)$. This means that the b-value increases from 0 to 1 (Figure (a)) Therefore, $\sin x$ increases from 0 to 1. As x increases from $\frac{\pi}{2}$ to $\frac{3\pi}{2}$, the corresponding point moves downward on the unit circle from $(0, 1)$ to $(-1, 0)$ and then to $(0, -1)$. This means that the b-value decreases from 1 to -1 (Figures (b) and (c)). Consequently, $\sin x$ decreases from 1 to -1. As x increases from $\frac{3\pi}{2}$ to 2π, the corresponding point moves upward from $(0, -1)$ to $(1, 0)$. This means that the b-value increases from -1 to 0 and so $\sin x$ increases from -1 to 0 (Figure (d)).

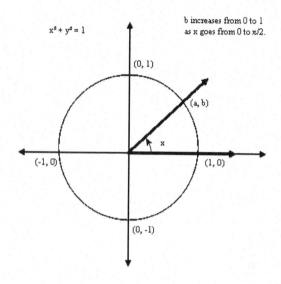

Figure (a)

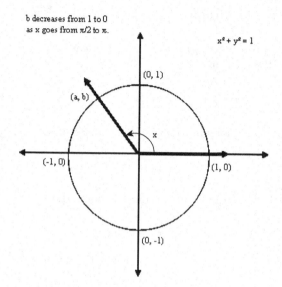

Figure (b)

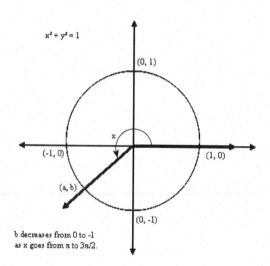

Figure (c)

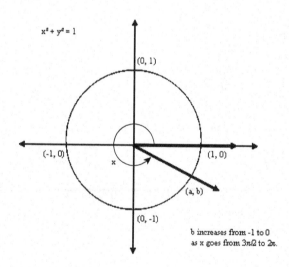

Figure (d)

Before we use the information above to graph $y = \sin x$, let's find some more points for the graph.

x	$y = \sin x$
$\frac{\pi}{6}$	$\sin \frac{\pi}{6} = \frac{1}{2}$
$\frac{5\pi}{6}$	$\sin \frac{5\pi}{6} = \sin \frac{\pi}{6} = \frac{1}{2}$
$\frac{7\pi}{6}$	$\sin \frac{7\pi}{6} = -\sin \frac{\pi}{6} = -\frac{1}{2}$
$\frac{11\pi}{6}$	$\sin \frac{11\pi}{6} - \sin \frac{\pi}{6} = -\frac{1}{2}$

The graph of $y = \sin x$ for the **restricted domain** $\{x \mid 0 \le x \le 2\pi\}$ is given in the following figure:

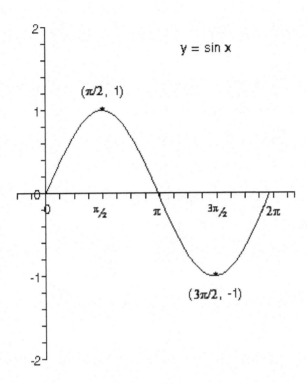

Notice that the graph contains two turning points, $\left(\frac{\pi}{2}, 1\right)$ and $\left(\frac{3\pi}{2}, -1\right)$. Furthermore, there are no breaks or cusps in the graph. This means that $y = \sin x$ is **continuous** and **smooth** on the restricted domain $\{x \mid 0 \le x \le 2\pi\}$. The graph in the figure above is one period, or one **cycle**, of the full graph of $y = \sin x$, which has a period of 2π. We can obtain the **whole graph** by simply repeating this cycle indefinitely to the left and to the right, obtaining infinitely many more cycles for the graph. A portion of the graph of $y = \sin x$ is given in the next figure.

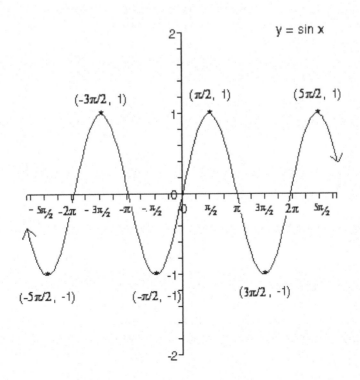

As you can see, the graph is symmetric about the origin and the cycle from $x = 0$ to $x = 2\pi$ looks exactly like the cycle from $x = -2\pi$ to $x = 0$. This is expected because of the periodicity of the sine function. Moreover, there are infinitely many turning points and x-intercepts on the graph and the sine function is continuous and smooth for all real numbers.

II) **The Graph of** $y = \cos x$

We will recall some properties of the cosine function.

1) $y = \cos x$ has period 2π.

2) The domain of $y = \cos x$ is the set of all real numbers, $\{x \mid -\infty < x < \infty\}$.

3) The range of $y = \cos x$ is the set $\{y \mid -1 \leq y \leq 1\}$.

4) The graph will contain the points $(0, 1)$, $\left(\frac{\pi}{2}, 0\right)$, $(\pi, -1)$, $\left(\frac{3\pi}{2}, 0\right)$, and $(2\pi, 1)$.

This is because:

$$\cos 0° = \cos 0 = 1 \qquad\qquad \cos 270° = \cos \tfrac{3\pi}{2} = 0$$

$$\cos 90° = \cos \tfrac{\pi}{2} = 0 \qquad\qquad \cos 360° = \cos 2\pi = 1$$

$$\cos 180° = \cos \pi = -1$$

5) $\cos(-x) = \cos x$

This property concerning negative angles shows us that the graph will have y-axis symmetry. If $g(x) = \cos x$, then

$$g(-x) = \cos(-x) = \cos x = g(x).$$

And so g is an even function. The graph of every even function has y-axis symmetry.

6) Every x-intercept for the graph has an x-value of the form $x = \frac{n\pi}{2}$, where n is an odd integer.

We know that $\left(\frac{\pi}{2}, 0\right)$ and $\left(\frac{3\pi}{2}, 0\right)$ are x-intercepts and their x-values have the form $\frac{n\pi}{2}$, where $n = 1$ and 3, respectively. By periodicity, we can obtain every x-intercept by adding integer multiples of 2π to these x-values. In fact, for negative angles, we can use the property that $\cos(-x) = \cos x$ and work with positive angles instead. For example, notice that:

$$\cos \tfrac{5\pi}{2} = \cos\left(\tfrac{\pi}{2} + 2\pi\right) = \cos \tfrac{\pi}{2} = 0 \qquad\qquad \cos\left(-\tfrac{\pi}{2}\right) = \cos \tfrac{\pi}{2} = 0$$

$$\cos \tfrac{7\pi}{2} = \cos\left(\tfrac{3\pi}{2} + 2\pi\right) = \cos \tfrac{3\pi}{2} = 0 \qquad\qquad \cos\left(-\tfrac{3\pi}{2}\right) = \cos \tfrac{3\pi}{2} = 0$$

$$\cos \tfrac{9\pi}{2} = \cos\left(\tfrac{5\pi}{2} + 2\pi\right) = \cos \tfrac{5\pi}{2} = 0 \qquad\qquad \cos\left(-\tfrac{5\pi}{2}\right) = \cos \tfrac{5\pi}{2} = 0$$

$$\vdots \qquad\qquad\qquad\qquad\qquad \vdots$$

Every angle measure is of the form $x = \frac{n\pi}{2}$, where n is an odd integer.

7) The graph will decrease from $x = 0$ to $x = \pi$, then increase from $x = \pi$ to $x = 2\pi$.

Recall that $\cos x = a$, where (a, b) is the point on the unit circle which corresponds to angle x. As x increases from 0 to π, the corresponding point moves to the left on the unit circle from $(1, 0)$ to $(0, 1)$ and then to $(-1, 0)$. This means that the a-value decreases from 1 to -1 (see Figures (a) and (b)). Therefore, $\cos x$ decreases from 1 to -1. As x increases from π to 2π, the corresponding point moves to the right on the unit circle from $(-1, 0)$ to $(0, -1)$ and then to $(1, 0)$ (see Figures (c) and (d)). This means that the a-value increases from -1 to 1. Consequently, $\cos x$ increases from -1 to 1. Figures (a)–(d) are on the next page.

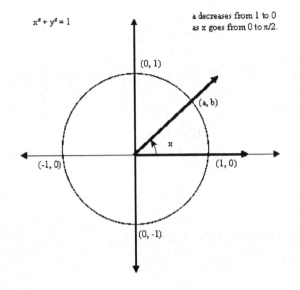

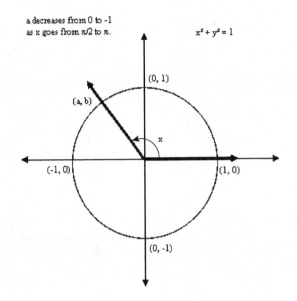

Figure (a)

Figure (b)

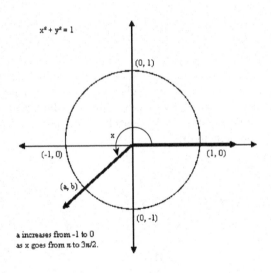

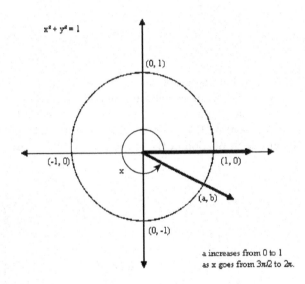

Figure (c)

Figure (d)

Some more points on the graph of $y = \cos x$ are given in the table below:

x	$y = \cos x$
$\frac{\pi}{3}$	$\cos \frac{\pi}{3} = \frac{1}{2}$
$\frac{2\pi}{3}$	$\cos \frac{2\pi}{3} = -\cos \frac{\pi}{3} = -\frac{1}{2}$
$\frac{4\pi}{3}$	$\cos \frac{4\pi}{3} = -\cos \frac{\pi}{3} = -\frac{1}{2}$
$\frac{5\pi}{3}$	$\cos \frac{5\pi}{3} = \cos \frac{\pi}{3} = \frac{1}{2}$

The graph of $y = \cos x$ for the restricted domain $\{x \mid 0 \leq x \leq 2\pi\}$ is given in the next figure.

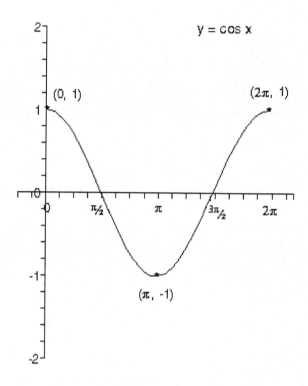

Notice that the graph has a turning point at $(\pi, -1)$. Since there are no breaks of cusps in the graph, $y = \cos x$ is continuous and smooth on the restricted domain $\{x \mid 0 \leq x \leq 2\pi\}$. The graph above is one cycle of the whole graph of $y = \cos x$, which has a period of 2π. By periodicity, we can obtain the whole graph by simply repeating this cycle indefinitely to the left and to the right, obtaining infinitely many more cycles for the graph. A portion of the graph of $y = \cos x$ is given in the next figure.

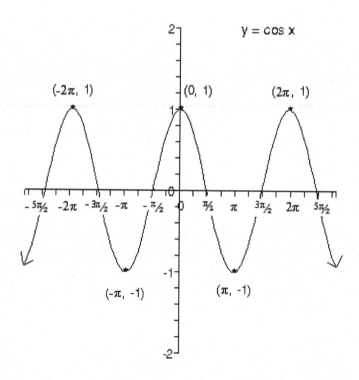

As you can see, the graph is symmetric about the y-axis and the cycle from $x = 0$ to $x = 2\pi$ looks exactly like the cycle from $x = -2\pi$ to $x = 0$. This is expected by the periodicity of the cosine function. There are infinitely many turning points and x-intercepts on the graph and the cosine function is continuous and smooth for all real numbers.

III) **The Graph of** $y = \tan x$

The following properties of the tangent function are useful in obtaining its graph:

1) $y = \tan x$ has period π.

2) The domain of $y = \tan x$ is the set $\left\{ x \mid x \neq \frac{n\pi}{2}, \text{ where } n \text{ is any odd integer} \right\}$.

3) The range of $y = \tan x$ is the set of all real numbers.

4) The graph will contain the points $(0, 0)$, $(\pi, 0)$, and $(2\pi, 0)$. Furthermore, there are infinitely many vertical asymptotes whose equations are of the form $x = \frac{n\pi}{2}$, where n is any odd integer.

We have:

$$\tan 0° = \tan 0 = 0 \qquad\qquad \tan 270° = \tan \tfrac{3\pi}{2} \text{ is undefined}$$

$$\tan 90° = \tan \tfrac{\pi}{2} \text{ is undefined} \qquad\qquad \tan 360° = \tan 2\pi = 0$$

$$\tan 180° = \tan \pi = 0$$

Observe that $x = \frac{\pi}{2}$ is a vertical asymptote (set $n = 1$ in the equation $x = \frac{n\pi}{2}$). Why is $x = \frac{\pi}{2}$ the equation of a vertical asymptote? Let's figure out what is happening when angle x is very close to $\frac{\pi}{2}$. By definition, if (a, b) is the point on the unit circle corresponding to angle x, then $\tan x = \frac{b}{a}$.

Case I. If x is in quadrant I, then $\underset{a \text{ is } +}{\underline{0 < a < 1}}$ and $\underset{b \text{ is } +}{\underline{0 < b < 1}}$. Let's suppose that x is increasing from 0 to $\frac{\pi}{2}$ and let (a, b) be the point on the unit circle which corresponds to x as x varies. As $x \to \frac{\pi}{2}^-$, $a \to 0$ and $b \to 1$ since the point (a, b) is getting closer to $(0, 1)$. The denominator of $\frac{b}{a}$ is getting closer to 0 and the numerator is getting closer to 1. Now, if you have a fraction whose denominator is **positive** and close to 0 and whose numerator is close to 1, then the fraction will have a **large positive value**. For example,

$$\frac{0.5}{0.000002} = 250,000 \quad \text{and} \quad \frac{0.998}{0.000000001} = 998,000,000.$$

If we allow the denominator of $\frac{b}{a}$ to become smaller and smaller while the numerator gets closer to 1, the fraction will become larger and larger without bound. This means that $\frac{b}{a} \to +\infty$ as $a \to 0^+$, that is, as $x \to \frac{\pi}{2}^-$. Consequently, we have that $\tan x \to +\infty$ as $x \to \frac{\pi}{2}^-$.

Case II. If x is in quadrant II, then $\underset{a \text{ is } -}{\underline{-1 < a < 0}}$ and $\underset{b \text{ is } +}{\underline{0 < b < 1}}$. Let's suppose that x is decreasing from π to $\frac{\pi}{2}$ and let (a, b) be the point on the unit circle which corresponds to x varies with x. Now, as $x \to \frac{\pi}{2}^+$, $a \to 0$ and $b \to 1$ as before. Once again, the denominator of $\frac{b}{a}$ is getting closer to 0 and the numerator gets closer to 1. If you have a fraction whose denominator is **negative** and close to 0 and whose numerator is close to 1, then the fraction will have a **large negative value**. For example,

$$\frac{0.5}{-0.000002} = -250,000 \quad \text{and} \quad \frac{0.998}{-0.000000001} = -998,000,000.$$

If we allow the denominator to become negatively smaller and smaller while the numerator approaches the value of 1, the fraction will become negatively larger and larger without bound. This means that $\frac{b}{a} \to -\infty$ as $a \to 0^-$ as $x \to \frac{\pi}{2}^+$. Consequently, we have that $\tan x \to -\infty$ as $x \to \frac{\pi}{2}^+$.

By definition, these results give us a vertical asymptote $x = \frac{\pi}{2}$. Since the tangent function has period π, we will have infinitely many vertical asymptotes:

$$x = \frac{\pi}{2} + \pi = \frac{3\pi}{2} \qquad\qquad x = \frac{\pi}{2} - \pi = -\frac{\pi}{2}$$

$$x = \frac{3\pi}{2} + \pi = \frac{5\pi}{2} \qquad\qquad x = -\frac{\pi}{2} - \pi = -\frac{3\pi}{2}$$

$$x = \frac{5\pi}{2} + \pi = \frac{7\pi}{2} \qquad\qquad x = -\frac{3\pi}{2} - \pi = -\frac{5\pi}{2}$$

$$\vdots \qquad\qquad\qquad \vdots$$

All of these equations have the form $x = \frac{n\pi}{2}$, where n is any odd integer.

5) $\tan(-x) = -\tan x$

The graph will have origin symmetry. Notice that if $f(x) = \tan x$, then

$$f(-x) = \tan(-x) = -\tan x = -f(x).$$

And so f is an odd function.

6) Every x-intercept for the graph has an x-value of the form $x = n\pi$, where n is any integer.

As you can see from 4) above, $(0, 0)$, $(\pi, 0)$, and $(2\pi, 0)$ are x-intercepts and their x-values have the form $n\pi$, where $n = 1$, 2, and 3, respectively. By periodicity, we can obtain every x-intercept by adding integer multiples of π to these x-values. For negative angles, we can use the property that $\tan(-x) = -\tan x$ and work with positive angles. For example:

$$\tan 3\pi = \tan(2\pi + \pi) = \tan 2\pi = 0 \qquad\qquad \tan(-\pi) = -\tan\pi = 0$$

$$\tan 4\pi = \tan(3\pi + \pi) = \tan 3\pi = 0 \qquad\qquad \tan(-2\pi) = -\tan 2\pi = 0$$

$$\tan 5\pi = \tan(4\pi + \pi) = \tan 4\pi = 0 \qquad\qquad \tan(-3\pi) = -\tan 3\pi = 0$$

$$\vdots \qquad\qquad\qquad\qquad \vdots$$

As you can see, every angle measure is of the form $n\pi$, where n is an integer. Some more points on the graph of $y = \tan x$ are given in the table below:

x	$y = \tan x$
$\frac{\pi}{4}$	$\tan\frac{\pi}{4} = 1$
$\frac{3\pi}{4}$	$\tan\frac{3\pi}{4} = -\tan\frac{\pi}{4} = -1$
$\frac{5\pi}{4}$	$\tan\frac{5\pi}{4} = \tan\frac{\pi}{4} = 1$
$\frac{7\pi}{4}$	$\tan\frac{7\pi}{4} = -\tan\frac{\pi}{4} = -1$

The graph of $y = \tan x$ for $\left\{x \mid 0 \leq x \leq 2\pi,\ x \neq \frac{\pi}{2},\ x \neq \frac{3\pi}{2}\right\}$ is given in the figure below.

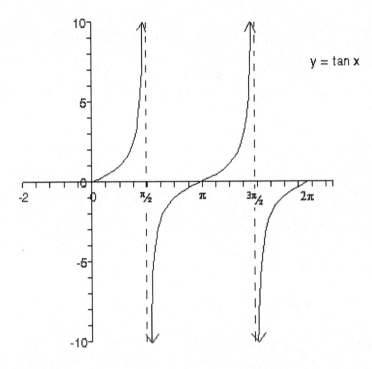

Notice that the graph has no turning points and is not continuous on the set $\{x \mid 0 \leq x \leq 2\pi\}$, since there are vertical asymptotes. The above figure shows two periods of the graph of $y = \tan x$. A larger portion of the graph of $y = \tan x$ is given in the next figure.

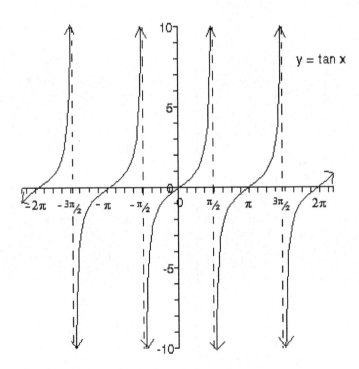

You can see that the graph is symmetric about the origin and the period from $x = 0$ to $x = \pi$ looks exactly like the period from $x = -\pi$ to $x = 0$. There are infinitely many vertical asymptotes whose equations are of the form $x = \frac{n\pi}{2}$, where n is any odd integer. There are infinitely many x-intercepts as well. The graph is discontinuous on the set $\{x \mid -\infty < x < \infty\}$ and has no turning points.

IV) The Graph of $y = \csc x$

Next, we have a list of some properties of the cosecant function. You should check each of these on your own.

1) $y = \csc x$ has period 2π.

2) The domain of $y = \csc x$ is the $\{x \mid x \neq n\pi,$ where n is any integer$\}$.

3) The range of $y = \csc x$ is the set $\{y \mid y \leq -1$ or $y \geq 1\}$.

4) The graph will contain the points $\left(\frac{\pi}{2}, 1\right)$ and $\left(\frac{3\pi}{2}, -1\right)$.

5) $\csc(-x) = -\csc x$, so the graph will have origin symmetry.

6) There are no intercepts for this graph (why not?).

7) There are vertical asymptotes $x = 0$, $x = \pi$, and $x = 2\pi$. Since $y = \csc x$ has period 2π, every vertical line whose equation is of the form $x = n\pi$ (where n is any integer) is a vertical asymptote.

Two periods of the graph of $y = \csc x$ are given below.

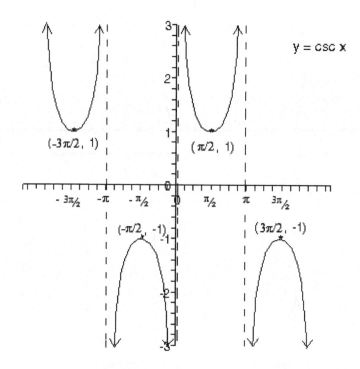

If you graph both $y = \csc x$ and $y = \sin x$, its reciprocal function, you will obtain:

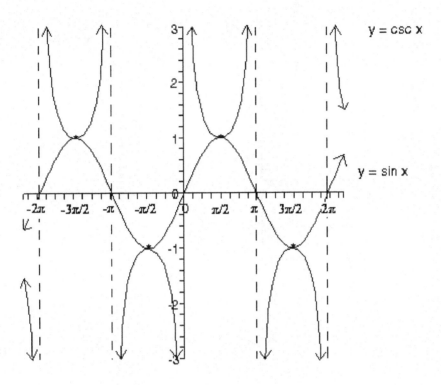

V) The Graph of $y = \sec x$

The secant function has the following properties, which are left for you to verify:

1) $y = \sec x$ has period 2π.

2) The domain of $y = \sec x$ is the set $\left\{ x \mid x \neq \frac{n\pi}{2}, \text{ where } n \text{ is any odd integer} \right\}$.

3) The range of $y = \sec x$ is the set $\left\{ y \mid y \leq -1 \text{ or } y \geq 1 \right\}$.

4) The graph will contain the points $(0, 1)$, $(\pi, -1)$, and $(2\pi, 1)$.

5) $\sec (-x) = \sec x$, so the graph will have y-axis symmetry.

6) There are no intercepts for this graph (why not?).

7) There are vertical asymptotes $x = \frac{\pi}{2}$ and $x = \frac{3\pi}{2}$. Since $y = \sec x$ has period 2π, every vertical line whose equation is of the form $x = \frac{n\pi}{2}$ (where n is any odd integer) is a vertical asymptote.

Two periods of the graph of $y = \sec x$ are given below.

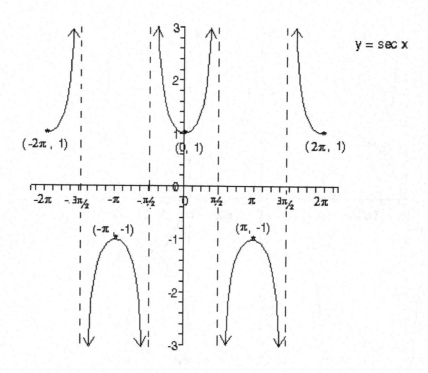

If you graph both $y = \sec x$ and $y = \cos x$, its reciprocal function, you will obtain:

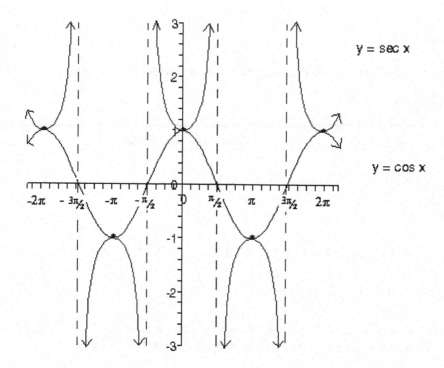

VI) The Graph of $y = \cot x$

The cotangent function has the following properties (verify these on your own):

1) $y = \cot x$ has period π.

2) The domain of $y = \cot x$ is the set $\{x \mid x \neq n\pi$, where n is any integer$\}$.

3) The range of $y = \cot x$ is the set of all real numbers.

4) The graph will contain the points $\left(\frac{\pi}{2}, 0\right)$ and $\left(\frac{3\pi}{2}, 0\right)$.

5) $\cot(-x) = -\cot x$, so the graph will have origin symmetry.

6) Every x-intercept for the graph has an x-value of the form $x = \frac{n\pi}{2}$, where n is any odd integer.

7) There are vertical asymptotes $x = 0$ and $x = \pi$. Since $y = \cot x$ has period π, every vertical line whose equation is of the form $x = n\pi$ (where n is any integer) is a vertical asymptote.

A portion of the graph of $y = \cot x$ is given in the following figure.

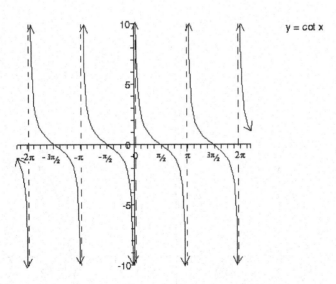

Section 5.2 Applying the Graphing Techniques

We can obtain the graphs of different functions which contain the trigonometric functions by using the graphing techniques discussed in Section R.5. Let's try some examples. We will focus our attention only on the sine, cosine, and tangent functions.

Examples. Graph.

1) $y = \cos\left(x - \frac{\pi}{4}\right)$

To graph $y = \cos\left(x - \frac{\pi}{4}\right)$, we will **shift** the graph of $y = \cos x$ **to the right** by $\frac{\pi}{4}$ units (see the figures below).

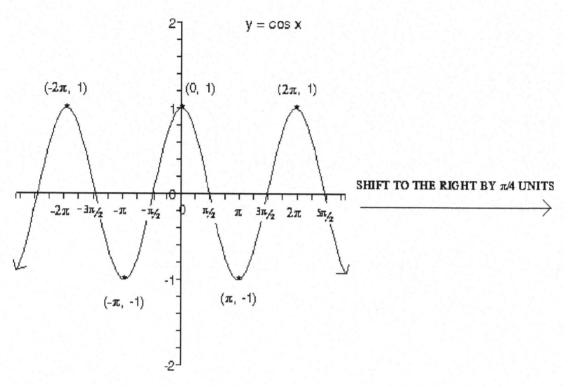

SHIFT TO THE RIGHT BY π/4 UNITS

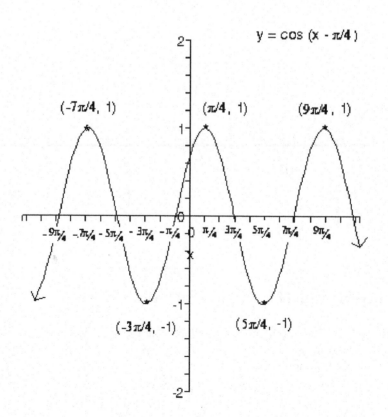

2) $y = \sin x - 3$

To graph $y = \sin x - 3$, we will **shift** the graph of $y = \sin x$ **downward** by three units (see the figures below).

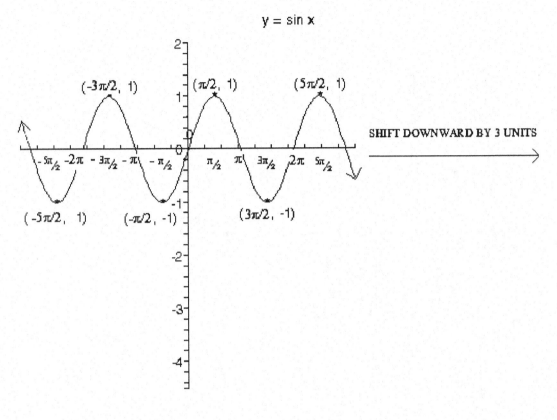

SHIFT DOWNWARD BY 3 UNITS

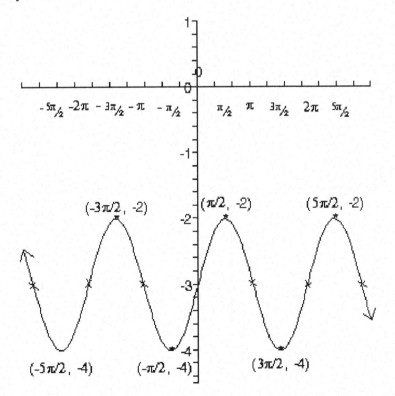

3) $y = -\tan x$

The graph $y = -\tan x$ is obtained by **reflecting** the graph of $y = \tan x$ about the x-axis (see the figures below).

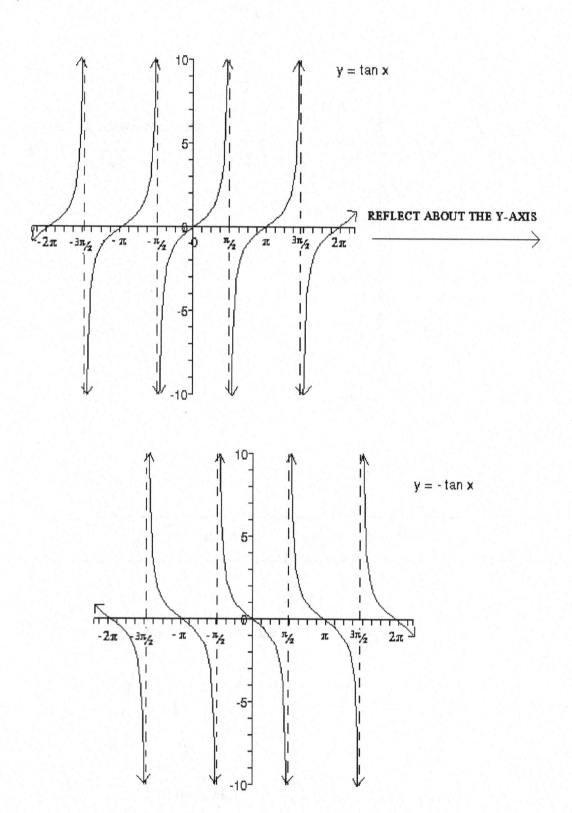

4) $y = \frac{3}{4} \sin x$

The graph $y = \frac{3}{4} \sin x$ is obtained by **vertically compressing** the graph of $y = \sin x$ by a factor of $\frac{3}{4}$ (see the figures below).

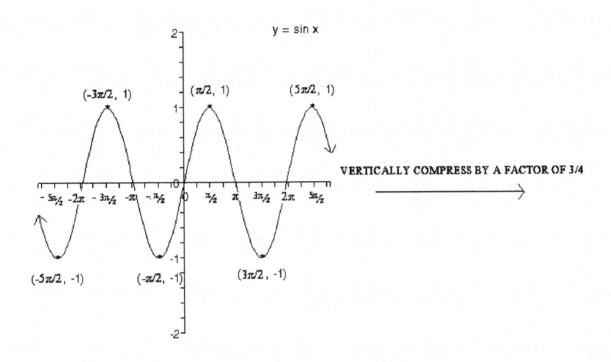

VERTICALLY COMPRESS BY A FACTOR OF 3/4

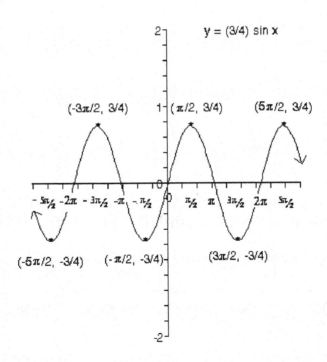

5) $y = \tan\left(x + \frac{\pi}{2}\right) + 2$

Let's first graph $y = \tan\left(x + \frac{\pi}{2}\right)$ by **shifting** the graph of $y = \tan x$ **to the left** by $\frac{\pi}{2}$ units. Next, we will **shift** the graph of $y = \tan\left(x + \frac{\pi}{2}\right)$ **upward** by two units, giving us the graph of $y = \tan\left(x + \frac{\pi}{2}\right) + 2$. The final graph is given below.

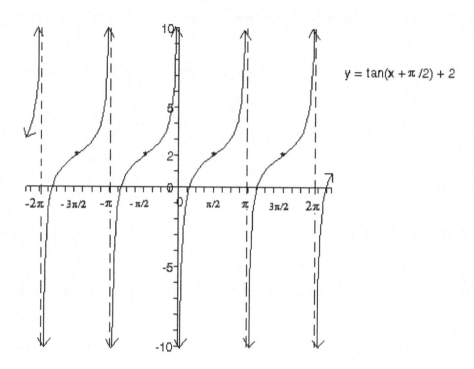

Try These (Set 1): Graph.

1) $y = \sin\left(x - \frac{\pi}{2}\right)$ 2) $y = \cos x + 2$ 3) $y = -\sin x$

Section 5.3   Sinusoidal Curves and Phase Shift

In this section, we will focus our attention on functions of the form $y = a\sin(bx - c)$ and $y = a\cos(bx - c)$, where $a \neq 0$ and $b > 0$ The graphs of these types of functions are called **sinusoidal curves**. We will start by looking at those sinusoidal curves whose equations are of the form $y = a\sin bx$ or $y = a\cos bx$. Notice that these are obtained by setting $c = 0$ in the general form. Afterwards, we will look at the case when $c \neq 0$.

Definition. The graph of $f(x) = a\sin bx$, where $a \neq 0$ and $b > 0$, is called a **sine curve**. The **amplitude** of f is $|a|$ and the **period** of f is $\frac{2\pi}{b}$.

The amplitude of $f(x) = a \sin bx$, which is $|a|$, tells us that the graph of f will have a maximum value of $|a|$ and a minimum value of $-|a|$. The period of f tells us that the x-values of one cycle of the sine curve will lie in the interval $\left[0, \frac{2\pi}{b}\right]$.

Notice that if $a = 1$ and $b = 1$, then we have the equation $y = \sin x$. By the formulas given in the definition, the amplitude is $|a| = |-1| = 1$ and the period is $\frac{2\pi}{b} = \frac{2\pi}{1} = 2\pi$. This coincides with the previously known results: the period of the sine function is 2π and the range of the sine function is $\{y \mid -1 \leq y \leq 1\}$, telling us that the minimum value of the sine function is -1 and the maximum value is 1.

Definition. The graph of $g(x) = a \cos bx$, where $a \neq 0$ and $b > 0$, is called a **cosine curve**. The **amplitude** of g is $|a|$ and the **period** of g is $\frac{2\pi}{b}$.

The amplitude of $g(x) = a \cos bx$ tells us that the graph of g will have a maximum value of $|a|$ and a minimum value of $-|a|$. The period of g tells us that the x-values of one cycle of the cosine curve will lie in the interval $\left[0, \frac{2\pi}{b}\right]$.

If $a = 1$ and $b = 1$, then we have the equation $y = \cos x$. Again, the amplitude is $|a| = |-1| = 1$ and the period is $\frac{2\pi}{b} = \frac{2\pi}{1} = 2\pi$. This coincides with the previously known results for the cosine function: it has period 2π and range $\{y \mid -1 \leq y \leq 1\}$.

Definition. The sine curves and cosine curves, collectively, are called **sinusoidal curves**.

By definition, the graph of any equation of the form $y = a \sin bx$ or $y = a \cos bx$, where $a \neq 0$ and $b > 0$, is a sinusoidal curve.

Examples. Find the amplitude and period of each function and sketch its graph.

1) $f(x) = 3 \sin 2x$

We have $a = 3$ and $b = 2$. The amplitude is $|3| = 3$ and the period is $\frac{2\pi}{b} = \frac{2\pi}{2} = \pi$. Now, the x-values of one cycle of the graph of f will lie in the interval $[0, \pi]$. Let's divide this interval into four **subintervals** of equal length (why this is done will soon be apparent). The length of each subinterval will be $\frac{\pi}{4}$ and our intervals are:

$$\left[0, \frac{\pi}{4}\right], \ \left[\frac{\pi}{4}, \frac{\pi}{2}\right], \ \left[\frac{\pi}{2}, \frac{3\pi}{4}\right], \text{ and } \left[\frac{3\pi}{4}, \pi\right].$$

Five major points on the cycle which come from using the endpoints of these intervals as the x-values are

$$(0, 0), \ \left(\frac{\pi}{4}, 3\right), \ \left(\frac{\pi}{2}, 0\right), \ \left(\frac{3\pi}{4}, -3\right), \text{ and } (\pi, 0).$$

The graph is given below.

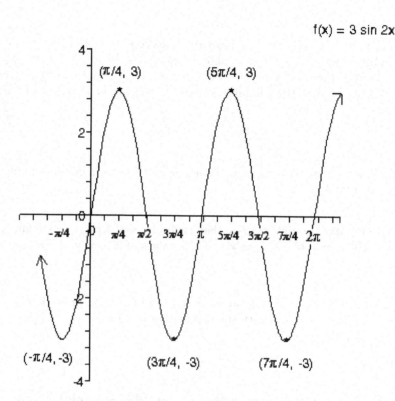

f(x) = 3 sin 2x

Notice how the x-axis is labeled by using increments of $\frac{\pi}{4}$, which was the length of each subinterval.

If the period of $y = a \sin bx$ **or** $y = a \cos bx$ **is** $\dfrac{2\pi}{b}$, **then the length of each subinterval is**

$$\frac{2\pi}{b} \div 4 = \frac{2\pi}{4b} = \frac{\pi}{2b}.$$

In this example, we have $\frac{\pi}{2b} = \frac{\pi}{2(2)} = \frac{\pi}{4}$ as expected.

2) $y = -2 \cos \frac{1}{2}x$

We have $a = -2$ and $b = \frac{1}{2}$. The amplitude is $|-2| = 2$ and the period is $\frac{2\pi}{\frac{1}{2}} = 4\pi$. The x-values of one cycle of the graph will lie in the interval $[0, 4\pi]$. If we divide this interval into four subintervals of equal length, then each subinterval will have length $\frac{\pi}{2b} = \frac{\pi}{2(\frac{1}{2})} = \pi$. Our intervals will be:

$$[0, \pi], \ [\pi, 2\pi], \ [2\pi, 3\pi], \ \text{and} \ [3\pi, 4\pi].$$

Five major points on the cycle which come from using the endpoints of these intervals as the x-values are

$$(0, -2), \ (\pi, 0), \ (2\pi, 2), \ (3\pi, 0), \ \text{and} \ (4\pi, -2).$$

The graph is given below.

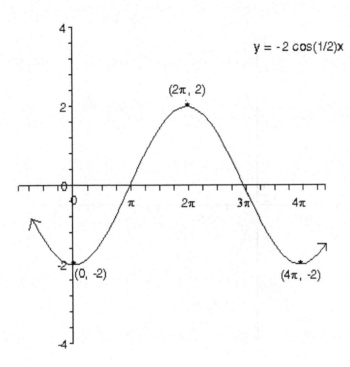

$$y = -2 \cos(1/2)x$$

Once again, notice how the x-axis is labeled by using increments of π, which was the length of each subinterval. Furthermore, the graph of $y = -2 \cos \frac{1}{2} x$ is a reflection of $y = 2 \cos \frac{1}{2} x$ about the x-axis.

3) $g(x) = \frac{1}{2} \sin(-\pi x)$

To begin with, let's rewrite our equation as

$$y = \underbrace{\frac{1}{2} \sin(-\pi x) = -\frac{1}{2} \sin \pi x}_{\sin(-\theta) = -\sin \theta}.$$

We have $a = -\frac{1}{2}$ and $b = \pi$. The amplitude is $\left| -\frac{1}{2} \right| = \frac{1}{2}$ and the period is $\frac{2\pi}{b} = \frac{2\pi}{\pi} = 2$. The x-values of one cycle of the graph of g will lie in the interval $[0,\ 2]$. Let's divide this interval into four subintervals of equal length. The length of each subinterval will be $\frac{\pi}{2b} = \frac{\pi}{2(\pi)} = \frac{1}{2}$ and our intervals are:

$$\left[0,\ \frac{1}{2}\right],\quad \left[\frac{1}{2},\ 1\right],\quad \left[1,\ \frac{3}{2}\right],\ \text{and}\ \left[\frac{3}{2},\ 2\right].$$

Five major points on the cycle which come from using the endpoints of these intervals as the x-values are

$$(0,\ 0),\quad \left(\frac{1}{2},\ -\frac{1}{2}\right),\quad (1,\ 0),\quad \left(\frac{3}{2},\ \frac{1}{2}\right),\ \text{and}\ (2,\ 0).$$

The graph is given below.

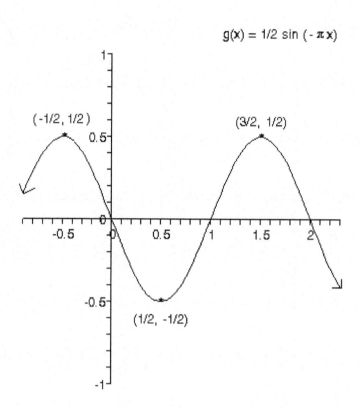

$g(x) = 1/2 \sin(-\pi x)$

The x-axis is labeled by using increments of $\frac{1}{2}$, which was the length of each subinterval. The graph of $y = -\frac{1}{2}\sin \pi x$ is the reflection of the graph of $y = \frac{1}{2}\sin \pi x$ about the x-axis.

Try These (Set 2): Find the amplitude and period of each function. Sketch the graph of each.

1) $y = 2\sin\frac{1}{2}x$ 2) $f(x) = -\cos 2\pi x$

We have seen that the graph of $y = a\sin bx$, where $a \neq 0$ and $b > 0$ has amplitude $|a|$ and period $\frac{2\pi}{b}$. If we graph one cycle of the sine curve from $x = 0$ to $x = \frac{2\pi}{b}$, we will obtain the graph in Figure (a) on the next page. Let's now graph $y = a\sin(bx - c)$, where $a \neq 0$, $b > 0$, and $c > 0$. Observe that

$$y = a\sin(bx - c) = a\sin\left[b\left(x - \frac{c}{b}\right)\right].$$

This means that we can obtain the graph of $y = a\sin(bx - c)$ by **shifting** the graph of $y = a\sin bx$ to **the right** by $\frac{c}{b}$ units, since we are subtracting $\frac{c}{b}$ from x. As Figure (b) on the next page shows, one cycle of the curve for $y = a\sin(bx - c)$ begins at $x = \frac{c}{b}$ and ends at $x = \frac{2\pi}{b} + \frac{c}{b}$. We call the number $\frac{c}{b}$ the **phase shift** of the graph of $y = a\sin(bx - c)$. Note that if $c < 0$, then the graph of $y = a\sin(bx - c)$ is obtained by **shifting** the graph of $y = a\sin bx$ **to the left** by $\left|\frac{c}{b}\right|$ units (why?). In this case, one cycle of the curve will begin at $x = -\left|\frac{c}{b}\right| = \frac{c}{b}$ and end at $x = \frac{2\pi}{b} - \left|\frac{c}{b}\right| = \frac{2\pi}{b} + \frac{c}{b}$.

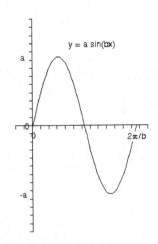

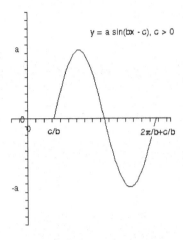

The same is true for the graph of $y = a \cos(bx - c)$, where $a \neq 0$, $b > 0$, and $c > 0$. If we graph one cycle of the cosine curve from $x = 0$ to $x = \frac{2\pi}{b}$, we will obtain the graph in Figure (a) below. The graph $y = a \cos(bx - c)$, where $a \neq 0$, $b > 0$ and $c > 0$, is obtained by **shifting** the graph of $y = a \cos bx$ **to the right** by $\frac{c}{b}$ units. Once again, this is due to the fact that

$$y = a \cos(bx - c) = a \cos\left[b\left(x - \frac{c}{b}\right)\right]$$

and we are subtracting $\frac{c}{b}$ from x, causing this type of shift to take place. As Figure (b) below shows, one cycle of the curve for $y = a \cos(bx - c)$ begins at $x = \frac{c}{b}$ and ends at $x = \frac{2\pi}{b} + \frac{c}{b}$. The number $\frac{c}{b}$ is called the **phase shift** of the graph of $y = a \cos(bx - c)$. If $c < 0$, then the graph of $y = a \cos(bx - c)$ is obtained by **shifting** the graph of $y = a \cos bx$ **to the left** by $\left|\frac{c}{b}\right|$ units. In this case, one cycle of the curve will begin at $x = -\left|\frac{c}{b}\right| = \frac{c}{b}$ and end at $x = \frac{2\pi}{b} - \left|\frac{c}{b}\right| = \frac{2\pi}{b} + \frac{c}{b}$.

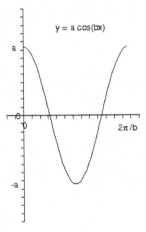

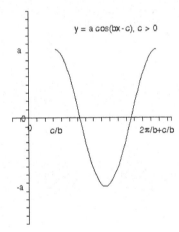

Let's summarize this information:

For the graphs of $y = a \sin(bx - c)$ or $y = a \cos(bx - c)$, where $a \neq 0$, $b > 0$, and c is any real number,

the amplitude is $|a|$,   **the period is $\frac{2\pi}{b}$,**   **and the phase shift is $\dfrac{c}{b}$.**

The phase shift is to the **right** if $c > 0$ and to the **left** if $c < 0$.

Examples. Find the amplitude, period, and phase shift of each function, then sketch its graph.

1) $y = 2\sin(3x - \pi)$

If we compare $y = 2\sin(3x - \pi)$ to $y = a\sin(bx - c)$, we see that $a = 2$, $b = 3$, and $c = \pi$. Therefore, the amplitude is $|a| = |2| = 2$, the period is $\frac{2\pi}{b} = \frac{2\pi}{3}$, and the phase shift is $\frac{c}{b} = \frac{\pi}{3}$. One cycle of the graph will begin at $x = \frac{c}{b} = \frac{\pi}{3}$ and end at $x = \frac{2\pi}{b} + \frac{c}{b} = \frac{2\pi}{3} + \frac{\pi}{3} = \pi$. Now, let's divide the interval $\left[\frac{\pi}{3}, \pi\right]$ into four subintervals of equal length. As we have seen before, each subinterval will have length $\frac{\pi}{2b} = \frac{\pi}{2(3)} = \frac{\pi}{6}$. Our intervals will be:

$$\left[\frac{\pi}{3}, \frac{\pi}{2}\right], \ \left[\frac{\pi}{2}, \frac{2\pi}{3}\right], \ \left[\frac{2\pi}{3}, \frac{5\pi}{6}\right], \text{ and } \left[\frac{5\pi}{6}, \pi\right].$$

Five major points on the cycle, which come from using the endpoints of these intervals as the x-values, are

$$\left(\frac{\pi}{3}, 0\right), \ \left(\frac{\pi}{2}, 2\right), \ \left(\frac{2\pi}{3}, 0\right), \ \left(\frac{5\pi}{6}, -2\right), \text{ and } (\pi, 0).$$

The graph is given below.

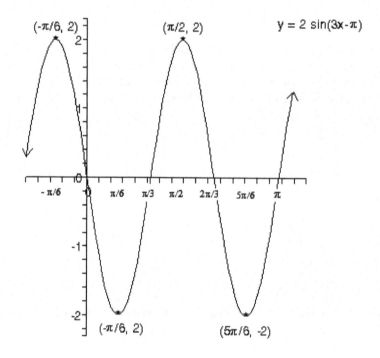

2) $y = \frac{1}{4}\cos\left(\frac{2}{3}x + 3\pi\right)$

Comparing $y = \frac{1}{4}\cos\left(\frac{2}{3}x + 3\pi\right)$ to $y = a\cos(bx - c)$, we see that $a = \frac{1}{4}$, $b = \frac{2}{3}$, and $c = -3\pi$. Therefore, the amplitude is $|a| = \left|\frac{1}{4}\right| = \frac{1}{4}$, the period is $\frac{2\pi}{b} = \frac{2\pi}{\frac{2}{3}} = 3\pi$, and the phase shift is $\frac{c}{b} = \frac{-3\pi}{\frac{2}{3}} = \frac{-9\pi}{2}$. One cycle of the graph will begin at $x = \frac{c}{b} = -\frac{9\pi}{2}$ and end at $x = \frac{2\pi}{b} + \frac{c}{b} = 3\pi - \frac{9\pi}{2} = -\frac{3\pi}{2}$. Next, we will divide the interval $\left[-\frac{9\pi}{2}, -\frac{3\pi}{2}\right]$ into four subintervals of equal length. Each subinterval will have length $\frac{\pi}{2b} = \frac{\pi}{2\left(\frac{2}{3}\right)} = \frac{3\pi}{4}$. Our intervals will be:

$$\left[-\frac{9\pi}{2}, -\frac{15\pi}{4}\right], \ \left[-\frac{15\pi}{4}, -3\pi\right], \ \left[-3\pi, -\frac{9\pi}{4}\right], \text{ and } \left[-\frac{9\pi}{4}, -\frac{3\pi}{2}\right].$$

Five major points on the cycle, which come from using the endpoints of these intervals as the x-values, are:

$$\left(-\frac{9\pi}{2}, \frac{1}{4}\right), \ \left(-\frac{15\pi}{4}, 0\right), \ \left(-3\pi, -\frac{1}{4}\right), \ \left(-\frac{9\pi}{4}, 0\right), \text{ and } \left(-\frac{3\pi}{2}, \frac{1}{4}\right).$$

The graph is given below.

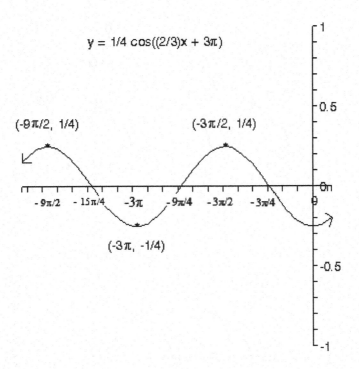

3) $y = -3\cos(\pi x - 2)$

Comparing $y = -3\cos(\pi x - 2)$ to $y = a\cos(bx - c)$, we see that $a = -3$, $b = \pi$, and $c = 2$. Therefore, the amplitude is $|a| = |-3| = 3$, the period is $\frac{2\pi}{b} = \frac{2\pi}{\pi} = 2$, and the phase shift is $\frac{c}{b} = \frac{2}{\pi}$. One cycle of the graph will begin at $x = \frac{c}{b} = \frac{2}{\pi}$ and end at $x = \frac{2\pi}{b} + \frac{c}{b} = 2 + \frac{2}{\pi} = \frac{2\pi+2}{\pi}$. Now we'll divide the interval $\left[\frac{2}{\pi}, \frac{2\pi+2}{\pi}\right]$ into four subintervals of equal length as before. Each subinterval will have length $\frac{\pi}{2b} = \frac{\pi}{2\pi} = \frac{1}{2}$. Our intervals will be:

$$\left[\frac{2}{\pi}, \frac{\pi+4}{2\pi}\right], \ \left[\frac{\pi+4}{2\pi}, \frac{\pi+2}{\pi}\right], \ \left[\frac{\pi+2}{\pi}, \frac{3\pi+4}{2\pi}\right], \text{ and } \left[\frac{3\pi+4}{2\pi}, \frac{2\pi+2}{\pi}\right].$$

Five major points on the cycle, which come from using the endpoints of these intervals as the x-values, are

$$\left(\frac{2}{\pi}, -3\right), \ \left(\frac{\pi+4}{2\pi}, 0\right), \ \left(\frac{\pi+2}{\pi}, 3\right), \ \left(\frac{3\pi+4}{2\pi}, 0\right), \text{ and } \left(\frac{2\pi+2}{\pi}, -3\right).$$

The graph is given below.

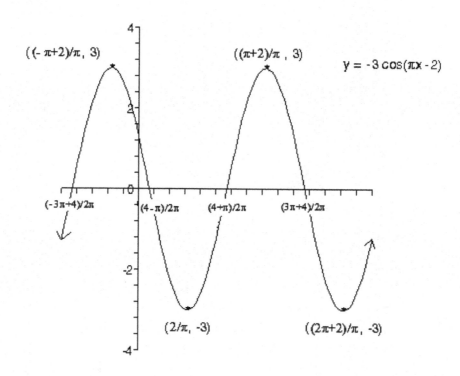

$$((-\pi+2)/\pi,\ 3)$$ $$((\pi+2)/\pi,\ 3)$$

$$y = -3\cos(\pi x - 2)$$

$$(-3\pi+4)/2\pi$$ $$(4-\pi)/2\pi$$ $$(4+\pi)/2\pi$$ $$(3\pi+4)/2\pi$$

$$(2/\pi,\ -3)$$ $$((2\pi+2)/\pi,\ -3)$$

Try These (Set 3): Find the amplitude, period, and phase shift of each function. Sketch the graph of each.

1) $y = \sin\left(\frac{1}{2}x - \pi\right)$

2) $y = -2\cos\left(2x + \frac{\pi}{3}\right)$

Exercise 5

In Exercises 1-12, graph each function on the given interval.

1. $f(x) = \sin x,\ 0 \le x \le 2\pi$

2. $f(\theta) = \sin\theta,\ -\pi \le \theta \le \pi$

3. $y = \tan\theta,\ 0 \le \theta \le 2\pi,\ \theta \ne \frac{\pi}{2}, \frac{3\pi}{2}$

4. $y = \sec\theta,\ 0 \le \theta \le 2\pi,\ \theta \ne \frac{\pi}{2}, \frac{3\pi}{2}$

5. $y = \csc x,\ 0 < x < 2\pi,\ x \ne \pi$

6. $h(x) = \cot x,\ 0 < x < \pi$

7. $h(\theta) = \cos\theta,\ -\pi \le \theta \le \pi$

8. $g(x) = \cos x,\ 0 \le x \le 2\pi$

9. $g(t) = \tan t,\ -\frac{\pi}{2} < t < \frac{\pi}{2}$

10. $y = \csc x,\ -\pi < x < \pi,\ x \ne 0$

11. $f(\alpha) = \sec\alpha,\ -\pi \le \alpha \le \pi,\ \alpha \ne \pm\frac{\pi}{2}$

12. $g(\beta) = \cot\beta,\ -\pi < \beta < \pi,\ \beta \ne 0$

In Exercises 13-32, graph each function.

13. $f(x) = \sin\left(x + \frac{\pi}{4}\right)$

14. $g(x) = \cos\left(x - \frac{\pi}{2}\right)$

15. $y = \tan\left(\theta - \frac{\pi}{2}\right)$

16. $y = \sin\left(\theta - \frac{3\pi}{2}\right)$

17. $f(x) = \cos x + 1$

18. $g(\theta) = \tan\theta - 2$

19. $y = \sin x - 3$

20. $y = \sec x + 2$

21. $f(x) = -\cos x$

22. $g(x) = -\sin x$

23. $y = -\csc\alpha$

24. $y = -\cot\alpha$

25. $f(\theta) = 2\sin(\theta - \pi)$ 26. $h(\theta) = 3\cos(\theta + \pi)$ 27. $y = -4\sec\left(x + \dfrac{3\pi}{2}\right)$

28. $y = -2\csc\left(x - \dfrac{\pi}{2}\right)$ 29. $y = \cos(2\pi x)$ 30. $y = \sin(2\pi x)$

31. $h(x) = \tan(\pi x)$ 32. $g(x) = \cot(\pi x)$

In Exercises 33-44, find the period and amplitude of each function. Graph at least one period of each function.

33. $y = \sin 2x$ 34. $y = \cos 3x$ 35. $y = 2\cos\dfrac{1}{2}x$ 36. $y = 3\sin\dfrac{1}{2}x$

37. $f(x) = \dfrac{1}{3}\sin 4x$ 38. $g(x) = \dfrac{2}{5}\cos 2x$ 39. $f(\theta) = 3\cos(\pi\theta)$ 40. $h(\theta) = \cos(2\pi\theta)$

41. $y = -2\cos 2x$ 42. $y = -3\sin 3x$ 43. $f(t) = -\sin\left(\dfrac{\pi}{2}t\right)$ 44. $g(t) = -\cos\left(\dfrac{\pi}{2}t\right)$

In Exercises 45-56, find the period, phase shift, and amplitude of each function. Graph at least one period of each function.

45. $y = \sin(2x - \pi)$ 46. $y = \cos(3x - \pi)$ 47. $y = 2\cos(4x + \pi)$

48. $y = 3\sin\left(2x + \dfrac{\pi}{2}\right)$ 49. $f(x) = -\dfrac{1}{4}\sin\left(3x - \dfrac{\pi}{2}\right)$ 50. $g(x) = -\dfrac{3}{5}\cos\left(2x + \dfrac{\pi}{3}\right)$

51. $f(x) = 2\sin(\pi x + 1)$ 52. $g(x) = 4\cos(\pi x + 2)$ 53. $f(\theta) = -\cos(2\pi\theta + 2)$

54. $f(\theta) = -\sin(2\pi\theta - 4)$ 55. $y = \cos\left(-2x + \dfrac{\pi}{2}\right)$ 56. $y = \sin\left(-2x + \dfrac{\pi}{2}\right)$

Chapter 6:   Trigonometric Identities and Formulas

In this chapter, we will learn about trigonometric identities and formulas. In order to verify a trigonometric identity or to derive a trigonometric formula, we need to know how to do algebraic manipulations with trigonometric expressions. This will be covered in Section 6.1. In Section 6.2, we will review the fundamental identities and the properties of negative angles. Several formulas will be discussed in Sections 6.3 through 6.6. These formulas include the sum and difference formulas, the double-angle formulas, the half-angle formulas, the product-to-sum formulas, and the sum-to-product formulas.

Section 6.1 Algebraic Operations of Trigonometric Expressions

It is often the case that our knowledge of algebra will come in handy when we want to work with trigonometric expressions. For example, suppose we want to add the trigonometric expressions $2\sin\theta$ and $3\sin\theta$ and obtain a single expression containing $\sin\theta$. Can we add these together? If so, how? In order to answer these questions, we need to resort to algebra. We know that we can add the monomials $2x$ and $3x$ to obtain $5x$. In the same way, we can add the trigonometric expressions $2\sin\theta$ and $3\sin\theta$ to obtain $5\sin\theta$ and write this as

$$2\sin\theta + 3\sin\theta = 5\sin\theta.$$

Notice that the equation $2\sin\theta + 3\sin\theta = 5\sin\theta$ is identical to $2x + 3x = 5x$, with x replaced by $\sin\theta$. Similarly, we can subtract $3\cos 5x$ from $12\cos 5x$ the same way we would subtract $3y$ from $12y$.

$$\underbrace{12\cos 5x - 3\cos 5x}_{12y-3y} = \underbrace{9\cos 5x}_{9y}$$

Observe that this method of combining works provided that the same trigonometric functions appear, as well as their respective angles. For example,

$$\underbrace{4\tan A + 3\tan A = 7\tan A}_{\text{same as } 4x+3x=7x}, \text{ but } \underbrace{4\tan A + 3\tan 2A}_{\text{same as } 4x+3y} \neq 7\tan 3A.$$

The reason why $4\tan A$ and $3\tan 2A$ don't combine in the way we've seen is because the angles are different (A and $2A$).

Here's another example of algebra in action. Suppose that we want to combine

$$\frac{1}{\sin x} + \cos x$$

into a single fraction. As we know, we can combine two fractions if they have common denominators. Observe that

$$\frac{1}{\sin x} + \cos x = \frac{1}{\sin x} + \frac{\cos x}{1}\left(\frac{\sin x}{\sin x}\right) \qquad \text{(The l.c.d. is } \sin x.)$$
$$= \frac{1 + \cos x \sin x}{\sin x}.$$

And we now have a single fraction. Whether or not this is reduced to lowest terms will be answered later. The idea that you need to keep in mind is that doing algebra with trigonometric expressions is no different than what you do with variables. Notice that we could think of

$$\frac{1}{\sin x} + \cos x \quad \text{as} \quad \frac{1}{A} + B, \quad \frac{1}{m} + n, \quad \text{or} \quad \frac{1}{s} + t.$$

And the method of combining is the same for each: find a common denominator, rewrite the second fraction with that denominator, and add the numerators together.

Here is a strategy that you should keep in mind when working with trigonometric expressions. After you get enough practice, this strategy will become embedded in your brain and you will be able to work with trigonometric expressions without resorting to variables.

> 1. When you are faced with a problem which contains trigonometric expressions, think of how the problem would be done if the expressions were variables instead.
>
> 2. Work out the problem with the variables first.
>
> 3. After the problem with the variables is done, change the variables back to the trigonometric expressions.

Adding and Subtracting Trigonometric Expressions

If two trigonometric expressions are **like terms** (that is, they contain the **same trigonometric terms**, the **same angle terms**, and the **same exponents**), we can combine them into a single trigonometric expression by adding their **coefficients**. For example, $6\sin^2 x$ and $3\sin^2 x$ are like terms because they both contain the trigonometric term $\sin^2 x$. Notice that the angle term, x, and the same exponent, 2, appear in both expressions. We can add $6\sin^2 x$ and $3\sin^2 x$ by adding the coefficients, 6 and 3, and keeping the trigonometric term the same:

$$\underbrace{6\sin^2 x + 3\sin^2 x}_{\text{Add the coefficients.}} = 9\sin^2 x$$

Observe that the method for adding $6\sin^2 x$ and $3\sin^2 x$ is the same as for adding $6y^2$ and $3y^2$:

$$6y^2 + 3y^2 = 9y^2$$

As we know from algebra, not all expressions are like terms. The same is true for trigonometric expressions. For example, the following expressions cannot be combined into a single trigonometric expression by using the method discussed:

$$\underbrace{\sin A + \cos A}_{\text{different trig. terms}} , \underbrace{4\tan 3\theta + 2\tan 5\theta}_{\text{different angle terms}}, \underbrace{\csc^2 \alpha + 8\csc \alpha - 1}_{\text{different exponents}}, \text{ and } \underbrace{6\cot (3t + 2) - 11\cot^3 (3t - 2)}_{\text{different angle terms and exponents}}$$

Notice how each of these examples look like algebraic expressions which do not combine into a single expression:

$$\underbrace{\sin A + \cos A}_{\text{Looks like } x+y.}, \underbrace{4\tan 3\theta + 2\tan 5\theta}_{\text{Looks like } 4x+2y.}, \underbrace{\csc^2 \alpha + 8\csc \alpha - 1}_{\text{Looks like } x^2+8x-1.}, \text{ and } \underbrace{6\cot (3t + 2) - 11\cot^3 (3t - 2)}_{\text{Looks like } 6x-11y^3.}$$

Let's do some examples with combining trigonometric expressions. Several 'bewares' are given to remind us of common mistakes. Be careful!

Examples. Combine into a single trigonometric expression (if possible).

1) $\underbrace{7\cos A + 4\cos A = 11\cos A}_{\text{same as } 7x+4x=11x}$

2) $\underbrace{-3\tan 2\theta + 11\tan 2\theta = 8\tan 2\theta}_{\text{same as } -3x+11x=8x}$

3) $\underbrace{9\sin 5\alpha - 16\sin 5\alpha + \sin 5\alpha = -6\sin 5\alpha}_{\text{same as } 9x-16x+x=-6x}$

4) $\underbrace{-6\csc (3\beta - 1) - 7\csc (3\beta - 1) = -13\csc (3\beta - 1)}_{\text{same as } -6x-7x=-13x}$

5) $\underbrace{12\sin t \cos 2t + 5\sin t \cos 2t = 17\sin t \cos 2t}_{\text{same as } 12xy+5xy=17xy}$

6) $\underbrace{-\cot^2 \theta \sin \theta + 11\sin \theta \cot^2 \theta = 10\cot^2 \theta \sin \theta}_{\text{same as } -x^2y+11yx^2=10x^2y}$

7) $\underbrace{-8\sec\left(7\beta+3\right)-\left(-8\sec\left(7\beta+3\right)\right)}=-8\sec\left(7\beta+3\right)+8\sec\left(7\beta+3\right)=0$
   same as $-8x-(-8x)=-8x+8x=0$

8) $\underbrace{\sec t+3}$ do not combine since $\sec t$ and 3 are not like terms.
   same as $x+3$

BEWARE: $\sec t+3\neq\sec\left(t+3\right)$

$\sec t+3\neq 3\sec t$

9) $\underbrace{4\sin A-5\cos A}$ do not combine since $4\sin A$ and $5\cos A$ have different trigonometric terms.
   same as $4x-5y$

BEWARE: $4\sin A-5\cos A\neq-\sin A\cos A$

10) $\underbrace{\sin^2 x+5\sin x}$ do not combine since $\sin^2 x$ and $5\sin x$ have different exponents.
    same as y^2+5y

BEWARE: $\sin^2 x+5\sin x\neq 6\sin^3 x$

11) $\underbrace{\cot\left(\alpha^2+\alpha+1\right)-\cot\alpha}$ do not combine since $\cot\left(\alpha^2+\alpha+1\right)$ and $\cot\alpha$ have different angle terms.
    same as $x-y$

BEWARE: $\cot\left(\alpha^2+\alpha+1\right)-\cot\alpha\neq\cot\left[\left(\alpha^2+\alpha+1\right)-\alpha\right]$

12) $\underbrace{9\sin^2\theta\cos^2\theta+7\sin^3\theta\cos^2\theta}$ do not combine since $\sin^2\theta$ appears in the first term and not the second
    same as $9x^2y^2+7x^3y^2$
term.

BEWARE: $9\sin^2\theta\cos^2\theta+7\sin^3\theta\cos^2\theta\neq 16\sin^5\theta\cos^4\theta$

Examples. Combine.

1) $\underbrace{\left(3\sin^2 A + 2\sin A - 8\right) + \left(4\sin^2 A - \sin A - 9\right) = 7\sin^2 A + \sin A - 17}_{\text{same as }(3x^2+2x-8)+(4x^2-x-9)=7x^2+x-17}$

2) $\underbrace{\left(\cos 3y - 5\cos 2y + 2\right) + \left(2\cos 3y + 2\cos 2y - 12\right) = 3\cos 3y - 3\cos 2y - 10}_{\text{same as }(x-5z+2)+(2x+2z-12)=3x-3z-10}$

Notice that we cannot combine $\cos 3y$ and $\cos 2y$ since they do not have the same angle term.

 BEWARE: $\cos 3y + \cos 2y \neq \cos 5y$

3) $\underbrace{\left(\tan^3 \theta + 2\tan^2 \theta + 2\right) + \left(3\tan^3 \theta - 9\tan^2 \theta + 8\right) = 4\tan^3 \theta - 7\tan^2 \theta + 10}_{\text{same as }(x^3+2x^2+2)+(3x^3-9x^2+8)=4x^3-7x^2+10}$

4) $(\tan \theta - \sec \theta - 4) - (\tan \theta - 7\sec \theta + 6) = \tan \theta - \sec \theta - 4 - \tan \theta + 7\sec \theta - 6 = 6\sec \theta - 10$

5) $\underbrace{\left(\cos^2 2y - 3\cos 2y\right) - \left(-4\cos^2 2y + \cos 2y\right) = \cos^2 2y - 3\cos 2y + 4\cos^2 2y - \cos 2y = 5\cos^2 2y - 4\cos 2y}_{\text{same as }(x^2-3x)-(-4x^2+x)=x^2-3x+4x^2-x=5x^2-4x}$

6) $\left(2\sin \theta \sin (\theta + 1) + 5\sin \theta \sin^2 (\theta + 1)\right) - \left(6\sin \theta \sin (\theta + 1) - 3\sin \theta \sin^2 (\theta + 1)\right)$
$= 2\sin \theta \sin (\theta + 1) + 5\sin \theta \sin^2 (\theta + 1) - 6\sin \theta \sin (\theta + 1) + 3\sin \theta \sin^2 (\theta + 1)$
$= -4\sin \theta \sin (\theta + 1) + 8\sin \theta \sin^2 (\theta + 1)$

 BEWARE: $-4\sin \theta \sin (\theta + 1) + 8\sin \theta \sin^2 (\theta + 1) \neq 4\sin \theta \sin^3 (\theta + 1)$

Try These (Set 1): Combine.

1) $(\sin x + 2\cos x) + (5\sin x - 11\cos x)$ 2) $\left(4\sin^2 A - 6\sin A + 10\right) + \left(-7\sin^2 A + \sin A - 2\right)$

3) $(3\tan 2\theta - 5) - (6\tan 2\theta - 3)$ 4) $\left(-2\csc^2 (x + 1) + 5\csc (x - 1)\right) - \left(-4\csc (x + 1) + 3\csc^2 (x + 1)\right)$

Multiplying and Dividing Trigonometric Expressions

The rules for multiplication and division of trigonometric expressions are the same as for polynomials.

Examples. Multiply.

1) $\underbrace{(2\cos \theta)\left(4\cos^2 \theta\right) = 8\cos^3 \theta}_{\text{same as }(2x)(4x^2)=8x^3}$ 2) $\underbrace{\left(-5\sin^3 x\right)\left(3\sin^4 x\right) = -15\sin^7 x}_{\text{same as }(-5y^3)(3y^4)=-15y^7}$

3) $\underbrace{\left(6\tan^2\alpha\right)\left(-9\sin^3\alpha\right) = -54\tan^2\alpha\sin^3\alpha}$

same as $(6x^2)(-9y^5)=-54x^2y^3$

4) $\underbrace{\left(-2\sec\theta\right)\left(-4\sec 3\theta\right) = 8\sec\theta\sec 3\theta}$

same as $(-2x)(-4y)=8xy$

5) $\underbrace{2\sin x\left(2\sin x + 3\right) = 4\sin^2 x + 6\sin x}$

same as $2y(2y+3)=4y^2+6y$

6) $\underbrace{-7\cot^2\beta\left(\cot^2\beta + 4\cot\beta - 2\right) = -7\cot^4\beta - 28\cot^3\beta + 14\cot^2\beta}$

same as $-7x^2(x^2+4x-2)=-7x^4-28x^3+14x^2$

7) $\underbrace{\left(3\sec\alpha + 2\right)\left(4\sec\alpha - 5\right) = 12\sec^2\alpha - 15\sec\alpha + 8\sec\alpha - 10 = 12\sec^2\alpha - 7\sec\alpha - 10}$

same as $(3x+2)(4x-5)=12x^2-15x+8x-10$ by the FOIL method

8) $\underbrace{\left(2\tan 5y + 1\right)\left(7\tan 5y + 6\right) = 14\tan^2 5y + 12\tan 5y + 7\tan 5y + 6 = 14\tan^2 5y + 19\tan 5y + 6}$

same as $(2x+1)(7x+6)=14x^2+12x+7x+6$ by the FOIL method

9) $\underbrace{\left(\sin A + \cos A\right)\left(\sin A - \cos A\right) = \sin^2 A - \cos^2 A}$

same as $(x+y)(x-y)=x^2-y^2$

10) $\underbrace{\left(\csc\left(4x - 1\right) + 5\right)^2 = \csc^2\left(4x - 1\right) + 10\csc\left(4x - 1\right) + 25}$

same as $(y+5)^2=y^2+10y+25$

Examples. Divide.

1) $\underbrace{\dfrac{\sin^6 x}{\sin^4 x} = \sin^2 x}$

same as $\frac{y^6}{y^4}=y^2$

2) $\underbrace{\dfrac{\tan^8 A\cos^7 B}{\tan^5 A\cos^2 B} = \tan^3 A\cos^5 B}$

same as $\frac{x^8y^7}{x^5y^2}=x^3y^5$

3) $\underbrace{\dfrac{\cot^3 4\theta}{\cot^2 4\theta} = \cot 4\theta}$

same as $\frac{x^3}{x^2}=x$

4) $\underbrace{\dfrac{\cos^4\beta\cos^3 2\beta}{\cos^3\beta\cos 2\beta} = \cos\beta\cos^2 2\beta}$

same as $\frac{x^4y^3}{x^3y}=xy^2$

5) $\underbrace{\dfrac{20\tan y + 15\sin y}{5} = \dfrac{20\tan y}{5} + \dfrac{15\sin y}{5} = 4\tan y + 3\sin y}$

same as $\frac{20a+15b}{5}=\frac{20a}{5}+\frac{15b}{5}$

6) $\underbrace{\dfrac{\sec^4 3A - 4\sec^3 3A}{\sec^2 3A} = \dfrac{\sec^4 3A}{\sec^2 3A} - \dfrac{4\sec^3 3A}{\sec^2 3A} = \sec^2 3A - 4\sec 3A}$

same as $\frac{x^4-4x^3}{x^2}=\frac{x^4}{x^2}-\frac{4x^3}{x^2}$

7) $\underbrace{\dfrac{\sin^3 B\tan B - 2\sin B\tan^2 B}{\sin B\tan B} = \dfrac{\sin^3 B\tan B}{\sin B\tan B} - \dfrac{2\sin B\tan^2 B}{\sin B\tan B} = \sin^2 B - 2\tan B}$

same as $\frac{x^3y-2xy^2}{xy}=\frac{x^3y}{xy}-\frac{2xy^2}{xy}=x^2-2y$

8) $\dfrac{\csc^2 y + 4\csc y + 2}{\csc y + 3} = \csc y + 1 - \dfrac{1}{\csc y + 3}$

If you think of this as $\dfrac{x^2 + 4x + 2}{x + 3}$ (replacing $\csc y$ by x in the original problem), the division problem goes as follows:

$$
\begin{array}{r}
x+1 \text{ R } -1 \\
x+3\overline{)\,x^2 + 4x + 2} \\
-\ \ x^2 + 3x \\
\hline
x + 2 \\
-\ \ \ \ \ \ x + 3 \\
\hline
-1
\end{array}
$$

Therefore, $\dfrac{x^2 + 4x + 2}{x + 3} = x + 1 + \dfrac{-1}{x + 3}$. Substituting $\csc y$ for x gives us our answer.

Try These (Set 2): Multiply or divide.

1) $\left(2\sin^2\theta \cos^3\theta\right)\left(-12\sin\theta \cos^5\theta\right)$ 2) $(3\cos\beta - 4)(2\cos\beta - 1)$

3) $\dfrac{16\tan^2 x + 8\tan x}{4\tan x}$ 4) $\dfrac{28\csc^3 A \sec^4 A - 7\csc^5 A \sec^2 A}{-7\csc^2 A \sec^2 A}$

Factoring Trigonometric Expressions

The methods of factoring which you have learned in algebra are used to factor trigonometric expressions.

Examples. Factor completely.

1) $\underbrace{\sin^2\theta - \sin\theta = \sin\theta\,(\sin\theta - 1)}_{\text{same as } x^2 - x = x(x-1)}$

2) $\underbrace{6\cos^2\alpha + 2\cos^3\alpha = 2\cos^2\alpha\,(3 + \cos\alpha)}_{\text{same as } 6x^2 + 2x^3 = 2x^2(3+x)}$

3) $\underbrace{\tan^2 A + \tan^2 A \sin A = \tan^2 A\,(1 + \sin A)}_{\text{same as } x^2 + x^2 y = x^2(1+y)}$

4) $\underbrace{\sec A \csc B + \sec^2 A \csc A = \sec A\,(\csc B + \sec A \csc A)}_{\text{same as } xy + x^2 z = x(y + xz)}$

5) $\underbrace{\sin^2 t - 9 = (\sin t + 3)(\sin t - 3)}_{\text{same as } x^2 - 9 = (x+3)(x-3)}$

6) $\underbrace{1 - \cot^2\theta = (1 + \cot\theta)(1 - \cot\theta)}_{\text{same as } 1 - x^2 = (1+x)(1-x)}$

7) $\underbrace{\tan^2\beta + 8\tan\beta + 12 = (\tan\beta + 6)(\tan\beta + 2)}_{\text{same as } x^2 + 8x + 12 = (x+6)(x+2)}$

8) $\underbrace{\csc^2 3x - \csc 3x - 6 = (\csc 3x + 2)(\csc 3x - 3)}_{\text{same as } y^2 - y - 6 = (y+2)(y-3)}$

9) $\underbrace{2\sec^2(A+1) + 3\sec(A+1) + 1 = (2\sec(A+1) + 1)(\sec(A+1) + 1)}_{\text{same as } 2x^2 + 3x + 1 = (2x+1)(x+1)}$

10) $\underbrace{9\sin^2 x - 12\sin x + 4 = (3\sin x - 2)(3\sin x - 2) = (3\sin x - 2)^2}_{\text{same as } 9y^2 - 12y + 4 = (3y-2)(3y-2)}$

11) $2\tan^2\alpha - 128 = 2\left(\tan^2\alpha - 64\right) = \underbrace{2(\tan\alpha + 8)(\tan\alpha - 8)}_{\text{same as } 2(x^2 - 64) = 2(x+8)(x-8)}$

12) $\underbrace{\cos^3 7t - \cos 7t = \cos 7t\left(\cos^2 7t - 1\right) = \cos 7t\,(\cos 7t + 1)(\cos 7t - 1)}_{\text{same as } x^3 - x = x(x^2 - 1) = x(x+1)(x-1)}$

Try These (Set 3): Factor completely.

1) $\tan^3 x + 6\tan x$ 2) $2\sin\theta \cos^2\theta - 3\sin^2\theta \cos\theta$ 3) $\csc^2\alpha - 2\csc\alpha - 63$

4) $\cot^2 A - \sin^2 A$ 5) $3\sin(3-x)\cos^2(5x-1) - 19\sin(3-x)\cos(5x-1) - 14\sin(3-x)$

Simplifying Fractions Which Contain Trigonometric Expressions

We will use factoring to simplify fractions which contain trigonometric expressions. As with rational expressions, we will use the following property:

> **Property:** If A, B, and C are trigonometric expressions and both B, $C \neq 0$, then $\dfrac{A\overset{1}{\cancel{C}}}{B\underset{1}{\cancel{C}}} = \dfrac{A}{B}$.

Examples. Simplify.

1) $\dfrac{3\sin^2\theta + 6\sin\theta}{\sin^3\theta + 2\sin^2\theta} = \dfrac{3\sin\theta\,(\sin\theta + 2)}{\sin^2\theta\,(\sin\theta + 2)} = \dfrac{3}{\sin\theta}$

  same as $\dfrac{3x^2 + 6x}{x^3 + 2x^2} = \dfrac{3x(x+2)}{x^2(x+2)} = \dfrac{3}{x}$

2) $\dfrac{4\tan^2 A + 8\tan A}{2\tan A \sec A} = \dfrac{\overset{2}{\cancel{4}}\tan A\,(\tan A + 2)}{\cancel{2}\tan A \sec A} = \dfrac{2\,(\tan A + 2)}{\sec A}$

  same as $\dfrac{4x^2 + 8x}{2xy} = \dfrac{4x(x+2)}{2xy} = \dfrac{2(x+2)}{y}$

3) $\dfrac{\cot^2\beta - 25}{\cot\beta - 5} = \dfrac{(\cot\beta + 5)(\cot\beta - 5)}{\cot\beta - 5} = \cot\beta + 5$

  same as $\dfrac{x^2 - 25}{x - 5} = \dfrac{(x+5)(x-5)}{x-5} = x+5$

4) $\dfrac{\cos x + 3}{\cos^2 x - 9} = \dfrac{\cos x + 3}{(\cos x + 3)(\cos x - 3)} = \dfrac{1}{\cos x - 3}$

  same as $\dfrac{y+3}{y^2 - 9} = \dfrac{y+3}{(y+3)(y-3)} = \dfrac{1}{y-3}$

5) $\dfrac{\sec^2 2\theta - \sin^2 2\theta}{\sin 2\theta - \sec 2\theta} = \dfrac{(\sec 2\theta + \sin 2\theta)(\sec 2\theta - \sin 2\theta)}{-1\,(\sin 2\theta - \sec 2\theta)} = -\,(\sec 2\theta + \sin 2\theta) = -\sec 2\theta - \sin 2\theta$

  same as $\dfrac{x^2 - y^2}{y - x} = \dfrac{(x+y)(x-y)}{-1(x-y)} = -(x+y)$

6) $\dfrac{\tan^2\left(t^2\right) + 9\tan\left(t^2\right) + 18}{\tan^2\left(t^2\right) - 2\tan\left(t^2\right) - 15} = \dfrac{\left(\tan\left(t^2\right) + 6\right)\left(\tan\left(t^2\right) + 3\right)}{\left(\tan\left(t^2\right) - 5\right)\left(\tan\left(t^2\right) + 3\right)} = \dfrac{\tan\left(t^2\right) + 6}{\tan\left(t^2\right) - 5}$

  same as $\dfrac{x^2 + 9x + 18}{x^2 - 2x - 15} = \dfrac{(x+6)(x+3)}{(x-5)(x+3)} = \dfrac{x+6}{x-5}$

Try These (Set 4): Simplify.

1) $\dfrac{6\cos^2 x - 9\cos x \sin x}{3\cos x \sin x}$

2) $\dfrac{\tan^2\theta - 4\tan\theta + 4}{\tan^2\theta - 14\tan\theta + 24}$

3) $\dfrac{5\sec^2\theta - \csc\theta \sec\theta}{25\sec^2\theta - 10\sec\theta \csc\theta + \csc^2\theta}$

Multiplying and Dividing Fractions Containing Trigonometric Expressions

Let's remind ourselves of how to multiply and divide fractions. Suppose A, B, C, and D are integers and both B, $D \neq 0$. Then $\dfrac{A}{B} \cdot \dfrac{C}{D} = \dfrac{AC}{BD}$. If $C \neq 0$ as well, then $\dfrac{A}{B} \div \dfrac{C}{D} = \dfrac{A}{B} \cdot \dfrac{D}{C} = \dfrac{AD}{BC}$. These same rules apply when A, B, C, and D are trigonometric expressions.

Examples. Multiply and simplify.

1) $\dfrac{\sin^2\theta \cos^3\theta}{8} \cdot \dfrac{\sin\theta \cos^4\theta}{3} = \dfrac{\left(\sin^2\theta \cos^3\theta\right)\left(\sin\theta \cos^4\theta\right)}{(8)(3)} = \dfrac{\sin^3\theta \cos^7\theta}{24}$

2) $\dfrac{\cot\alpha}{2\cot\alpha+4}\cdot\dfrac{6}{7\cot\alpha}=\dfrac{\cancel{\cot\alpha}}{\underset{1}{\cancel{2}}(\cot\alpha+2)}\cdot\dfrac{\overset{3}{\cancel{6}}}{7\cancel{\cot\alpha}}=\dfrac{3}{7(\cot\alpha+2)}$

3) $\dfrac{3\tan^3 x}{4\tan^2 x-1}\cdot\dfrac{2\tan x+1}{6\tan x}=\dfrac{\overset{1}{\cancel{3}}\tan^3 x}{\underset{1}{(\cancel{2\tan x+1})}(2\tan x-1)}\cdot\dfrac{\overset{1}{(\cancel{2\tan x+1})}}{\underset{2}{\cancel{6}}\tan x}$

$$=\dfrac{\tan^{\overset{2}{\cancel{3}}} x}{2\,\cancel{\tan x}\,(2\tan x-1)}=\dfrac{\tan^2 x}{2(2\tan x-1)}$$

4) $\dfrac{\sec^3 A-\sec^2 A-6\sec A}{8\sec^2 A-24\sec A}\cdot\dfrac{12\sec^2 A+12}{2\sec^3 A+2\sec A}=\dfrac{\sec A\left(\sec^2 A-\sec A-6\right)}{8\sec A(\sec A-3)}\cdot\dfrac{12\left(\sec^2 A+1\right)}{2\sec A\left(\sec^2 A+1\right)}$

$$=\dfrac{\cancel{\sec A}\,\cancel{(\sec A-3)}(\sec A+2)}{8\cancel{\sec A}\,\cancel{(\sec A-3)}}\cdot\dfrac{12\,\cancel{\left(\sec^2 A+1\right)}}{2\sec A\,\cancel{\left(\sec^2 A+1\right)}}$$

$$=\dfrac{3(\sec A+2)}{4\sec A}$$

Examples. Divide and simplify.

1) $\dfrac{\tan^4\theta}{2}\div\dfrac{\tan^5\theta}{9}=\dfrac{\tan^4\theta}{2}\cdot\dfrac{9}{\tan^5\theta}=\dfrac{9}{2\tan\theta}$

2) $\dfrac{1-\csc A}{\cos A+\csc A}\div\dfrac{1+\csc A}{12\cos A+12\csc A}=\dfrac{1-\csc A}{\cos A+\csc A}\cdot\dfrac{12\cos A+12\csc A}{1+\csc A}$

$$=\dfrac{1-\csc A}{\cancel{\cos A+\csc A}}\cdot\dfrac{12\,\cancel{(\cos A+\csc A)}}{1+\csc A}=\dfrac{12(1-\csc A)}{1+\csc A}$$

3) $\dfrac{1}{3\sin x-6}\div\dfrac{2\sin^2 x-2\sin x}{\sin^2 x-4}=\dfrac{1}{3\sin x-6}\cdot\dfrac{\sin^2 x-4}{2\sin^2 x-2\sin x}=\dfrac{1}{3\,\cancel{(\sin x-2)}}\cdot\dfrac{(\sin x+2)\,\cancel{(\sin x-2)}}{2\sin x(\sin x-1)}$

$$=\dfrac{\sin x+2}{6\sin x(\sin x-1)}$$

4) $\dfrac{\cot^2 x-3\cot x-10}{\cot^2 x-\cot x}\div\dfrac{\cot^2 x-25}{\cot x}=\dfrac{\cot^2 x-3\cot x-10}{\cot^2 x-\cot x}\cdot\dfrac{\cot x}{\cot^2 x-25}$

$$=\dfrac{\cancel{(\cot x-5)}(\cot x+2)}{\cancel{\cot x}(\cot x-1)}\cdot\dfrac{\cancel{\cot x}}{(\cot x+5)\cancel{(\cot x-5)}}$$

$$=\dfrac{\cot x+2}{(\cot x-1)(\cot x+5)}$$

Try These (Set 5): Multiply or divide and simplify.

1) $\dfrac{2\tan^3\alpha}{3\cos^4\beta}\cdot\dfrac{6\cos^2\beta}{7\tan^2\alpha}$ 2) $\dfrac{8\sin^2 x}{25\sin^2 x-9}\cdot\dfrac{5\sin x+3}{12\sin^2 x}$ 3) $\dfrac{\sec^2\theta+10\sec\theta+25}{\sec^2\theta+5\sec\theta}\div\dfrac{\sec^2\theta-3\sec\theta}{\sec^2\theta}$

Adding and Subtracting Fractions Containing Trigonometric Expressions

In order to add or subtract two fractions, they must have common denominators. Suppose A, B, and C are integers and $C \neq 0$. Then $\dfrac{A}{C} + \dfrac{B}{C} = \dfrac{A+B}{C}$ and $\dfrac{A}{C} - \dfrac{B}{C} = \dfrac{A-B}{C}$. If the denominators are not common, we may apply algebraic techniques to find the least common denominator (abbreviated as l.c.d.).

1. Common Denominators

When the denominators are the same, just combine (add or subtract) the numerators together.

Examples. Combine and simplify.

1) $\dfrac{4}{3\sin t + 1} + \dfrac{3}{3\sin t + 1} = \dfrac{4+3}{3\sin t + 1} = \dfrac{7}{3\sin t + 1}$

2) $\dfrac{\cot\alpha + 3}{\cot\alpha + 5} + \dfrac{3\cot\alpha - 4}{\cot\alpha + 5} = \dfrac{(\cot\alpha + 3) + (3\cot\alpha - 4)}{\cot\alpha + 5} = \dfrac{4\cot\alpha - 1}{\cot\alpha + 5}$

3) $\dfrac{2\sec A}{\sec^2 A - 1} - \dfrac{\sec A + 1}{\sec^2 A - 1} = \dfrac{2\sec A - (\sec A + 1)}{\sec^2 A - 1} = \dfrac{2\sec A - \sec A - 1}{\sec^2 A - 1} = \dfrac{\sec A - 1}{\sec^2 A - 1}$

$$= \dfrac{\overset{1}{\cancel{\sec A - 1}}}{(\sec A + 1)\left(\underset{1}{\cancel{\sec A - 1}}\right)} = \dfrac{1}{\sec A + 1}$$

2. Additive Inverse Denominators

Recall that when the denominators are additive inverses of each other (that is, they add up to zero), they can be made into common denominators by changing the second denominator into the first denominator and by changing the operation. This technique is demonstrated in the examples below.

Examples. Combine and simplify.

1) $\dfrac{2\tan x - 9}{3\tan x - 4} - \dfrac{5\tan x - 12}{4 - 3\tan x} = \underbrace{\dfrac{2\tan x - 9}{3\tan x - 4} + \dfrac{5\tan x - 12}{3\tan x - 4}}_{3\tan x - 4 \text{ and } 4 - 3\tan x \text{ are additive inverses of each other.}} = \dfrac{(2\tan x - 9) + (5\tan x - 12)}{3\tan x - 4}$

$$= \dfrac{7\tan x - 21}{3\tan x - 4} = \dfrac{7(\tan x - 3)}{3\tan x - 4}$$

2) $\underbrace{\dfrac{\cos^2\theta + 3\cos\theta - 2}{-\cos\theta + 1} + \dfrac{\cos^2\theta - 4\cos\theta + 6}{\cos\theta - 1}}_{-\cos\theta + 1 \text{ and } \cos\theta - 1 \text{ are additive inverses of each other.}} = \dfrac{\cos^2\theta + 3\cos\theta - 2}{-\cos\theta + 1} - \dfrac{\cos^2\theta - 4\cos\theta + 6}{-\cos\theta + 1}$

$$= \dfrac{\left(\cos^2\theta + 3\cos\theta - 2\right) - \left(\cos^2\theta - 4\cos\theta + 6\right)}{-\cos\theta + 1}$$

$$= \dfrac{\cos^2\theta + 3\cos\theta - 2 - \cos^2\theta + 4\cos\theta - 6}{-\cos\theta + 1}$$

$$= \dfrac{7\cos\theta - 8}{-\cos\theta + 1}$$

3. Uncommon Denominators Which Are Not Factorable

If two fractions have denominators which are not common, not additive inverses, and are not factorable (they are **prime**), then the common denominator is the product of the two denominators.

Examples. Combine and simplify.

1) $\dfrac{\sin A}{\cos B} + \dfrac{\cos A}{\sin B} = \dfrac{\sin B}{\sin B}\left(\dfrac{\sin A}{\cos B}\right) + \dfrac{\cos B}{\cos B}\left(\dfrac{\cos A}{\sin B}\right) = \dfrac{\sin B \sin A + \cos B \cos A}{\sin B \cos B}$

2) $\dfrac{\cos\theta}{\sin\theta} + \dfrac{\sin\theta}{1+\cos\theta} = \left(\dfrac{1+\cos\theta}{1+\cos\theta}\right)\dfrac{\cos\theta}{\sin\theta} + \left(\dfrac{\sin\theta}{\sin\theta}\right)\dfrac{\sin\theta}{1+\cos\theta} = \dfrac{\cos\theta\,(1+\cos\theta) + \sin^2\theta}{\cos\theta\,(1+\cos\theta)}$

$$= \underbrace{\dfrac{\cos\theta + \cos^2\theta + \sin^2\theta}{\cos\theta\,(1+\cos\theta)} = \dfrac{\cancel{\cos\theta + 1}^{\;1}}{\cos\theta\,\cancel{(1+\cos\theta)}\,1}}_{\text{since } \sin^2\theta + \cos^2\theta = 1} = \dfrac{1}{\cos\theta} = \sec\theta$$

3) $\dfrac{1}{\tan y} + \tan y = \dfrac{1}{\tan y} + \dfrac{\tan y}{\tan y}\left(\dfrac{\tan y}{1}\right) = \dfrac{1+\tan^2 y}{\tan y} = \dfrac{\sec^2 y}{\tan y}$

By using our fundamental trigonometric identities and some algebraic manipulation, we can simplify our answer further. Observe that

$$\dfrac{\sec^2 y}{\tan y} = \dfrac{\frac{1}{\cos^2 y}}{\frac{\sin y}{\cos y}} = \dfrac{\frac{1}{\cos^2 y}\left(\frac{\cos^2 y}{1}\right)}{\frac{\sin y}{\cos y}\left(\frac{\cos^2 y}{1}\right)} = \dfrac{1}{\sin y \cos y} = \dfrac{1}{\sin y}\cdot\dfrac{1}{\cos y} = \csc y \sec y.$$

4. Uncommon Denominators Which Are Factorable

If one or more of the denominators are factorable, we factor them and find the l.c.d. the same way as we do for rational expressions.

Examples. Combine and simplify.

1) $\underbrace{\dfrac{7\sin A}{5\tan A\sec^2 A} + \dfrac{3\sin A}{10\tan A\sec A}}_{\text{The denominators are already factored.}} = \left(\dfrac{2}{2}\right)\dfrac{7\sin A}{5\tan A\sec^2 A} + \left(\dfrac{\sec A}{\sec A}\right)\dfrac{3\sin A}{10\tan A\sec A}$

$$= \dfrac{14\sin A + 3\sin A\sec A}{10\tan A\sec^2 A}$$

2) $\underbrace{\dfrac{4}{\sin^3\theta\cos^2\theta} - \dfrac{5\tan\theta}{\sin\theta\cos^5\theta}}_{\text{The denominators are already factored.}} = \left(\dfrac{\cos^3\theta}{\cos^3\theta}\right)\dfrac{4}{\sin^3\theta\cos^2\theta} - \left(\dfrac{\sin^2\theta}{\sin^2\theta}\right)\dfrac{5\tan\theta}{\sin\theta\cos^5\theta}$

$$= \dfrac{4\cos^3\theta - 5\tan\theta\sin^2\theta}{\sin^3\theta\cos^5\theta}$$

3) $\dfrac{5}{\csc^2 t - 4} + \dfrac{1}{\csc t - 2} = \dfrac{5}{(\csc t + 2)(\csc t - 2)} + \left(\dfrac{\csc t + 2}{\csc t + 2}\right)\dfrac{1}{\csc t - 2}$

$$= \dfrac{5 + (\csc t + 2)}{(\csc t + 2)(\csc t - 2)} = \dfrac{7 + \csc t}{(\csc t + 2)(\csc t - 2)}$$

4) $\dfrac{2}{\cos^2 x + \cos x} - \dfrac{7}{\cos^2 x + 2\cos x + 1} = \dfrac{2}{\cos x(\cos x + 1)} - \dfrac{7}{(\cos x + 1)(\cos x + 1)}$

$$= \left(\dfrac{\cos x + 1}{\cos x + 1}\right)\dfrac{2}{\cos x(\cos x + 1)} - \left(\dfrac{\cos x}{\cos x}\right)\dfrac{7}{(\cos x + 1)(\cos x + 1)}$$

$$= \dfrac{2(\cos x + 1) - 7\cos x}{\cos x(\cos x + 1)(\cos x + 1)} = \dfrac{2\cos x + 2 - 7\cos x}{\cos x(\cos x + 1)(\cos x + 1)}$$

$$= \dfrac{-5\cos x + 2}{\cos x(\cos x + 1)(\cos x + 1)} = \dfrac{-5\cos x + 2}{\cos x(\cos x + 1)^2}$$

Try These (Set 6): Combine and simplify.

1) $\dfrac{\sin x - 8\cos x}{\sin x + 2\cos x} + \dfrac{5\cos x + 12\sin x}{\sin x + 2\cos x}$

2) $\dfrac{3\cot\alpha - 7}{\cot^2\alpha - 16} + \dfrac{2\cot\alpha - 3}{16 - \cot^2\alpha}$

3) $\cos A + \dfrac{\sin^2 A}{\cos A}$

4) $\dfrac{\sec\theta - 2}{2\sec^2\theta - 6\sec\theta} - \dfrac{\sec\theta + 1}{\sec^2\theta - 7\sec\theta + 12}$

Simplifying Complex Fractions Containing Trigonometric Expressions

A **complex fraction** is a fraction whose numerator and denominator contain rational expressions. For example, the expressions

$$\dfrac{\dfrac{1}{6} + \dfrac{3}{2}}{2}, \quad \dfrac{5 - \dfrac{1}{x^2}}{\dfrac{x}{8} - \dfrac{x}{7}}, \quad \dfrac{3x + \dfrac{4x}{y} - \dfrac{2x}{5}}{x + \dfrac{x}{y}}, \quad \text{and} \quad \dfrac{a^2 + 8a + \dfrac{1}{a^2 - 9}}{a^2 - 10a + \dfrac{2}{a^2 - 16}}$$

are complex fractions. We are interested in simplifying such fractions when they contain trigonometric expressions. There are two methods which are commonly used to do this. I will demonstrate both methods in the examples that follow.

Examples. Simplify.

1) $\dfrac{\dfrac{1}{\sin\theta}}{\dfrac{2}{\cos\theta} + \dfrac{5}{\sin\theta}}$

Method 1. Find the least common multiple (abbreviated as l.c.m.) of the denominators of the fractions within the 'big fraction' and multiply the numerator and denominator of the 'big fraction' by this l.c.m.

$$\frac{\dfrac{1}{\sin\theta}}{\dfrac{2}{\cos\theta}+\dfrac{5}{\sin\theta}} = \left(\frac{\dfrac{1}{\sin\theta}}{\dfrac{2}{\cos\theta}+\dfrac{5}{\sin\theta}}\right)\underbrace{\left(\frac{\dfrac{\cos\theta\sin\theta}{1}}{\dfrac{\cos\theta\sin\theta}{1}}\right)}_{\text{The l.c.m. of } \sin\theta,\ \cos\theta,\ \text{and }\sin\theta \text{ is } \cos\theta\sin\theta.} = \frac{\dfrac{1}{\sin\theta}\left(\dfrac{\cos\theta\sin\theta}{1}\right)}{\dfrac{2}{\cos\theta}\left(\dfrac{\cos\theta\sin\theta}{1}\right)+\dfrac{5}{\sin\theta}\left(\dfrac{\cos\theta\sin\theta}{1}\right)}$$

$$= \frac{\cos\theta}{2\sin\theta+5\cos\theta}$$

Method 2. Combine the fractions in the numerator and denominator of the 'big fraction'. Rewrite the 'big fraction' as division problem of the numerator and denominator and work it out.

$$\frac{\dfrac{1}{\sin\theta}}{\dfrac{2}{\cos\theta}+\dfrac{5}{\sin\theta}} = \frac{\dfrac{1}{\sin\theta}}{\left(\dfrac{\sin\theta}{\sin\theta}\right)\dfrac{2}{\cos\theta}+\left(\dfrac{\cos\theta}{\cos\theta}\right)\dfrac{5}{\sin\theta}} = \frac{\dfrac{1}{\sin\theta}}{\dfrac{2\sin\theta+5\cos\theta}{\sin\theta\cos\theta}} = \left(\dfrac{1}{\sin\theta}\right)\div\left(\dfrac{2\sin\theta+5\cos\theta}{\sin\theta\cos\theta}\right)$$

$$= \left(\dfrac{1}{\sin\theta}\right)\left(\dfrac{\sin\theta\cos\theta}{2\sin\theta+5\cos\theta}\right) = \frac{\cos\theta}{2\sin\theta+5\cos\theta}$$

2) $\dfrac{\dfrac{\cos A}{6\tan A}-\dfrac{2}{\tan^2 A}}{\dfrac{5}{4\tan^2 A}-3\sin A}$

Method 1. Using the l.c.m.

$$\frac{\dfrac{\cos A}{6\tan A}-\dfrac{2}{\tan^2 A}}{\dfrac{5}{4\tan^2 A}-3\sin A} = \left(\frac{\dfrac{\cos A}{6\tan A}-\dfrac{2}{\tan^2 A}}{\dfrac{5}{4\tan^2 A}-3\sin A}\right)\underbrace{\left(\frac{\dfrac{12\tan^2 A}{1}}{\dfrac{12\tan^2 A}{1}}\right)}_{\text{The l.c.m. of } 6\tan A,\ \tan^2 A,\ \text{and } 4\tan^2 A \text{ is } 12\tan^2 A.} = \frac{\dfrac{\cos A}{6\tan A}\left(\dfrac{12\tan^2 A}{1}\right)-\dfrac{2}{\tan^2 A}\left(\dfrac{12\tan^2 A}{1}\right)}{\dfrac{5}{4\tan^2 A}\left(\dfrac{12\tan^2 A}{1}\right)-3\sin A\left(\dfrac{12\tan^2 A}{1}\right)}$$

$$= \frac{2\tan A\cos A-24}{15-36\sin A\tan^2 A} \quad\text{or}\quad \frac{2\left(\tan A\cos A-12\right)}{3\left(5-12\sin A\tan^2 A\right)}$$

Method 2. By dividing fractions.

$$\frac{\dfrac{\cos A}{6\tan A}-\dfrac{2}{\tan^2 A}}{\dfrac{5}{4\tan^2 A}-3\sin A} = \frac{\left(\dfrac{\tan A}{\tan A}\right)\dfrac{\cos A}{6\tan A}-\left(\dfrac{6}{6}\right)\dfrac{2}{\tan^2 A}}{\dfrac{5}{4\tan^2 A}-\left(\dfrac{4\tan^2 A}{4\tan^2 A}\right)\dfrac{3\sin A}{1}} = \frac{\dfrac{\tan A\cos A-12}{6\tan^2 A}}{\dfrac{5-12\tan^2 A\sin A}{4\tan^2 A}}$$

$$= \left(\dfrac{\tan A\cos A-12}{6\tan^2 A}\right)\div\left(\dfrac{5-12\tan^2 A\sin A}{4\tan^2 A}\right)$$

$$= \left(\dfrac{\tan A\cos A-12}{6\tan^2 A}\right)\left(\dfrac{4\tan^2 A}{5-12\tan^2 A\sin A}\right)$$

$$= \frac{2\left(\tan A\cos A-12\right)}{3\left(5-12\sin A\tan^2 A\right)} \quad\text{or}\quad \frac{2\tan A\cos A-24}{15-36\sin A\tan^2 A}$$

3) $\dfrac{\dfrac{1}{1+\sin\theta}-1}{\dfrac{1}{1-\sin\theta}+1}$

Method 1. Using the l.c.m.

$$\dfrac{\dfrac{1}{1+\sin\theta}-1}{\dfrac{1}{1-\sin\theta}-1}=\left(\dfrac{\dfrac{1}{1+\sin\theta}-1}{\dfrac{1}{1-\sin\theta}-1}\right)\left(\dfrac{\dfrac{(1+\sin\theta)\,(1-\sin\theta)}{1}}{\dfrac{(1+\sin\theta)\,(1-\sin\theta)}{1}}\right)$$

The l.c.m. of $1+\sin\theta$ and $1-\sin\theta$ is $(1+\sin\theta)(1-\sin\theta)$.

$$=\dfrac{\dfrac{1}{1+\sin\theta}\left(\dfrac{(1+\sin\theta)\,(1-\sin\theta)}{1}\right)-1\left(\dfrac{(1+\sin\theta)\,(1-\sin\theta)}{1}\right)}{\dfrac{1}{1-\sin\theta}\left(\dfrac{(1+\sin\theta)\,(1-\sin\theta)}{1}\right)-1\left(\dfrac{(1+\sin\theta)\,(1-\sin\theta)}{1}\right)}$$

$$=\dfrac{1-\sin\theta-(1+\sin\theta)\,(1-\sin\theta)}{1+\sin\theta-(1+\sin\theta)\,(1-\sin\theta)}=\dfrac{1-\sin\theta-\left(1-\sin^{2}\theta\right)}{1+\sin\theta-\left(1-\sin^{2}\theta\right)}=\dfrac{1-\sin\theta-1+\sin^{2}\theta}{1+\sin\theta-1+\sin^{2}\theta}$$

$$=\dfrac{\sin^{2}\theta-\sin\theta}{\sin^{2}\theta+\sin\theta}=\dfrac{\sin\theta(\sin\theta-1)}{\sin\theta(\sin\theta+1)}=\dfrac{\sin\theta-1}{\sin\theta+1}$$

Method 2. By dividing fractions.

$$\dfrac{\dfrac{1}{1+\sin\theta}-1}{\dfrac{1}{1-\sin\theta}-1}=\dfrac{\dfrac{1}{1+\sin\theta}-\left(\dfrac{1+\sin\theta}{1+\sin\theta}\right)\dfrac{1}{1}}{\dfrac{1}{1-\sin\theta}-\left(\dfrac{1-\sin\theta}{1-\sin\theta}\right)\dfrac{1}{1}}=\dfrac{\dfrac{1-(1+\sin\theta)}{1+\sin\theta}}{\dfrac{1-(1-\sin\theta)}{1-\sin\theta}}=\dfrac{\dfrac{1-1-\sin\theta}{1+\sin\theta}}{\dfrac{1-1+\sin\theta}{1-\sin\theta}}=\dfrac{\dfrac{-\sin\theta}{1+\sin\theta}}{\dfrac{\sin\theta}{1-\sin\theta}}$$

$$=\left(\dfrac{-\sin\theta}{1+\sin\theta}\right)\div\left(\dfrac{\sin\theta}{1-\sin\theta}\right)=\left(\dfrac{-\sin\theta}{1+\sin\theta}\right)\left(\dfrac{1-\sin\theta}{\sin\theta}\right)=-\dfrac{1-\sin\theta}{1+\sin\theta}$$

Notice that

$$-\dfrac{1-\sin\theta}{1+\sin\theta}=\dfrac{-(1-\sin\theta)}{1+\sin\theta}=\dfrac{-1+\sin\theta}{1+\sin\theta}=\dfrac{\sin\theta-1}{\sin\theta+1},$$

the same answer that we found using Method 1.

Try These (Set 7): Simplify.

1) $\dfrac{\tan\alpha-\dfrac{2}{\tan\alpha}}{4}$ 2) $\dfrac{\dfrac{\csc x+\sin x}{2}}{\dfrac{\sin x}{4}+\dfrac{3}{8\cos x}}$ 3) $\dfrac{\dfrac{1}{\cos^{2}A-9}+\dfrac{2}{\cos A+3}}{\dfrac{6}{\cos A-3}}$

Exercise 6.1

In Exercises 1-20, combine.

1. $5\sin\theta+8\sin\theta$ 2. $7\cos\theta+12\cos\theta$ 3. $-6\tan x+2\tan x$ 4. $9\sec x+(-3\sec x)$

5. $-\cos 2\alpha-7\cos 2\alpha$ 6. $-10\csc 3\alpha+12\csc 3\alpha$ 7. $11\cot^{2}x-\left(-2\cot^{2}x\right)$ 8. $\sin^{2}\theta-\left(-5\sin^{2}\theta\right)$

9. $(-3\sin A + 6\cos A) + (4\sin A - \cos A)$

10. $(7\tan B - 4\csc B) + (\tan B - 3\csc B)$

11. $\left(12\sec^2 x - 7\csc y\right) - \left(16\sec^2 x - 11\csc y\right)$

12. $\left(6\sin A + 4\cos^2 B\right) - \left(-3\cos^2 B + 2\sin A\right)$

13. $\left(7\sin^2 A - 2\sin A - 3\right) + \left(-\sin^2 A + 5\sin A - 3\right)$

14. $\left(-3\tan^2\theta + 8\tan\theta + 12\right) + \left(7\tan^2\theta - 6\tan\theta - 1\right)$

15. $\left(8\sec^2 4\alpha + \sec 4\alpha + 1\right) - \left(2\sec^2 4\alpha - 11\sec 4\alpha - 16\right)$

16. $\left(-\csc^2 2\alpha + 9\csc 2\alpha - 3\right) - \left(-5\csc^2 2\alpha + 5\csc 4\alpha - 3\right)$

17. $(3\tan(5x - 1) + 7\cot 6x) + (8\tan(5x - 1) - 13\cot 6x)$

18. $(-2\sin 7x + 8\cos(2x + 3)) + (\sin 7x - 48\cos(2x + 3))$

19. $\left(4\cos^2(5x - 1) - 11\cos^2(5x + 1)\right) - \left(12\cos^2(5x + 1) - 3\cos^2(5x - 1)\right)$

20. $\left(-\sec^2\left(x^2 + 1\right) + 6\sec^2\left(y^2 + 1\right)\right) - \left(7\sec^2\left(y^2 + 1\right) + 4\sec^2\left(x^2 + 1\right)\right)$

In Exercises 21-38, multiply and simplify.

21. $(8\sin\theta\cos\theta)\left(3\sin^2\theta\cos^3\theta\right)$

22. $\left(7\tan^2 x\cos x\right)\left(-5\tan^2 x\cos^3 x\right)$

23. $\left(-2\cos^4\alpha\csc^3\alpha\right)\left(-9\cos^2\alpha\csc^5\alpha\right)$

24. $\left(-6\sec^2\alpha\cot^5\alpha\right)\left(4\sec^2\alpha\cot^2\alpha\right)$

25. $\sin x\,(4\sin x + 5)$

26. $\cos y\,(3\cos y + 6)$

27. $7\tan\theta\,(9\tan\theta - 2)$

28. $3\sec\theta\,(2\sec\theta - 3)$

29. $(2\sin\beta + 5)(3\sin\beta + 4)$

30. $(6\tan\beta - 1)(2\tan\beta + 7)$

31. $(4\cot\theta - 3)(2\cot\theta - 3)$

32. $(7\csc\theta + 5)(2\csc\theta - 3)$

33. $(\sin x + \cos x)(\sin x - \cos x)$

34. $(\tan x - \sec x)(\tan x + \sec x)$

35. $(\sin x - 2)^2$

36. $(\cos y + 4)^2$

37. $(5\csc A + 3)^2$

38. $(8\cot B - 2)^2$

In Exercises 39-48, divide and simplify.

39. $\dfrac{9\sin^2 x + \sin x}{\sin x}$

40. $\dfrac{2\cos^2 x - 5\cos x}{\cos x}$

41. $\dfrac{20\tan^2\theta - 4\tan\theta}{2\tan\theta}$

42. $\dfrac{14\sec^2\beta + 6\sec\beta}{2\sec\beta}$

43. $\dfrac{4\sin x\sec x + 12\sec x}{4\sec x}$

44. $\dfrac{18\cos A\sin A - 16\sin A}{2\sin A}$

45. $\dfrac{12\csc B\tan^3 B - 10\tan^2 B}{2\tan^2 B}$

46. $\dfrac{25\sec^2 B\sin B + 10\sec B\sin B}{5\sec B\sin B}$

47. $\dfrac{8\cos^3 A\sin^2 A - 4\cos^2 A\sin A}{-2\cos A\sin A}$

48. $\dfrac{\tan^4 x\sec x - 12\tan^2 x\sec^3 x}{-\tan x\sec x}$

In Exercises 49-76, factor completely.

49. $\sin^2 x + 2\sin x$

50. $3\tan^2 y + \tan y$

51. $6\cos^2\theta - 9\cos\theta$

52. $15\csc^2 y - 10\csc y$

53. $\cot^2\theta - \sin^2\theta$

54. $\sin^2\beta - \tan^2\beta$

55. $9\sec^2\alpha - 4$

56. $25\tan^2 y - 49$

57. $5\sin^2\theta\cos\theta + 4\sin\theta\cos^3\theta$ 58. $9\sec^4\theta\cot^3\theta - \sec^2\theta\cot^2\theta$ 59. $12\tan^2 x\csc x - 18\tan^3 x\csc^4 x$

60. $7\cos^2 A\cot^2 A + 11\cos^4 A\cot A$ 61. $\tan^2\alpha - 2\tan\alpha - 15$ 62. $\sin^2 A + 6\sin A + 8$

63. $\cos^2\theta - 7\cos\theta + 12$ 64. $\csc^2\theta - \csc\theta - 12$ 65. $2\sin^2\theta - \sin\theta - 1$

66. $4\cos^2 x - 4\cos x + 1$ 67. $3\tan^2 x + \tan x - 2$ 68. $2\cot^2\theta + \cot\theta - 1$

69. $\cos^2 5x + 3\cos 5x - 28$ 70. $\sec^2 8\theta - 6\sec 8\theta + 5$ 71. $\cot^2(x+4) + 6\cot(x+4) + 9$

72. $\csc^2(2x-3) - 12\csc(2x-3) + 36$ 73. $\sin^3 5\alpha - 16\sin 5\alpha$ 74. $\cot^4 7\beta - 4\cot^2 7\beta$

75. $9\cos^4\theta - \cos^2\theta$ 76. $81\sec^3\theta - \sec\theta$

In Exercises 77-88, simplify each expression.

77. $\dfrac{2\tan^2\theta + 16\sec\theta\tan\theta}{2\tan\theta}$ 78. $\dfrac{6\sec\theta - 9\sec^2\theta\sin\theta}{3\sec\theta}$ 79. $\dfrac{\cos^2 x - 6\cos x + 9}{\cos^2 x - 10\cos x + 21}$

80. $\dfrac{\cot^2 x + 12\cot x + 35}{\cot^2 x - 25}$ 81. $\dfrac{\sin^2 A - \cos^2 A}{\sin A + \cos A}$ 82. $\dfrac{\csc A - \tan A}{\csc^2 A - \tan^2 A}$

83. $\dfrac{3\tan^2 B - \tan B\csc B}{9\tan^2 B - \csc^2 B}$ 84. $\dfrac{\sec^2 B - \sec B - 2}{\sec^2 B - 2\sec B}$ 85. $\dfrac{3\sin^2 4\alpha + \sin 4\alpha - 2}{\sin^3 4\alpha - \sin 4\alpha}$

86. $\dfrac{\cos^3 7\theta - \cos 7\theta}{2\cos^2 7\theta - \cos 7\theta - 1}$ 87. $\dfrac{\cos^3 2\beta - 7\cos^2 2\beta + 12\cos 2\beta}{\cos^2 2\beta\sin 2\beta - 4\cos 2\beta\sin 2\beta}$ 88. $\dfrac{12\cot^3 9\beta - 3\cot 9\beta}{4\cot^2 9\beta - 4\cot 9\beta + 1}$

In Exercises 89-142, perform the indicated operation and simplify.

89. $\dfrac{8\sin^4 A}{7\cos^2 B}\cdot\dfrac{7\cos B}{6\sin^2 A}$ 90. $\dfrac{9\tan\theta}{10\csc^5\alpha}\cdot\dfrac{8\csc^3\alpha}{\tan^2\theta}$ 91. $\dfrac{22\sec^2 x}{5\cot y}\cdot\left(-\dfrac{25\cot^3 y}{16\sec^2 x}\right)$

92. $\left(-\dfrac{4\cos A}{13\tan^4 B}\right)\cdot\dfrac{11\tan^3 B}{10\cos A}$ 93. $\dfrac{6\csc^2 u}{16\csc^2 u - 25}\cdot\dfrac{4\csc u - 5}{12\csc^3 u}$ 94. $\dfrac{-3\cos^2 t}{4 - \cos t}\cdot\dfrac{\cos^2 t - 16}{12\cos t}$

95. $\dfrac{\cos^2\beta - \sin^2\beta}{9\sin^2\beta - 18\sin\beta}\cdot\dfrac{12\sin\beta}{\sin\beta + \cos\beta}$ 96. $\dfrac{\tan\beta + \csc\beta}{\tan^2\beta + 2\tan\beta\csc\beta + \sec^2\beta}\cdot\dfrac{15\csc^2\beta}{6\csc^2\beta + 24\csc\beta}$

97. $\dfrac{4\sin^3 x}{11\cos^4 y}\div\dfrac{3\sin x}{22\cos^2 y}$ 98. $\dfrac{18\sec\theta}{5\sin^2\alpha}\div\dfrac{9\sec^2\theta}{\sin^2\alpha}$ 99. $\left(-\dfrac{2\tan^2 A}{\cot B}\right)\div\left(-\dfrac{3\tan A\cot^2 B}{14}\right)$

100. $\dfrac{9\cos^2 u}{13\sin v}\div\left(-\dfrac{18\sin v\cos^3 u}{3}\right)$ 101. $\dfrac{16\tan^2\alpha}{\tan^2\alpha - 36}\div\dfrac{18\tan\alpha}{\tan\alpha - 6}$ 102. $\dfrac{\sin^2\beta - 4}{\sin\beta + 4}\div\dfrac{5}{\sin^2\beta - 2\sin\beta}$

103. $\dfrac{\cos^2\theta - 16\cos\theta + 64}{\cos^2\theta - 8\cos\theta}\div\dfrac{\cos^2\theta - 2\cos\theta}{2\cos^2\theta}$ 104. $\dfrac{\csc^2 x - \csc x + 12}{\cos^2 x + 3\csc x}\div\dfrac{\csc^4 x - 4\csc^3 x}{5\csc x}$

105. $\dfrac{3\cos y}{1 + 2\cos y} + \dfrac{8\cos y - 5}{1 + 2\cos y}$ 106. $\dfrac{3\tan t}{\sec t - 8} + \dfrac{1 - 6\tan t}{\sec t - 8}$ 107. $\dfrac{1 - 5\sin\theta}{2\cos\theta} + \dfrac{1 + 3\sin\theta}{2\cos\theta}$

108. $\dfrac{3\sin\beta+7}{4\sec\beta}+\dfrac{5-\sin\beta}{4\sec\beta}$

109. $\dfrac{\tan x+3\sin x}{\sin x+2\cos x}-\dfrac{3\tan x-\sin x}{\sin x+2\cos x}$

110. $\dfrac{6-10\cot y}{3\cos y-1}-\dfrac{5-2\cot y}{3\cos y-1}$

111. $\dfrac{4\csc^2 A-3\csc A+3}{\csc A-1}-\dfrac{3\csc^2 A-3\csc A+2}{\csc A-1}$

112. $\dfrac{\tan^2 B+5\tan B-7}{\tan^2 B-9}-\dfrac{\tan^2 B+4\tan B-4}{\tan^2 B-9}$

113. $\dfrac{8\sec x+3}{\sec x-2}+\dfrac{2\sec x-5}{2-\sec x}$

114. $\dfrac{7\csc u-13}{3\csc u-5}+\dfrac{2-3\csc u}{5-3\csc u}$

115. $\dfrac{3\cos x}{16-\cos^2 x}-\dfrac{4-2\cos x}{\cos^2 x-16}$

116. $\dfrac{\sin y-3}{4\sin^2 y-25}-\dfrac{\sin y-2}{25-4\sin^2 y}$

117. $\dfrac{\cos x}{\sin y}+\dfrac{\sin x}{\cos y}$

118. $\dfrac{\tan A}{\sec B}+\dfrac{\sec A}{\tan B}$

119. $\dfrac{\cos\theta}{1+\sin\theta}-\dfrac{\sin\theta}{\cos\theta}$

120. $\dfrac{\sin\theta}{\tan\theta+1}-\dfrac{\tan\theta}{\sin\theta}$

121. $\dfrac{3}{\csc A+\cos A}+\dfrac{2}{\csc A-\cos A}$

122. $\dfrac{1}{\sec B-2\cos B}+\dfrac{4}{\sec B+\cos B}$

123. $\dfrac{\sin x+\cos x}{\sin x-\cos x}-\dfrac{\sin x-\cos x}{\sin x+\cos x}$

124. $\dfrac{\tan x-\csc x}{\csc x+\tan x}+\dfrac{\tan x+\csc x}{\csc x-\tan x}$

125. $\dfrac{\sin^2 y}{\cos y}+\cos y$

126. $\tan x+\dfrac{1}{\tan x}$

127. $3\sin\theta-\dfrac{2}{5\sin\theta}$

128. $5\tan\alpha-\dfrac{3}{4\tan\alpha}$

129. $\dfrac{1}{\sec A}-\cos A$

130. $\tan B-\dfrac{1}{\cot B}$

131. $\dfrac{2}{3\sin A\tan^3 A}+\dfrac{5}{6\sin^2 A\tan A}$

132. $\dfrac{1}{4\csc^2 B\sec B}+\dfrac{3}{10\csc B\sec B}$

133. $\dfrac{\cos^2 x+2}{7\cos^2 x\sin x}-\dfrac{\sin x\cos x-1}{2\cos x\sin^2 x}$

134. $\dfrac{\sin\beta\tan^2\beta-3}{6\sin^2\beta\tan\beta}-\dfrac{\tan\beta+4\sin\beta}{16\sin^3\beta}$

135. $\dfrac{4}{\tan^2 A+6\tan A}+\dfrac{3}{\tan^2 A-6\tan A}$

136. $\dfrac{2\cot B}{\cot^2 B-3\cot B}+\dfrac{10}{\cot^2 B-9}$

137. $\dfrac{\cot\theta+6}{\cot^2\theta-5\cot\theta+6}+\dfrac{\cot\theta-3}{\cot^2\theta-4}$

138. $\dfrac{\sec\alpha-10}{\sec^2\alpha+12\sec\alpha}+\dfrac{5}{\sec^2\alpha+14\sec\alpha+24}$

139. $\dfrac{2-\cos t}{\cos^2 t-25}-\dfrac{1-\cos t}{\cos t-5}$

140. $\dfrac{2\sin x+9}{\sin x+2}-\dfrac{4\sin x}{\sin^2 x+2\sin x}$

141. $\dfrac{6\tan A}{\tan^2 A-4}+\dfrac{3-\tan A}{\tan^2 A-12\tan A+20}$

142. $\dfrac{\csc B+3}{\csc^2 B+3\csc B-18}+\dfrac{\csc B}{\csc^2 B+12\csc B+36}$

In Exercises 143-152, simplify.

143. $\dfrac{\sin x+\dfrac{2}{\sin x}}{3}$

144. $\dfrac{\dfrac{4}{\sec x}+1}{5}$

145. $\dfrac{\dfrac{\cos\theta}{2}-\sin\theta}{\dfrac{4}{\sin\theta}}$

146. $\dfrac{\cot\theta-\dfrac{\cot\theta}{3}}{\dfrac{2}{\cot\theta}}$

147. $\dfrac{\dfrac{\csc x+2\cos x}{2}}{4-\dfrac{5}{6\csc x}}$

148. $\dfrac{9+\dfrac{1}{8\sec y}}{\dfrac{\sec y-3\cos y}{4}}$

149. $\dfrac{\dfrac{2}{\tan^2 A-4\tan A}-\dfrac{6}{\tan A}}{7+\dfrac{1}{\tan A-4}}$

150. $\dfrac{\dfrac{3}{2\csc B+3}+5}{\dfrac{1}{4\csc^2 B-9}}$

151. $\dfrac{\dfrac{\sin x}{\sin x+\cos x}-1}{\dfrac{\cos x}{\sin x-\cos x}+1}$

152. $\dfrac{1-\dfrac{\tan x}{\tan x-\cos x}}{1+\dfrac{\tan x}{\tan x+\cos x}}$

Section 6.2 Trigonometric Identities

Section 6.2.1   Review of the Fundamental Identities

By now, you should be familiar with the fundamental identities and the properties of negative angles. We will review them in this section because they are extremely important and useful for verifying trigonometric identities. Before we recall these identities, let's remind ourselves of what identities and conditional equations are.

Definition: An **identity** is an equation which is true for every choice of the variable for which both sides are defined.

Examples.

1) The equation

$$7(x+3) = 7x + 21$$

is an identity. If we replace x with any real number, then the equation is true. Notice, for instance, that if $x = -1$, then

$$7(-1+3) \stackrel{?}{=} 7(-1) + 21$$
$$7(2) \stackrel{?}{=} -7 + 21$$
$$14 \stackrel{\checkmark}{=} 14$$

which is a true sentence.

2) The equation

$$\frac{x^2 - x - 6}{x - 3} = x + 2, x \neq 3$$

is an identity since the value of 3 for x has been omitted. This value of x would make the denominator of the fraction equal to zero, making the fraction undefined. This is the only value for which this would occur. All other values of x satisfy this equation since

$$\frac{x^2 - x - 6}{x - 3} = \frac{\overset{1}{(\cancel{x-3})}(x+2)}{\underset{1}{\cancel{x-3}}} = x + 2.$$

3) The equation

$$9y - 2 = 25$$

is not an identity, since the **only** number for which the equation is true is $y = 3$. If it was an identity, then the equation would be true for all values of y.

4) The equation

$$\frac{5y + 10}{y + 2} = 5$$

is not an identity. The value of -2 for y makes the denominator of the fraction equal to zero, creating an undefined expression. In fact, any value for y **except** -2 would satisfy the equation since

$$\frac{5y + 10}{y + 2} = \frac{5\overset{1}{(\cancel{y+2})}}{\underset{1}{\cancel{y+2}}} = 5.$$

Notice that the difference between the equation $\dfrac{5y+10}{y+2} = 5$ in Example 4 and the equation $\dfrac{x^2-x-6}{x-3} =$ $x+2$, $x \neq 3$, in Example 2 is that we are not told to omit the 'bad' value of -2 for y.

The equations in Examples 3 and 4 are examples of **conditional equations**.

Definition: A **conditional equation** is an equation which is true for (possibly) some choices of the variable for which both sides are defined, but not others.

Some more examples of conditional equations are

$$-x + 8 = 3, \quad y^2 - 15y + 56 = 0, \quad \text{and} \quad \frac{2}{x^2-1} = \frac{1}{x-1}.$$

Notice that $-x + 8 = 3$ is true **only** if $x = 5$, $y^2 - 15y + 56 = 0$ is true **only** if $y = 7$ or $y = 8$, and $\dfrac{2}{x^2-1} = \dfrac{1}{x-1}$ has no solution (it is **never** true). None of these equations are identities.

Let's now recall the fundamental trigonometric identities. They were verified in Section 3.2. We will assume that all values of θ for which an identity is undefined have been excluded.

The Fundamental Identities

The Reciprocal Identities

$$\sin\theta = \frac{1}{\csc\theta} \qquad\qquad \cos\theta = \frac{1}{\sec\theta} \qquad\qquad \tan\theta = \frac{1}{\cot\theta}$$

$$\csc\theta = \frac{1}{\sin\theta} \qquad\qquad \sec\theta = \frac{1}{\cos\theta} \qquad\qquad \cot\theta = \frac{1}{\tan\theta}$$

The Quotient Identities

$$\frac{\sin\theta}{\cos\theta} = \tan\theta \qquad\qquad\qquad \frac{\cos\theta}{\sin\theta} = \cot\theta$$

The Pythagorean Identities

$$\sin^2\theta + \cos^2\theta = 1 \qquad\qquad \tan^2\theta + 1 = \sec^2\theta \qquad\qquad 1 + \cot^2\theta = \csc^2\theta$$

Notice that the reciprocal identities can also be written as follows:

$$\sin\theta\csc\theta = 1 \qquad\qquad \cos\theta\sec\theta = 1 \qquad\qquad \tan\theta\cot\theta = 1.$$

It is important that you memorize the reciprocal identities in this form. They will frequently occur in verifying identities. Similarly, the Pythagorean identities often appear in different forms. Below is a list that you should memorize (or at least be able to recognize):

$$1 - \sin^2\theta = \cos^2\theta \qquad\qquad \sec^2\theta - 1 = \tan^2\theta \qquad\qquad \csc^2\theta - 1 = \cot^2\theta$$

$$1 - \cos^2\theta = \sin^2\theta \qquad\qquad \sec^2\theta - \tan^2\theta = 1 \qquad\qquad \csc^2\theta - \cot^2\theta = 1$$

Another set of identities which is useful are the negative angle identities (see Section 3.4).

The Negative Angle Identities

$$\cos\left(-\theta\right) = \cos\theta \qquad \sec\left(-\theta\right) = \sec\theta$$
$$\sin\left(-\theta\right) = -\sin\theta \qquad \csc\left(-\theta\right) = -\csc\theta$$
$$\tan\left(-\theta\right) = -\tan\theta \qquad \cot\left(-\theta\right) = -\cot\theta$$

Examples. Express the given expressions in terms of $\sin\theta$, $\cos\theta$, or both. Write your answers in simplest terms.

1) $\underbrace{\csc\theta + \sec\theta = \dfrac{1}{\sin\theta} + \dfrac{1}{\cos\theta}}_{\text{by reciprocal identities}} = \left(\dfrac{\cos\theta}{\cos\theta}\right)\dfrac{1}{\sin\theta} + \left(\dfrac{\sin\theta}{\sin\theta}\right)\dfrac{1}{\cos\theta} = \dfrac{\cos\theta + \sin\theta}{\sin\theta\cos\theta}$

2) $\underbrace{\cot\theta\sin\theta\sec\theta = \left(\dfrac{\cancel{\cos\theta}}{\cancel{\sin\theta}}\right)\left(\dfrac{\cancel{\sin\theta}}{1}\right)\left(\dfrac{1}{\cancel{\cos\theta}}\right) = 1}_{\text{by the quotient and reciprocal identities}}$

3) $\underbrace{\dfrac{\tan\theta}{\sin\theta} = \dfrac{\frac{\sin\theta}{\cos\theta}}{\sin\theta}}_{\text{by a quotient identity}} = \dfrac{\frac{\sin\theta}{\cos\theta}}{\frac{\sin\theta}{1}}\left(\dfrac{\frac{\cos\theta}{1}}{\frac{\cos\theta}{1}}\right) = \dfrac{\frac{\sin\theta}{\cos\theta}\left(\frac{\cancel{\cos\theta}}{1}\right)}{\frac{\sin\theta}{1}\left(\frac{\cos\theta}{1}\right)} = \dfrac{\frac{1}{\cancel{\sin\theta}}}{\frac{\cancel{\sin\theta}\cos\theta}{1}} = \dfrac{1}{\cos\theta}$

Another way to simplify $\dfrac{\tan\theta}{\sin\theta}$ is to manipulate the quotient identity as follows:

$$\frac{\sin\theta}{\cos\theta} = \tan\theta$$

$$\frac{\sin\theta}{\cos\theta} = \frac{\tan\theta}{1}$$

$$\sin\theta = \cos\theta\tan\theta$$

$$\frac{\frac{1}{\cancel{\sin\theta}}}{\cos\theta\cancel{\sin\theta}} = \frac{\cancel{\cos\theta}\tan\theta}{\cancel{\cos\theta}\sin\theta}$$

$$\frac{1}{\cos\theta} = \frac{\tan\theta}{\sin\theta}$$

$$\overbrace{\text{Note that } \tan^2\theta = \left(\tfrac{\sin\theta}{\cos\theta}\right)^2 = \tfrac{\sin^2\theta}{\cos^2\theta}.}$$

4) $\underbrace{\cos^2\theta\left(\sec^2\theta - 1\right) = \cos^2\theta\tan^2\theta = \cos^2\theta\left(\dfrac{\sin^2\theta}{\cos^2\theta}\right)}_{\text{by a Pythagorean and a quotient identity}} = \dfrac{\frac{1}{\cancel{\cos^2\theta}}}{1}\left(\dfrac{\sin^2\theta}{\cancel{\cos^2\theta}}\right) = \sin^2\theta$

5) $\underbrace{\cot\theta + \tan\theta = \frac{\cos\theta}{\sin\theta} + \frac{\sin\theta}{\cos\theta}}_{\text{by the quotient identities}} = \left(\frac{\cos\theta}{\cos\theta}\right)\frac{\cos\theta}{\sin\theta} + \left(\frac{\sin\theta}{\sin\theta}\right)\frac{\sin\theta}{\cos\theta} = \underbrace{\frac{\cos^2\theta + \sin^2\theta}{\cos\theta\sin\theta}}_{\sin^2\theta + \cos^2\theta = 1} = \frac{1}{\cos\theta\sin\theta}$

6) $\dfrac{\sin^3(-\theta)}{\sin\theta} = \underbrace{\dfrac{(\sin(-\theta))^3}{\sin\theta} = \dfrac{(-\sin\theta)^3}{\sin\theta}}_{\sin(-\theta) = -\sin\theta} = \dfrac{-\sin^{\overset{2}{3}}\theta}{\underset{1}{\cancel{\sin\theta}}} = -\sin^2\theta$

Try These (Set 8): Express the given expressions in terms of $\sin\alpha$, $\cos\alpha$, or both. Write your answers in simplified form.

1) $\csc\alpha\sec\alpha$ 2) $\dfrac{\cos\alpha}{\sec\alpha}$ 3) $\tan\alpha(\csc\alpha + \cos\alpha)$ 4) $\dfrac{1 - \cos^2(-\alpha)}{\tan^2(-\alpha)}$

Section 6.2.2   Verifying Trigonometric Identities

Now, we will learn how to verify that a given trigonometric equation is an identity (for those values of the variable for which the equation is well-defined). We will rely on our fundamental identities, along with our knowledge of algebra, to do this task. Knowing how to verify an identity is an important skill and it is useful in Calculus and more advanced mathematics courses.

The solutions of the first two examples below are accompanied by a step-by-step procedure and strategy for verifying an identity. When we verify an identity, we can either work on one side of the equation only or work on both sides (for more complicated identities).

Examples. Verify that each equation is an identity.

1) $\cot\theta\sin\theta = \cos\theta$

Step 1. In the equation, choose a side of the equation which you will rewrite to equal the other. To decide which side of the equation is best to work with, follow these strategies:

Strategies for Choosing a Side

Choose a side which
      1. has several terms in it (or more terms than the other).
      2. contains complicated expressions.
      3. contains terms that remind you of the fundamental identities.
      4. contains tangent or cotangent.
      5. requires algebraic manipulation (combining fractions, factoring, etc.).
      6. has terms that can be rewritten in terms of sine, cosine, or both.

Note that this strategy may not work for all identities. Some identities require alternative techniques (I like to call them 'tricks.').

In our example, the left-hand side of the equation $\cot\theta\sin\theta = \cos\theta$ has more terms, (as well as the cotangent function), in it. Furthermore, we know that $\cot\theta$ can be written in terms of $\sin\theta$ and $\cos\theta$. Our strategy list suggests that we will work with the left-hand side of the equation.

Step 2. Using your fundamental identities and negative angle identities, rewrite the side that you choose to equal the other side.

We know that $\cot\theta = \dfrac{\cos\theta}{\sin\theta}$ is one of our quotient identities. We will replace $\cot\theta$ by $\dfrac{\cos\theta}{\sin\theta}$ on the left-hand side of the equation.

$$\cot\theta\sin\theta = \left(\frac{\cos\theta}{\sin\theta}\right)\sin\theta$$

$$= \left(\frac{\cos\theta}{\sin\theta}\right)\frac{\sin\theta}{1}$$

$$= \cos\theta$$

Since $\cot\theta\sin\theta = \cos\theta$, the identity is verified.

2) $\cos\alpha + \tan\alpha = \sin\alpha\,(\cot\alpha + \sec\alpha)$

Let's think about which side is better to work with. It seems to me that the right-hand side of the equation is preferable because it requires an algebraic manipulation, the Distributive Property (Strategy 5). It also has more terms than the left-hand side (Strategy 1) and seems more complicated to work with (Strategy 2). It is true that the left-hand side contains the tangent function (Strategy 4), but the right-hand side satisfies more things in our strategy list.

Our goal is to manipulate the right-hand side of the equation in such a way that our result will equal the left-hand side of the equation. Since the left-hand side is $\cos\alpha + \tan\alpha$, it makes perfect sense to try to get $\cos\alpha$ and $\tan\alpha$ when manipulating the right-hand side. This means that whatever identities we choose to use, they must produce the terms $\cos\alpha$ and $\tan\alpha$. Let's see what will happen.

$$\sin\alpha\,(\cot\alpha + \sec\alpha) = \sin\alpha\cot\alpha + \sin\alpha\sec\alpha \qquad \text{(by the Distributive Property)}$$

$$= \sin\alpha\left(\frac{\cos\alpha}{\sin\alpha}\right) + \sin\alpha\left(\frac{1}{\cos\alpha}\right) \qquad \left(\cot\alpha = \frac{\cos\alpha}{\sin\alpha}\ \text{ and }\ \sec\alpha = \frac{1}{\cos\alpha}\right)$$

$$= \frac{\sin\alpha}{1}\left(\frac{\cos\alpha}{\sin\alpha}\right) + \frac{\sin\alpha}{1}\left(\frac{1}{\cos\alpha}\right)$$

$$= \cos\alpha + \frac{\sin\alpha}{\cos\alpha}$$

$$= \cos\alpha + \tan\alpha$$

This shows that our identity is true. Notice that by replacing $\cot\alpha$ by $\dfrac{\cos\alpha}{\sin\alpha}$ and $\sec\alpha$ by $\dfrac{1}{\cos\alpha}$, we were able to obtain $\cos\alpha + \tan\alpha$. This obeys Strategy 3 and Strategy 6.

3) $(\sec A + 1)(\sec A - 1) = \tan^2 A$

The left-hand side requires some algebraic manipulation (the FOIL method). Let's expand it out and see what will happen. Not only am I following Strategy 5, but I am doing what makes sense to me: working out the more complicated side of the equation (Strategy 2).

$$(\sec A + 1)(\sec A - 1) = \sec^2 A - 1 \qquad \text{(recall that } (a+b)(a-b) = a^2 - b^2)$$
$$= \tan^2 A \qquad (\tan^2 A + 1 = \sec^2 A)$$

This verifies the identity.

4) $\dfrac{1}{1 - \sin x} = \dfrac{1 + \sin x}{\cos^2 x}$

Notice that both sides of the equation contain $\sin x$ and the right-hand side contains $\cos^2 x$. Whenever I see $\cos^2 x$, I think of the identity $\sin^2 x + \cos^2 x = 1$. For this reason, I will rewrite the right-hand side (Strategy 3).

$$\frac{1 + \sin x}{\cos^2 x} = \frac{1 + \sin x}{1 - \sin^2 x} \qquad (\sin^2 x + \cos^2 x = 1 \text{ becomes } \cos^2 x = 1 - \sin^2 x)$$

$$= \frac{\overset{1}{\cancel{1 + \sin x}}}{\underset{1}{(\cancel{1 + \sin x})}(1 - \sin x)} \qquad \text{(recall that } a^2 - b^2 = (a+b)(a-b))$$

$$= \frac{1}{1 - \sin x} \qquad \text{(simplify the fraction)}$$

As you can see, some algebra (factoring a difference of two squares) is required here. This will usually be the case.

5) $\dfrac{\cot \beta + 1}{\cot \beta - 1} = \dfrac{1 + \tan \beta}{1 - \tan \beta}$

There are two trigonometric functions in this equation, $\cot \beta$ and $\tan \beta$. Do you know any identity which relates them together? How about the reciprocal identity? Let's replace $\cot \beta$ by $\dfrac{1}{\tan \beta}$ on the left-hand side of the equation and see where it will take us.

$$\frac{\cot \beta + 1}{\cot \beta - 1} = \frac{\dfrac{1}{\tan \beta} + 1}{\dfrac{1}{\tan \beta} - 1} \qquad \left(\cot \beta = \frac{1}{\tan \beta}\right)$$

$$= \frac{\left(\dfrac{1}{\tan \beta} + 1\right)\left(\dfrac{\tan \beta}{1}\right)}{\left(\dfrac{1}{\tan \beta} - 1\right)\left(\dfrac{\tan \beta}{1}\right)} \qquad \text{(the l.c.m. is } \tan \beta)$$

$$= \frac{\dfrac{1}{\cancel{\tan \beta}}\left(\dfrac{\cancel{\tan \beta}}{1}\right) + 1\left(\dfrac{\tan \beta}{1}\right)}{\dfrac{1}{\cancel{\tan \beta}}\left(\dfrac{\cancel{\tan \beta}}{1}\right) - 1\left(\dfrac{\tan \beta}{1}\right)} \qquad \text{(distribute)}$$

$$= \frac{1 + \tan \beta}{1 - \tan \beta} \qquad \text{(simplify the fraction)}$$

The identity if verified. Once again, this example required some algebra.

6) $\csc B + 1 = \dfrac{\sin B + 1}{\sin B}$

Let's work on the right-hand side of the equation (since it contains a fraction). The first thing we need to do is to get rid of the fraction. To do this, we will decompose it into two fractions and simplify each.

$$\dfrac{\sin B + 1}{\sin B} = \dfrac{\sin B}{\sin B} + \dfrac{1}{\sin B} \qquad \left(\dfrac{a+b}{c} = \dfrac{a}{c} + \dfrac{b}{c} \right)$$

$$= 1 + \csc B \qquad\qquad\qquad \left(\dfrac{1}{\sin B} = \csc B \right)$$

$$= \csc B + 1$$

7) $\dfrac{1 + \cos\theta}{\sin\theta} + \dfrac{\sin\theta}{1 + \cos\theta} = 2\csc\theta$

Let's combine the fractions on the left-hand side. After doing so, we will use our fundamental identities and some algebra to 'clean up things'.

$$\dfrac{1+\cos\theta}{\sin\theta} + \dfrac{\sin\theta}{1+\cos\theta} = \left(\dfrac{1+\cos\theta}{1+\cos\theta} \right)\left(\dfrac{1+\cos\theta}{\sin\theta} \right) + \left(\dfrac{\sin\theta}{\sin\theta} \right)\left(\dfrac{\sin\theta}{1+\cos\theta} \right)$$

$$= \dfrac{(1+\cos\theta)(1+\cos\theta) + \sin^2\theta}{\sin\theta\,(1+\cos\theta)} \qquad \text{(combine the fractions)}$$

$$= \dfrac{1 + 2\cos\theta + \cos^2\theta + \sin^2\theta}{\sin\theta\,(1+\cos\theta)} \qquad \text{(expand } (1+\cos\theta)(1+\cos\theta) \text{ by FOIL)}$$

$$= \dfrac{1 + 2\cos\theta + 1}{\sin\theta\,(1+\cos\theta)} \qquad \left(\cos^2\theta + \sin^2\theta = 1\right)$$

$$= \dfrac{2 + 2\cos\theta}{\sin\theta\,(1+\cos\theta)}$$

$$= \dfrac{2\cancel{(1+\cos\theta)}^{\,1}}{\sin\theta\cancel{(1+\cos\theta)}_{\,1}} \qquad \text{(factor } 2 + 2\cos\theta = 2\,(1+\cos\theta)\,)$$

$$= \dfrac{2}{\sin\theta} \qquad \text{(simplify the fraction)}$$

$$= 2\csc\theta \qquad \left(\dfrac{1}{\sin\theta} = \csc\theta \right)$$

8) $\dfrac{1 + \sin A}{\cos A} = \dfrac{\cos A}{1 - \sin A}$

It seems that none of the items in our strategy list are satisfied. This example requires a trick. What we will do is multiply the right-hand side of the equation by $\dfrac{1 + \sin A}{1 + \sin A}$. Let's do this and see what happens.

$$\frac{\cos A}{1 - \sin A} = \left(\frac{\cos A}{1 - \sin A}\right)\left(\frac{1 + \sin A}{1 + \sin A}\right) \qquad \text{(the trick!)}$$

$$= \frac{\cos A\,(1 + \sin A)}{(1 - \sin A)\,(1 + \sin A)}$$

$$= \frac{\cos A\,(1 + \sin A)}{1 - \sin^2 A} \qquad \left((a - b)\,(a + b) = a^2 - b^2\right)$$

$$= \frac{\overset{1}{\cancel{\cos A}}\,(1 + \sin A)}{\cos^{\cancel{2}} A} \qquad \left(1 - \sin^2 A = \cos^2 A\right)$$

$$= \frac{1 + \sin A}{\cos A} \qquad \text{(simplify the fraction)}$$

This verifies the identity. As you can see, the trick allowed us to create the denominator

$$(1 - \sin A)\,(1 + \sin A) = 1 - \sin^2 A = \cos^2 A$$

which is what we needed in order to verify our identity. A similar trick could've been done on the left-hand side. If you multiply $\dfrac{1 + \sin A}{\cos A}$ by $\dfrac{1 - \sin A}{1 - \sin A}$, the identity will be verified. Why don't you give it a try?

Try These (Set 9): Verify that each equation is an identity.

1) $\sin x \sec x = \dfrac{1}{\cot x}$ 　　　 2) $\tan \beta + \cot \beta = \csc \beta \sec \beta$ 　　　 3) $\dfrac{1 - \cos \theta}{\sin^2 \theta} = \dfrac{\sec \theta}{1 + \sec \theta}$

Exercise 6.2

In Exercises 1-28, express the given expressions in terms of $\sin x$, $\cos x$, or both. Write your answers in simplest terms.

1. $\tan x \cos x$ 　　　 2. $\cot x \sin x$ 　　　 3. $\dfrac{\csc x}{\sin x}$ 　　　 4. $\dfrac{\sec x}{\cos x}$

5. $\tan x \,(\cos x + \cot x)$ 　　 6. $\cos x \,(\sec x + \tan x)$ 　　 7. $\sin(-x)\cos(-x)$ 　　 8. $\cos(-x)\sec x$

9. $\csc(-x)\sin x$ 　　 10. $\tan(-x)\cos x$ 　　 11. $\sec x - \csc x$ 　　 12. $\csc x + 1$

13. $\tan x \csc x \cos^2 x$ 　　 14. $\cot x \cos x \sin x$ 　　 15. $\dfrac{\sin x}{\tan x}$ 　　 16. $\dfrac{\cot x}{\csc x}$

17. $\sin^2 x \,(\csc^2 x - 1)$ 　　 18. $\cos^2 x \,(1 - \sec^2 x)$ 　　 19. $\sec x + \tan x$ 　　 20. $\csc x + \cot x$

21. $\tan x - \cot x$ 　　 22. $\sec x + \cos x$ 　　 23. $(\tan^2 x + 1)\,(1 - \sin^2 x)$ 　　 24. $(1 - \sec^2 x)\,(1 - \cos^2 x)$

25. $1 - \sin^2(-x)$ 　　 26. $1 - \cos^2(-x)$ 　　 27. $\dfrac{\tan^2(-x) + 1}{\cos(-x)}$ 　　 28. $\dfrac{\cot^2(-x) + 1}{\sin(-x)}$

In Exercises 29-62, verify that each equation is an identity.

29. $\cot\theta = \csc\theta\cos\theta$ 30. $\tan\theta\csc\theta = \sec\theta$ 31. $\sin^2\alpha = \tan\alpha\cot\alpha - \cos^2\alpha$

32. $\sec^2\alpha - \tan^2\alpha = \sec\alpha\cos\alpha$ 33. $\sin x + 1 = \cos x\,(\tan x + \sec x)$

34. $\sec y - 1 = \tan y\,(\csc y - \cot y)$ 35. $(\sin A + \cos A)^2 = 1 + 2\sin A\cos A$

36. $(\sin B - \cos B)^2 = 1 - 2\sin B\cos B$ 37. $(\cos x + \sin x)(\cos x - \sin x) = 1 - 2\sin^2 x$

38. $(\tan y - \sec y)(\tan y + \sec y) = -1$ 39. $\cos^4\beta - \sin^4\beta = \cos^2\beta - \sin^2\beta$

40. $\tan^4\beta - \sec^4\beta = -\tan^2\beta - \sec^2\beta$ 41. $\sin\alpha\cot\alpha = \dfrac{1}{\sec\alpha}$ 42. $\tan\theta\cos\theta = \dfrac{1}{\csc\theta}$

43. $\dfrac{\tan A}{\sec A} = \dfrac{\cos A}{\cot A}$ 44. $\dfrac{\sin A}{\cot A} = \dfrac{\tan A}{\csc A}$ 45. $\dfrac{\cos B - \tan B}{\sin B} = \cot B - \sec B$

46. $\dfrac{\csc B + \cot B}{\csc B} = \cos B + 1$ 47. $\dfrac{\sin x + 1}{\tan x} = \cos x + \cot x$ 48. $\dfrac{1 - \cos y}{\sec y} = \cos y - \cos^2 y$

49. $\dfrac{\sec\beta}{\tan\beta + \cot\beta} = \sin\beta$ 50. $\dfrac{\csc\beta}{\cot\beta + \tan\beta} = \cos\beta$ 51. $\dfrac{1 + \sin\alpha}{1 - \sin\alpha} = \dfrac{\csc\alpha + 1}{\csc\alpha - 1}$

52. $\dfrac{1 + \sec\theta}{1 - \sec\theta} = \dfrac{\cos\theta + 1}{\cos\theta - 1}$ 53. $\dfrac{\cos\theta}{1 - \sin\theta} + \dfrac{1 - \sin\theta}{\cos\theta} = 2\sec\theta$ 54. $\dfrac{1 + \sin\theta}{\cos\theta} + \dfrac{\cos\theta}{1 + \sin\theta} = 2\sec\theta$

55. $\dfrac{(1 - \sin x)^2}{\cos^2 x} = \dfrac{1 - \sin x}{1 + \sin x}$ 56. $\dfrac{\sin^2 x}{(\cos x - 1)^2} = \dfrac{1 + \cos x}{1 - \cos x}$ 57. $\dfrac{\tan^2 y - 1}{\tan^2 y + 1} + 2\cos^2 y = 1$

58. $\dfrac{\cot^2 y - 1}{\cot^2 y + 1} - 1 = 2\cos^2 y$ 59. $\dfrac{1 + \cos\beta}{1 - \cos\beta} - \dfrac{1 - \cos\beta}{1 + \cos\beta} = 4\cot\beta\csc\beta$

60. $\dfrac{1 - \sin\beta}{1 + \sin\beta} + \dfrac{\sin\beta}{1 - \sin\beta} = -\dfrac{2\sin\beta + 1}{\sin\beta + 1}$ 61. $\dfrac{1 - \tan^2\alpha}{\cos^2\alpha - \sin^2\alpha} = \sec^2\alpha$ 62. $\dfrac{1 - \cos^2\alpha}{1 - \sin^2\alpha} = \tan^2\alpha$

Section 6.3 Sum and Difference Formulas

Suppose that we want to rewrite the expression $\cos(A + B)$ in such a way that each angle which appears in each term of the new expression is either A or B, but not $A + B$ or $A - B$. Is it possible to obtain such an expression? Well, our first guess would be to write

$$\cos(A + B) \overset{?}{=} \cos A + \cos B.$$

Our guess, however, would be incorrect. To demonstrate, observe that

$$\cos(30° + 60°) = \cos 90° = 0 \ \text{ and } \ \cos 30° + \cos 60° = \frac{\sqrt{3}}{2} + \frac{1}{2} = \frac{\sqrt{3} + 1}{2}.$$

And so $\cos(30° + 60°) \neq \cos 30° + \cos 60°$. In fact, it turns out that there are no values for A and B such that $\cos(A + B)$ equals $\cos A + \cos B$. This means that $\cos(A + B) \neq \cos A + \cos B$. What is the correct formula? Similarly, what would be the formula for $\sin(A - B)$ or for $\tan(A + B)$? Let's see.

The Sum and Difference Formulas for Cosine

We'll begin by deriving the formula for $\cos(A-B)$. Let's suppose that angles A and B satisfy the inequality $A > B > 0$. If we graph A and B in standard position on the unit circle, we will obtain the figure below.

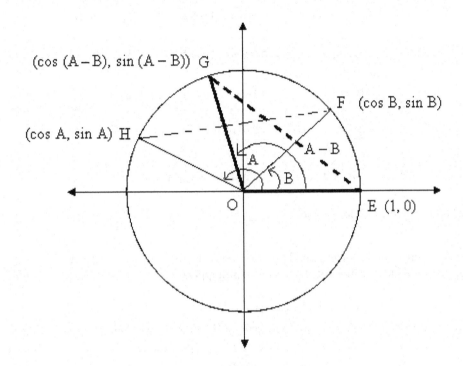

Notice that angle EOH is A, angle EOF is B, and angle EOG is found to be $A - B$. As the diagram shows, $\triangle FOH$ is obtained by rotating $\triangle EOG$ through angle B. This means that $\triangle FOH$ is congruent to $\triangle EOG$. Consequently, side EG of $\triangle EOG$ has the same length as side FH of $\triangle FOH$ (marked with the dotted lines in the figure above). By the Distance Formula, this can be written as

$$\sqrt{[\cos(A-B) - 1]^2 + [\sin(A-B) - 0]^2} = \sqrt{(\cos A - \cos B)^2 + (\sin A - \sin B)^2}.$$

We simplify this expression and obtain

$$\left(\sqrt{[\cos(A-B) - 1]^2 + [\sin(A-B) - 0]^2}\right)^2 = \left(\sqrt{(\cos A - \cos B)^2 + (\sin A - \sin B)^2}\right)^2$$

$$[\cos(A-B) - 1]^2 + \sin^2(A-B) = (\cos A - \cos B)^2 + (\sin A - \sin B)^2.$$

By applying the formula

$$(x - y)^2 = x^2 - 2xy + y^2$$

to each of the expressions

$$[\cos(A-B) - 1]^2, (\cos A - \cos B)^2, \text{ and } (\sin A - \sin B)^2,$$

we obtain

$$\cos^2(A-B) - 2\cos(A-B) + 1 + \sin^2(A-B) = \cos^2 A - 2\cos A\cos B + \cos^2 B + \sin^2 A - 2\sin A\sin B + \sin^2 B.$$

Now, since $\sin^2(A-B) + \cos^2(A-B) = 1$, $\sin^2 A + \cos^2 A = 1$, and $\sin^2 A + \cos^2 A = 1$, we obtain

$$1 - 2\cos(A-B) + 1 = 1 - 2\cos A\cos B + 1 - 2\sin A\sin B$$

$$2 - 2\cos(A-B) = 2 - 2\cos A\cos B - 2\sin A\sin B$$

$$-2\cos(A-B) = -2\cos A\cos B - 2\sin A\sin B$$

$$\frac{\cancel{-2}\cos(A-B)}{\cancel{-2}} = \frac{\cancel{-2}(\cos A\cos B + \sin A\sin B)}{\cancel{-2}}$$

$$\cos(A-B) = \cos A\cos B + \sin A\sin B$$

and this is the difference formula for cosine.

Let's derive the sum formula for cosine. The trick we will use here is to write $A + B$ as $A - (-B)$ and use the difference formula for cosine. Let's see what will happen.

$$\begin{aligned}
\cos(A+B) &= \cos(A - (-B)) \\
&= \cos A\cos(-B) + \sin A\sin(-B) \\
&= \cos A\cos B + \sin A(-\sin B) \\
&= \cos A\cos B - \sin A\sin B
\end{aligned}$$

and we now have the sum formula for cosine.

Sum and Difference Formulas for Cosine

$$\cos(A+B) = \cos A\cos B - \sin A\sin B$$
$$\cos(A-B) = \cos A\cos B + \sin A\sin B$$

Notice that the identities are almost identical, with the exception of the sign in between the terms. Be careful not to make the following common mistakes.

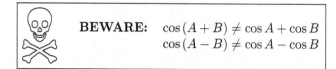

BEWARE: $\cos(A+B) \neq \cos A + \cos B$
$\cos(A-B) \neq \cos A - \cos B$

Let's practice using these formulas by doing a few of examples.

Examples. Find the exact value of each of the expression.

1) $\cos 75° = \underbrace{\cos(30° + 45°) = \cos 30° \cos 45° - \sin 30° \sin 45°}_{\text{Use the sum formula with } A=30° \text{ and } B=45°.} = \left(\frac{\sqrt{3}}{2}\right)\left(\frac{\sqrt{2}}{2}\right) - \left(\frac{1}{2}\right)\left(\frac{\sqrt{2}}{2}\right) = \frac{\sqrt{6}-\sqrt{2}}{4}$

2) $\cos 15° = \underbrace{\cos(60° - 45°) = \cos 60° \cos 45° + \sin 60° \sin 45°}_{\text{Use the difference formula with } A=60° \text{ and } B=45°.} = \left(\frac{1}{2}\right)\left(\frac{\sqrt{2}}{2}\right) + \left(\frac{\sqrt{3}}{2}\right)\left(\frac{\sqrt{2}}{2}\right) = \frac{\sqrt{2}+\sqrt{6}}{4}$

3) $\cos \frac{7\pi}{12} = \cos\left(\frac{4\pi}{12} + \frac{3\pi}{12}\right) = \cos\left(\frac{\pi}{3} + \frac{\pi}{4}\right) = \cos \frac{\pi}{3} \cos \frac{\pi}{4} - \sin \frac{\pi}{3} \sin \frac{\pi}{4} = \left(\frac{1}{2}\right)\left(\frac{\sqrt{2}}{2}\right) - \left(\frac{\sqrt{3}}{2}\right)\left(\frac{\sqrt{2}}{2}\right) = \frac{\sqrt{2}-\sqrt{6}}{4}$

4) $\cos 19° \cos 251° - \sin 19° \sin 251° = \cos(19° + 251°) = \cos 270° = 0$

5) $\cos \frac{35\pi}{18} \cos \frac{17\pi}{18} + \sin \frac{35\pi}{18} \sin \frac{17\pi}{18} = \cos\left(\frac{35\pi}{18} - \frac{17\pi}{18}\right) = \cos\left(\frac{18\pi}{18}\right) = \cos \pi = -1$

Examples.

1) Suppose that $\sin A = -\frac{4}{5}$ and $\cos B = \frac{5}{13}$. If A lies in quadrant III and B lies in quadrant IV, find the exact value of $\cos(A + B)$.

Let's start by writing down our sum formula for cosine. The formula is

$$\cos(A + B) = \cos A \cos B - \sin A \sin B.$$

We need to know the values of $\cos A$, $\cos B$, $\sin A$, and $\sin B$ in order to find $\cos(A + B)$. We are given the values of $\sin A$ and $\cos B$ already. Let's find $\cos A$ and $\sin B$ by using the definitions of the trigonometric functions. Recall that if $(a,\ b)$ lies on the terminal side of θ, $(a,\ b) \neq (0,\ 0)$, and $r = \sqrt{a^2 + b^2}$, then

$$\sin \theta = \frac{b}{r}, \qquad \cos \theta = \frac{a}{r}, \qquad \tan \theta = \frac{b}{a} \ \text{(if it exists)},$$

and the remaining functions are reciprocals of these. Notice that $r > 0$ for any values of a and b, provided that they are not both zero (which cannot occur since $(a,\ b) \neq (0,\ 0)$).

Step 1. Let's find $\cos A$.

Observe that $\sin A = -\frac{4}{5} = \frac{-4}{5} = \frac{b}{r}$, so we may choose $b = -4$ and $r = 5$ (see the next figure). We need to find a since $\cos A = \frac{a}{r}$. Note that $a < 0$ since A lies in quadrant III and both coordinates (a and b) of a point in this quadrant are negative. Well, since $r = \sqrt{a^2 + b^2}$, we have that

$$5 = \sqrt{a^2 + (-4)^2}$$
$$5 = \sqrt{a^2 + 16}$$
$$(5)^2 = \left(\sqrt{a^2 + 16}\right)^2$$
$$25 = a^2 + 16$$
$$9 = a^2$$
$$a = \pm\sqrt{9} = \pm 3.$$

And so $a = -3$ (we reject $a = 3$ because $a < 0$ in quadrant III). Therefore,

$$\cos A = \frac{a}{r} = \frac{-3}{5}.$$

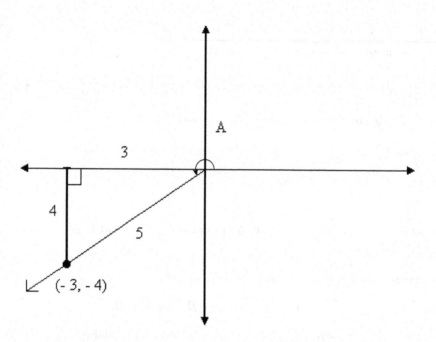

Step 2. Let's find $\sin B$.

Since $\cos B = \frac{5}{13} = \frac{a}{r}$, we may choose $a = 5$ and $r = 13$ (see the next figure). We need to find b since $\sin B = \frac{b}{r}$. Note that $b < 0$ since B lies in quadrant IV and the y-coordinate (our b value) of a point in this quadrant is negative. We can use the formula $r = \sqrt{a^2 + b^2}$ to find b as we did in Step 1:

$$13 = \sqrt{5^2 + b^2}$$
$$13 = \sqrt{25 + b^2}$$
$$(13)^2 = \left(\sqrt{25 + b^2}\right)^2$$
$$169 = 25 + b^2$$
$$144 = b^2$$
$$b = \pm\sqrt{144} = \pm 12$$

And so $b = -12$ (we reject $b = 12$ because $b < 0$ in quadrant IV). Therefore,

$$\sin B = \frac{b}{r} = \frac{-12}{13}.$$

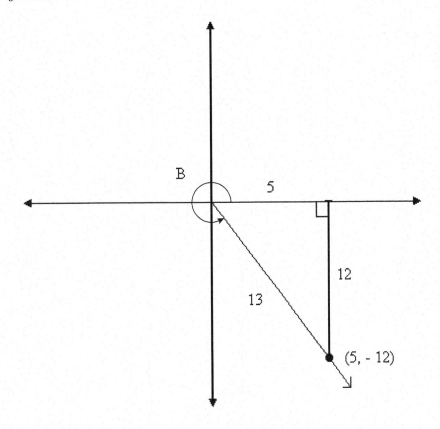

Step 3. Let's find $\cos(A+B)$.

Now that we have all of the quantities, we can calculate $\cos(A+B)$.

$$\cos(A+B) = \cos A \cos B - \sin A \sin B$$
$$= \frac{-3}{5}\left(\frac{5}{13}\right) - \left(-\frac{4}{5}\right)\left(\frac{-12}{13}\right)$$
$$= \frac{-15}{65} - \frac{48}{65}$$
$$= -\frac{63}{65}$$

2) Suppose that $\cos\alpha = -\frac{\sqrt{5}}{4}$ and $\tan\beta = \sqrt{2}$. If $\frac{\pi}{2} < \alpha < \pi$ and $0 < \beta < \frac{\pi}{2}$, find the exact value of $\cos(\alpha - \beta)$.

We will follow the same method that we used in the previous example. Let's write down our difference formula for cosine. The formula is

$$\cos(\alpha - \beta) = \cos\alpha\cos\beta + \sin\alpha\sin\beta.$$

The only value that we are given is for $\cos\alpha$. We need to find the values for $\cos\beta$, $\sin\alpha$ and $\sin\beta$.

Step 1. Let's find $\cos\beta$ and $\sin\beta$.

Observe that $\tan\beta = \sqrt{2} = \frac{\sqrt{2}}{1} = \frac{b}{a}$, so we may choose $b = \sqrt{2}$ and $a = 1$ (see the next figure). Notice that both a and b must be positive numbers because β lies in quadrant I. We need to find r since $\cos\beta = \frac{a}{r}$

and $\sin\beta = \dfrac{b}{r}$. Using the formula $r = \sqrt{a^2 + b^2}$, we have that:

$$r = \sqrt{1^2 + \left(\sqrt{2}\right)^2}$$
$$r = \sqrt{1+2}$$
$$r = \sqrt{3}$$

And so $r = \sqrt{3}$. Therefore,

$$\cos\beta = \frac{a}{r} = \frac{1}{\sqrt{3}} \quad \text{and} \quad \sin\beta = \frac{b}{r} = \frac{\sqrt{2}}{\sqrt{3}}.$$

We will rationalize the denominator of our final answer at the end.

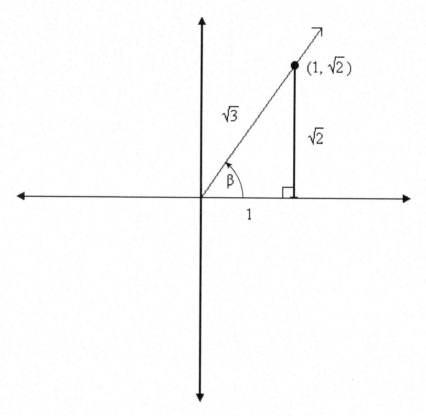

Step 2. Let's find $\sin\alpha$.

Since $\cos\alpha = -\dfrac{\sqrt{5}}{4} = \dfrac{-\sqrt{5}}{4} = \dfrac{a}{r}$, we may choose $a = -\sqrt{5}$ and $r = 4$ (see the next figure). We need to find b since $\sin\alpha = \dfrac{b}{r}$. Note that $b > 0$ since α lies in quadrant II and the y-coordinate (our b value) of a point in this quadrant is positive. Once again, we use the formula $r = \sqrt{a^2 + b^2}$ to find b:

$$4 = \sqrt{\left(-\sqrt{5}\right)^2 + b^2}$$
$$4 = \sqrt{5 + b^2}$$
$$(4)^2 = \left(\sqrt{5 + b^2}\right)^2$$
$$16 = 5 + b^2$$
$$11 = b^2$$
$$b = \pm\sqrt{11}$$

And so $b = \sqrt{11}$ (we reject $b = -11$ because $b > 0$ in quadrant II). Therefore,

$$\sin\alpha = \frac{b}{r} = \frac{\sqrt{11}}{4}.$$

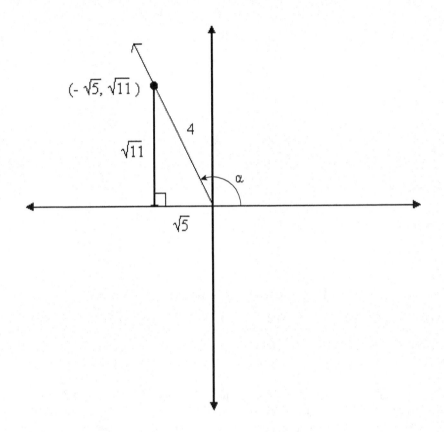

Step 3. Let's find $\cos(A - B)$.

$$\cos(\alpha - \beta) = \cos\alpha\cos\beta + \sin\alpha\sin\beta$$

$$= -\frac{\sqrt{5}}{4}\left(\frac{1}{\sqrt{3}}\right) - \frac{\sqrt{11}}{4}\left(\frac{\sqrt{2}}{\sqrt{3}}\right)$$

$$= \frac{-\sqrt{5}}{4\sqrt{3}} - \frac{\sqrt{22}}{4\sqrt{3}}$$

$$= \frac{-\sqrt{5} - \sqrt{22}}{4\sqrt{3}}$$

$$= \left(\frac{-\sqrt{5} - \sqrt{22}}{4\sqrt{3}}\right)\left(\frac{\sqrt{3}}{\sqrt{3}}\right)$$

$$= \frac{-\sqrt{15} - \sqrt{66}}{12}$$

3) Verify the identity: $\cos\left(\frac{3\pi}{2} - \theta\right) = -\sin\theta$

We will use the difference formula for cosines to expand the left-hand side.

$$\cos(A - B) = \cos A \cos B + \sin A \sin B$$

$$\cos\left(\frac{3\pi}{2} - \theta\right) = \cos\frac{3\pi}{2}\cos\theta + \sin\frac{3\pi}{2}\sin\theta$$

$$= 0\left(\cos\theta\right) + (-1)\sin\theta$$

$$= -\sin\theta$$

Try These (Set 10):

1) Suppose that $\sin x = \frac{2}{3}$ and $\sec y = 4$. If x lies in quadrant II and y lies in quadrant IV, find the exact value of $\cos(x + y)$.

2) Find the exact value of $\cos 74° \cos 14° + \sin 74° \sin 14°$.

3) Verify the identity: $\cos(\pi + \theta) = -\cos\theta$

The Cofunction Identities

The sum and difference formulas for cosine can be used to derive the sum and difference formulas for sine and tangent. The first step to deriving these formulas requires the use of two cofunction identities.

Recall that two acute angles, β and α, are complementary angles if $\beta + \alpha = 90°$ (or $\frac{\pi}{2}$ radians). Notice that if β and α are complementary angles, then $\alpha = 90° - \beta$ (or $\frac{\pi}{2} - \beta$). In other words, if β is an acute angle, then β and $90° - \beta$ (or $\frac{\pi}{2} - \beta$) are complementary. Let's remind ourselves of the Complementary Angle Theorem (in terms of degrees and radians).

The Complementary Angle Theorem

Suppose that β is an acute angle. Then:

$$\sin\beta = \cos(90° - \beta) \qquad \cos\beta = \sin(90° - \beta)$$
$$\sin\beta = \cos\left(\frac{\pi}{2} - \beta\right) \qquad \cos\beta = \sin\left(\frac{\pi}{2} - \beta\right)$$

$$\tan\beta = \cot(90° - \beta) \qquad \cot\beta = \tan(90° - \beta)$$
$$\tan\beta = \cot\left(\frac{\pi}{2} - \beta\right) \qquad \cot\beta = \tan\left(\frac{\pi}{2} - \beta\right)$$

$$\sec\beta = \csc(90° - \beta) \qquad \csc\beta = \sec(90° - \beta)$$
$$\sec\beta = \csc\left(\frac{\pi}{2} - \beta\right) \qquad \csc\beta = \sec\left(\frac{\pi}{2} - \beta\right)$$

We will prove that the identities stated in the Complementary Angle Theorem are true for any angle, β (not just when β is an acute angle). We call these generalized identities the **cofunction identities**. I will write these identities in radian measure. The same identities are true if we replace $\frac{\pi}{2}$ by $90°$.

The Cofunction Identities

Suppose that β is **any angle**. Then

(1) $\sin \beta = \cos \left(\dfrac{\pi}{2} - \beta \right)$ $\qquad$ (2) $\cos \beta = \sin \left(\dfrac{\pi}{2} - \beta \right)$

(3) $\tan \beta = \cot \left(\dfrac{\pi}{2} - \beta \right)$ $\qquad$ (4) $\cot \beta = \tan \left(\dfrac{\pi}{2} - \beta \right)$

(5) $\sec \beta = \csc \left(\dfrac{\pi}{2} - \beta \right)$ $\qquad$ (6) $\csc \beta = \sec \left(\dfrac{\pi}{2} - \beta \right)$

Note that these identities hold provided that they are well-defined. For example,

$$\underbrace{\cot 0}_{\text{undefined}} \neq \tan \left(\frac{\pi}{2} - 0 \right) = \underbrace{\tan \frac{\pi}{2}}_{\text{undefined}} .$$

Proofs of the cofunction identities:

(1) We will use the difference formula for cosine.

$$\begin{aligned}
\cos \left(\frac{\pi}{2} - \beta \right) &= \cos \frac{\pi}{2} \cos \beta + \sin \frac{\pi}{2} \sin \beta \\
&= 0 \left(\cos \beta \right) + 1 \left(\sin \beta \right) \\
&= \sin \beta
\end{aligned}$$

(2) We can use identity (1) above. Observe that

$$\underbrace{\sin \left(\frac{\pi}{2} - \beta \right) = \cos \left(\frac{\pi}{2} - \left(\frac{\pi}{2} - \beta \right) \right)}_{\text{by identity (1)}} = \cos \left(\frac{\pi}{2} - \frac{\pi}{2} + \beta \right) = \cos \beta.$$

(3) By a quotient identity and identities (1) and (2), we have

$$\cot \left(\frac{\pi}{2} - \beta \right) = \frac{\cos \left(\frac{\pi}{2} - \beta \right)}{\sin \left(\frac{\pi}{2} - \beta \right)} = \frac{\sin \beta}{\cos \beta} = \tan \beta.$$

(4) Using the identity (3) and fact that tangent and cotangent are reciprocals of one another, we have

$$\tan \left(\frac{\pi}{2} - \beta \right) = \frac{1}{\cot \left(\frac{\pi}{2} - \beta \right)} = \frac{1}{\tan \beta} = \cot \beta.$$

Try to prove (5) and (6) by yourself.

The Sum and Difference Formulas for Sine

We will now find formulas for $\sin(A+B)$ and $\sin(A-B)$. To derive the formula for $\sin(A+B)$, we use the cofunction identities (1) and (2) and the difference formula for cosine.

$$\sin(A+B) = \cos\left(\frac{\pi}{2} - (A+B)\right)$$
$$= \cos\left(\left(\frac{\pi}{2} - A\right) - B\right)$$
$$= \cos\left(\frac{\pi}{2} - A\right)\cos B + \sin\left(\frac{\pi}{2} - A\right)\sin B$$
$$= \sin A \cos B + \cos A \sin B$$

We now have our sum formula for sine. To derive the difference formula, we simply write $A - B = A + (-B)$ and use the sum formula for sine.

$$\sin(A-B) = \sin(A + (-B))$$
$$= \sin A \cos(-B) + \cos A \sin(-B)$$
$$= \sin A \cos B + \cos A (-\sin B)$$
$$= \sin A \cos B - \cos A \sin B$$

and we have the difference formula for sine.

Sum and Difference Formulas for Sine

$$\sin(A+B) = \sin A \cos B + \cos A \sin B$$
$$\sin(A-B) = \sin A \cos B - \cos A \sin B$$

The identities are almost identical, except for the sign in between the terms. As with the formulas for cosine, be careful not to make the following common mistakes.

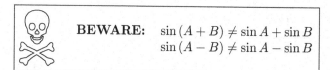 **BEWARE:** $\sin(A+B) \neq \sin A + \sin B$
$\sin(A-B) \neq \sin A - \sin B$

Examples. Find the exact value of each of the expression.

1) $\sin 15° = \underbrace{\sin(60° - 45°) = \sin 60° \cos 45° - \cos 60° \sin 45°}_{\text{Use the difference formula with } A=60° \text{ and } B=45°.} = \left(\frac{\sqrt{3}}{2}\right)\left(\frac{\sqrt{2}}{2}\right) - \left(\frac{1}{2}\right)\left(\frac{\sqrt{2}}{2}\right) = \frac{\sqrt{6}-\sqrt{2}}{4}$

2) $\sin 195° = \underbrace{\sin(135° + 60°) = \sin 135° \cos 60° + \cos 135° \sin 60°}_{\text{Use the sum formula with } A=135° \text{ and } B=60°.} = \left(\frac{\sqrt{2}}{2}\right)\left(\frac{1}{2}\right) + \left(-\frac{\sqrt{2}}{2}\right)\left(\frac{\sqrt{3}}{2}\right) = \frac{\sqrt{2}-\sqrt{6}}{4}$

3) $\sin\frac{5\pi}{12} = \sin\left(\frac{2\pi}{12} + \frac{3\pi}{12}\right) = \sin\left(\frac{\pi}{6} + \frac{\pi}{4}\right) = \sin\frac{\pi}{6}\cos\frac{\pi}{4} + \cos\frac{\pi}{6}\sin\frac{\pi}{4} = \left(\frac{1}{2}\right)\left(\frac{\sqrt{2}}{2}\right) + \left(\frac{\sqrt{3}}{2}\right)\left(\frac{\sqrt{2}}{2}\right) = \frac{\sqrt{2}+\sqrt{6}}{4}$

4) $\sin 92° \cos 2° - \cos 92° \sin 2° = \sin(92° - 2°) = \sin 90° = 1$

5) $\sin\frac{2\pi}{15}\cos\frac{28\pi}{15} + \cos\frac{2\pi}{15}\sin\frac{28\pi}{15} = \sin\left(\frac{2\pi}{15} + \frac{28\pi}{15}\right) = \sin\left(\frac{30\pi}{15}\right) = \sin 2\pi = 0$

Examples.

1) Suppose that $\cos \alpha = \frac{\sqrt{7}}{3}$ and $\sin \beta = \frac{1}{4}$. If α lies in quadrant I and β lies in quadrant II, find the exact value of $\sin (\alpha - \beta)$.

The difference formula for sine is

$$\sin (\alpha - \beta) = \sin \alpha \cos \beta - \cos \alpha \sin \beta.$$

We need to find the values for $\sin \alpha$ and $\cos \beta$.

Step 1. Let's find $\sin \alpha$.

Since $\cos \alpha = \dfrac{\sqrt{7}}{3} = \dfrac{a}{r}$, so we may choose $a = \sqrt{7}$ and $r = 3$ (see the next figure). Notice that a must be a positive number because α lies in quadrant I. We need to find b. Using the formula $r = \sqrt{a^2 + b^2}$, we have that:

$$3 = \sqrt{\left(\sqrt{7}\right)^2 + b^2}$$
$$3 = \sqrt{7 + b^2}$$
$$(3)^2 = \left(\sqrt{7 + b^2}\right)^2$$
$$9 = 7 + b^2$$
$$2 = b^2$$
$$b = \pm\sqrt{2}$$

And so $b = \sqrt{2}$ (since α lies in quadrant I). Therefore,

$$\sin \alpha = \frac{b}{r} = \frac{\sqrt{2}}{3}.$$

We will rationalize the denominator of our final answer at the end.

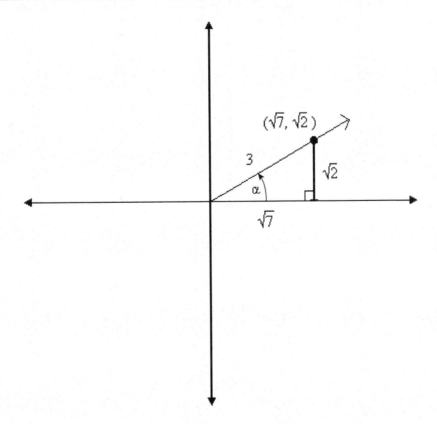

Step 2. Let's find $\cos \beta$.

Since $\sin \beta = \dfrac{1}{4} = \dfrac{b}{r}$, we may choose $b = 1$ and $r = 4$ (see the next figure). We need to find a. Observe that $a < 0$ since β lies in quadrant II. Using the formula $r = \sqrt{a^2 + b^2}$, we have:

$$4 = \sqrt{a^2 + (1)^2}$$
$$4 = \sqrt{a^2 + 1}$$
$$(4)^2 = \left(\sqrt{a^2 + 1}\right)^2$$
$$16 = a^2 + 1$$
$$15 = a^2$$
$$a = \pm\sqrt{15}$$

And so $a = -\sqrt{15}$. Therefore,

$$\cos \beta = \frac{a}{r} = \frac{-\sqrt{15}}{4}.$$

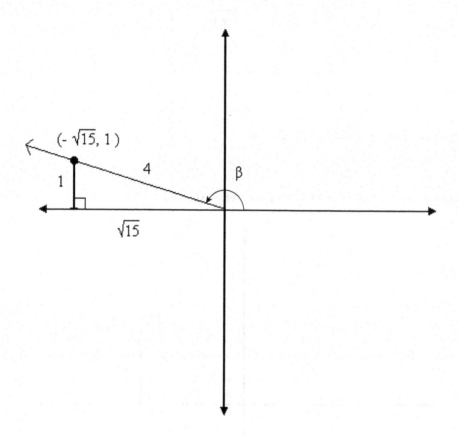

Step 3. Let's find $\sin (\alpha - \beta)$.

$$
\begin{aligned}
\sin (\alpha - \beta) &= \sin \alpha \cos \beta - \cos \alpha \sin \beta \\
&= \frac{\sqrt{2}}{3} \left(\frac{-\sqrt{15}}{4}\right) - \frac{\sqrt{7}}{3} \left(\frac{1}{4}\right) \\
&= \frac{-\sqrt{30}}{12} - \frac{\sqrt{7}}{12} \\
&= \frac{-\sqrt{30} - \sqrt{7}}{12}
\end{aligned}
$$

2) Verify the identity: $\sin\left(-\frac{\pi}{2} + \theta\right) = -\cos\theta$

We will use the sum formula for sine.

$$\sin(A + B) = \sin A \cos B + \cos A \sin B$$

$$\sin\left(-\frac{\pi}{2} + \theta\right) = \sin\left(-\frac{\pi}{2}\right)\cos\theta + \cos\left(-\frac{\pi}{2}\right)\sin\theta$$

$$= -\sin\frac{\pi}{2}\cos\theta + \cos\frac{\pi}{2}\sin\theta$$

$$= -1(\cos\theta) + 0(\sin\theta)$$

$$= -\cos\theta$$

3) Verify the identity: $\frac{1}{2}\left[\sin(x+y) - \sin(x-y)\right] = \cos x \sin y$

Let's work on the left-hand side of the equation. Both of the formulas for sine will be used.

$$\frac{1}{2}\left[\sin(x+y) - \sin(x-y)\right] = \frac{1}{2}\left[\sin x \cos y + \cos x \sin y - (\sin x \cos y - \cos x \sin y)\right]$$

$$= \frac{1}{2}\left[\sin x \cos y + \cos x \sin y - \sin x \cos y + \cos x \sin y\right]$$

$$= \frac{1}{\cancel{2}}\left[\cancel{2}\cos x \sin y\right]$$

$$= \cos x \sin y$$

Try These (Set 11):

1) Suppose that $\cos A = -\frac{4}{5}$ and $\cot B = \frac{\sqrt{2}}{3}$. If $180° < A < 270°$ and $0° < B < 90°$, find the exact value of $\sin(A + B)$.

2) Find the exact value of $\sin\frac{8\pi}{9}\cos\frac{\pi}{18} - \cos\frac{8\pi}{9}\sin\frac{\pi}{18}$.

3) Verify the identity: $\sin\left(\frac{\pi}{4} + t\right) + \sin\left(\frac{\pi}{4} - t\right) = \sqrt{2}\cos t$

The Sum and Difference Formulas for Tangent

The sum and difference formulas for tangent will be derived by using the formulas for sine and cosine. Let's begin by deriving the sum formula for tangent, $\tan(A + B)$. There is a trick involved which allows us to produce a nice formula. The trick (which appears in the second line) is to divide the numerator and denominator of the fraction by $\cos A \cos B$.

$$\tan(A+B) = \frac{\sin(A+B)}{\cos(A+B)} = \frac{\sin A \cos B + \cos A \sin B}{\cos A \cos B - \sin A \sin B}$$

$$= \frac{\dfrac{\sin A \cos B + \cos A \sin B}{\cos A \cos B}}{\dfrac{\cos A \cos B - \sin A \sin B}{\cos A \cos B}} = \frac{\dfrac{\sin A \cos B}{\cos A \cos B} + \dfrac{\cos A \sin B}{\cos A \cos B}}{\dfrac{\cos A \cos B}{\cos A \cos B} - \dfrac{\sin A \sin B}{\cos A \cos B}}$$

$$= \frac{\dfrac{\sin A}{\cos A} + \dfrac{\sin B}{\cos B}}{1 - \dfrac{\sin A}{\cos A}\dfrac{\sin B}{\cos B}} = \frac{\tan A + \tan B}{1 - \tan A \tan B}$$

We now have our sum formula for tangent. The difference formula is found by writing $A - B = A + (-B)$ and applying the sum formula for tangent.

$$\tan(A - B) = \tan(A + (-B))$$

$$= \frac{\tan A + \tan(-B)}{1 - \tan A \tan(-B)}$$

$$= \frac{\tan A + (-\tan B)}{1 - \tan A (-\tan B)}$$

$$= \frac{\tan A - \tan B}{1 + \tan A \tan B}$$

And we're done. As with the cosine and sine formulas, notice that the tangent formulas are almost identical, except for some differences in signs.

Sum and Difference Formulas for Tangent

$$\tan(A + B) = \frac{\tan A + \tan B}{1 - \tan A \tan B}$$

$$\tan(A - B) = \frac{\tan A - \tan B}{1 + \tan A \tan B}$$

Once again, don't make the following common mistakes.

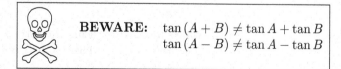

BEWARE: $\tan(A + B) \neq \tan A + \tan B$

$\tan(A - B) \neq \tan A - \tan B$

Examples. Find the exact value of each of the expression.

1) $\tan 75° = \underbrace{\tan\left(45° + 30°\right) = \dfrac{\tan 45° + \tan 30°}{1 - \tan 45° \tan 30°}}_{\text{Use the sum formula with } A=45° \text{ and } B=30°.} = \dfrac{1 + \frac{1}{\sqrt{3}}}{1 - 1\left(\frac{1}{\sqrt{3}}\right)} = \dfrac{1 + \frac{1}{\sqrt{3}}}{1 - \frac{1}{\sqrt{3}}}$

$= \left(\dfrac{1 + \frac{1}{\sqrt{3}}}{1 - \frac{1}{\sqrt{3}}}\right)\left(\dfrac{\frac{\sqrt{3}}{1}}{\frac{\sqrt{3}}{1}}\right) = \dfrac{1\left(\frac{\sqrt{3}}{1}\right) + \frac{1}{\sqrt{3}}\left(\frac{\sqrt{3}}{1}\right)}{1\left(\frac{\sqrt{3}}{1}\right) - \frac{1}{\sqrt{3}}\left(\frac{\sqrt{3}}{1}\right)} = \dfrac{\sqrt{3} + 1}{\sqrt{3} - 1}$

2) $\dfrac{\tan \frac{8\pi}{7} - \tan \frac{\pi}{7}}{1 + \tan \frac{8\pi}{7} \tan \frac{\pi}{7}} = \tan\left(\frac{8\pi}{7} - \frac{\pi}{7}\right) = \tan\left(\frac{7\pi}{7}\right) = \tan \pi = 0$

3) $\tan \frac{19\pi}{12} = \tan\left(\frac{16\pi}{12} + \frac{3\pi}{12}\right) = \tan\left(\frac{4\pi}{3} + \frac{\pi}{4}\right) = \dfrac{\tan \frac{4\pi}{3} + \tan \frac{\pi}{4}}{1 - \tan \frac{4\pi}{3} \tan \frac{\pi}{4}} = \dfrac{\sqrt{3} + 1}{1 - \left(\sqrt{3}\right)(1)} = \dfrac{\sqrt{3} + 1}{1 - \sqrt{3}}$

Examples.

1) If $\sin A = -\frac{4}{5}$, $\frac{3\pi}{2} < A < 2\pi$, and $\cos B = -\frac{1}{2}$, $\pi < B < \frac{3\pi}{2}$, find the exact value of $\tan\left(A - B\right)$.

The difference formula for tangent is

$$\tan\left(A - B\right) = \dfrac{\tan A - \tan B}{1 + \tan A \tan B}.$$

We need to find the values for $\tan A$ and $\tan B$.

<u>**Step 1.**</u> Let's find $\tan A$.

Since $\sin A = -\dfrac{4}{5} = \dfrac{-4}{5} = \dfrac{b}{r}$ and A is in quadrant IV, we may choose $b = -4$ and $r = 5$ (see the next figure). Notice that a must be a positive number because A lies in quadrant IV. We need to find a. Using the formula $r = \sqrt{a^2 + b^2}$, we have that:

$$5 = \sqrt{a^2 + (-4)^2}$$
$$5 = \sqrt{a^2 + 16}$$
$$(5)^2 = \left(\sqrt{a^2 + 16}\right)^2$$
$$25 = a^2 + 16$$
$$9 = a^2$$
$$a = \pm\sqrt{9} = \pm 3$$

And so $a = 3$ (since A lies in quadrant IV). Therefore,

$$\tan A = \dfrac{b}{a} = \dfrac{-4}{3} = -\dfrac{4}{3}.$$

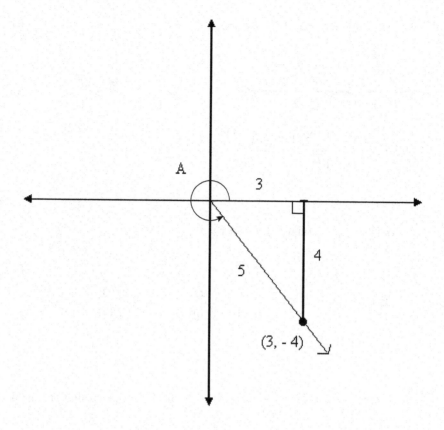

Step 2. Let's find $\tan B$.

Since $\cos B = -\dfrac{1}{2} = \dfrac{-1}{2} = \dfrac{a}{r}$ and B is in quadrant III, we may choose $a = -1$ and $r = 2$ (see the next figure). We need to find b. Observe that $b < 0$ since B lies in quadrant III. Using the formula $r = \sqrt{a^2 + b^2}$, we have:

$$2 = \sqrt{(-1)^2 + b^2}$$
$$2 = \sqrt{1 + b^2}$$
$$(2)^2 = \left(\sqrt{1 + b^2}\right)^2$$
$$4 = 1 + b^2$$
$$3 = b^2$$
$$b = \pm\sqrt{3}$$

And so $b = -\sqrt{3}$. Therefore,

$$\tan B = \frac{b}{a} = \frac{-\sqrt{3}}{-1} = \sqrt{3}.$$

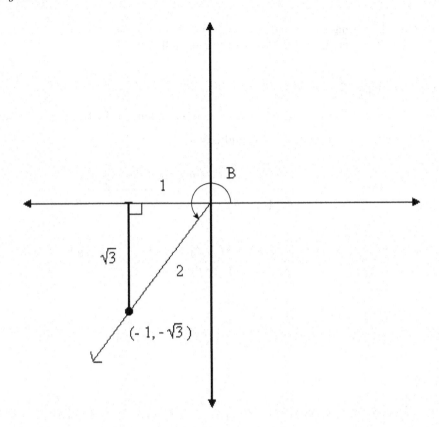

Step 3. Let's find $\tan(A-B)$.

$$\tan(A-B) = \frac{\tan A - \tan B}{1 + \tan A \tan B}$$

$$= \frac{-\dfrac{4}{3} - \sqrt{3}}{1 + \left(-\dfrac{4}{3}\right)(\sqrt{3})} = \left(\frac{-\dfrac{4}{3} - \sqrt{3}}{1 - \dfrac{4\sqrt{3}}{3}}\right)\left(\frac{\dfrac{3}{1}}{\dfrac{3}{1}}\right)$$

$$= \frac{-\dfrac{4}{\cancel{3}}\left(\dfrac{\cancel{3}}{1}\right) - \sqrt{3}\left(\dfrac{3}{1}\right)}{1\left(\dfrac{3}{1}\right) - \dfrac{4\sqrt{3}}{\cancel{3}}\left(\dfrac{\cancel{3}}{1}\right)} = \frac{-4 - 3\sqrt{3}}{3 - 4\sqrt{3}}$$

2) Verify the identity: $\tan\left(\frac{\pi}{4} + \theta\right) = \dfrac{1 + \tan\theta}{1 - \tan\theta}$

We will use the sum formula for tangent.

$$\tan\left(\frac{\pi}{4} + \theta\right) = \frac{\tan\dfrac{\pi}{4} + \tan\theta}{1 - \tan\dfrac{\pi}{4}\tan\theta} = \frac{1 + \tan\theta}{1 - 1(\tan\theta)} = \frac{1 + \tan\theta}{1 - \tan\theta}$$

You must be careful when using the formulas for tangent. They can only be used when $\tan A$, $\tan B$, and $\tan(A + B)$ (or $\tan(A - B)$ if you are using this one) are all well-defined.

3) Verify the identity: $\tan\left(\frac{\pi}{2} + \theta\right) = -\cot\theta$

We cannot use the sum formula for tangent, since $\tan\frac{\pi}{2}$ is undefined. Instead, we will use the identity $\tan\theta = \dfrac{\sin\theta}{\cos\theta}$, as well as the sum formulas for sine and cosine.

$$\tan\left(\frac{\pi}{2} + \theta\right) = \frac{\sin\left(\frac{\pi}{2} + \theta\right)}{\cos\left(\frac{\pi}{2} + \theta\right)} = \frac{\sin\frac{\pi}{2}\cos\theta + \cos\frac{\pi}{2}\sin\theta}{\cos\frac{\pi}{2}\cos\theta - \sin\frac{\pi}{2}\sin\theta}$$

$$= \frac{1(\cos\theta) + 0(\sin\theta)}{0(\cos\theta) - 1(\sin\theta)} = \frac{\cos\theta}{-\sin\theta} = -\frac{\cos\theta}{\sin\theta}$$

$$= -\cot\theta$$

Try These (Set 12):

1) Suppose that $\tan\alpha = \sqrt{5}$ and $\sec\beta = -\frac{4}{3}$. If $180° < \alpha < 270°$ and $90° < \beta < 180°$, find the exact value of $\tan(\alpha - \beta)$.

2) Find the exact value of $\dfrac{\tan 310° + \tan 20°}{1 - \tan 310° \tan 20°}$.

3) Verify the identity: $\tan(2\pi - x) = -\tan x$

Verifying Identities Containing a Sum and/or Difference of Angles

We will look at some more examples on verifying identities which contain a sum of angles and/or a difference of angles. Let's begin by summarizing our formulas.

The Sum and Difference Formulas

$$\cos(A + B) = \cos A \cos B - \sin A \sin B$$

$$\cos(A - B) = \cos A \cos B + \sin A \sin B$$

$$\sin(A + B) = \sin A \cos B + \cos A \sin B$$

$$\sin(A - B) = \sin A \cos B - \cos A \sin B$$

$$\tan(A + B) = \frac{\tan A + \tan B}{1 - \tan A \tan B}$$

$$\tan(A - B) = \frac{\tan A - \tan B}{1 + \tan A \tan B}$$

Examples. Verify the identities.

1) $\dfrac{\sin{(A-B)}}{\sin{(A+B)}} = \dfrac{\tan A - \tan B}{\tan A + \tan B}$

Let's work on the left-hand side of the equation. I've chosen this side for the obvious reason that it contains a sum and a difference of angles. Therefore, our sine formulas will be used. The trick needed to verify this identity is to create terms with tangent in it. In the second equality, you will see that I divided each term in the numerator and denominator by $\cos A \cos B$. The reason that I did this is because I noticed that the first fraction in the numerator will become

$$\frac{\sin A \cos B}{\cos A \cos B} = \frac{\sin A}{\cos A} = \tan A,$$

which is exactly one of the terms in the expression that I'm trying to obtain. Let's see what happens.

$$\frac{\sin{(A-B)}}{\sin{(A+B)}} = \frac{\sin A \cos B - \cos A \sin B}{\sin A \cos B + \cos A \sin B} = \frac{\dfrac{\sin A \cos B}{\cos A \cos B} - \dfrac{\cos A \sin B}{\cos A \cos B}}{\dfrac{\sin A \cos B}{\cos A \cos B} + \dfrac{\cos A \sin B}{\cos A \cos B}}$$

$$= \frac{\dfrac{\sin A}{\cos A} - \dfrac{\sin B}{\cos B}}{\dfrac{\sin A}{\cos A} + \dfrac{\sin B}{\cos B}} = \frac{\tan A - \tan B}{\tan A + \tan B}$$

By remembering that I can create $\tan A$ by dividing $\sin A$ by $\cos A$, I was able to come up with a plan to prove the identity to be true. After going through with my plan, I see that my identity comes out the way that I hoped for.

2) $\dfrac{\cos{(x+y)}}{\cos{(x-y)}} = \dfrac{1 - \tan x \tan y}{1 + \tan x \tan y}$

Let's work out the left-hand side. As in the previous example, there is a **technique** involved (no longer referred to as a 'trick'). Let's do this one step by step. First, let's expand $\cos{(x+y)}$ and $\cos{(x-y)}$ by using our formulas:

$$\frac{\cos{(x+y)}}{\cos{(x-y)}} = \frac{\cos x \cos y - \sin x \sin y}{\cos x \cos y + \sin x \sin y}$$

Now, the first term in the numerator (and denominator) is $\cos x \cos y$. We would like to somehow transform this into a 1 since the right-hand side of the identity has a 1 in its numerator (and denominator). This suggests that we should divide every term in our fraction by $\cos x \cos y$. Let's see what happens.

$$\frac{\cos{(x+y)}}{\cos{(x-y)}} = \frac{\cos x \cos y - \sin x \sin y}{\cos x \cos y + \sin x \sin y} = \frac{\dfrac{\overset{1}{\cancel{\cos x \cos y}}}{\cancel{\cos x \cos y}} - \dfrac{\sin x \sin y}{\cos x \cos y}}{\dfrac{\cancel{\cos x \cos y}}{\underset{1}{\cancel{\cos x \cos y}}} + \dfrac{\sin x \sin y}{\cos x \cos y}}$$

$$= \frac{1 - \dfrac{\sin x}{\cos x}\dfrac{\sin y}{\cos y}}{1 + \dfrac{\sin x}{\cos x}\dfrac{\sin y}{\cos y}} = \frac{1 - \tan x \tan y}{1 + \tan x \tan y}$$

3) $\cot(\alpha + \beta) = \dfrac{\cot\alpha\cot\beta - 1}{\cot\alpha + \cot\beta}$

We don't have a formula for the sum of angles for cotangent. In fact, this identity is a formula. How do we derive it? Well, let's take a look at the right-hand side. We know the formula for the sum of angles for tangent. Our plan, therefore, is to convert the cotangent terms into tangent terms. We can do this by taking reciprocals. Let's see what happens.

$$\frac{\cot\alpha\cot\beta - 1}{\cot\alpha + \cot\beta} = \frac{\dfrac{1}{\tan\alpha}\dfrac{1}{\tan\beta} - 1}{\dfrac{1}{\tan\alpha} + \dfrac{1}{\tan\beta}} = \left(\frac{\dfrac{1}{\tan\alpha}\dfrac{1}{\tan\beta} - 1}{\dfrac{1}{\tan\alpha} + \dfrac{1}{\tan\beta}}\right)\left(\frac{\dfrac{\tan\alpha\tan\beta}{1}}{\dfrac{\tan\alpha\tan\beta}{1}}\right)$$

$$= \frac{\dfrac{1}{\tan\alpha}\dfrac{1}{\tan\beta}\left(\dfrac{\tan\alpha\tan\beta}{1}\right) - 1\left(\dfrac{\tan\alpha\tan\beta}{1}\right)}{\dfrac{1}{\tan\alpha}\left(\dfrac{\tan\alpha\tan\beta}{1}\right) + \dfrac{1}{\tan\beta}\left(\dfrac{\tan\alpha\tan\beta}{1}\right)} = \frac{1 - \tan\alpha\tan\beta}{\tan\beta + \tan\alpha}$$

Now I'm not happy because this doesn't look like $\cot(\alpha + \beta)$ ... yet! Observe that

$$\frac{1 - \tan\alpha\tan\beta}{\tan\beta + \tan\alpha} \text{ is the reciprocal of } \frac{\tan\beta + \tan\alpha}{1 - \tan\alpha\tan\beta} = \tan(\alpha + \beta).$$

Therefore,

$$\frac{\cot\alpha\cot\beta - 1}{\cot\alpha + \cot\beta} = \frac{1 - \tan\alpha\tan\beta}{\tan\beta + \tan\alpha}$$

$$= \frac{1}{\dfrac{\tan\beta + \tan\alpha}{1 - \tan\alpha\tan\beta}}$$

$$= \frac{1}{\tan(\alpha + \beta)}$$

$$= \cot(\alpha + \beta)$$

and we have our identity.

4) $\sin(\theta + k\pi) = (-1)^k \sin\theta$, where k is any integer.

Using the sum formula for sine, we have

$$\sin(\theta + k\pi) = \sin\theta\cos k\pi + \cos\theta\sin k\pi.$$

We need to figure out what $\cos k\pi$ and $\sin k\pi$ are. Let's start with $\cos k\pi$. Recall that $\cos 0 = 1$ and $\cos \pi = -1$. This implies that for any integer n, we have

$$\cos{(0 + 2\pi n)} = \underbrace{\cos{[(2n)\,\pi]} = \cos{k\pi}}_{\text{Let } k=2n \text{ (an even integer).}} = 1 \quad \text{and} \quad \cos{(\pi + 2\pi n)} = \underbrace{\cos{[(2n+1)\,\pi]} = \cos{k\pi}}_{\text{Let } k=2n+1 \text{ (an odd integer).}} = -1$$

because cosine is periodic with period 2π. This shows us that $\cos{k\pi} = 1$ if k is even and $\cos{k\pi} = -1$ if k is odd. We can represent this information by the formula $\cos{k\pi} = (-1)^k$. Notice that $(-1)^k = 1$ if k is even and $(-1)^k = -1$ if k is odd, which is what we wanted.

Next let's work out $\sin{k\pi}$. Recall that $\sin{0} = 0$ and $\sin{\pi} = 0$. By the periodicity of sine, this implies that for any integer n,

$$\sin{(0 + 2\pi n)} = \underbrace{\sin{[(2n)\,\pi]} = \sin{k\pi}}_{\text{Let } k=2n \text{ (an even integer).}} = 0 \quad \text{and} \quad \sin{(\pi + 2\pi n)} = \underbrace{\sin{[(2n+1)\,\pi]} = \sin{k\pi}}_{\text{Let } k=2n+1 \text{ (an odd integer).}} = 0$$

Therefore, $\sin{k\pi} = 0$ when k is either an even integer or an odd integer. Let's go back to our identity that we are trying to verify.

$$\begin{aligned}
\sin{(\theta + k\pi)} &= \sin{\theta}\cos{k\pi} + \cos{\theta}\sin{k\pi} \\
&= (\sin{\theta})\,(-1)^k + (\cos{\theta})\,(0) \\
&= (-1)^k \sin{\theta}
\end{aligned}$$

Try These (Set 13): Verify each identity.

1) $\dfrac{\sin{(A+B)}}{\cos{A}\cos{B}} = \tan{A} + \tan{B}$

2) $\dfrac{\sin{(\alpha+\beta)}}{\cos{(\alpha-\beta)}} = \dfrac{\cot{\alpha} + \cot{\beta}}{1 + \cot{\alpha}\cot{\beta}}$

Exercise 6.3

In Exercises 1-30, find the exact value of each of the expression.

1. $\sin{75°}$
2. $\sin{15°}$
3. $\sin{\frac{7\pi}{12}}$
4. $\sin{\frac{\pi}{12}}$

5. $\cos{195°}$
6. $\cos{105°}$
7. $\cos{\frac{\pi}{12}}$
8. $\cos{\frac{17\pi}{12}}$

9. $\tan{105°}$
10. $\tan{165°}$
11. $\tan{\frac{19\pi}{12}}$
12. $\tan{\frac{\pi}{12}}$

13. $\sin{(-165°)}$
14. $\tan{(-75°)}$
15. $\cos{\left(-\frac{7\pi}{12}\right)}$
16. $\cos{\left(-\frac{\pi}{12}\right)}$

17. $\cos{44°}\cos{46°} - \sin{44°}\sin{46°}$
18. $\cos{160°}\cos{40°} + \sin{160°}\sin{40°}$

19. $\cos{305°}\cos{170°} + \sin{305°}\sin{170°}$
20. $\cos{185°}\cos{25°} - \sin{185°}\sin{25°}$

21. $\cos{\frac{7\pi}{12}}\cos{\frac{5\pi}{12}} - \sin{\frac{7\pi}{12}}\sin{\frac{5\pi}{12}}$
22. $\cos{\frac{5\pi}{12}}\cos{\frac{\pi}{12}} + \sin{\frac{5\pi}{12}}\sin{\frac{\pi}{12}}$

23. $\sin{100°}\cos{55°} - \cos{100°}\sin{55°}$
24. $\sin{160°}\cos{200°} + \cos{160°}\sin{200°}$

25. $\sin{\frac{5\pi}{18}}\cos{\frac{\pi}{18}} + \cos{\frac{5\pi}{18}}\sin{\frac{\pi}{18}}$
26. $\sin{\frac{7\pi}{12}}\cos{\frac{\pi}{12}} - \cos{\frac{7\pi}{12}}\sin{\frac{\pi}{12}}$

27. $\dfrac{\tan 50° + \tan 130°}{1 - \tan 50° \tan 130°}$

28. $\dfrac{\tan 305° - \tan 185°}{1 + \tan 305° \tan 185°}$

29. $\dfrac{\tan \frac{7\pi}{9} + \tan \frac{7\pi}{18}}{1 - \tan \frac{7\pi}{9} \tan \frac{7\pi}{18}}$

30. $\dfrac{\tan \frac{20\pi}{9} - \tan \frac{5\pi}{9}}{1 + \tan \frac{20\pi}{9} \tan \frac{5\pi}{9}}$

In Exercises 31-36, use the given information to find the exact value of each of the following:

(a) $\cos(\alpha + \beta)$ (b) $\sin(\alpha + \beta)$ (c) $\tan(\alpha - \beta)$ (d) $\cos(\alpha - \beta)$

31. $\sin \alpha = \frac{4}{5}$, $0 < \alpha < \frac{\pi}{2}$; $\cos \beta = \frac{2\sqrt{2}}{5}$, $\frac{3\pi}{2} < \beta < 2\pi$

32. $\cos \alpha = \frac{1}{3}$, $0 < \alpha < \frac{\pi}{2}$; $\sin \beta = \frac{\sqrt{3}}{3}$, $\frac{\pi}{2} < \beta < \pi$

33. $\tan \alpha = -4$, $270° < \alpha < 360°$; $\cos \beta = \frac{3}{5}$, $0° < \beta < 90°$

34. $\sin \alpha = -\frac{3\sqrt{2}}{7}$, $270° < \alpha < 360°$; $\tan \beta = 2$, $180° < \beta < 270°$

35. $\cos \alpha = -\frac{2}{3}$, $-\pi < \alpha < -\frac{\pi}{2}$; $\tan \beta = -\frac{\sqrt{6}}{4}$, $-\frac{\pi}{2} < \beta < 0$

36. $\tan \alpha = -\frac{5}{4}$, $-\frac{3\pi}{2} < \alpha < -\pi$; $\sin \beta = -\frac{5\sqrt{2}}{8}$, $-\frac{\pi}{2} < \beta < 0$

In Exercises 37-64, establish the identity.

37. $\cos\left(\frac{\pi}{2} + x\right) = -\sin x$

38. $\sin\left(\frac{\pi}{2} + x\right) = \cos x$

39. $\sin(\pi - A) = \sin A$

40. $\sin(\pi + A) = -\sin A$

41. $\cos(\pi + \theta) = -\cos \theta$

42. $\cos(\pi - \theta) = -\cos \theta$

43. $\sin\left(\frac{3\pi}{2} + \alpha\right) = -\cos \alpha$

44. $\cos\left(\frac{3\pi}{2} + \beta\right) = \sin \beta$

45. $\tan(\pi + x) = \tan x$

46. $\tan(\pi - x) = -\tan x$

47. $\tan\left(\frac{3\pi}{2} - \alpha\right) = \cot \alpha$

48. $\tan\left(\frac{\pi}{2} + \beta\right) = -\cot \beta$

49. $\sin(x + y) + \sin(x - y) = 2\sin x \cos y$

50. $\sin(x + y) - \sin(x - y) = 2\cos x \sin y$

51. $\cos(x + y) - \cos(x - y) = -2\sin x \sin y$

52. $\cos(x + y) + \cos(x - y) = 2\cos x \cos y$

53. $\dfrac{\sin(A + B)}{\sin(A - B)} = \dfrac{\tan A + \tan B}{\tan A - \tan B}$

54. $\dfrac{\sin(A - B)}{\cos A \cos B} = \tan A - \tan B$

55. $\dfrac{\cos(A - B)}{\sin A \cos B} = \tan B + \cot A$

56. $\dfrac{\cos(A + B)}{\cos A \cos B} = 1 - \tan A \tan B$

57. $\sec(\theta + \alpha) = \dfrac{\csc \theta \csc \alpha}{\cot \theta \cot \alpha - 1}$

58. $\csc(\theta + \alpha) = \dfrac{\csc \theta \csc \alpha}{1 + \cot \theta \tan \alpha}$

59. $\tan(\alpha + \beta) + \tan(\alpha - \beta) = \dfrac{2\tan \alpha \sec^2 \beta}{1 - \tan^2 \alpha \tan^2 \beta}$

60. $\tan(\alpha + \beta) - \tan(\alpha - \beta) = \dfrac{2\tan \beta \sec^2 \alpha}{1 - \tan^2 \alpha \tan^2 \beta}$

61. $\cos(\theta + k\pi) = (-1)^k \cos \theta$, where k is any integer.

62. $\sin(\theta - k\pi) = (-1)^k \sin\theta$, where k is any integer.

63. $\tan(\alpha + k\pi) = \tan\alpha$, where k is any integer.

64. $\tan(\beta - k\pi) = \tan\beta$, where k is any integer.

65. Suppose that $f(x) = \cos x$. Show that

$$\frac{f(x+h) - f(x)}{h} = -\sin x\left(\frac{\sin h}{h}\right) - \cos x\left(\frac{1 - \cos h}{h}\right).$$

66. Suppose that $g(x) = \sin x$. Show that

$$\frac{g(x+h) - g(x)}{h} = \cos x\left(\frac{\sin h}{h}\right) - \sin x\left(\frac{1 - \cos h}{h}\right).$$

Section 6.4 Double-Angle Formulas

By using the sum formulas from Section 6.3, we can derive another collection of important formulas called the **double-angle formulas**. These formulas appear very frequently in Calculus and higher mathematics, so you should eventually memorize them.

Let's start by deriving a formula for $\sin 2A$. The idea is to write $\sin 2A = \sin(A + A)$ and use the sum formula for sine.

$$\begin{aligned} \sin 2A &= \sin(A + A) \\ &= \sin A\cos A + \cos A\sin A \\ &= 2\sin A\cos A \end{aligned}$$

Next, let's derive the formulas for $\cos 2A$. Again, we will write $2A = A + A$ and proceed as before.

$$\begin{aligned} \cos 2A &= \cos(A + A) \\ &= \cos A\cos A - \sin A\sin A \\ &= \cos^2 A - \sin^2 A \end{aligned}$$

Now, recall that $\sin^2 A = 1 - \cos^2 A$ by the Pythagorean identity. Replacing $\sin^2 A$ by $1 - \cos^2 A$ gives us another formula for $\cos 2A$.

$$\begin{aligned} \cos 2A &= \cos^2 A - \sin^2 A \\ &= \cos^2 A - (1 - \cos^2 A) \\ &= \cos^2 A - 1 + \cos^2 A \\ &= 2\cos^2 A - 1 \end{aligned}$$

We also know that $\cos^2 A = 1 - \sin^2 A$ by the Pythagorean identity. Replacing $\cos^2 A$ by $1 - \sin^2 A$ gives us a third formula for $\cos 2A$.

$$\begin{aligned} \cos 2A &= \cos^2 A - \sin^2 A \\ &= 1 - \sin^2 A - \sin^2 A \\ &= 1 - 2\sin^2 A \end{aligned}$$

To derive the formula for $\tan 2A$, we do the same as before.

$$\tan 2A = \frac{\tan A + \tan A}{1 - \tan A \tan A}$$

$$= \frac{2 \tan A}{1 - \tan^2 A}$$

The collection of our new formulas is given below.

Double-Angle Formulas

$$\sin 2A = 2 \sin A \cos A \qquad\qquad \tan 2A = \frac{2 \tan A}{1 - \tan^2 A}$$

$$\cos 2A = \cos^2 A - \sin^2 A$$
$$\cos 2A = 2 \cos^2 A - 1$$
$$\cos 2A = 1 - 2 \sin^2 A$$

Solving for the square terms in last two cosine formulas, we obtain the following useful formulas which represent $\cos^2 A$ and $\sin^2 A$ in terms of $\cos 2A$.

$$\cos^2 A = \frac{1 + \cos 2A}{2}$$

$$\sin^2 A = \frac{1 - \cos 2A}{2}$$

Since $\dfrac{\sin^2 A}{\cos^2 A} = \left(\dfrac{\sin A}{\cos A}\right)^2 = \tan^2 A$, we can use the previous formulas to obtain a formula for $\tan^2 A$ in terms of $\cos 2A$.

$$\tan^2 A = \frac{1 - \cos 2A}{1 + \cos 2A}$$

Examples.

1) Suppose that $\sin \theta = \frac{4}{5}$ and $\cos \theta < 0$. Find the exact value of $\sin 2\theta$ and $\cos 2\theta$.

Let's begin by finding the value of $\sin 2\theta$. The formula for $\sin 2\theta$ contains $\cos \theta$ in it, so we ought to find the value of $\cos \theta$ first. Observe that θ is in quadrant II since $\sin \theta = \dfrac{4}{5} > 0$ and $\cos \theta < 0$. Since $\sin \theta = \dfrac{4}{5} = \dfrac{b}{r}$

and θ is in quadrant II, we may choose $b = 4$ and $r = 5$ (see the figure below). Note that a must be a negative number because θ lies in quadrant II. We need to find a. Using the formula $r = \sqrt{a^2 + b^2}$, we have:

$$5 = \sqrt{a^2 + (4)^2}$$
$$5 = \sqrt{a^2 + 16}$$
$$(5)^2 = \left(\sqrt{a^2 + 16}\right)^2$$
$$25 = a^2 + 16$$
$$9 = a^2$$
$$a = \pm\sqrt{9} = \pm 3$$

And so $a = -3$. Therefore,

$$\cos\theta = \frac{a}{r} = \frac{-3}{5} = -\frac{3}{5}.$$

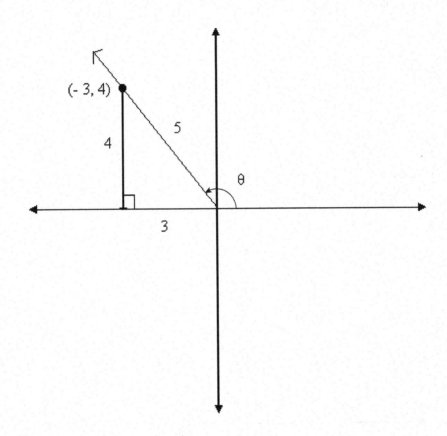

We can now find the exact value of $\sin 2\theta$.

$$\sin 2\theta = 2\sin\theta\cos\theta = 2\left(\frac{4}{5}\right)\left(-\frac{3}{5}\right) = -\frac{24}{25}$$

To find the exact value of $\cos 2\theta$, you can use any one of the double-angle formulas for cosine.

$$\cos 2\theta = 1 - 2\sin^2\theta = 1 - 2\left(\frac{4}{5}\right)^2 = 1 - \frac{2}{1}\left(\frac{16}{25}\right)$$

$$= 1 - \frac{32}{25} = -\frac{7}{25}$$

2) If $\cos x = \frac{2\sqrt{3}}{7}$, find the exact value of $\cos 2x$.

To find the exact value of $\cos 2x$, we will use the double-angle formula for cosine which contains $\cos x$ only. Using one of the other two formulas would require more work.

$$\cos 2x = 2\cos^2 x - 1 = 2\left(\frac{2\sqrt{3}}{7}\right)^2 - 1$$

$$= 2\left(\frac{12}{49}\right) - 1 = \frac{24}{49} - 1 = -\frac{25}{49}$$

3) If $\sec B = \sqrt{5}$ and $\sin B < 0$, find the exact value of $\tan 2B$.

The formula for $\tan 2B$ contains $\tan B$ in it, so let's find the value of $\tan B$ first. Notice that B is in quadrant IV since $\sec B = \sqrt{5} > 0$ and $\sin B < 0$. Since $\sec B = \frac{\sqrt{5}}{1} = \frac{r}{a}$ and θ is in quadrant IV, we may choose $a = 1$ and $r = \sqrt{5}$ (see the figure below). Note that b must be a negative number because B lies in quadrant IV. We need to find b. Using the formula $r = \sqrt{a^2 + b^2}$, we have:

$$\sqrt{5} = \sqrt{(1)^2 + b^2}$$
$$\sqrt{5} = \sqrt{1 + b^2}$$
$$\left(\sqrt{5}\right)^2 = \left(\sqrt{1 + b^2}\right)^2$$
$$5 = 1 + b^2$$
$$4 = b^2$$
$$b = \pm\sqrt{4} = \pm 2$$

And so $b = -2$. Therefore,

$$\tan B = \frac{b}{a} = \frac{-2}{1} = -2$$

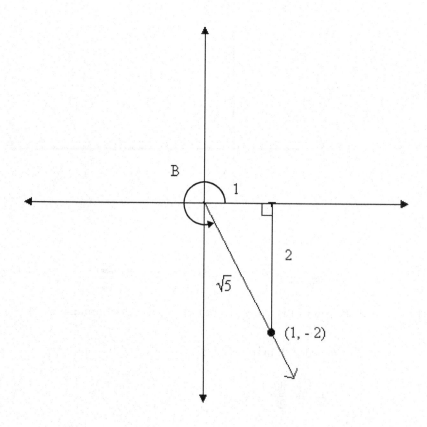

Let's find the exact value of $\tan 2B$.

$$\tan 2B = \frac{2 \tan B}{1 - \tan^2 B} = \frac{2(-2)}{1 - (-2)^2} = \frac{-4}{1-4} = \frac{4}{3}$$

4) Find the exact value of $2 \sin 15° \cos 15°$.

The expression resembles the right hand side of the formula $\sin 2A = 2 \sin A \cos A$, where $A = 15°$. Using this formula backwards, we have

$$2 \sin 15° \cos 15° = \sin [2(15°)] = \sin 30° = \frac{1}{2}.$$

4) Find the exact value of $\cos^2 \frac{\pi}{12} - \sin^2 \frac{\pi}{12}$.

The expression resembles the right hand side of the formula $\cos 2A = \cos^2 A - \sin^2 A$, where $A = \frac{\pi}{12}$. Using this formula backwards gives us

$$\cos^2 \frac{\pi}{12} - \sin^2 \frac{\pi}{12} = \cos \left[2 \left(\frac{\pi}{12} \right) \right] = \cos \frac{\pi}{6} = \frac{\sqrt{3}}{2}.$$

Try These (Set 14):

1) If $\cos x = \frac{2\sqrt{3}}{9}$, find the exact value of $\cos 2x$.

2) Find the exact value of $\dfrac{2 \tan 15°}{1 - \tan^2 15°}$.

3) If $\csc \beta = -\frac{4}{3}$ and $\sec \beta > 0$, find the exact value of $\sin 2\beta$.

Verifying Identities Containing a Double-Angle

Examples. Verify the identities.

1) $(\sin \theta + \cos \theta)^2 = \sin 2\theta + 1$

Let's expand the left-hand side of the equation and see what happens.

$$\begin{aligned}
(\sin \theta + \cos \theta)^2 &= \sin^2 \theta + 2 \sin \theta \cos \theta + \cos^2 \theta && \text{(using the formula } (A+B)^2 = A^2 + 2AB + B^2) \\
&= \sin^2 \theta + \cos^2 \theta + 2 \sin \theta \cos \theta && \text{(commuting terms)} \\
&= 1 + \sin 2\theta && (\sin^2 \theta + \cos^2 \theta = 1 \text{ and } 2 \sin \theta \cos \theta = \sin 2\theta)
\end{aligned}$$

2) $\tan 2x = \dfrac{2\tan x}{\sec^2 x - 2\tan^2 x}$

We will begin by rewriting $\tan 2x$ by using the double-angle formula. Afterwards, we will use one of the Pythagorean identities in order to create the $\sec^2 x$ term.

$$\tan 2x = \frac{2\tan x}{1 - \tan^2 x} \qquad\qquad \text{(the double-angle formula for } \tan 2x)$$

$$= \frac{2\tan x}{(\sec^2 x - \tan^2 x) - \tan^2 x} \qquad (\tan^2 x + 1 = \sec^2 x)$$

$$= \frac{2\tan x}{\sec^2 x - 2\tan^2 x}$$

3) $\tan A = \dfrac{1 - \cos 2A}{\sin 2A}$

We have to use the double-angle formulas to rewrite $\cos 2A$ and $\sin 2A$. However, there are three different formulas for $\cos 2A$. Which one should we use? Well, since we know that $\tan A = \dfrac{\sin A}{\cos A}$, we should use the formula which has $\sin A$ in it.

$$\frac{1 - \cos 2A}{\sin 2A} = \frac{1 - (1 - 2\sin^2 A)}{2\sin A \cos A} \qquad (\cos 2A = 1 - 2\sin^2 A \text{ is the preferred formula})$$

$$= \frac{1 - 1 + 2\sin^2 A}{2\sin A \cos A}$$

$$= \frac{\overset{1}{\cancel{2}}\sin^{\overset{1}{\cancel{2}}} A}{2\cancel{\sin} A \cos A}$$

$$= \frac{\sin A}{\cos A}$$

$$= \tan A$$

4) $\sin 3t = 3\sin t - 4\sin^3 t$

If we write $\sin 3t$ as $\sin(2t + t)$, we can use the sum formula for sine to remove the parenthesis. As you will see, it is preferable to use the formula $\cos 2t = 1 - 2\sin^2 t$ because our identity contains $\sin^3 t$ in it. Furthermore, we will replace all cosine terms because the identity that we want to verify only contains sine in it.

$$\begin{aligned}
\sin 3t &= \sin(2t + t) \\
&= \sin 2t \cos t + \cos 2t \sin t & \text{(sum formula for sine)} \\
&= (2\sin t \cos t)\cos t + (1 - 2\sin^2 t)\sin t & \text{(double-angle formulas)} \\
&= 2\sin t \cos^2 t + \sin t - 2\sin^3 t & \text{(Distributive Property)} \\
&= 2\sin t (1 - \sin^2 t) + \sin t - 2\sin^3 t & (\sin^2 t + \cos^2 t = 1) \\
&= 2\sin t - 2\sin^3 t + \sin t - 2\sin^3 t & \text{(Distributive Property)} \\
&= 3\sin t - 4\sin^3 t
\end{aligned}$$

In the next example, we will derive a new formula from a known one. This technique is important to know in order to do some problems in calculus.

Example. Using the formula $\cos^2 A = \dfrac{1 + \cos 2A}{2}$, derive a formula for $\cos^4 \theta$ which contains **both** $\cos 2\theta$ and $\cos 4\theta$.

$$\cos^4 \theta = \left(\cos^2 \theta\right)^2 = \left(\frac{1 + \cos 2\theta}{2}\right)^2 = \frac{(1 + \cos 2\theta)^2}{4}$$

$$= \frac{1 + 2\cos 2\theta + \cos^2 2\theta}{4} \qquad \text{(using the formula } (A+B)^2 = A^2 + 2AB + B^2)$$

$$= \frac{1}{4} + \frac{2\cos 2\theta}{4} + \frac{\cos^2 2\theta}{4}$$

$$= \frac{1}{4} + \frac{1}{2}\cos 2\theta + \frac{1}{4}\left(\frac{1 + \cos 2\,(2\theta)}{2}\right) \qquad \text{(using } \cos^2 A = \frac{1 + \cos 2A}{2} \text{ with } A = 2\theta)$$

$$= \frac{1}{4} + \frac{1}{2}\cos 2\theta + \frac{1}{8}\left(1 + \cos 4\theta\right)$$

$$= \frac{1}{4} + \frac{1}{2}\cos 2\theta + \frac{1}{8} + \frac{1}{8}\cos 4\theta$$

$$= \frac{3}{8} + \frac{1}{2}\cos 2\theta + \frac{1}{8}\cos 4\theta$$

Try These (Set 15): Verify each identity.

1) $(\sin A - \cos A)^2 = 1 - \sin 2A$

2) $\cos 4\theta = 8\cos^4 \theta - 8\cos^2 \theta + 1$ (Hint: use the formula $\cos 2A = 2\cos^2 A - 1$ twice.)

Exercise 6.4

In Exercises 1-8, find the exact value of each expression.

1. $2\sin 22.5° \cos 22.5°$ 2. $2\sin 75° \cos 75°$ 3. $\cos^2 15° - \sin^2 15°$ 4. $1 - 2\sin^2 22.5°$

5. $2\cos^2 105° - 1$ 6. $\cos^2 165° - \sin^2 165°$ 7. $\dfrac{2\tan 15°}{1 - \tan^2 15°}$ 8. $\dfrac{2\tan 22.5°}{1 - \tan^2 22.5°}$

In Exercises 9-20, use the given information to find the exact value of:

(a) $\sin 2x$ (b) $\cos 2x$ (c) $\tan 2x$

9. $\sin x = \frac{5}{13},\ 0° < x < 90°$ 10. $\cos x = \frac{3}{5},\ 0° < x < 90°$ 11. $\tan x = \sqrt{2},\ \pi < x < \frac{3\pi}{2}$

12. $\tan x = \frac{\sqrt{6}}{5},\ \pi < x < \frac{3\pi}{2}$ 13. $\cos x = -\frac{\sqrt{3}}{5},\ \frac{\pi}{2} < x < \pi$ 14. $\sin x = -\frac{\sqrt{2}}{6},\ \frac{3\pi}{2} < x < 2\pi$

15. $\tan x = -\frac{1}{5}$, $\cos x < 0$ 16. $\cos x = \frac{\sqrt{3}}{5}$, $\sin x < 0$ 17. $\sec x = -\frac{8}{5}$, $\tan x > 0$

18. $\sec x = 3\sqrt{2}$, $\sin x < 0$ 19. $\csc x = \frac{5\sqrt{2}}{6}$, $\cos x < 0$ 20. $\cot x = -\frac{3\sqrt{3}}{4}$, $\csc x < 0$

In Exercises 21-44, establish the identity.

21. $(\cos\theta - \sin\theta)^2 = 1 - \sin 2\theta$ 22. $(\cos\alpha + \sin\alpha)^2 = 1 - \sin 2\alpha$

23. $(\cos x + \sin x)(\cos x - \sin x) = \cos 2x$ 24. $2\sin^2 x = \tan x \sin 2x$

25. $\cos 2\beta = \dfrac{2 - \sec^2\beta}{\sec^2\beta}$ 26. $\sin 2\beta = \dfrac{2\tan\beta}{\tan^2\beta + 1}$ 27. $\csc 2A = \dfrac{\sec A}{2\sin A}$

28. $\sec 2A = \dfrac{\sec^2 A}{1 - \tan^2 A}$ 29. $\dfrac{\tan\theta - \cot\theta}{\tan\theta + \cot\theta} = -\cos 2\theta$ 30. $\cot 2\theta = \dfrac{(\cot\theta + 1)(\cot\theta - 1)}{2\cot\theta}$

31. $\cos^4 x - \sin^4 x = \cos 2x$ 32. $\sec^4 x - \tan^4 x = 2\tan^2 x + 1$ 33. $\sin^2 x = \frac{1}{2} - \frac{1}{2}\cos 2x$

34. $\cos^2 x = \frac{1}{2} + \frac{1}{2}\cos 2x$ 35. $\cos 3\theta = 4\cos^3\theta - 3\cos\theta$ 36. $\sin 3\theta = 3\sin\theta\cos^2\theta - \sin^3\theta$

37. $\tan 3x = \dfrac{\tan^3 x - 3\tan x}{3\tan^2 x - 1}$ 38. $\tan 2x = \dfrac{2\cot x}{\csc^2 x - 2}$ 39. $\sin 4A = 4\sin A\cos A - 8\sin^3 A\cos A$

40. $\cos 4A = \cos^2 2A - \sin^2 2A$ 41. $\sin 2x = \dfrac{2\cot x}{1 + \cot^2 x}$ 42. $\dfrac{\cos 2\theta}{\cos\theta} = -\sec\theta + 2\cos\theta$

43. $\sin^4 x = \frac{3}{8} - \frac{1}{2}\cos 2x + \frac{1}{8}\cos 4x$ (Hint: use Exercises 33 and 34.)

44. $\cos^4 x = \frac{3}{8} + \frac{1}{2}\cos 2x + \frac{1}{8}\cos 4x$ (Hint: use Exercises 33 and 34.)

Section 6.5   Half-Angle Formulas

We will now derive the **half-angle formulas** for sine, cosine, and tangent. In Section 6.4, we derived three double-angle formulas for cosine. Two of these led us to the formulas which allow us to represent $\cos^2\theta$, $\sin^2\theta$, and $\tan^2\theta$ in terms of $\cos 2\theta$. In particular, we have:

$$\cos^2\theta = \frac{1 + \cos 2\theta}{2} \qquad \sin^2\theta = \frac{1 - \cos 2\theta}{2}$$

$$\tan^2\theta = \frac{1 - \cos 2\theta}{1 + \cos 2\theta}$$

If we replace θ by $\dfrac{A}{2}$, we obtain the **half-angle formulas**. Let's derive the formula for $\cos \dfrac{A}{2}$. Observe that:

$$\cos^2 \theta = \frac{1 + \cos 2\theta}{2}$$

$$\cos^2 \frac{A}{2} = \frac{1 + \cos \left[2\left(\dfrac{A}{2}\right) \right]}{2}$$

$$\cos^2 \frac{A}{2} = \frac{1 + \cos A}{2}$$

$$\cos \frac{A}{2} = \pm\sqrt{\frac{1 + \cos A}{2}}$$

And we have the half-angle formula for cosine. In a similar way, we can establish the half-angle formulas for sine and tangent (try these on your own).

The Half-Angle Formulas

$$\cos \frac{A}{2} = \pm\sqrt{\frac{1 + \cos A}{2}} \qquad \sin \frac{A}{2} = \pm\sqrt{\frac{1 - \cos A}{2}}$$

$$\tan \frac{A}{2} = \pm\sqrt{\frac{1 - \cos A}{1 + \cos A}}$$

Note that the $\pm$ in front of the square root symbol indicates that the answer will be positive or negative, depending on the quadrant in which the angle $\dfrac{A}{2}$ lies. For example, if $\dfrac{A}{2}$ lies in quadrant IV, then $\cos \dfrac{A}{2}$ is positive, whereas $\sin \dfrac{A}{2}$ and $\tan \dfrac{A}{2}$ are both negative. We will sometimes need these formulas without the square root present.

The Half-Angle Formulas (Alternative Form)

$$\cos^2 \frac{A}{2} = \frac{1 + \cos A}{2} \qquad \sin^2 \frac{A}{2} = \frac{1 - \cos A}{2}$$

$$\tan^2 \frac{A}{2} = \frac{1 - \cos A}{1 + \cos A}$$

Two other useful formulas for $\tan \dfrac{A}{2}$ are

$$\tan \frac{A}{2} = \frac{\sin A}{1 + \cos A} \qquad \text{and} \qquad \tan \frac{A}{2} = \frac{1 - \cos A}{\sin A}.$$

Notice that these formulas do not require a choice of sign (positive or negative) and do not contain a square root as in the original formulas. Let's derive the first formulas. Some tricks are involved, so go through each step carefully.

$$\tan \frac{A}{2} = \frac{\sin \frac{A}{2}}{\cos \frac{A}{2}} \qquad \left(\tan x = \frac{\sin x}{\cos x}\right)$$

$$= \frac{2\sin \frac{A}{2}\cos \frac{A}{2}}{2\cos^2 \frac{A}{2}} \qquad \left(\text{multiply numerator and denominator by } 2\cos \frac{A}{2}\right)$$

$$= \frac{\sin\left[2\left(\frac{A}{2}\right)\right]}{1 + \cos\left[2\left(\frac{A}{2}\right)\right]} \qquad \left(\text{use } \sin 2x = 2\sin x \cos x \text{ and } \cos 2x = 2\cos^2 x - 1, \text{ where } x = \frac{A}{2}\right)$$

$$= \frac{\sin A}{1 + \cos A}$$

To establish the second formula, we will verify that $\dfrac{\sin A}{1 + \cos A} = \dfrac{1 - \cos A}{\sin A}$.

$$\frac{\sin A}{1 + \cos A} = \left(\frac{\sin A}{1 + \cos A}\right)\left(\frac{1 - \cos A}{1 - \cos A}\right)$$

$$= \frac{\sin A\,(1 - \cos A)}{1 - \cos^2 A} \qquad (\text{use } (x + y)(x - y) = x^2 - y^2)$$

$$= \frac{\sin A\,(1 - \cos A)}{\sin^2 A} \qquad (\sin^2 A + \cos^2 A = 1)$$

$$= \frac{1 - \cos A}{\sin A}$$

This verifies the formulas for $\tan \dfrac{A}{2}$.

Examples.

1) Suppose that $\tan x = \frac{4}{3}$ and $\pi < x < \frac{3\pi}{2}$. Find the exact value of $\sin \frac{x}{2}$ and $\cos \frac{x}{2}$.

The formulas for $\sin \dfrac{x}{2}$ and $\cos \dfrac{x}{2}$ both contain $\cos x$ in them, so let's find the value of $\cos x$ first. We are given that x is in quadrant III. This means that $\dfrac{x}{2}$ is in quadrant II since

$$\pi < x < \frac{3\pi}{2} \qquad \text{implies that} \qquad \frac{\pi}{2} < \frac{x}{2} < \frac{3\pi}{4}.$$

From this, we now know that $\sin \dfrac{x}{2}$ will be positive (sine is positive in quadrant II) and $\cos \dfrac{x}{2}$ will be negative (cosine is negative in quadrant II). Now, since $\tan x = \dfrac{4}{3} = \dfrac{b}{a}$ and x is in quadrant III, we may choose

$b = -4$ and $a = -3$. Note that both a and b must be a negative number because x lies in quadrant III. We need to find r. Using the formula $r = \sqrt{a^2 + b^2}$, we have that

$$r = \sqrt{a^2 + b^2} = \sqrt{(-3)^2 + (-4)^2} = \sqrt{9 + 16} = \sqrt{25} = 5.$$

This gives us

$$\cos x = \frac{a}{r} = \frac{-3}{5}.$$

Therefore,

$$\sin \frac{x}{2} = \pm\sqrt{\frac{1 - \cos x}{2}} = \sqrt{\frac{1 - \left(-\frac{3}{5}\right)}{2}} \qquad \left(\text{since } \sin \frac{x}{2} > 0\right)$$

$$= \sqrt{\frac{1 + \frac{3}{5}}{2}} = \sqrt{\frac{1(5) + \frac{3}{\cancel{5}}(\cancel{5})}{2(5)}} = \sqrt{\frac{5 + 3}{10}}$$

$$= \sqrt{\frac{8}{10}} = \sqrt{\frac{4}{5}} = \frac{2}{\sqrt{5}} = \frac{2\sqrt{5}}{5}$$

and

$$\cos \frac{x}{2} = \pm\sqrt{\frac{1 + \cos x}{2}} = -\sqrt{\frac{1 + \left(-\frac{3}{5}\right)}{2}} \qquad \left(\text{since } \cos \frac{x}{2} < 0\right)$$

$$= -\sqrt{\frac{1 - \frac{3}{5}}{2}} = -\sqrt{\frac{1(5) - \frac{3}{\cancel{5}}(\cancel{5})}{2(5)}} = -\sqrt{\frac{5 - 3}{10}}$$

$$= -\sqrt{\frac{2}{10}} = -\sqrt{\frac{1}{5}} = -\frac{1}{\sqrt{5}} = -\frac{\sqrt{5}}{5}$$

2) If $\cos \theta = \frac{\sqrt{2}}{3}$ and $\frac{3\pi}{2} < \theta < 2\pi$, find the exact value of $\tan \frac{\theta}{2}$.

Since $\frac{3\pi}{2} < \theta < 2\pi$, we know that $\frac{\theta}{2}$ is in quadrant II because

$$\frac{3\pi}{2} < \theta < 2\pi \qquad \text{implies that} \qquad \frac{3\pi}{4} < \frac{\theta}{2} < \pi.$$

Therefore, $\tan \frac{\theta}{2}$ will be negative (tangent is negative in quadrant II). Since the half-angle formula for tangent only contains $\cos \theta$ in it, we can immediately find its value.

$$\tan \frac{\theta}{2} = \pm\sqrt{\frac{1 - \cos \theta}{1 + \cos \theta}} = -\sqrt{\frac{1 - \frac{\sqrt{2}}{3}}{1 + \frac{\sqrt{2}}{3}}} \qquad \left(\text{since } \tan \frac{\theta}{2} < 0\right)$$

$$= -\sqrt{\frac{1(3) - \frac{\sqrt{2}}{\cancel{3}}(\cancel{3})}{1(3) + \frac{\sqrt{2}}{\cancel{3}}(\cancel{3})}} = -\sqrt{\frac{3 - \sqrt{2}}{3 + \sqrt{2}}}$$

3) Find the exact value of $\cos 15°$ using the half-angle formula for cosine.

Observe that $15° = \dfrac{30°}{2}$ and $A = 15°$ lies in quadrant I.

$$\cos 15° = \underbrace{\cos \frac{30°}{2} = \sqrt{\frac{1 + \cos 30°}{2}}}_{\text{Let } A=15° \text{ in the formula.}} = \sqrt{\frac{1 + \dfrac{\sqrt{3}}{2}}{2}}$$

$$= \sqrt{\frac{1\,(2) + \dfrac{\sqrt{3}}{\cancel{2}}\,(\cancel{2})}{2\,(2)}} = \sqrt{\frac{2 + \sqrt{3}}{4}} = \frac{\sqrt{2 + \sqrt{3}}}{2}$$

4) Find the exact value of $\sin 195°$ using the half-angle formula for sine.

Observe that $195° = \dfrac{390°}{2}$ and $A = 195°$ lies in quadrant III.

$$\sin 195° = \underbrace{\sin \frac{390°}{2} = -\sqrt{\frac{1 - \cos 390°}{2}}}_{\text{Let } A=195° \text{ in the formula.}} \qquad \text{(negative, because } A = 195° \text{ lies in quadrant III)}$$

$$= -\sqrt{\frac{1 - \cos 30°}{2}} \qquad (\cos 390° = \cos 30°)$$

$$= -\sqrt{\frac{1 - \dfrac{\sqrt{3}}{2}}{2}} = -\sqrt{\frac{1\,(2) - \dfrac{\sqrt{3}}{\cancel{2}}\,(\cancel{2})}{2\,(2)}}$$

$$= -\sqrt{\frac{2 - \sqrt{3}}{4}} = -\frac{\sqrt{2 - \sqrt{3}}}{2}$$

5) Find the exact value of $\tan \frac{\pi}{8}$ using a half-angle formula for tangent.

There are three ways to do this. One way is to use the formula containing the square root:

$$\tan \frac{\pi}{8} = \tan \frac{\frac{\pi}{4}}{2} = \sqrt{\frac{1 - \cos \dfrac{\pi}{4}}{1 + \cos \dfrac{\pi}{4}}} = \sqrt{\frac{1 - \dfrac{\sqrt{2}}{2}}{1 + \dfrac{\sqrt{2}}{2}}}$$

$$= \sqrt{\frac{1\,(2) - \dfrac{\sqrt{2}\,(\cancel{2})}{\cancel{2}}}{1\,(2) + \dfrac{\sqrt{2}}{\cancel{2}}\,(\cancel{2})}} = \sqrt{\frac{2 - \sqrt{2}}{2 + \sqrt{2}}}$$

Another way to do this is to use the formula $\tan \dfrac{A}{2} = \dfrac{1 - \cos A}{\sin A}$:

$$\tan \frac{\pi}{8} = \tan \frac{\frac{\pi}{4}}{2} = \frac{1 - \cos \frac{\pi}{4}}{\sin \frac{\pi}{4}} = \frac{1 - \dfrac{1}{\sqrt{2}}}{\dfrac{1}{\sqrt{2}}}$$

$$= \frac{1\left(\sqrt{2}\right) - \dfrac{1}{\sqrt{2}}\left(\dfrac{1}{\sqrt{2}}\right)}{\dfrac{1}{\sqrt{2}}\left(\dfrac{1}{\sqrt{2}}\right)} = \frac{\sqrt{2} - 1}{1} = \sqrt{2} - 1$$

Even though the answers look totally different from each other, they are the same. Try to verify this on your own. The third way that this problem could've been done is to use the formula $\tan \dfrac{A}{2} = \dfrac{\sin A}{1 + \cos A}$. Try this one on your own and verify that this answer is the same as the others.

Try These (Set 16):

1) If $\tan \theta = 2$ and $\pi < \theta < \dfrac{3\pi}{2}$, find the exact value of $\sin \dfrac{\theta}{2}$, $\cos \dfrac{\theta}{2}$, and $\tan \dfrac{\theta}{2}$.

2) Find the exact value of $\cos 105°$ using the half-angle formula for cosine.

Verifying Identities Containing a Half-Angle

Examples. Verify the identities.

1) $\sec^2 \dfrac{A}{2} = \dfrac{2}{1 + \cos A}$

Since we know that $\sec \theta = \dfrac{1}{\cos \theta}$ (which implies that $\sec^2 \theta = \dfrac{1}{\cos^2 \theta}$), we should work on the left-hand side.

$$\sec^2 \frac{A}{2} = \frac{1}{\cos^2 \dfrac{A}{2}}$$

$$= \frac{1}{\dfrac{1 + \cos A}{2}} \qquad \left(\cos^2 \frac{A}{2} = \frac{1 + \cos A}{2}\right)$$

$$= \frac{2}{1 + \cos A}$$

2) $\cos x = \dfrac{1 - \tan^2 \dfrac{x}{2}}{1 + \tan^2 \dfrac{x}{2}}$

The right-hand side needs to be cleaned up.

$$\frac{1 - \tan^2 \frac{x}{2}}{1 + \tan^2 \frac{x}{2}} = \frac{1 - \dfrac{1 - \cos x}{1 + \cos x}}{1 + \dfrac{1 - \cos x}{1 + \cos x}} \qquad \left(\tan^2 \frac{x}{2} = \frac{1 - \cos x}{1 + \cos x} \right)$$

$$= \frac{1 (1 + \cos x) - \dfrac{1 - \cos x}{1 + \cos x} (1 + \cos x)}{1 (1 + \cos x) + \dfrac{1 - \cos x}{1 + \cos x} (1 + \cos x)}$$

$$= \frac{1 + \cos x - (1 - \cos x)}{1 + \cos x + (1 - \cos x)}$$

$$= \frac{1 + \cos x - 1 + \cos x}{1 + \cos x + 1 - \cos x}$$

$$= \frac{\overset{1}{\cancel{2}} \cos x}{\underset{1}{\cancel{2}}}$$

$$= \cos x$$

Another nice way to verify this identity is to derive it from scratch. Observe that

$$\cos x = \cos \left[2 \left(\frac{x}{2} \right) \right] = \cos^2 \frac{x}{2} - \sin^2 \frac{x}{2} \qquad \left(\text{let } \theta = \frac{x}{2} \text{ in the identity } \cos 2\theta = \cos^2 \theta - \sin^2 \theta \right)$$

$$= \frac{\cos^2 \frac{x}{2} - \sin^2 \frac{x}{2}}{1} = \frac{\cos^2 \frac{x}{2} - \sin^2 \frac{x}{2}}{\sin^2 \frac{x}{2} + \cos^2 \frac{x}{2}} \qquad \left(\text{let } \theta = \frac{x}{2} \text{ in the identity } \sin^2 \theta + \cos^2 \theta = 1 \right)$$

$$= \left(\frac{\cos^2 \frac{x}{2} - \sin^2 \frac{x}{2}}{\sin^2 \frac{x}{2} + \cos^2 \frac{x}{2}} \right) \left(\frac{\dfrac{1}{\cos^2 \frac{x}{2}}}{\dfrac{1}{\cos^2 \frac{x}{2}}} \right) = \frac{\cos^2 \frac{x}{2} \left(\dfrac{1}{\cos^2 \frac{x}{2}} \right) - \sin^2 \frac{x}{2} \left(\dfrac{1}{\cos^2 \frac{x}{2}} \right)}{\sin^2 \frac{x}{2} \left(\dfrac{1}{\cos^2 \frac{x}{2}} \right) + \cos^2 \frac{x}{2} \left(\dfrac{1}{\cos^2 \frac{x}{2}} \right)}$$

$$= \frac{1 - \dfrac{\sin^2 \frac{x}{2}}{\cos^2 \frac{x}{2}}}{\dfrac{\sin^2 \frac{x}{2}}{\cos^2 \frac{x}{2}} + 1} = \frac{1 - \left(\dfrac{\sin \frac{x}{2}}{\cos \frac{x}{2}} \right)^2}{\left(\dfrac{\sin \frac{x}{2}}{\cos \frac{x}{2}} \right)^2 + 1} = \frac{1 - \tan^2 \frac{x}{2}}{\tan^2 \frac{x}{2} + 1} \qquad \left(\text{let } \theta = \frac{x}{2} \text{ in the identity } \frac{\sin \theta}{\cos \theta} = \tan \theta \right)$$

The trick here is to write $\cos x$ in terms of $\cos^2 \frac{x}{2}$ and $\sin^2 \frac{x}{2}$, then create $\tan^2 \frac{x}{2}$ by dividing every term in the fraction by $\cos^2 \frac{x}{2}$. Try to derive a similar formula for $\sin x$ in terms of $\tan \frac{x}{2}$ and $\tan^2 \frac{x}{2}$ (see the Try These Exercises).

3) $\cot \dfrac{\alpha}{2} - \tan \dfrac{\alpha}{2} = 2 \cot \alpha$

We will work on the left-hand side.

$$\cot \frac{\alpha}{2} - \tan \frac{\alpha}{2} = \frac{1}{\tan \dfrac{\alpha}{2}} - \tan \frac{\alpha}{2} \qquad\qquad \left(\cot A = \frac{1}{\tan A} \right)$$

$$= \frac{1}{\dfrac{\sin \alpha}{1 + \cos \alpha}} - \frac{\sin \alpha}{1 + \cos \alpha} \qquad\qquad \left(\tan \frac{\alpha}{2} = \frac{\sin \alpha}{1 + \cos \alpha} \right)$$

$$= \frac{1 + \cos \alpha}{\sin \alpha} - \frac{\sin \alpha}{1 + \cos \alpha}$$

$$= \left(\frac{1 + \cos \alpha}{\sin \alpha} \right) \left(\frac{1 + \cos \alpha}{1 + \cos \alpha} \right) - \left(\frac{\sin \alpha}{1 + \cos \alpha} \right) \left(\frac{\sin \alpha}{\sin \alpha} \right)$$

$$= \frac{(1 + \cos \alpha)(1 + \cos \alpha) - \sin^2 \alpha}{\sin \alpha (1 + \cos \alpha)}$$

$$= \frac{1 + 2\cos \alpha + \cos^2 \alpha - \sin^2 \alpha}{\sin \alpha (1 + \cos \alpha)}$$

$$= \frac{1 + 2\cos \alpha + \cos^2 \alpha - \left(1 - \cos^2 \alpha \right)}{\sin \alpha (1 + \cos \alpha)}$$

$$= \frac{1 + 2\cos \alpha + \cos^2 \alpha - 1 + \cos^2 \alpha}{\sin \alpha (1 + \cos \alpha)}$$

$$= \frac{2\cos \alpha + 2\cos^2 \alpha}{\sin \alpha (1 + \cos \alpha)}$$

$$= \frac{2\cos \alpha \,(\cancel{1 + \cos \alpha})}{\sin \alpha \,(\cancel{1 + \cos \alpha})}$$

$$= \frac{2\cos \alpha}{\sin \alpha}$$

$$= 2\cot \alpha$$

Another method of verifying this identity goes as follows:

$$\cot \frac{\alpha}{2} - \tan \frac{\alpha}{2} = \frac{\cos \dfrac{\alpha}{2}}{\sin \dfrac{\alpha}{2}} - \frac{\sin \dfrac{\alpha}{2}}{\cos \dfrac{\alpha}{2}}$$

$$= \left(\frac{\cos \dfrac{\alpha}{2}}{\cos \dfrac{\alpha}{2}} \right) \frac{\cos \dfrac{\alpha}{2}}{\sin \dfrac{\alpha}{2}} - \left(\frac{\sin \dfrac{\alpha}{2}}{\sin \dfrac{\alpha}{2}} \right) \frac{\sin \dfrac{\alpha}{2}}{\cos \dfrac{\alpha}{2}}$$

$$= \frac{\cos^2 \dfrac{\alpha}{2} - \sin^2 \dfrac{\alpha}{2}}{\sin \dfrac{\alpha}{2} \cos \dfrac{\alpha}{2}}$$

$$= \frac{2\cos \alpha}{2 \sin \dfrac{\alpha}{2} \cos \dfrac{\alpha}{2}} \qquad\qquad \left(\cos^2 \frac{\alpha}{2} - \sin^2 \frac{\alpha}{2} = \cos \left[2 \left(\frac{\alpha}{2} \right) \right] = \cos \alpha \right)$$

$$= \frac{2\cos\alpha}{\sin\alpha} \qquad\qquad \left(2\sin\frac{\alpha}{2}\cos\frac{\alpha}{2} = \sin\left[2\left(\frac{\alpha}{2}\right)\right] = \sin\alpha\right)$$

$$= 2\cot\alpha$$

Try These (Set 17): Verify each identity.

1) $\csc^2\dfrac{\theta}{2} = \dfrac{2\sec\theta}{\sec\theta - 1}$

2) $\sin x = \dfrac{2\tan\dfrac{x}{2}}{1 + \tan^2\dfrac{x}{2}}$

Exercise 6.5

In Exercises 1-14, find the exact value of each expression.

1. $\cos 15°$ 2. $\tan 22.5°$ 3. $\sin 105°$ 4. $\sin 75°$

5. $\tan 195°$ 6. $\cos 165°$ 7. $\cos\dfrac{\pi}{8}$ 8. $\tan\dfrac{9\pi}{8}$

9. $\sin\dfrac{7\pi}{8}$ 10. $\cos\dfrac{5\pi}{8}$ 11. $\tan\left(-\dfrac{\pi}{8}\right)$ 12. $\sin\left(-\dfrac{3\pi}{8}\right)$

13. $\cos\left(-\dfrac{5\pi}{8}\right)$ 14. $\tan\left(-\dfrac{7\pi}{8}\right)$

In Exercises 15-26, use the given information to find the exact value of:

    (a) $\sin\dfrac{x}{2}$ (b) $\cos\dfrac{x}{2}$ (c) $\tan\dfrac{x}{2}$

15. $\sin x = \frac{3}{5},\ 0° < x < 90°$ 16. $\cos x = \frac{5}{6},\ 0° < x < 90°$ 17. $\tan x = \frac{\sqrt{10}}{8},\ \pi < x < \frac{3\pi}{2}$

18. $\sin x = \frac{\sqrt{2}}{7},\ \frac{\pi}{2} < x < \pi$ 19. $\cos x = -\frac{\sqrt{3}}{5},\ \pi < x < \frac{3\pi}{2}$ 20. $\tan x = -4\sqrt{2},\ \frac{\pi}{2} < x < \pi$

21. $\tan x = -5,\ \frac{3\pi}{2} < x < 2\pi$ 22. $\cos x = \frac{2\sqrt{5}}{3},\ 0 < x < \frac{\pi}{2}$ 23. $\csc x = \frac{7}{2},\ \frac{\pi}{2} < x < \pi$

24. $\sec x = 2\sqrt{6},\ \frac{3\pi}{2} < x < 2\pi$ 25. $\cot x = \frac{8\sqrt{3}}{5},\ \pi < x < \frac{3\pi}{2}$ 26. $\csc x = -\frac{10}{7},\ \frac{3\pi}{2} < x < 2\pi$

In Exercises 27-38, establish the identity.

27. $\sin^2\dfrac{x}{2} = \dfrac{\csc x - \cot x}{2\csc x}$ 28. $\sin^2\dfrac{x}{2} = \dfrac{\sin^2 x}{2(1 + \cos x)}$ 29. $\csc^2\dfrac{\alpha}{2} = \dfrac{2}{1 - \cos\alpha}$

30. $\cot^2\dfrac{\theta}{2} = \dfrac{\sec\theta + 1}{\sec\theta - 1}$ 31. $\tan\dfrac{\alpha}{2} = \csc\alpha - \cot\alpha$ 32. $\cot\dfrac{\alpha}{2} = \dfrac{\sec\alpha\sin\alpha}{\sec\alpha - 1}$

33. $\tan^2\dfrac{A}{2} = \dfrac{\sin^2 A}{(1 + \cos A)^2}$ 34. $\sin^2\dfrac{B}{2} = \dfrac{\tan B - \sin B}{2\tan B}$ 35. $\cot\dfrac{\alpha}{2} + \tan\dfrac{\alpha}{2} = 2\csc\alpha$

36. $\tan\dfrac{\beta}{2} - \cot\dfrac{\beta}{2} = -2\cot\beta$ 37. $\sin x\csc\dfrac{x}{2} = 2\cos\dfrac{x}{2}$ 38. $\cos^2\dfrac{x}{2} - \cos x = \sin^2\dfrac{x}{2}$

Section 6.6 Product-to-Sum and Sum-to-Product Formulas

In this section, we will derive two sets of formulas, the **product-to-sum formulas** and the **sum-to-product formulas**.

Product-to-Sum Formulas

The **product-to-sum formulas** are as follows:

Product-to-Sum Formulas

(1) $\sin A \cos B = \dfrac{1}{2} \left[\sin (A + B) + \sin (A - B) \right]$

(2) $\cos A \cos B = \dfrac{1}{2} \left[\cos (A + B) + \cos (A - B) \right]$

(3) $\sin A \sin B = \dfrac{1}{2} \left[\cos (A - B) - \cos (A + B) \right]$

Let's verify that these formulas are true by recalling the sum formulas for sine and cosine.

$$\sin (A + B) = \sin A \cos B + \cos A \sin B \qquad \cos (A + B) = \cos A \cos B - \sin A \sin B$$
$$\sin (A - B) = \sin A \cos B - \cos A \sin B \qquad \cos (A - B) = \cos A \cos B + \sin A \sin B$$

We obtain a formula for the product $\sin A \cos B$ by adding the sine formulas together as follows:

$$\sin (A + B) + \sin (A - B) = (\sin A \cos B + \cos A \sin B) + (\sin A \cos B - \cos A \sin B)$$
$$= 2 \sin A \cos B$$

After dividing each side of the equation by 2, we obtain

$$\frac{1}{2} \left[\sin (A + B) + \sin (A - B) \right] = \sin A \cos B.$$

To get the formula for the product $\cos A \cos B$, we add the cosine formulas together:

$$\cos (A + B) + \cos (A - B) = (\cos A \cos B - \sin A \sin B) + (\cos A \cos B + \sin A \sin B)$$
$$= 2 \cos A \cos B$$

After dividing each side of the equation by 2, we obtain

$$\frac{1}{2} \left[\cos (A + B) + \cos (A - B) \right] = \cos A \cos B.$$

To derive the formula for $\sin A \sin B$, we subtract one cosine formula from the other:

$$\cos(A - B) - \cos(A + B) = (\cos A \cos B + \sin A \sin B) - (\cos A \cos B - \sin A \sin B)$$
$$= \cos A \cos B + \sin A \sin B - \cos A \cos B + \sin A \sin B$$
$$= 2 \sin A \sin B.$$

Now, divide by 2:

$$\frac{1}{2}\left[\cos(A - B) - \cos(A + B)\right] = \sin A \cos B$$

Notice that the $\sin A \cos B$ formula comes from the sum of sines formula and this formula has terms involving sine times cosine. The $\sin A \sin B$ and $\cos A \cos B$ formulas, however, both come from the sum of cosines formula and this formula has terms involving sine times sine and cosine times cosine.

Example. Verify formula (2) for $A = 30°$ and $B = 60°$.

Substituting $A = 30°$ and $B = 60°$ into the formula

$$\cos A \cos B = \frac{1}{2}\left[\cos(A + B) + \cos(A - B)\right]$$

gives us

$$\cos 30° \cos 60° = \frac{1}{2}\left[\cos(30° + 60°) + \cos(30° - 60°)\right]$$
$$\frac{1}{2}\left(\frac{\sqrt{3}}{2}\right) = \frac{1}{2}\left[\cos 90° + \cos(-30°)\right]$$
$$\frac{\sqrt{3}}{4} = \frac{1}{2}\left(0 + \frac{\sqrt{3}}{2}\right) \qquad (\cos(-30°) = \cos 30°)$$
$$\frac{\sqrt{3}}{4} = \frac{\sqrt{3}}{4}, \text{ which is true.}$$

Example. Verify formula (1) for $A = 120°$ and $B = -270°$.

Substituting $A = 120°$ and $B = -270°$ into the formula

$$\sin A \cos B = \frac{1}{2}\left[\sin(A + B) + \sin(A - B)\right]$$

gives us

$$\sin 120° \cos(-270°) = \frac{1}{2}\left[\sin(120° + (-270°)) + \sin(120° - (-270°))\right]$$
$$\sin 60° \cos 270° = \frac{1}{2}\left[\sin(-150°) + \sin 390°\right] \qquad (\sin 120° = \sin 60° \text{ and } \cos(-270°) = \cos 270°)$$
$$\frac{\sqrt{3}}{2}(0) = \frac{1}{2}\left[-\sin 150° + \sin 30°\right] \qquad (\sin(-150°) = -\sin 150° \text{ and } \sin 390° = \sin 30°)$$
$$0 = \frac{1}{2}\left[-\frac{1}{2} + \frac{1}{2}\right] \qquad (\sin 150° = \sin 30° = \frac{1}{2})$$
$$0 = \frac{1}{2}(0)$$
$$0 = 0, \text{ which is true.}$$

Examples. Rewrite each expression as a sum or difference of sine(s) and cosine(s). Simplify your answer (if possible).

1) $\sin 3x \cos 2x = \dfrac{1}{2}\left[\sin(3x+2x) + \sin(3x-2x)\right] = \dfrac{1}{2}\left(\sin 5x + \sin x\right) = \dfrac{1}{2}\sin 5x + \dfrac{1}{2}\sin x$

Using (1), with $A=3x$ and $B=2x$.

2) $4\sin 5\theta \sin 8\theta = 4\left[\dfrac{1}{2}\left(\cos(5\theta-8\theta) - \cos(5\theta+8\theta)\right)\right] = 2\left(\cos(-3\theta) - \cos 13\theta\right) = 2\cos 3\theta - 2\cos 13\theta$

Using (3), with $A=5\theta$ and $B=8\theta$.   Note that $\cos(-3\theta)=\cos 3\theta$.

3) $2\cos\dfrac{\pi}{12}\cos\dfrac{\pi}{4} = 2\left[\dfrac{1}{2}\left(\cos\left(\dfrac{\pi}{12}+\dfrac{\pi}{4}\right) + \cos\left(\dfrac{\pi}{12}-\dfrac{\pi}{4}\right)\right)\right] = \cos\dfrac{\pi}{3} + \cos\left(-\dfrac{\pi}{6}\right) = \dfrac{1}{2} + \dfrac{\sqrt{3}}{2} = \dfrac{1+\sqrt{3}}{2}$

Using (2), with $A=\frac{\pi}{12}$ and $B=\frac{\pi}{4}$. $\cos\frac{\pi}{3}=\frac{1}{2}$ and $\cos\left(-\frac{\pi}{6}\right)=\cos\frac{\pi}{6}=\frac{\sqrt{3}}{2}$.

Try These (Set 18): Rewrite each expression as a sum or difference of sine(s) and cosine(s).

1) $\cos 3x \cos 4x$ 2) $6\sin\theta\sin 7\theta$ 3) $-\cos 2t \sin 9t$

Sum-to-Product Formulas

The **sum-to-product formulas** are as follows:

Sum-to-Product Formulas

(1) $\sin A + \sin B = 2\sin\left(\dfrac{A+B}{2}\right)\cos\left(\dfrac{A-B}{2}\right)$

(2) $\sin A - \sin B = 2\cos\left(\dfrac{A+B}{2}\right)\sin\left(\dfrac{A-B}{2}\right)$

(3) $\cos A + \cos B = 2\cos\left(\dfrac{A+B}{2}\right)\cos\left(\dfrac{A-B}{2}\right)$

(4) $\cos A - \cos B = -2\sin\left(\dfrac{A+B}{2}\right)\sin\left(\dfrac{A-B}{2}\right)$

Let's derive formula (1). By adding the sum and difference formulas for sine together, we obtain

$$\sin(x+y) + \sin(x-y) = 2\sin x \cos y.$$

Notice that both sides of this equation look like the corresponding sides in formula (1). In particular, we would like to make $\sin(x+y)+\sin(x-y)$ look like $\sin A + \sin B$. In order to do this, we'll set $A = x+y$ and $B = x-y$. Our goal is to determine what the values of x and y are in terms of A and B. Well, to find these values, we'll need to solve a system of linear equations. We will proceed by using the process of elimination. By adding the equations $A = x+y$ and $B = x-y$ together, we obtain

$$x + y = A$$
$$+ \quad \underline{x - y = B}$$
$$2x = A + B$$

and so $x = \dfrac{A + B}{2}$. To find the value for y, we replace x by $\dfrac{A + B}{2}$ into either one of the equations and solve for y. I'll use the equation $x + y = A$.

$$x + y = A$$

$$\dfrac{A + B}{2} + y = A$$

$$-\dfrac{A + B}{2} \qquad\qquad -\dfrac{A + B}{2}$$

$$y = A - \dfrac{A + B}{2}$$

Combining the right-hand side into a single fraction gives us

$$A - \frac{A + B}{2} = \frac{2A}{2} - \frac{A + B}{2} = \frac{2A - (A + B)}{2}$$
$$= \frac{2A - A - B}{2} = \frac{A - B}{2}$$

and so $y = \dfrac{A - B}{2}$. If we now replace x and y in the equation $\sin(x + y) + \sin(x - y) = 2\sin x \cos y$ by $\dfrac{A + B}{2}$ and $\dfrac{A - B}{2}$, respectively, we will obtain formula (1). Formulas (2), (3), and (4) can be obtained the same way: add or subtract the sum/difference formulas for sine and cosine and replace x and y by $\dfrac{A + B}{2}$ and $\dfrac{A - B}{2}$, respectively. Try to derive these on your own.

Example. Verify formula (3) for $A = 300°$ and $B = 180°$.

Substituting $A = 300°$ and $B = 180°$ into the formula

$$\cos A + \cos B = 2\cos\left(\frac{A + B}{2}\right)\cos\left(\frac{A - B}{2}\right)$$

gives us

$$\cos 300° + \cos 180° = 2\cos\left(\frac{300° + 180°}{2}\right)\cos\left(\frac{300° - 180°}{2}\right)$$

$$\frac{1}{2} + (-1) = 2\cos\left(\frac{480°}{2}\right)\cos\left(\frac{120°}{2}\right) \qquad \left(\cos 300° = \cos 60° = \frac{1}{2}\right)$$

$$-\frac{1}{2} = 2\cos 240° \cos 60°$$

$$-\frac{1}{2} = 2\left(-\frac{1}{2}\right)\left(\frac{1}{2}\right) \qquad\qquad (\cos 240° = -\cos 60°)$$

$$-\frac{1}{2} = -\frac{1}{2}, \text{ which is true.}$$

Examples. Rewrite as a product of sine(s) and/or cosine(s). Simplify your answer(if possible).

1) $\sin 6x + \sin 4x = 2 \sin \left(\dfrac{6x + 4x}{2} \right) \cos \left(\dfrac{6x - 4x}{2} \right) = 2 \sin \left(\dfrac{10x}{2} \right) \cos \left(\dfrac{2x}{2} \right) = 2 \sin 5x \cos x$

$\underbrace{\hspace{6cm}}$
$\text{Using (1), with } A=6x \text{ and } B=4x.$

2) $\cos 3\alpha - \cos 2\alpha = -2 \sin \left(\dfrac{3\alpha + 2\alpha}{2} \right) \sin \left(\dfrac{3\alpha - 2\alpha}{2} \right) = -2 \sin \dfrac{5\alpha}{2} \sin \dfrac{\alpha}{2}$

$\underbrace{\hspace{6cm}}$
$\text{Using (4), with } A=3\alpha \text{ and } B=2\alpha.$

3) $\sin \dfrac{7\pi}{12} - \sin \dfrac{\pi}{12} = 2 \cos \left(\dfrac{\frac{7\pi}{12} + \frac{\pi}{12}}{2} \right) \sin \left(\dfrac{\frac{7\pi}{12} - \frac{\pi}{12}}{2} \right) = 2 \cos \left(\dfrac{\frac{7\pi}{12}(12) + \frac{\pi}{12}(12)}{2(12)} \right) \sin \left(\dfrac{\frac{7\pi}{12}(12) - \frac{\pi}{12}(12)}{2(12)} \right)$

$\underbrace{\hspace{6cm}}$
$\text{Using (2), with } A=\frac{7\pi}{12} \text{ and } B=\frac{\pi}{12}.$

$= 2 \cos \left(\dfrac{7\pi + \pi}{24} \right) \sin \left(\dfrac{7\pi - \pi}{24} \right) = 2 \cos \dfrac{8\pi}{24} \sin \dfrac{6\pi}{24}$

$= 2 \cos \dfrac{\pi}{3} \sin \dfrac{\pi}{4} = \cancel{2} \left(\dfrac{\sqrt{3}}{\cancel{2}} \right) \left(\dfrac{\sqrt{2}}{2} \right) = \dfrac{\sqrt{6}}{2}$

Try These (Set 19): Rewrite as a product of sine(s) and/or cosine(s). Simplify your answer (if possible).

1) $\cos 8x + \cos 4x$ 2) $\sin \beta - \sin 7\beta$ 3) $\cos 3A - \cos A$

Verifying Identities

Examples. Verify each identity.

1) $\cot A = \dfrac{\sin 4A + \sin 6A}{\cos 4A - \cos 6A}$

Observe that the numerator is a sum of sines and the denominator is a difference of cosines. This suggests that we should rewrite each as a product of sine(s) and/or cosine(s). Let's do this and see what happens.

$$\frac{\sin 4A + \sin 6A}{\cos 4A - \cos 6A} = \frac{2 \sin \left(\dfrac{4A + 6A}{2} \right) \cos \left(\dfrac{4A - 6A}{2} \right)}{-2 \sin \left(\dfrac{4A + 6A}{2} \right) \sin \left(\dfrac{4A - 6A}{2} \right)}$$

$$= \frac{2 \sin \left(\dfrac{10A}{2} \right) \cos \left(\dfrac{-2A}{2} \right)}{-2 \sin \left(\dfrac{10A}{2} \right) \sin \left(\dfrac{-2A}{2} \right)}$$

$$= \frac{2 \sin 5A \cos (-A)}{-2 \sin 5A \sin (-A)}$$

$$= \frac{2\overset{1}{\cancel{\sin 5A}}\cos A}{2\underset{1}{\cancel{\sin 5A}}\sin A} \qquad (\sin(-A) = -\sin A)$$

$$= \frac{\cos A}{\sin A}$$

$$= \cot A$$

2) $\dfrac{\sin\theta + \sin\alpha}{\cos\theta + \cos\alpha} = \tan\left(\dfrac{\theta + \alpha}{2}\right)$

We will work on the left-hand side since we know formulas for the numerator and denominator.

$$\frac{\sin\theta + \sin\alpha}{\cos\theta + \cos\alpha} = \frac{2\sin\left(\dfrac{\theta+\alpha}{2}\right)\cos\left(\dfrac{\theta-\alpha}{2}\right)}{2\cos\left(\dfrac{\theta+\alpha}{2}\right)\cos\left(\dfrac{\theta-\alpha}{2}\right)}$$

$$= \frac{\sin\left(\dfrac{\theta+\alpha}{2}\right)}{\cos\left(\dfrac{\theta+\alpha}{2}\right)}$$

$$= \tan\left(\frac{\theta+\alpha}{2}\right) \qquad \left(\frac{\sin A}{\cos A} = \tan A\right)$$

3) $\dfrac{\sin 3x - \sin 5x}{\cos^2 2x - \sin^2 2x} = -2\sin x$

Working on the left-hand side gives us:

$$\frac{\sin 3x - \sin 5x}{\cos^2 2x - \sin^2 2x} = \frac{2\cos\left(\dfrac{3x+5x}{2}\right)\sin\left(\dfrac{3x-5x}{2}\right)}{\cos 2\,(2x)} \qquad (\cos^2 A - \sin^2 A = \cos 2A)$$

$$= \frac{2\cos\left(\dfrac{8x}{2}\right)\sin\left(\dfrac{-2x}{2}\right)}{\cos 4x}$$

$$= \frac{2\cos 4x\sin(-x)}{\cos 4x}$$

$$= \frac{-2\overset{1}{\cancel{\cos 4x}}\sin x}{\underset{1}{\cancel{\cos 4x}}} \qquad (\sin(-x) = -\sin x)$$

$$= -2\sin x$$

Try These (Set 20): Verify the identities.

1) $\dfrac{\sin A - \sin B}{\cos A - \cos B} = -\cot\left(\dfrac{A+B}{2}\right)$

2) $\dfrac{\sin x + \sin 3x}{4\sin x\cos x} = \cos x$

Exercise 6.6

In Exercises 1-12, rewrite each expression as a sum or difference of sine(s) and cosine(s). Simplify if possible.

1. $\sin 7x \cos 3x$

2. $\sin 9\theta \cos 4\theta$

3. $6 \sin 2\theta \sin 5\theta$

4. $8 \sin 8\theta \sin 2\theta$

5. $\cos 6x \cos x$

6. $\cos 4x \cos 3x$

7. $\sin 2t \cos 8t$

8. $\sin 3A \cos 7A$

9. $\sin 3\alpha \sin 6\alpha$

10. $\sin \alpha \sin 4\alpha$

11. $3 \cos 2x \cos 6x$

12. $7 \cos 3x \cos 4x$

In Exercises 13-26, rewrite each sum or difference as a product of sine(s) and/or cosine(s). Simplify if possible.

13. $\cos 2x + \cos 6x$

14. $\cos 8x + \cos 4x$

15. $\cos 5A - \cos A$

16. $\cos 9B - \cos 3B$

17. $\sin 3\theta + \sin 4\theta$

18. $\sin \alpha + \sin 6\alpha$

19. $\sin 2\beta - \sin 11\beta$

20. $\sin 6\beta - \sin 7\beta$

21. $\dfrac{1}{2} (\cos 3x - \cos 8x)$

22. $\dfrac{1}{2} (\cos 4y + \cos 9y)$

23. $\dfrac{1}{8} (\sin 4\theta + \sin 6\theta)$

24. $\dfrac{1}{4} (\sin 3\theta - \sin 4\theta)$

25. $-\dfrac{1}{4} (\cos 7A - \cos 8A)$

26. $-\dfrac{1}{6} (\sin 2B + \sin 3B)$

In Exercises 27-38, find the exact value of each expression.

27. $\sin 15° \sin 45°$

28. $\sin 45° \cos 15°$

29. $\cos 15° \cos 105°$

30. $\sin 15° \sin 105°$

31. $\sin 15° \cos 375°$

32. $\cos 345° \cos 15°$

33. $\sin \frac{\pi}{12} \cos \frac{\pi}{4}$

34. $\sin \frac{\pi}{4} \sin \frac{\pi}{12}$

35. $\cos \frac{7\pi}{12} + \cos \frac{\pi}{12}$

36. $\sin \frac{\pi}{12} + \sin \frac{7\pi}{12}$

37. $\sin \frac{\pi}{12} - \sin \frac{5\pi}{12}$

38. $\cos \frac{5\pi}{12} - \cos \frac{\pi}{12}$

In Exercises 39-48, establish each identity.

39. $\cos x = \dfrac{\cos 3x + \cos x}{2 \cos 2x}$

40. $\cos x = \dfrac{\sin 3x + \sin x}{2 \sin 2x}$

41. $\tan \theta = \dfrac{\cos 4\theta - \cos 6\theta}{\sin 4\theta + \sin 6\theta}$

42. $\tan \theta = \dfrac{\sin 3\theta - \sin \theta}{\cos 3\theta + \cos \theta}$

43. $\cot 2\alpha = \dfrac{\sin 3\alpha - \sin \alpha}{\cos \alpha - \cos 3\alpha}$

44. $\cot 3\alpha = \dfrac{\cos 4\alpha + \cos 2\alpha}{\sin 4\alpha + \sin 2\alpha}$

45. $\dfrac{\sin A + \sin B}{\sin A - \sin B} = \tan \left(\dfrac{A+B}{2} \right) \cot \left(\dfrac{A-B}{2} \right)$

46. $\dfrac{\cos A + \cos B}{-\cos A + \cos B} = \cot \left(\dfrac{A+B}{2} \right) \cot \left(\dfrac{A-B}{2} \right)$

47. $\cot \left(\dfrac{x+y}{2} \right) = \dfrac{\cos x + \cos y}{\sin x + \sin y}$

48. $-\tan \left(\dfrac{x+y}{2} \right) = \dfrac{\cos x - \cos y}{\sin x - \sin y}$

Chapter 7: Inverse Trigonometric Functions and Trigonometric Equations

In this chapter, we will learn about inverse trigonometric functions and methods of solving trigonometric equations.

Section 7.1   Inverse Trigonometric Functions

In Section R.7, we have reviewed inverse functions. We have seen that if a function is one-to-one, then it has an inverse function and its graph passes the horizontal line test. If a function is not one-to-one, then we can restrict its domain in a suitable way so that the function is one-to-one on the restricted domain. For example, $f(x) = x^2$ is not one-to-one on its natural domain $(-\infty, \infty)$. However, the horizontal line test shows that $g(x) = x^2$ is one-to-one on the restricted domain $[0, \infty)$.

After glancing at the graphs of the six trigonometric functions, you will be convinced that none of the graphs pass the horizontal line test. This means that none of the functions are one-to-one on their natural domain. As mentioned above, we can restrict the domain of each trigonometric function to a suitable domain on which each of them is one-to-one. In this section, we will discuss how to restrict the domain for each function and define the inverse trigonometric functions.

The Inverse Sine Function

Let's take a look at the graph of the sine function.

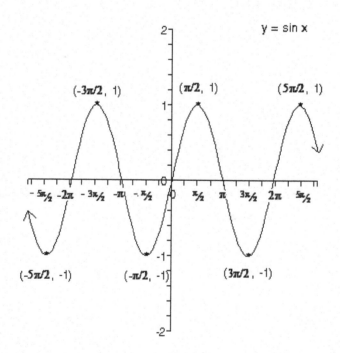

Recall that the domain of $y = \sin x$ is $\{x \mid -\infty < x < \infty\} = (-\infty, \infty)$ and the range is $\{y \mid -1 \le y \le 1\} = [-1, 1]$. Observe that the sine graph fails the horizontal line test, implying that $y = \sin x$ is not one-to-one on $(-\infty, \infty)$. If we restrict the domain of $y = \sin x$ to the interval $\left[-\frac{\pi}{2}, \frac{\pi}{2}\right]$, then the graph on this interval will pass the horizontal line test. Consequently, $y = \sin x$ is one-to-one and has an inverse function on the interval $\left[-\frac{\pi}{2}, \frac{\pi}{2}\right]$ (see the next figure).

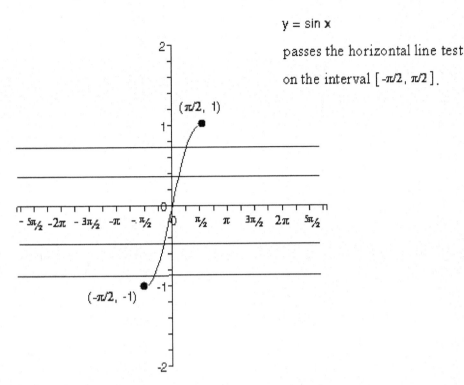

To find the inverse function, we interchange x and y in the equation $y = \sin x$ to obtain the implicit form of the inverse function, namely $x = \sin y$ (where $-\frac{\pi}{2} \leq y \leq \frac{\pi}{2}$). To write this function in explicit form, we define the **inverse sine function** as follows:

$$y = \sin^{-1} x, \quad \text{where} \quad -\frac{\pi}{2} \leq y \leq \frac{\pi}{2} \quad \text{and} \quad -1 \leq x \leq 1.$$

We read $y = \sin^{-1} x$ as 'y equals sine inverse of x'. Note that $y = \sin^{-1} x$ is the same as $x = \sin y$. It is useful to think of $y = \sin^{-1} x$ as 'y equals the angle whose sine is x'. Sometimes we write $\sin^{-1} x$ as $\arcsin x$ and read this as the '**arc sine** of x'.

Examples. Find the exact value.

1) $\sin^{-1} \frac{1}{2}$

Let $\sin^{-1} \frac{1}{2} = \theta$. We want to find the angle θ, $-\frac{\pi}{2} \leq \theta \leq \frac{\pi}{2}$, whose sine is $\frac{1}{2}$. In other words, we want to solve the equation

$$\sin \theta = \frac{1}{2}, \quad \text{where} \quad -\frac{\pi}{2} \leq \theta \leq \frac{\pi}{2}.$$

Well, we know that $\sin \frac{\pi}{6} = \frac{1}{2}$ and $-\frac{\pi}{2} \leq \frac{\pi}{6} \leq \frac{\pi}{2}$. Therefore, $\theta = \frac{\pi}{6}$ and so $\sin^{-1} \frac{1}{2} = \frac{\pi}{6}$. Once again, observe that

$$\sin^{-1} \frac{1}{2} = \frac{\pi}{6} \quad \text{is the same as} \quad \sin \frac{\pi}{6} = \frac{1}{2}.$$

2) $\sin^{-1} 0$

Let $\sin^{-1} 0 = \theta$. We want to find the angle θ, $-\frac{\pi}{2} \leq \theta \leq \frac{\pi}{2}$, whose sine is 0. In other words, we want to solve the equation

$$\sin \theta = 0, \quad \text{where} \quad -\frac{\pi}{2} \leq \theta \leq \frac{\pi}{2}.$$

We know that $\sin 0 = 0$ and $-\frac{\pi}{2} \leq 0 \leq \frac{\pi}{2}$. Therefore, $\theta = 0$ and so $\sin^{-1} 0 = 0$.

3) $\sin^{-1}\left(-\frac{\sqrt{2}}{2}\right)$

Let $\sin^{-1}\left(-\frac{\sqrt{2}}{2}\right) = \theta$. We want to find the angle θ, $-\frac{\pi}{2} \leq \theta \leq \frac{\pi}{2}$, such that $\sin\theta = -\frac{\sqrt{2}}{2}$. We know that $\sin\frac{\pi}{4} = \frac{\sqrt{2}}{2}$. Multiplying both sides of this equation by -1 and using the property of negative angles for sine give us

$$-\sin\frac{\pi}{4} = -\frac{\sqrt{2}}{2}$$

$$\sin\left(-\frac{\pi}{4}\right) = -\frac{\sqrt{2}}{2}$$

Since $-\frac{\pi}{2} \leq -\frac{\pi}{4} \leq \frac{\pi}{2}$, we have that $\theta = -\frac{\pi}{4}$. Therefore, $\sin^{-1}\left(-\frac{\sqrt{2}}{2}\right) = -\frac{\pi}{4}$.

The following property of the inverse sine function can be used to evaluate the inverse sine of any negative number in an easy way.

Property of the Inverse Sine Function

If $-1 \leq x \leq 1$, then $\sin^{-1}(-x) = -\sin^{-1}x$.

This property can also be written in terms of arc sine as follows:

If $-1 \leq x \leq 1$, then $\arcsin(-x) = -\arcsin x$.

Proof: Let $\sin^{-1}(-x) = \theta$. This can be written as $\sin\theta = -x$. Observe that:

$$-x = \sin\theta$$

$$x = -\sin\theta$$

$$x = \sin(-\theta)$$

$$\sin^{-1}x = -\theta$$

$$-\sin^{-1}x = \theta$$

And so $\sin^{-1}(-x) = -\sin^{-1}x$.

4) $\sin^{-1}\left(-\frac{\sqrt{3}}{2}\right)$

First let's find $\sin^{-1}\frac{\sqrt{3}}{2}$. By definition, $\theta = \sin^{-1}\frac{\sqrt{3}}{2}$ becomes $\sin\theta = \frac{\sqrt{3}}{2}$. The solution to this equation in the interval $-\frac{\pi}{2} \leq \theta \leq \frac{\pi}{2}$ is $\theta = \frac{\pi}{3}$. This means that $\sin^{-1}\frac{\sqrt{3}}{2} = \frac{\pi}{3}$. By our property, we have that $\sin^{-1}\left(-\frac{\sqrt{3}}{2}\right) = -\sin^{-1}\left(\frac{\sqrt{3}}{2}\right) = -\frac{\pi}{3}$.

5) $\arcsin\frac{\sqrt{2}}{2}$

Evaluating $\arcsin\frac{\sqrt{2}}{2}$ is the same as evaluating $\sin^{-1}\frac{\sqrt{2}}{2}$. If we set $\arcsin\frac{\sqrt{2}}{2} = \theta$, then $\sin\theta = \frac{\sqrt{2}}{2}$ where $-\frac{\pi}{2} \leq \theta \leq \frac{\pi}{2}$. This implies that $\theta = \frac{\pi}{4}$, so $\arcsin\frac{\sqrt{2}}{2} = \frac{\pi}{4}$.

6) $\sin^{-1}\frac{2}{5}$ (in radians, to three decimal places)

Your calculator can evaluate this for you. Make sure that the calculator is in radian mode. On the TI-30XII calculator, type in

$$\boxed{\text{2nd}}\;\boxed{\sin}\;\boxed{2}\;\boxed{\div}\;\boxed{5}\;\boxed{)}\;\boxed{=}$$

and you will obtain approximately 0.412. Therefore, $\sin^{-1}\frac{2}{5}\approx 0.412$.

We can obtain the graph of $y=\sin^{-1}x$ by reflecting the graph of $y=\sin x$, $-\frac{\pi}{2}\le x\le\frac{\pi}{2}$, about the line $y=x$. The graph is given below.

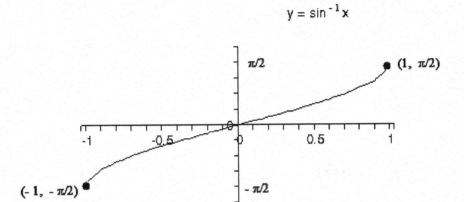

Recall that if f is a one-to-one function, then $f\left(f^{-1}\left(x\right)\right)=x$ (where x is in the domain of $f^{-1}\left(x\right)$) and $f^{-1}\left(f\left(x\right)\right)=x$ (where x is in the domain of $f\left(x\right)$). If $f\left(x\right)=\sin x$, $-\frac{\pi}{2}\le x\le\frac{\pi}{2}$, then $f^{-1}\left(x\right)=\sin^{-1}x$ and we have that

$$\sin\left(\sin^{-1}x\right)=x,\quad\text{where}-1\le x\le 1\text{ and}$$
$$\sin^{-1}\left(\sin x\right)=x,\quad\text{where}-\frac{\pi}{2}\le x\le\frac{\pi}{2}.$$

Equivalently, we write:

$$\sin\left(\arcsin x\right)=x,\quad\text{where }-1\le x\le 1\text{ and}$$
$$\arcsin\left(\sin x\right)=x,\quad\text{where }-\frac{\pi}{2}\le x\le\frac{\pi}{2}.$$

Examples. Find the exact value.

1) $\underbrace{\sin\left(\sin^{-1}\frac{1}{5}\right)=\frac{1}{5}}_{\text{since }-1\le\frac{1}{5}\le 1}$

2) $\underbrace{\sin\left(\sin^{-1}0.826\right)=0.826}_{\text{since }-1\le 0.826\le 1}$

3) $\underbrace{\sin\left(\arcsin(-1)\right)=-1}_{\text{since }-1\le -1\le 1}$

4) $\underbrace{\sin^{-1}\left(\sin\frac{\pi}{5}\right)=\frac{\pi}{5}}_{\text{since }-\frac{\pi}{2}\le\frac{\pi}{5}\le\frac{\pi}{2}}$

5) $\underbrace{\arcsin\left(\sin 0\right)=0}_{\text{since }-\frac{\pi}{2}\le 0\le\frac{\pi}{2}}$

6) $\underbrace{\sin^{-1}\left(\sin\left(-1.02\right)\right)=-1.02}_{\text{since }-\frac{\pi}{2}\le -1.02\le\frac{\pi}{2}}$

7) $\underbrace{\sin^{-1}\left(\sin\frac{3\pi}{4}\right)=\sin^{-1}\left(\frac{\sqrt{2}}{2}\right)=\frac{\pi}{4}}_{\sin\frac{3\pi}{4}=\sin\frac{\pi}{4}=\frac{\sqrt{2}}{2}}$

Notice that $\sin^{-1}\left(\sin\frac{3\pi}{4}\right) \neq \frac{3\pi}{4}$. The property does not apply because $\frac{3\pi}{4}$ is not in the interval $\left[-\frac{\pi}{2}, \frac{\pi}{2}\right]$. Be careful!

 BEWARE: $\sin^{-1}\left(\sin x\right) \neq x$ **unless** $-\frac{\pi}{2} \leq x \leq \frac{\pi}{2}$.

8) $\underbrace{\arcsin\left(\sin\frac{11\pi}{6}\right) = \arcsin\left(-\frac{1}{2}\right)}_{\sin\frac{11\pi}{6}=-\sin\frac{\pi}{6}=-\frac{1}{2}} = -\arcsin\left(\frac{1}{2}\right) = -\frac{\pi}{6}$ \qquad (observe that $\sin\left(-\frac{\pi}{6}\right) = -\frac{1}{2}$)

9) $\underbrace{\sin^{-1}\left(\sin\left(-\frac{7\pi}{2}\right)\right)}_{\sin\left(-\frac{7\pi}{2}\right)=-\sin\frac{7\pi}{2}=-(-1)=1} = \sin^{-1}1 = \frac{\pi}{2}$ \qquad (since $\sin\frac{\pi}{2} = 1$)

Try These (Set 1): Find the exact value.

1) $\sin^{-1}\frac{\sqrt{3}}{2}$ \qquad 2) $\arcsin\left(-\frac{\sqrt{2}}{2}\right)$ \qquad 3) $\sin\left(\arcsin\left(-\frac{7}{9}\right)\right)$ \qquad 4) $\sin^{-1}\left(\sin\frac{7\pi}{3}\right)$

The Inverse Cosine Function

Let's remind ourselves of the graph of the cosine function.

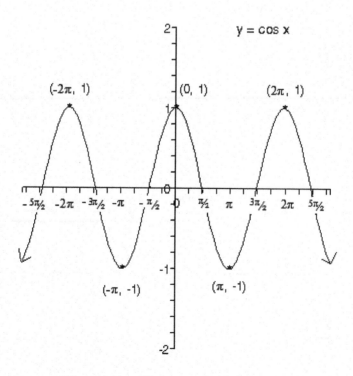

The domain of $y = \cos x$ is $\{x \mid -\infty < x < \infty\} = (-\infty, \infty)$ and the range is $\{y \mid -1 \leq y \leq 1\} = [-1, 1]$. Notice that the cosine graph fails the horizontal line test, implying that $y = \cos x$ is not one-to-one on $(-\infty, \infty)$. If we restrict the domain of $y = \cos x$ to the interval $[0, \pi]$, then the graph on this interval will pass the horizontal line test. As a result, $y = \cos x$ is one-to-one and has an inverse function on the interval $[0, \pi]$ (see the graph below).

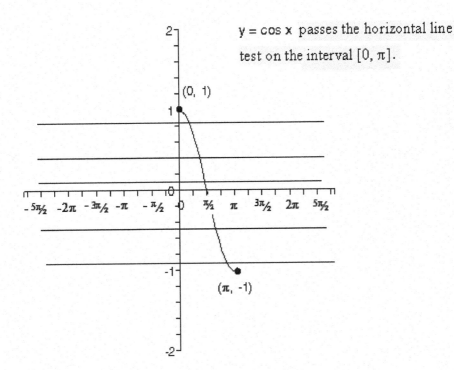

To find the inverse function, we interchange x and y in the equation $y = \cos x$ to obtain the implicit form of the inverse function, namely $x = \cos y$ (where $0 \leq y \leq \pi$). To write this function in explicit form, we define the **inverse cosine function** as follows:

$$y = \cos^{-1} x, \quad \text{where} \quad 0 \leq y \leq \pi \quad \text{and} \quad -1 \leq x \leq 1.$$

We read $y = \cos^{-1} x$ as 'y equals cosine inverse of x'. Note that $y = \cos^{-1} x$ is the same as $x = \cos y$. It is useful to think of $y = \cos^{-1} x$ as 'y equals the angle whose cosine is x'. Sometimes we write $\cos^{-1} x$ as $\arccos x$ and read this as the '**arc cosine** of x'.

The following property will be useful in evaluating the inverse cosine of a negative number.

Property of the Inverse Cosine Function

If $-1 \leq x \leq 1$, then $\cos^{-1}(-x) = \pi - \cos^{-1} x$.

This property can also be written in terms of arc cosine as follows:

If $-1 \leq x \leq 1$, then $\arccos(-x) = \pi - \arccos x$.

Proof. If we set $\cos^{-1}(-x) = \theta$, then $\cos\theta = -x$. Using the identity $\cos(\pi - \theta) = -\cos\theta$, we obtain:

$$-x = \cos\theta$$
$$x = -\cos\theta$$
$$x = \cos(\pi - \theta)$$
$$\cos^{-1}x = \pi - \theta$$
$$\cos^{-1}x = \pi - \cos^{-1}(-x)$$

And so $\cos^{-1}(-x) = \pi - \cos^{-1}x$.

Examples. Find the exact value.

1) $\cos^{-1}\frac{1}{2}$

Let $\cos^{-1}\frac{1}{2} = \theta$. We want to find the angle θ, $0 \leq \theta \leq \pi$, whose cosine is 1. In other words, we want to solve the equation

$$\cos\theta = \frac{1}{2}, \quad \text{where } 0 \leq \theta \leq \pi.$$

We know that $\cos\frac{\pi}{3} = \frac{1}{2}$ and $-\frac{\pi}{2} \leq \frac{\pi}{3} \leq \frac{\pi}{2}$. Therefore, $\theta = \frac{\pi}{3}$ and so $\cos^{-1}\frac{1}{2} = \frac{\pi}{3}$. Notice that

$$\cos^{-1}\left(\frac{1}{2}\right) = \frac{\pi}{3} \quad \text{is the same as} \quad \cos\frac{\pi}{3} = \frac{1}{2}.$$

2) $\cos^{-1}(-1)$

Let $\cos^{-1}(-1) = \theta$. We want to find the angle θ, $0 \leq \theta \leq \pi$, whose cosine is -1. In other words, we want to solve the equation

$$\cos\theta = -1, \quad \text{where } 0 \leq \theta \leq \pi.$$

Well, we know that $\cos\pi = -1$ and $0 \leq \pi \leq \pi$. Therefore, $\theta = \pi$ and so $\cos^{-1}(-1) = \pi$.

3) $\arccos\left(-\frac{\sqrt{3}}{2}\right)$

First let's find the value of $\arccos\left(\frac{\sqrt{3}}{2}\right)$. Observe that $\arccos\left(\frac{\sqrt{3}}{2}\right) = \theta$ (equivalently, $\cos^{-1}\left(\frac{\sqrt{3}}{2}\right) = \theta$) implies that $\cos\theta = \frac{\sqrt{3}}{2}$. The solution to this equation on the interval $[0, \pi]$ is $\theta = \frac{\pi}{6}$. This means that $\arccos\left(\frac{\sqrt{3}}{2}\right) = \frac{\pi}{6}$. Now, using our property, we obtain

$$\arccos\left(-\frac{\sqrt{3}}{2}\right) = \pi - \arccos\left(\frac{\sqrt{3}}{2}\right) = \pi - \frac{\pi}{6} = \frac{6\pi}{6} - \frac{\pi}{6} = \frac{5\pi}{6}.$$

Notice that $\underbrace{\cos\frac{5\pi}{6}}_{\frac{5\pi}{6} \text{ is in quadrant II.}} = -\cos\frac{\pi}{6} = -\frac{\sqrt{3}}{2}$ as expected.

4) $\cos^{-1}\left(-\frac{\sqrt{2}}{2}\right)$

Observe that $\cos^{-1}\left(\frac{\sqrt{2}}{2}\right) = \frac{\pi}{4}$ (since $\cos\frac{\pi}{4} = \frac{\sqrt{2}}{2}$). Therefore, our property gives us

$$\cos^{-1}\left(-\frac{\sqrt{2}}{2}\right) = \pi - \cos^{-1}\left(\frac{\sqrt{2}}{2}\right) = \pi - \frac{\pi}{4} = \frac{4\pi}{4} - \frac{\pi}{4} = \frac{3\pi}{4}.$$

Notice that $\underbrace{\cos\frac{3\pi}{4}}_{\frac{3\pi}{4} \text{ is in quadrant II.}} = -\cos\frac{\pi}{4} = -\frac{\sqrt{2}}{2}$ as expected.

5) arccos 0

Evaluating arccos 0 is the same as evaluating $\cos^{-1} 0$. If we let $\cos^{-1} 0 = \theta$, then $\cos \theta = 0$ where $0 \leq \theta \leq \pi$. The solution to this equation on the given interval is $\theta = \frac{\pi}{2}$. Therefore, arccos 0 $= \frac{\pi}{2}$.

6) $\cos^{-1}(-0.1662)$ (in radians, to four decimal places)

Make sure that your calculator is in radian mode. On the TI-30XII calculator, you type in

$$\boxed{\text{2nd}} \,\, \boxed{\text{cos}} \,\, \boxed{(\text{-})} \,\, \boxed{.1662} \,\, \boxed{)} \,\, \boxed{=}$$

and will get approximately 1.7378. Therefore, $\cos^{-1}(-0.1662) \approx 1.7378$.

The graph of $y = \cos^{-1} x$ is obtained by reflecting the graph of $y = \cos x$, $0 \leq x \leq \pi$, about the line $y = x$. The graph is given below.

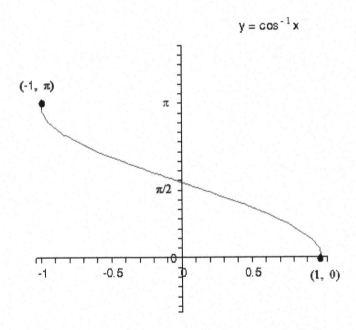

The following properties for the cosine function and its inverse hold (compare these to the properties for sine and its inverse):

$$\cos\left(\cos^{-1} x\right) = x, \quad \text{where } -1 \leq x \leq 1 \quad \text{and}$$

$$\cos^{-1}\left(\cos x\right) = x, \quad \text{where } 0 \leq x \leq \pi.$$

Equivalently, we have

$$\cos\left(\arccos x\right) = x, \quad \text{where } -1 \leq x \leq 1 \quad \text{and}$$

$$\arccos\left(\cos x\right) = x, \quad \text{where } 0 \leq x \leq \pi.$$

Examples. Find the exact value.

1) $\underbrace{\cos\left(\cos^{-1}\frac{2}{3}\right) = \frac{2}{3}}_{\text{since } -1 \le \frac{2}{3} \le 1}$
2) $\underbrace{\cos\left(\cos^{-1}(-0.902)\right) = -0.902}_{\text{since } -1 \le -0.902 \le 1}$
3) $\underbrace{\cos(\arccos 1) = 1}_{\text{since } -1 \le 1 \le 1}$

4) $\underbrace{\arccos\left(\cos\frac{\pi}{7}\right) = \frac{\pi}{7}}_{\text{since } 0 \le \frac{\pi}{7} \le \pi}$
5) $\underbrace{\cos^{-1}(\cos 0) = 0}_{\text{since } 0 \le 0 \le \pi}$
6) $\underbrace{\cos^{-1}(\cos 2.88) = 2.88}_{\text{since } 0 \le 2.88 \le \pi}$

7) $\underbrace{\arccos\left(\cos\frac{5\pi}{3}\right) = \arccos\left(\frac{1}{2}\right)}_{\cos\frac{5\pi}{3} = \cos\frac{\pi}{3} = \frac{1}{2}} = \frac{\pi}{3}$

Notice that $\arccos\left(\cos\frac{5\pi}{3}\right) \ne \frac{5\pi}{3}$. The property cannot be used here because $\frac{5\pi}{3}$ is not in the interval $[0, \pi]$. Be careful!

 BEWARE: $\cos^{-1}(\cos x) \ne x$ **unless** $0 \le x \le \pi$.

8) $\underbrace{\cos^{-1}\left(\cos\frac{5\pi}{4}\right) = \cos^{-1}\left(-\frac{\sqrt{2}}{2}\right)}_{\cos\frac{5\pi}{4} = -\cos\frac{\pi}{4} = -\frac{\sqrt{2}}{2}} = \underbrace{\pi - \cos^{-1}\frac{\sqrt{2}}{2}}_{\text{Observe that } \cos\frac{\pi}{4} = \frac{\sqrt{2}}{2}.} = \pi - \frac{\pi}{4} = \frac{4\pi}{4} - \frac{\pi}{4} = \frac{3\pi}{4}$

9) $\underbrace{\cos^{-1}(\cos(-5\pi)) = \cos^{-1}(-1)}_{\cos(-5\pi) = \cos 5\pi = \cos\pi = -1} = \pi$

10) $\underbrace{\cos^{-1}\left(\cos\frac{7\pi}{6}\right) = \cos^{-1}\left(-\frac{\sqrt{3}}{2}\right)}_{\cos\frac{7\pi}{6} = -\cos\frac{\pi}{6} = -\frac{\sqrt{3}}{2}} = \underbrace{\pi - \cos^{-1}\frac{\sqrt{3}}{2}}_{\text{Note that } \cos\frac{\pi}{6} = \frac{\sqrt{3}}{2}.} = \pi - \frac{\pi}{6} = \frac{6\pi}{6} - \frac{\pi}{6} = \frac{5\pi}{6}$

Try These (Set 2): Find the exact value.

1) $\cos^{-1}\frac{\sqrt{2}}{2}$
2) $\arccos\left(-\frac{1}{2}\right)$
3) $\cos\left(\cos^{-1}\left(-\frac{3}{4}\right)\right)$
4) $\arccos\left(\cos\left(-\frac{7\pi}{6}\right)\right)$

The Inverse Tangent Function

The graph of the tangent function fails the horizontal line test (see the next figure). This means that $y = \tan x$ is not one-to-one on its natural domain, $\left\{x \mid x \ne \frac{n\pi}{2}\right\}$, where n is an odd integer.

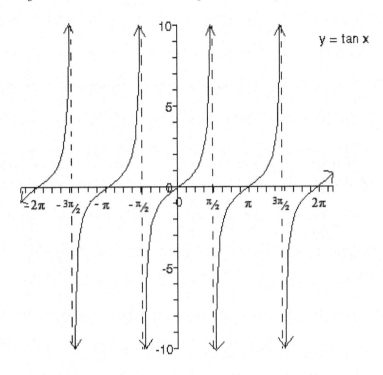

If we restrict the domain of $y = \tan x$ to the interval $\left(-\frac{\pi}{2}, \frac{\pi}{2}\right)$, then the graph on this interval will pass the horizontal line test. Consequently, $y = \tan x$ is one-to-one and has an inverse function on the interval $\left(-\frac{\pi}{2}, \frac{\pi}{2}\right)$ (see the figure below).

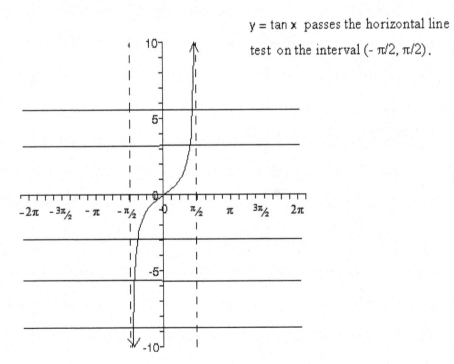

To find the inverse function, we interchange x and y in the equation $y = \tan x$ to obtain the implicit form of the inverse function, namely $x = \tan y$ (where $-\frac{\pi}{2} < y < \frac{\pi}{2}$). To write this function in explicit form, we define the **inverse tangent function** as follows:

$$y = \tan^{-1} x, \quad \text{where} \quad -\frac{\pi}{2} < y < \frac{\pi}{2} \quad \text{and} \quad -\infty < x < \infty.$$

We read $y = \tan^{-1} x$ as 'y equals tangent inverse of x'. Keep in mind that $y = \tan^{-1} x$ is the same as $x = \tan y$. It is useful to think of $y = \tan^{-1} x$ as 'y equals the angle whose tangent is x'. Sometimes we write $\tan^{-1} x$ as $\arctan x$ and read this as the '**arctan** of x'.

The following property of the inverse tangent function can be used to evaluate the inverse tangent of any negative number in an easy way:

Property of the Inverse Tangent Function

If x is **any** real number, then $\tan^{-1}(-x) = -\tan^{-1} x$.

Using arctan, we write this property as follows:

If x is **any** number, then $\arctan(-x) = -\arctan x$.

Proof. Let $\tan^{-1}(-x) = \theta$. This can be written as $\tan\theta = -x$. Observe that:

$$-x = \tan\theta$$
$$x = -\tan\theta$$
$$x = \tan(-\theta)$$
$$\tan^{-1} x = -\theta$$
$$-\tan^{-1} x = \theta$$

And so $\tan^{-1}(-x) = -\tan^{-1} x$.

Examples. Find the exact value.

1) $\tan^{-1} 1$

Let $\tan^{-1} 1 = \theta$. We want to find the angle θ, $-\frac{\pi}{2} < \theta < \frac{\pi}{2}$, whose tangent is 1. In other words, we want to solve the equation

$$\tan\theta = 1, \quad \text{where} \quad -\frac{\pi}{2} < \theta < \frac{\pi}{2}.$$

Since $\tan\frac{\pi}{4} = 1$ and $-\frac{\pi}{2} < \frac{\pi}{4} < \frac{\pi}{2}$, we have that $\theta = \frac{\pi}{4}$ which means that $\tan^{-1} 1 = \frac{\pi}{4}$. Observe that

$$\tan^{-1} 1 = \frac{\pi}{4} \quad \text{is the same as} \quad \tan\frac{\pi}{4} = 1.$$

2) $\arctan 0$

Let $\arctan 0 = \theta$. We want to find the angle θ, $-\frac{\pi}{2} < \theta < \frac{\pi}{2}$, whose tangent is 0. In other words, we want to solve the equation

$$\tan\theta = 0, \quad \text{where} \quad -\frac{\pi}{2} < \theta < \frac{\pi}{2}.$$

Well, we know that $\tan 0 = 0$ and $-\frac{\pi}{2} < 0 < \frac{\pi}{2}$. Therefore, $\theta = 0$ and so $\arctan 0 = 0$.

3) $\tan^{-1}\left(-\sqrt{3}\right)$

First let's find $\tan^{-1}\left(\sqrt{3}\right)$. By definition, $\theta = \tan^{-1}\left(\sqrt{3}\right)$ becomes $\tan\theta = \sqrt{3}$. The solution to this equation in the interval $-\frac{\pi}{2} < \theta < \frac{\pi}{2}$ is $\theta = \frac{\pi}{3}$. This means that $\tan^{-1}\left(\sqrt{3}\right) = \frac{\pi}{3}$. By our property, we have that $\tan^{-1}\left(-\sqrt{3}\right) = -\tan^{-1}\left(\sqrt{3}\right) = -\frac{\pi}{3}$.

4) $\tan^{-1}\left(-\frac{\sqrt{3}}{3}\right)$

We begin by finding $\tan^{-1}\left(\frac{\sqrt{3}}{3}\right)$. By definition, $\theta = \tan^{-1}\left(\frac{\sqrt{3}}{3}\right)$ becomes $\tan\theta = \frac{\sqrt{3}}{3}$. The solution to this equation in the interval $-\frac{\pi}{2} < \theta < \frac{\pi}{2}$ is $\theta = \frac{\pi}{6}$. This means that $\tan^{-1}\left(\frac{\sqrt{3}}{3}\right) = \frac{\pi}{6}$. By our property, we have that $\tan^{-1}\left(-\frac{\sqrt{3}}{3}\right) = -\tan^{-1}\left(\frac{\sqrt{3}}{3}\right) = -\frac{\pi}{6}$.

5) $\arctan(37.981)$ (in radians, to three decimal places)

Using the calculator, we type

$$\boxed{\text{2nd}}\ \boxed{\text{tan}}\ \boxed{\text{37.981}}\ \boxed{)}\ \boxed{=}$$

and obtain approximately 1.544. Therefore, $\arctan(37.981) \approx 1.544$.

The graph of $y = \tan^{-1} x$ is found by reflecting the graph of $y = \tan x$, $-\frac{\pi}{2} < x < \frac{\pi}{2}$, about the line $y = x$. The graph is given below.

$$y = \tan^{-1} x$$

The following properties for the tangent function and its inverse hold (compare these to the properties for sine and cosine and their inverses):

$$\tan\left(\tan^{-1} x\right) = x, \qquad \text{where } -\infty < x < \infty \quad \text{and}$$

$$\tan^{-1}\left(\tan x\right) = x, \qquad \text{where } -\frac{\pi}{2} < x < \frac{\pi}{2}.$$

Equivalently, we have

$$\tan\left(\arctan x\right) = x, \qquad \text{where } -\infty < x < \infty \quad \text{and}$$

$$\arctan\left(\tan x\right) = x, \qquad \text{where } -\tfrac{\pi}{2} < x < \tfrac{\pi}{2}.$$

Examples. Find the exact value.

1) $\tan\left(\tan^{-1} 12\right) = 12$ 　　　2) $\tan\left(\arctan 27.12\right) = 27.12$ 　　　3) $\tan\left(\tan^{-1} \tfrac{30}{17}\right) = \tfrac{30}{17}$

4) $\underbrace{\tan^{-1}\left(\tan \tfrac{\pi}{6}\right) = \tfrac{\pi}{6}}_{\text{since } -\frac{\pi}{2} < \frac{\pi}{6} < \frac{\pi}{2}}$ 　　5) $\underbrace{\arctan\left(\tan 1.5\right) = 1.5}_{\text{since } -\frac{\pi}{2} < 1.5 < \frac{\pi}{2}}$ 　　6) $\underbrace{\tan^{-1}\left(\tan\left(-\tfrac{\pi}{8}\right)\right) = -\tfrac{\pi}{8}}_{\text{since } -\frac{\pi}{2} < -\frac{\pi}{8} < \frac{\pi}{2}}$

7) $\underbrace{\tan^{-1}\left(\tan \tfrac{7\pi}{4}\right) = \tan^{-1}\left(-1\right)}_{\tan \frac{7\pi}{4} = -\tan \frac{\pi}{4} = -1} = -\tan^{-1} 1 = -\tfrac{\pi}{4}$

Notice that $\tan^{-1}\left(\tan \tfrac{7\pi}{4}\right) \neq \tfrac{7\pi}{4}$. The property does not apply because $\tfrac{7\pi}{4}$ is not in the interval $\left(-\tfrac{\pi}{2}, \tfrac{\pi}{2}\right)$. Be careful!

 BEWARE: $\tan^{-1}\left(\tan x\right) \neq x$ **unless** $-\tfrac{\pi}{2} < x < \tfrac{\pi}{2}$.

---

8) $\underbrace{\arctan\left(\tan \tfrac{4\pi}{3}\right) = \arctan\left(\sqrt{3}\right)}_{\tan \frac{4\pi}{3} = \tan \frac{\pi}{3} = \sqrt{3}} = \tfrac{\pi}{3}$

9) $\underbrace{\tan^{-1}\left(\tan\left(-6\pi\right)\right) = \tan^{-1} 0}_{\tan(-6\pi) = -\tan 6\pi = -(0) = 0} = 0 \qquad \left(\text{since } \tan 0 = 0\right)$

Try These (Set 3): Find the exact value.

1) $\tan^{-1} \sqrt{3}$ 　　　2) $\arctan\left(-1\right)$ 　　　3) $\tan\left(\tan^{-1}\left(4.71\right)\right)$ 　　　4) $\tan^{-1}\left(\tan \tfrac{17\pi}{6}\right)$

Some More Examples

Before we take a look at the remaining inverse trigonometric functions, let's do some more examples with the inverse trigonometric functions that we have so far.

Examples. Find the exact value.

1) $\sin\left(\tan^{-1} 1\right)$

Let $\theta = \tan^{-1} 1$. We want to find θ, $-\frac{\pi}{2} < \theta < \frac{\pi}{2}$, such that $\tan \theta = 1$. Since $\tan \frac{\pi}{4} = 1$ and $-\frac{\pi}{2} < \frac{\pi}{4} < \frac{\pi}{2}$, we have that $\theta = \frac{\pi}{4}$. Therefore,

$$\sin\left(\tan^{-1} 1\right) = \sin \theta = \sin \frac{\pi}{4} = \frac{\sqrt{2}}{2}.$$

2) $\cos\left(\sin^{-1} \frac{\sqrt{3}}{2}\right)$

Let $\theta = \sin^{-1} \frac{\sqrt{3}}{2}$. We want to find θ, $-\frac{\pi}{2} \le \theta \le \frac{\pi}{2}$, such that $\sin \theta = \frac{\sqrt{3}}{2}$. Since $\sin \frac{\pi}{3} = \frac{\sqrt{3}}{2}$ and $-\frac{\pi}{2} \le \frac{\pi}{3} \le \frac{\pi}{2}$, we have that $\theta = \frac{\pi}{3}$. Therefore,

$$\cos\left(\sin^{-1} \frac{\sqrt{3}}{2}\right) = \cos \theta = \cos \frac{\pi}{3} = \frac{1}{2}.$$

3) $\tan\left[\arccos\left(-1\right)\right]$

Let $\theta = \arccos\left(-1\right)$. We want to find θ, $0 \le \theta \le \pi$, such that $\cos \theta = -1$. Since $\cos \pi = -1$ and $0 \le \pi \le \pi$, we have that $\theta = \pi$. Therefore,

$$\tan\left[\arccos\left(-1\right)\right] = \tan \theta = \tan \pi = 0.$$

4) $\cos\left(\tan^{-1} \frac{1}{3}\right)$

Let $\theta = \tan^{-1} \frac{1}{3}$. Then $\tan \theta = \frac{1}{3}$, where $-\frac{\pi}{2} < \theta < \frac{\pi}{2}$. To solve this problem, we will draw a picture of θ in standard position. Notice that θ lies in quadrant I since $\tan \theta = \frac{1}{3} > 0$ and $0 < \theta < \frac{\pi}{2}$.

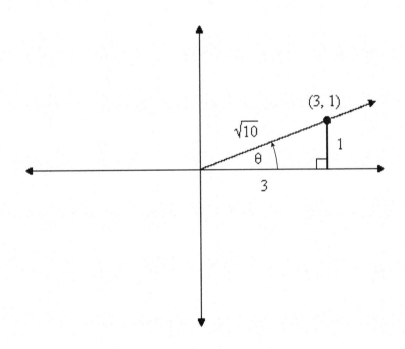

Using the figure above, we can solve the problem.

$$\cos\left(\tan^{-1} \frac{1}{3}\right) = \cos \theta = \frac{3}{\sqrt{10}} = \frac{3\sqrt{10}}{10}.$$

5) $\cos\left(\arcsin\left(-\frac{3}{5}\right)\right)$

Let $\theta = \arcsin\left(-\frac{3}{5}\right)$. Then $\sin \theta = -\frac{3}{5}$, where $-\frac{\pi}{2} \le \theta \le \frac{\pi}{2}$. As in Example 4, we will draw a picture of θ in standard position. Notice that θ lies in quadrant IV since $\sin \theta = -\frac{3}{5} < 0$ and $-\frac{\pi}{2} < \theta < 0$.

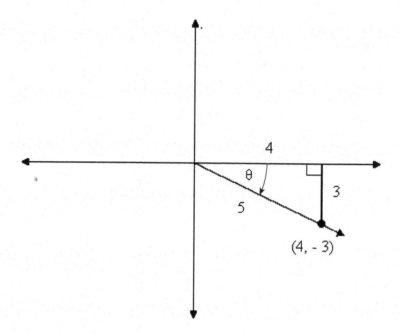

Using the figure above, we find that

$$\cos\left[\arcsin\left(-\tfrac{3}{5}\right)\right] = \cos\theta = \tfrac{4}{5}.$$

6) $\sin\left[\arctan\left(-4\right)\right]$

Let $\theta = \arctan\left(-4\right)$. Then $\tan\theta = -4$, where $-\tfrac{\pi}{2} < \theta < \tfrac{\pi}{2}$. The figure below shows angle θ in standard position. Notice that θ lies in quadrant IV since $\tan\theta = -4 < 0$ and $-\tfrac{\pi}{2} < \theta < 0$.

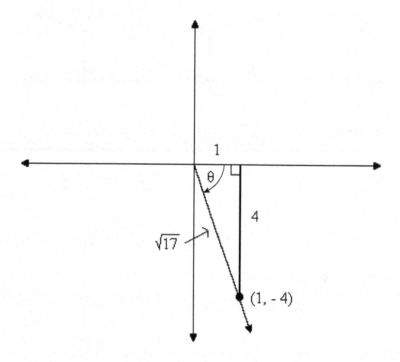

The figure shows that

$$\sin\left[\arctan\left(-4\right)\right] = \sin\theta = -\tfrac{4}{\sqrt{17}} = -\tfrac{4\sqrt{17}}{17}.$$

7) $\tan\left[\cos^{-1}\left(-\frac{2\sqrt{2}}{7}\right)\right]$

Let $\theta = \cos^{-1}\left(-\frac{2\sqrt{2}}{7}\right)$. Then $\cos\theta = -\frac{2\sqrt{2}}{7}$, where $0 \le \theta \le \pi$. The figure below shows angle θ in standard form. Notice that θ lies in quadrant II since $\cos\theta = -\frac{2\sqrt{2}}{7} < 0$ and $\frac{\pi}{2} < \theta < \pi$.

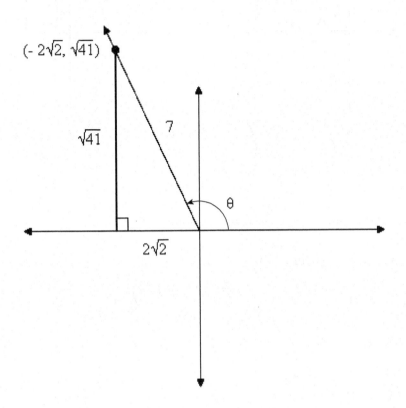

The figure shows that

$$\tan\left[\cos^{-1}\left(-\frac{2\sqrt{2}}{7}\right)\right] = \tan\theta = -\frac{\sqrt{41}}{2\sqrt{2}} = -\frac{\sqrt{82}}{4}.$$

8) $\underbrace{\arcsin\left(\cos\frac{2\pi}{3}\right) = \arcsin\left(-\frac{1}{2}\right)}_{\cos\frac{2\pi}{3} = -\cos\frac{\pi}{3} = -\frac{1}{2}} = \underbrace{-\arcsin\frac{1}{2} = -\frac{\pi}{6}}_{\sin\frac{\pi}{6} = \frac{1}{2}}$

9) $\underbrace{\tan^{-1}\left(\csc\frac{\pi}{2}\right) = \tan^{-1}1}_{\csc\frac{\pi}{2} = 1} = \frac{\pi}{4}$ (since $\tan\frac{\pi}{4} = 1$)

10) $\sin\left(\cos^{-1}\frac{\sqrt{2}}{2} + \sin^{-1}\frac{12}{13}\right)$

Let $A = \cos^{-1}\frac{\sqrt{2}}{2}$ and $B = \sin^{-1}\frac{12}{13}$. Then we have that $\cos A = \frac{\sqrt{2}}{2}$, where $0 \le A \le \pi$, and $\sin B = \frac{12}{13}$, where $-\frac{\pi}{2} \le B \le \frac{\pi}{2}$. Both angle A and angle B are in quadrant I since $\cos A = \frac{\sqrt{2}}{2} > 0$ with $0 < A < \frac{\pi}{2}$ and $\sin B = \frac{12}{13} > 0$ with $0 < B < \frac{\pi}{2}$ (see the next figures).

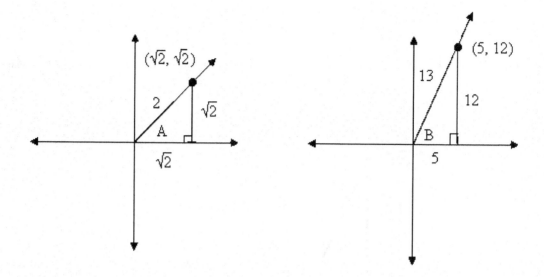

By using the sum formula for sine and the diagrams above, we have

$$\sin\left(\cos^{-1}\tfrac{\sqrt{2}}{2} + \sin^{-1}\tfrac{12}{13}\right) = \sin(A+B) = \sin A \cos B + \sin B \cos A$$

$$= \tfrac{\sqrt{2}}{2}\left(\tfrac{5}{13}\right) + \tfrac{12}{13}\left(\tfrac{\sqrt{2}}{2}\right)$$

$$= \tfrac{5\sqrt{2}}{26} + \tfrac{12\sqrt{2}}{26} = \tfrac{17\sqrt{2}}{26}.$$

11) $\tan\left[\arcsin\left(-\tfrac{\sqrt{7}}{4}\right) - \arccos\left(-\tfrac{3}{5}\right)\right]$

Let $A = \arcsin\left(-\tfrac{\sqrt{7}}{4}\right)$ and $B = \arccos\left(-\tfrac{3}{5}\right)$. Then we have that $\sin A = -\tfrac{\sqrt{7}}{4}$, where $-\tfrac{\pi}{2} \le A \le \tfrac{\pi}{2}$, and $\cos B = -\tfrac{3}{5}$, where $0 \le B \le \pi$. The graph of angles A and B are shown in the figures below. Notice that angle A is in quadrant IV since $\sin A = -\tfrac{\sqrt{7}}{4} < 0$ with $-\tfrac{\pi}{2} < A < 0$ and angle B is in quadrant II since $\cos B = -\tfrac{3}{5} < 0$ with $\tfrac{\pi}{2} < B < \pi$.

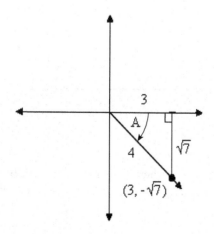

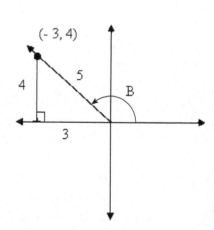

By using the difference formula for tangent and the figure above, we obtain:

$$\tan\left[\arcsin\left(-\tfrac{\sqrt{7}}{4}\right) - \arccos\left(-\tfrac{3}{5}\right)\right] = \tan(A-B) = \frac{\tan A - \tan B}{1 + \tan A \tan B}$$

$$= \frac{\left(-\tfrac{\sqrt{7}}{3}\right) - \left(-\tfrac{4}{3}\right)}{1 + \left(-\tfrac{\sqrt{7}}{3}\right)\left(-\tfrac{4}{3}\right)} = \frac{\frac{-\sqrt{7}+4}{3}}{1 + \frac{4\sqrt{7}}{9}}$$

$$= \frac{\left(\frac{-\sqrt{7}+4}{3}\right)\left(\tfrac{9}{1}\right)}{1\left(\tfrac{9}{1}\right) + \frac{4\sqrt{7}}{9}\left(\tfrac{9}{1}\right)} = \frac{3\left(-\sqrt{7}+4\right)}{9 + 4\sqrt{7}}$$

$$= \frac{-3\sqrt{7} + 12}{9 + 4\sqrt{7}}$$

12) $\cos\left(2\sin^{-1}\tfrac{\sqrt{2}}{6}\right)$

Before we tackle this problem, let's recall the different versions of the double-angle formula for cosine.

$$\cos 2\theta = \cos^2\theta - \sin^2\theta$$
$$= 2\cos^2\theta - 1$$
$$= 1 - 2\sin^2\theta$$

Now, if we let $\theta = \sin^{-1}\left(-\tfrac{\sqrt{2}}{6}\right)$, then we have that $\sin\theta = -\tfrac{\sqrt{2}}{6}$, where $-\tfrac{\pi}{2} \le \theta \le \tfrac{\pi}{2}$. Observe that the last double-angle formula listed contains the sine function only. Therefore, the easiest way to solve this problem would be to use the identity $\cos 2\theta = 1 - 2\sin^2\theta$.

$$\cos\left(2\sin^{-1}\tfrac{\sqrt{2}}{6}\right) = \cos 2\theta = 1 - 2\sin^2\theta$$

$$= 1 - 2\left(-\tfrac{\sqrt{2}}{6}\right)^2 = 1 - 2\left(\tfrac{2}{36}\right)$$

$$= 1 - \tfrac{4}{36} = \tfrac{8}{9}$$

13) $\sin\left[2\arctan\left(-\tfrac{10}{11}\right)\right]$

If we let $\theta = \arctan\left(-\tfrac{10}{11}\right)$, then we have that $\tan\theta = -\tfrac{10}{11}$, where $-\tfrac{\pi}{2} < \theta < \tfrac{\pi}{2}$. Angle θ lies in quadrant IV since $\tan\theta = -\tfrac{10}{11} < 0$ and $-\tfrac{\pi}{2} < \theta < 0$. The next figure shows angle θ in standard position.

Using the double-angle formula for sine and the figure, we obtain:

$$\sin\left[2\arctan\left(-\tfrac{10}{11}\right)\right] = \sin 2\theta = 2\sin\theta\cos\theta$$

$$= 2\left(-\tfrac{10}{\sqrt{221}}\right)\left(\tfrac{11}{\sqrt{221}}\right) = -\tfrac{220}{221}$$

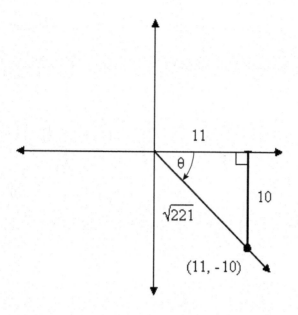

14) $\cos\left[\frac{1}{2}\sin^{-1}\left(\frac{\sqrt{3}}{3}\right)\right]$

If we let $\theta = \sin^{-1}\left(\frac{\sqrt{3}}{3}\right)$, then we have that $\sin\theta = \frac{\sqrt{3}}{3}$, where $-\frac{\pi}{2} \le \theta \le \frac{\pi}{2}$. Angle θ lies in quadrant I since $\sin\theta = \frac{\sqrt{3}}{3} > 0$ and $0 < \theta < \frac{\pi}{2}$. The figure below shows angle θ in standard position. Note that angle $\frac{\theta}{2}$ also lies in quadrant I since

$$0 < \theta < \frac{\pi}{2} \quad \text{implies that} \quad 0 < \frac{1}{2}\theta < \frac{\pi}{4}$$

(just multiply each term of the inequality by $\frac{1}{2}$).

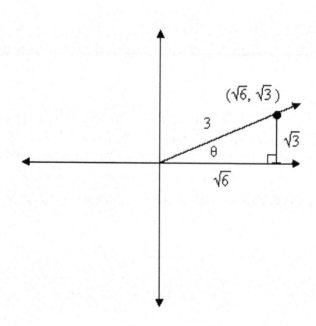

Using the half-angle formula for cosine and the figure, we have

$$\cos\left[\tfrac{1}{2}\sin^{-1}\left(\tfrac{\sqrt{3}}{3}\right)\right] = \underbrace{\cos\tfrac{1}{2}\theta = \sqrt{\frac{1+\cos\theta}{2}}}_{\text{It is positive because }\frac{\theta}{2}\text{ lies in quadrant I.}}$$

$$= \sqrt{\frac{1+\frac{\sqrt{6}}{3}}{2}} = \sqrt{\frac{1\left(\frac{3}{1}\right)+\frac{\sqrt{6}}{3}\left(\frac{3}{1}\right)}{2\left(\frac{3}{1}\right)}}$$

$$= \sqrt{\frac{3+\sqrt{6}}{6}}.$$

Examples. Rewrite without any trigonometric functions.

1) $\tan\left(\sin^{-1}x\right)$, where $x \neq \pm 1$

Let $\theta = \sin^{-1}x$, where $x \neq \pm 1$. Then $\sin\theta = x$, where $-\tfrac{\pi}{2} < \theta < \tfrac{\pi}{2}$ (since $x \neq \pm 1$, we exclude the possibility that $\theta = \pm\tfrac{\pi}{2}$). Notice that $\cos\theta > 0$ since angle θ must lie in either quadrant I or on the positive x-axis. By one of our Pythagorean identities, we have

$$\cos\theta = +\sqrt{1-\sin^2\theta} = \sqrt{1-x^2}.$$

Therefore,

$$\tan\left(\sin^{-1}x\right) = \tan\theta = \frac{\sin\theta}{\cos\theta} = \frac{x}{\sqrt{1-x^2}}.$$

Notice that $\tan\left(\sin^{-1}x\right)$ is undefined when $x = \pm 1$.

2) $\sin\left(\arccos x - \arcsin y\right)$

Let $A = \arccos x$ and $B = \arcsin y$. Then $\cos A = x$, $0 \leq A \leq \pi$, and $\sin B = y$, $-\tfrac{\pi}{2} \leq B \leq \tfrac{\pi}{2}$. Now, the difference formula for sine contains the terms $\sin A$, $\cos A$, $\sin B$, and $\cos B$. We need to find expressions for $\sin A$ and $\cos B$. Well, since $0 \leq A \leq \pi$, we know that $\sin A \geq 0$. Therefore, using one of the Pythagorean identities, we have

$$\sin A = +\sqrt{1-\cos^2 A} = \sqrt{1-x^2}.$$

Similarly, $\cos B \geq 0$ because $-\tfrac{\pi}{2} \leq B \leq \tfrac{\pi}{2}$. Again, using one of the Pythagorean identities, we have

$$\cos B = +\sqrt{1-\sin^2 B} = \sqrt{1-y^2}.$$

Therefore,

$$\sin\left(\arccos x - \arcsin y\right) = \sin\left(A-B\right) = \sin A\cos B - \sin B\cos A$$
$$= \sqrt{1-x^2}\sqrt{1-y^2} - yx.$$

3) $\cos\left(2\tan^{-1}x\right)$

If we let $\theta = \tan^{-1}x$, then $\tan\theta = x$, where $-\tfrac{\pi}{2} < \theta < \tfrac{\pi}{2}$. Notice that $\tan\theta$ could be positive or negative, depending on whether $-\tfrac{\pi}{2} < \theta < 0$ or $0 < \theta < \tfrac{\pi}{2}$, respectively. However, notice that in any version of the double-angle formula for cosine, the trigonometric functions are squared:

$$\cos 2\theta = \underbrace{\cos^2\theta} - \underbrace{\sin^2\theta} = 2\underbrace{\cos^2\theta} - 1 = 1 - 2\underbrace{\sin^2\theta}$$

This means that it doesn't matter which quadrant θ lies in; the squaring which takes place will give a nonnegative result. Now, which of these versions of the identity should we use? Well, first let's think of an identity which relates tangent to sine or cosine. In the previous example, a Pythagorean identity helped us out. Let's think along those lines; do we know any Pythagorean identity which contains tangent? Yes, we do! However, that identity contains tangent and secant (and not cosine or sine). This is no problem since we know that secant is the reciprocal of cosine. Let's use all of this information to solve our problem.

We have that:

$$\sec \theta = \pm\sqrt{\tan^2 \theta + 1}$$

$$\frac{1}{\cos \theta} = \pm\sqrt{\tan^2 \theta + 1}$$

$$\cos \theta = \pm\frac{1}{\sqrt{\tan^2 \theta + 1}} = \pm\frac{1}{\sqrt{x^2 + 1}}$$

And so

$$\cos\left(2\tan^{-1} x\right) = \cos 2\theta = 2\cos^2 \theta - 1$$

$$= 2\left(\pm\frac{1}{\sqrt{x^2 + 1}}\right)^2 - 1$$

$$= 2\left(\frac{1}{x^2 + 1}\right) - 1 = \frac{2}{x^2 + 1} - 1$$

$$= \frac{2}{x^2 + 1} - \frac{x^2 + 1}{x^2 + 1} = \frac{1 - x^2}{x^2 + 1}.$$

Examples. Establish the identities.

1) $\sin\left(\arccos x\right) = \sqrt{1 - x^2}$

Let $\theta = \arccos x$. Then $\cos \theta = x$, where $0 \leq \theta \leq \pi$. Observe that $\sin \theta \geq 0$ for these values of x. Using one of the Pythagorean identities, we have

$$\sin\left(\arccos x\right) = \sin \theta = +\sqrt{1 - \cos^2 \theta} = \sqrt{1 - x^2}.$$

And the identity is verified.

2) $\tan^{-1}\left(\dfrac{1}{x}\right) + \tan^{-1} x = \dfrac{\pi}{2}$, where $x > 0$.

If we set $\theta = \tan^{-1}\left(\dfrac{1}{x}\right)$, then $\tan \theta = \dfrac{1}{x}$, where $-\frac{\pi}{2} < \theta < \frac{\pi}{2}$. Since we are assuming that $x > 0$, we have that $0 < \theta < \frac{\pi}{2}$ (because $\tan \theta = \dfrac{1}{x} > 0$). Similarly, if we set $\alpha = \tan^{-1} x$, then $\tan \alpha = x$, where $0 < \alpha < \frac{\pi}{2}$ (since $\tan \alpha = x > 0$). Now, observe that

$$\tan \theta = \frac{1}{x} \quad \text{becomes} \quad \frac{1}{\tan \theta} = x$$

which is the same as $\cot \theta = x$. Since $\tan \alpha = x$ as well, we have

$$\cot \theta = \tan \alpha$$

which implies that θ and α are complementary angles (that is, $\theta + \alpha = \frac{\pi}{2}$). To see this, recall that if we let $\theta = \frac{\pi}{2} - \alpha$ (so that $\theta + \alpha = \frac{\pi}{2}$), then:

$$\cot \theta = \cot \left(\frac{\pi}{2} - \alpha \right) = \frac{\cos \left(\frac{\pi}{2} - \alpha \right)}{\sin \left(\frac{\pi}{2} - \alpha \right)}$$

$$= \frac{\cos \frac{\pi}{2} \cos \alpha + \sin \frac{\pi}{2} \sin \alpha}{\sin \frac{\pi}{2} \cos \alpha - \cos \frac{\pi}{2} \sin \alpha}$$

$$= \frac{0 \cdot \cos \alpha + 1 \cdot \sin \alpha}{1 \cdot \cos \alpha - 0 \cdot \sin \alpha}$$

$$= \frac{\sin \alpha}{\cos \alpha} = \tan \alpha$$

Therefore,

$$\tan^{-1} \left(\frac{1}{x} \right) + \tan^{-1} x = \theta + \alpha = \frac{\pi}{2}$$

and we have established the identity.

3) $\sec \left(2 \cos^{-1} x \right) = \dfrac{1}{2x^2 - 1}$

Let $\theta = \cos^{-1} x$. Then $\cos \theta = x$, where $0 \leq \theta \leq \pi$. Using the fact that secant is the reciprocal of cosine, we have:

$$\sec \left(2 \cos^{-1} x \right) = \sec 2\theta = \frac{1}{\cos 2\theta}$$

$$= \frac{1}{2 \cos^2 \theta - 1}$$

$$= \frac{1}{2x^2 - 1}$$

Notice that the double angle formula that we chose to use was the easiest one. The other two versions of it contain sine, which is not known to us. To find it would require more work than necessary.

Try These (Set 4):

I) Find the exact value.

1) $\cos^{-1} \left(\sin \frac{7\pi}{6} \right)$ 2) $\sin \left[\tan^{-1} 5 + \sin^{-1} \left(-\frac{2}{3} \right) \right]$ 3) $\cos \left(2 \sin^{-1} \frac{5}{6} \right)$ 4) $\tan \left[\frac{1}{2} \cos^{-1} \left(-\frac{\sqrt{6}}{4} \right) \right]$

II) Establish the identities.

1) $\tan \left(\cos^{-1} x \right) = \dfrac{\sqrt{1 - x^2}}{x}$ 2) $\sin \left(\sin^{-1} x - \frac{\pi}{2} \right) = -\sqrt{1 - x^2}$

The Inverse Secant, Inverse Cosecant and Inverse Cotangent Functions

The inverse secant, inverse cosecant, and inverse cotangent functions are now defined. We will see that these are related to the other inverse trigonometric functions.

Definitions of the Inverse Secant, Inverse Cosecant and Inverse Cotangent Functions

1. If $x = \sec y$, then we define $y = \sec^{-1} x$, where $|x| \geq 1$ and $0 \leq y \leq \pi$, $y \neq \frac{\pi}{2}$.

2. If $x = \csc y$, then we define $y = \csc^{-1} x$, where $|x| \geq 1$ and $-\frac{\pi}{2} \leq y \leq \frac{\pi}{2}$, $y \neq 0$.

3. If $x = \cot y$, then we define $y = \cot^{-1} x$, where $-\infty < x < \infty$ and $0 < y < \pi$.

These definitions are determined in the same way that the definitions for inverse sine, inverse cosine, and inverse tangent were.

We will now prove a set of identities which will allow us to convert each of our new inverse trigonometric functions into the inverse sine, inverse cosine, or inverse tangent function.

Inverse Secant, Cosecant and Cotangent Identities

1. $\sec^{-1} x = \cos^{-1}\left(\dfrac{1}{x}\right)$ for all $|x| \geq 1$.

2. $\csc^{-1} x = \sin^{-1}\left(\dfrac{1}{x}\right)$ for all $|x| \geq 1$.

3. $\cot^{-1} x = \tan^{-1}\left(\dfrac{1}{x}\right)$ for all $x > 0$.

Proof. We will prove the first identity together. Let $\theta = \sec^{-1} x$. Then, by definition, $\sec\theta = x$ for $0 \leq \theta \leq \pi$, $\theta \neq \frac{\pi}{2}$. Observe that

$$\sec\theta = x \text{ becomes } \frac{1}{\cos\theta} = x, \text{ which is the same as } \cos\theta = \frac{1}{x}.$$

However, $\cos\theta = \dfrac{1}{x}$ can be written as $\theta = \cos^{-1}\left(\dfrac{1}{x}\right)$. Therefore,

$$\sec^{-1} x = \theta = \cos^{-1}\left(\frac{1}{x}\right)$$

And the first identity is verified. I'll leave the other identities for you to verify.

Notice that $\cot^{-1} x = \tan^{-1}\left(\dfrac{1}{x}\right)$ **only** when $x > 0$ (Why?). If $x < 0$, then the identity

$$\cot^{-1} x = \frac{\pi}{2} - \tan^{-1} x$$

is useful. In fact, this identity is true for **any** value of x (see Exercise 114).

Examples. Find the exact value.

1) $\sec^{-1} 2 = \sec^{-1} \frac{2}{1} = \cos^{-1} \frac{1}{2} = \frac{\pi}{3}$ $\left(\text{since } \cos \frac{\pi}{3} = \frac{1}{2}\right)$

2) $\csc^{-1} \sqrt{2} = \csc^{-1} \frac{\sqrt{2}}{1} = \sin^{-1} \frac{1}{\sqrt{2}} = \frac{\pi}{4}$ $\left(\text{since } \sin \frac{\pi}{4} = \frac{1}{\sqrt{2}} = \frac{\sqrt{2}}{2}\right)$

3) $\underbrace{\cot^{-1}\left(-\frac{\sqrt{3}}{3}\right) = \frac{\pi}{2} - \tan^{-1}\left(-\frac{\sqrt{3}}{3}\right)}_{\text{Use } \cot^{-1} x = \frac{\pi}{2} - \tan^{-1} x \text{ since } -\frac{\sqrt{3}}{2} < 0.} = \frac{\pi}{2} - \left(-\tan^{-1} \frac{\sqrt{3}}{3}\right) = \underbrace{\frac{\pi}{2} + \frac{\pi}{6} = \frac{2\pi}{3}}_{\text{Note that } \tan \frac{\pi}{6} = \frac{\sqrt{3}}{3}.}$

4) $\sec^{-1}\left(-\frac{2\sqrt{3}}{3}\right) = \cos^{-1}\left(-\frac{3}{2\sqrt{3}}\right) = \underbrace{\cos^{-1}\left(-\frac{\sqrt{3}}{2}\right) = \pi - \cos^{-1}\frac{\sqrt{3}}{2} = \pi - \frac{\pi}{6} = \frac{5\pi}{6}}$

$$\text{observe that } \cos\tfrac{5\pi}{6} = -\cos\tfrac{\pi}{6} = -\tfrac{\sqrt{3}}{2}$$

5) $\sin\left(\cot^{-1}1\right)$

Let $\theta = \cot^{-1}1$. Then

$$\theta = \cot^{-1}1 = \cot^{-1}\tfrac{1}{1} = \tan^{-1}\tfrac{1}{1} = \underbrace{\tan^{-1}1 = \tfrac{\pi}{4}}_{\tan\frac{\pi}{4}=1}.$$

Therefore,

$$\sin\left(\cot^{-1}1\right) = \sin\theta = \sin\tfrac{\pi}{4} = \tfrac{\sqrt{2}}{2}.$$

6) $\tan\left[\csc^{-1}(-2)\right]$

Let $\theta = \csc^{-1}(-2)$. Then

$$\theta = \csc^{-1}(-2) = \csc^{-1}\left(\tfrac{-2}{1}\right) = \sin^{-1}\left(-\tfrac{1}{2}\right) = -\sin^{-1}\tfrac{1}{2} = -\tfrac{\pi}{6}.$$

Therefore,

$$\tan\left[\csc^{-1}(-2)\right] = \tan\theta = \tan\left(-\tfrac{\pi}{6}\right) = -\tan\tfrac{\pi}{6} = -\tfrac{1}{\sqrt{3}} = -\tfrac{\sqrt{3}}{3}.$$

7) $\cos\left[\sec^{-1}\left(-\sqrt{2}\right)\right]$

Let $\theta = \sec^{-1}\left(-\sqrt{2}\right)$. Then

$$\theta = \sec^{-1}\left(-\sqrt{2}\right) = \sec^{-1}\left(-\tfrac{\sqrt{2}}{1}\right) = \cos^{-1}\left(-\tfrac{1}{\sqrt{2}}\right) = \underbrace{\pi - \cos^{-1}\tfrac{1}{\sqrt{2}} = \pi - \tfrac{\pi}{4} = \tfrac{3\pi}{4}}.$$

$$\text{Note that } \cos\tfrac{\pi}{4} = \tfrac{1}{\sqrt{2}} = \tfrac{\sqrt{2}}{2}.$$

And so

$$\cos\left[\sec^{-1}\left(-\sqrt{2}\right)\right] = \cos\theta = \cos\tfrac{3\pi}{4} = -\cos\tfrac{\pi}{4} = -\tfrac{\sqrt{2}}{2}.$$

Try These (Set 5): Find the exact value.

1) $\csc^{-1}2$ 2) $\cot^{-1}\left(-\sqrt{3}\right)$ 3) $\sec^{-1}(-1)$ 4) $\sin\left[\cot^{-1}\left(\tfrac{\sqrt{3}}{3}\right)\right]$

Exercise 7.1

In Exercises 1-26, find the exact value of the given expression.

1. $\sin^{-1}\tfrac{1}{2}$ 2. $\sin^{-1}\tfrac{\sqrt{2}}{2}$ 3. $\tan^{-1}\sqrt{3}$ 4. $\tan^{-1}\tfrac{\sqrt{3}}{3}$ 5. $\cos^{-1}\tfrac{\sqrt{3}}{2}$

6. $\cos^{-1}0$ 7. $\arcsin(-1)$ 8. $\arctan(0)$ 9. $\arccos(1)$ 10. $\arcsin(1)$

11. $\arctan\left(-\tfrac{\sqrt{3}}{3}\right)$ 12. $\arctan(-1)$ 13. $\arccos\left(-\tfrac{1}{2}\right)$ 14. $\arccos\left(-\tfrac{\sqrt{2}}{2}\right)$

15. $\arcsin\left(-\tfrac{1}{2}\right)$ 16. $\arcsin\left(-\tfrac{\sqrt{3}}{2}\right)$ 17. $\sin^{-1}0$ 18. $\cos^{-1}(-1)$

19. $\sec^{-1}2$ 20. $\sec^{-1}\tfrac{2\sqrt{3}}{3}$ 21. $\csc^{-1}\tfrac{2\sqrt{3}}{3}$ 22. $\csc^{-1}\sqrt{2}$

23. $\cot^{-1}\left(-\tfrac{\sqrt{3}}{3}\right)$ 24. $\cot^{-1}(-1)$ 25. $\csc^{-1}(-1)$ 26. $\sec^{-1}(-1)$

In Exercises 27-52, find the exact value of the given expression.

27. $\sin\left(\sin^{-1}\frac{2}{3}\right)$ 28. $\sin\left(\sin^{-1}\frac{1}{5}\right)$ 29. $\tan\left(\tan^{-1}\frac{5}{2}\right)$ 30. $\tan\left(\tan^{-1}\frac{3}{10}\right)$

31. $\cos\left(\cos^{-1}\frac{4}{7}\right)$ 32. $\cos\left(\cos^{-1}\frac{1}{9}\right)$ 33. $\tan\left(\arctan\left(-\frac{\sqrt{11}}{2}\right)\right)$ 34. $\sin\left(\arcsin\left(-\frac{\sqrt{3}}{12}\right)\right)$

35. $\cos\left(\arccos\left(-\frac{7}{10}\right)\right)$ 36. $\cos\left(\arccos\left(-\frac{\sqrt{2}}{3}\right)\right)$ 37. $\sin^{-1}\left(\sin\frac{\pi}{3}\right)$ 38. $\tan^{-1}\left(\tan\frac{\pi}{4}\right)$

39. $\cos^{-1}\left(\cos\pi\right)$ 40. $\cos^{-1}\left(\cos 0\right)$ 41. $\arctan\left(\tan\frac{5\pi}{4}\right)$ 42. $\arcsin\left(\sin\frac{5\pi}{6}\right)$

43. $\arccos\left(\cos\frac{2\pi}{3}\right)$ 44. $\arccos\left(\cos 2\pi\right)$ 45. $\sin^{-1}\left(\sin\left(-\frac{3\pi}{4}\right)\right)$ 46. $\tan^{-1}\left(\tan\left(-\frac{5\pi}{4}\right)\right)$

47. $\cos^{-1}\left(\cos\left(-2\pi\right)\right)$ 48. $\cos^{-1}\left(\cos\left(-\frac{3\pi}{2}\right)\right)$ 49. $\arctan\left(\tan\left(-\frac{5\pi}{6}\right)\right)$ 50. $\arcsin\left(\sin\left(-\frac{5\pi}{3}\right)\right)$

51. $\arccos\left(\cos\left(-\frac{9\pi}{4}\right)\right)$ 52. $\arccos\left(\cos\left(-\frac{13\pi}{6}\right)\right)$

In Exercises 53-98, find the exact value of the given expression.

53. $\sin^{-1}\left(\cos\frac{\pi}{6}\right)$ 54. $\sin^{-1}\left(\cos\frac{\pi}{3}\right)$ 55. $\arctan\left(\sin\frac{\pi}{2}\right)$

56. $\arctan\left(\sin\pi\right)$ 57. $\cos^{-1}\left(\sin\frac{5\pi}{4}\right)$ 58. $\cos^{-1}\left(\tan\frac{2\pi}{3}\right)$

59. $\arcsin\left(\cos\pi\right)$ 60. $\arcsin\left(\cos\frac{\pi}{2}\right)$ 61. $\sin\left(\tan^{-1}\sqrt{3}\right)$

62. $\tan\left(\cos^{-1}\frac{1}{2}\right)$ 63. $\cos\left(\arcsin\frac{\sqrt{3}}{2}\right)$ 64. $\sin\left(\arctan\sqrt{2}\right)$

65. $\cos\left(\tan^{-1}\left(-1\right)\right)$ 66. $\tan\left(\sin^{-1}\left(-\frac{\sqrt{2}}{2}\right)\right)$ 67. $\tan\left(\arccos\left(-\frac{\sqrt{3}}{2}\right)\right)$

68. $\sin\left(\arctan\left(-1\right)\right)$ 69. $\cos\left(2\sin^{-1}\frac{1}{3}\right)$ 70. $\cos\left(2\tan^{-1}4\right)$

71. $\sin\left(2\sin^{-1}\frac{\sqrt{3}}{4}\right)$ 72. $\sin\left(2\cos^{-1}\frac{\sqrt{5}}{6}\right)$ 73. $\cos\left(2\tan^{-1}\left(-\frac{\sqrt{7}}{2}\right)\right)$

74. $\cos\left(2\sin^{-1}\left(-\frac{2}{5}\right)\right)$ 75. $\tan\left(2\tan^{-1}\frac{7}{3}\right)$ 76. $\tan\left(2\cos^{-1}\frac{1}{7}\right)$

77. $\tan\left(2\sin^{-1}\left(-\frac{\sqrt{5}}{5}\right)\right)$ 78. $\tan\left(2\tan^{-1}\left(-3\right)\right)$ 79. $\sin\left(\frac{1}{2}\sin^{-1}\frac{2}{5}\right)$

80. $\sin\left(\frac{1}{2}\cos^{-1}\frac{4}{7}\right)$ 81. $\cos\left(\frac{1}{2}\tan^{-1}\frac{\sqrt{7}}{2}\right)$ 82. $\tan\left(\frac{1}{2}\cos^{-1}\frac{2}{5}\right)$

83. $\tan\left(\frac{1}{2}\sin^{-1}\left(-\frac{2\sqrt{3}}{7}\right)\right)$ 84. $\cos\left(\frac{1}{2}\tan^{-1}\left(-\frac{9}{4}\right)\right)$ 85. $\sin\left(\frac{1}{2}\cos^{-1}\left(-\frac{3}{5}\right)\right)$

86. $\cos\left(\frac{1}{2}\sin^{-1}\left(-\frac{5}{8}\right)\right)$ 87. $\tan\left(\frac{1}{2}\sec^{-1}\frac{5}{2}\right)$ 88. $\sin\left(\frac{1}{2}\csc^{-1}\frac{7}{3}\right)$

89. $\sin\left(\sin^{-1}\frac{1}{3}+\cos^{-1}\frac{2}{3}\right)$ 90. $\sin\left(\tan^{-1}\frac{6}{7}-\sin^{-1}\frac{1}{4}\right)$ 91. $\cos\left(\cos^{-1}\frac{\sqrt{3}}{3}-\tan^{-1}4\right)$

92. $\cos\left(\sin^{-1}\frac{3}{4}+\cos^{-1}\frac{\sqrt{2}}{4}\right)$ 93. $\tan\left(\tan^{-1}\left(-\frac{5}{3}\right)-\cos^{-1}\frac{7}{8}\right)$ 94. $\tan\left(\sin^{-1}\left(-\frac{9}{10}\right)+\tan^{-1}4\right)$

95. $\sin\left(\arccos\frac{\sqrt{2}}{3}-\pi\right)$ 96. $\cos\left(\arcsin\frac{3}{7}-\pi\right)$ 97. $\cos\left(\arcsin\left(-\frac{12}{13}\right)-\arctan\frac{4}{3}\right)$

98. $\sin\left(\arctan\left(-\frac{13}{5}\right)+\arccos\frac{1}{4}\right)$

In Exercises 99-108, write each expression as an algebraic expression containing x and y.

99. $\cos\left(\sin^{-1} x - \cos^{-1} y\right)$

100. $\cos\left(\sin^{-1} x + \cos^{-1} y\right)$

101. $\sin\left(\tan^{-1} x + \sin^{-1} y\right)$

102. $\sin\left(\cos^{-1} x - \tan^{-1} y\right)$

103. $\tan\left(\cos^{-1} x + \sin^{-1} y\right)$

104. $\tan\left(\sin^{-1} x - \sin^{-1} y\right)$

105. $\cos\left(2\sin^{-1} x\right)$

106. $\cos\left(2\cos^{-1} x\right)$

107. $\sin\left(2\sin^{-1} x\right)$

108. $\sin\left(2\cos^{-1} x\right)$

In Exercises 109-116, establish each of the identities.

109. $\tan\left(\sin^{-1} x\right) = \dfrac{x}{\sqrt{1-x^2}}$

110. $\sin\left(\cos^{-1} x\right) = \sqrt{1-x^2}$

111. $\cos\left(\sin^{-1} x\right) = \sqrt{1-x^2}$

112. $\cos\left(\tan^{-1} x\right) = \dfrac{1}{\sqrt{1+x^2}}$

113. $\sin^{-1} x + \cos^{-1} x = \frac{\pi}{2}$

114. $\tan^{-1} x + \cot^{-1} x = \frac{\pi}{2}$

115. $\sin\left(2\tan^{-1} x\right) = \dfrac{2x}{1+x^2}$

116. $\cos\left(2\tan^{-1} x\right) = \dfrac{1-x^2}{1+x^2}$

Section 7.2 First-Degree Trigonometric Equations

In this section, we will learn how to solve trigonometric equations which resemble first-degree (or linear) equations. Examples of such equations are

$$\cos\theta = \frac{1}{2}, \quad \underbrace{2\sin\alpha - 1 = 0}_{\text{Resembles } 2x-1=0.}, \quad \underbrace{3\tan\left(5y - \frac{\pi}{2}\right) + 1 = 0}_{\text{Resembles } 3x+1=0.}, \quad \underbrace{7\cos t = -1.95}_{\text{Resembles } 7x=-1.95.}, \quad \text{and } \underbrace{1 - 2\csc\left(\frac{1}{4}\beta\right) = -9}_{\text{Resembles } 1-2x=-9.}.$$

To solve a first-degree trigonometric equation, we solve for the trigonometric function first. Once this is done, there are different techniques available which enable us to solve the equation. These techniques are discussed in the examples.

Examples. Find all of the solutions to the equations. Express your answers in radian measure.

1) $2\sin\theta - 1 = 0$

This equation resembles the equation $2x - 1 = 0$ (if we replace $\sin\theta$ by x) and we can easily solve for x. The same steps can be applied to solve for $\sin\theta$ in the equation $2\sin\theta - 1 = 0$. Notice that this is a conditional equation since it is satisfied by some values of θ but not others (unlike an identity, which is satisfied by all values).

$$2\sin\theta - 1 = 0$$
$$\underline{ +1 \quad +1}$$
$$\frac{2\sin\theta}{2} = \frac{1}{2}$$
$$\sin\theta = \frac{1}{2}$$

Now that we have solved for $\sin\theta$, how do we find the values of θ for which $\sin\theta = \frac{1}{2}$? Well, notice that $\sin\theta > 0$ in quadrant I and II. In order to find a value of θ in quadrant I, we evaluate the inverse sine of $\frac{1}{2}$:

$$\theta = \sin^{-1}\frac{1}{2} = \frac{\pi}{6}$$

Notice that $\frac{\pi}{6}$ is the **reference angle** of any angle θ for which $\sin\theta = \frac{1}{2}$. To find a value of θ in quadrant II, we use the fact that the reference angle of θ (which is $\frac{\pi}{6}$) in quadrant II equals π minus θ:

$$\frac{\pi}{6} = \pi - \theta$$

Solving for θ gives us

$$\theta = \pi - \frac{\pi}{6} = \frac{5\pi}{6}.$$

These two solutions determine all of the others. Recall that $\sin\theta = \sin(\theta + 2\pi k)$, where k is any integer (sine has periodicity 2π). This means that we can obtain the rest of the solutions by adding $2\pi k$ to the values of θ that we found so far. In other words, the solutions are

$$\theta = \frac{\pi}{6} + 2\pi k \quad \text{or} \quad \theta = \frac{5\pi}{6} + 2\pi k,$$

where k is any integer. Let's find some of the solutions.

When $k = 0$, we obtain $\quad \theta = \frac{\pi}{6} + 2\pi(0) = \frac{\pi}{6} + 0 = \frac{\pi}{6} \quad$ and $\quad \theta = \frac{5\pi}{6} + 2\pi(0) = \frac{5\pi}{6} + 0 = \frac{5\pi}{6}.$

When $k = 1$, we obtain $\quad \theta = \frac{\pi}{6} + 2\pi(1) = \frac{\pi}{6} + 2\pi = \frac{13\pi}{6} \quad$ and $\quad \theta = \frac{5\pi}{6} + 2\pi(1) = \frac{5\pi}{6} + 2\pi = \frac{17\pi}{6}.$

When $k = 2$, we obtain $\quad \theta = \frac{\pi}{6} + 2\pi(2) = \frac{\pi}{6} + 4\pi = \frac{25\pi}{6} \quad$ and $\quad \theta = \frac{5\pi}{6} + 2\pi(2) = \frac{5\pi}{6} + 4\pi = \frac{29\pi}{6}.$

When $k = -1$, we obtain $\quad \theta = \frac{\pi}{6} + 2\pi(-1) = \frac{\pi}{6} - 2\pi = -\frac{11\pi}{6} \quad$ and $\quad \theta = \frac{5\pi}{6} + 2\pi(-1) = \frac{5\pi}{6} - 2\pi = -\frac{7\pi}{6}.$

When $k = -2$, we obtain $\quad \theta = \frac{\pi}{6} + 2\pi(-2) = \frac{\pi}{6} - 4\pi = -\frac{23\pi}{6} \quad$ and $\quad \theta = \frac{5\pi}{6} + 2\pi(-2) = \frac{5\pi}{6} - 4\pi = -\frac{19\pi}{6}.$

We have just found that some of the solutions are $\dfrac{5\pi}{6}, \dfrac{17\pi}{6}, \dfrac{29\pi}{6}, -\dfrac{7\pi}{6},$ and $-\dfrac{19\pi}{6}.$

2) $\sqrt{2}\cos\beta + 1 = 0$

Let's begin by isolating the term $\cos\beta$.

$$\sqrt{2}\cos\beta + \cancel{1} = 0$$
$$\underline{\quad \cancel{1} \quad -1 \quad}$$
$$\frac{\cancel{\sqrt{2}}\cos\beta}{\cancel{\sqrt{2}}} = \frac{-1}{\sqrt{2}}$$

$$\cos\beta = -\frac{1}{\sqrt{2}}$$

Now let's find those values of β for which $\cos\beta = -\frac{1}{\sqrt{2}}$. To begin with, we will find the acute angle α which satisfies the equation $\cos\alpha = \frac{1}{\sqrt{2}}$. Well, this equation leads us to

$$\alpha = \cos^{-1}\left(\frac{1}{\sqrt{2}}\right) = \frac{\pi}{4} \text{ and so } \cos\frac{\pi}{4} = \frac{1}{\sqrt{2}}.$$

How can this information be used to solve the equation $\cos\beta = -\frac{1}{\sqrt{2}}$? Well, recall that $\cos\beta < 0$ in quadrants II and III. The reason that we found $\alpha = \frac{\pi}{4}$ first is because α is the reference angle of each solution of β that we're looking for. The chart below shows us how to determine β by using α.

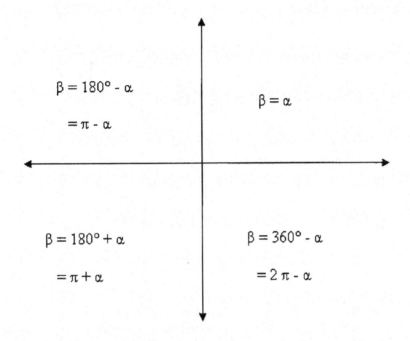

Using the formulas in the chart above, we have

$$\beta = \underbrace{\pi - \frac{\pi}{4} = \frac{3\pi}{4}}_{\text{in quadrant II}} \quad \text{or} \quad \beta = \underbrace{\pi + \frac{\pi}{4} = \frac{5\pi}{4}}_{\text{in quadrant III}}.$$

These two solutions determine all of the others. Since $\cos\beta = \cos(\beta + 2\pi k)$, where k is any integer (cosine has periodicity 2π), the solutions are

$$\beta = \frac{3\pi}{4} + 2\pi k \quad \text{or} \quad \beta = \frac{5\pi}{4} + 2\pi k,$$

where k is any integer.

3) $6\tan x - 6\sqrt{3} = 0$

$$6\tan x - 6\sqrt{3} = 0$$
$$\underline{+6\sqrt{3} \quad +6\sqrt{3}}$$
$$\frac{\cancel{6}\tan x}{\cancel{6}} = \frac{6\sqrt{3}}{6}$$

$$\tan x = \sqrt{3}$$

Let's find those values of x for which $\tan x = \sqrt{3}$. One value of x is

$$x = \tan^{-1}\left(\sqrt{3}\right) = \frac{\pi}{3}.$$

Unlike the sine and cosine functions, the tangent function has periodicity π. This means that $\tan x = \tan(x + \pi k)$, where k is any integer. Hence, all of the solutions of the equation can be obtained by adding πk to $\frac{\pi}{3}$, where k represents any integer. Therefore, our solutions are

$$x = \frac{\pi}{3} + \pi k, \text{ where } k \text{ is any integer.}$$

Let's write down some of the solutions.

When $k = 0$, we obtain $\quad x = \frac{\pi}{3} + \pi\,(0) = \frac{\pi}{3} + 0 = \frac{\pi}{3}$.

When $k = 1$, we obtain $\quad x = \frac{\pi}{3} + \pi\,(1) = \frac{\pi}{3} + \pi = \frac{4\pi}{3}$.

When $k = 2$, we obtain $\quad x = \frac{\pi}{3} + \pi\,(2) = \frac{\pi}{3} + 2\pi = \frac{7\pi}{3}$.

When $k = -1$, we obtain $\quad x = \frac{\pi}{3} + \pi\,(-1) = \frac{\pi}{3} - \pi = -\frac{2\pi}{3}$.

When $k = -2$, we obtain $\quad x = \frac{\pi}{3} + \pi\,(-2) = \frac{\pi}{3} - 2\pi = -\frac{5\pi}{3}$.

4) $\sin\left(\theta + \frac{\pi}{3}\right) = 1$

We will repeat the procedure used before. First let's solve the equation $\sin x = 1$ (I'm creating an easier equation to solve by replacing $\theta + \frac{\pi}{3}$ by x). Well, observe that $\sin x = 1$ when $x = \frac{\pi}{2}$. Therefore, every number of the form $x = \frac{\pi}{2} + 2\pi k$ (where k is any integer) is a solution. If we now go back to our original equation, we have that

$$\sin\left(\theta + \frac{\pi}{3}\right) = 1 \text{ implies that } \theta + \frac{\pi}{3} = \frac{\pi}{2} + 2\pi k, \text{ where } k \text{ is any integer.}$$

We now solve for θ.

$$
\begin{array}{r}
\theta + \cancel{\dfrac{\pi}{3}} = \dfrac{\pi}{2} + 2\pi k \\[2mm]
-\cancel{\dfrac{\pi}{3}} \qquad -\dfrac{\pi}{3} \\[1mm]
\hline
\theta = \dfrac{\pi}{6} + 2\pi k
\end{array}
$$

5) $\cos 4t = 0$

This is an example of a multiple angle equation. First let's solve the equation $\cos x = 0$ (I'm creating an easier equation to solve by replacing $4t$ by x). Notice that $\cos x = 0$ when $x = \frac{\pi}{2}$ and $x = \frac{3\pi}{2}$. Therefore, every number of the form $x = \frac{\pi}{2} + 2\pi k$ or $x = \frac{3\pi}{2} + 2\pi k$ (where k is any integer) is a solution. Let's return to our original equation. We have that

$$\cos 4t = 0 \text{ implies that } 4t = \frac{\pi}{2} + 2\pi k \text{ or } 4t = \frac{3\pi}{2} + 2\pi k, \text{ where } k \text{ is any integer.}$$

We now solve for t.

$$4t = \frac{\pi}{2} + 2\pi k \quad \text{or} \quad 4t = \frac{3\pi}{2} + 2\pi k$$

$$\frac{1}{4}(4t) = \frac{1}{4}\left(\frac{\pi}{2} + 2\pi k\right) \quad \text{or} \quad \frac{1}{4}(4t) = \frac{1}{4}\left(\frac{3\pi}{2} + 2\pi k\right)$$

$$t = \frac{\pi}{8} + \frac{\pi}{2}k \quad \text{or} \quad t = \frac{3\pi}{8} + \frac{\pi}{2}k$$

Examples. Find the solutions to the equations in the given interval.

1) $3\tan x + \sqrt{3} = 0$ in the interval $0° < x < 360°$.

Notice that we want our solutions in degree measure. Let's solve for $\tan x$ first.

$$3\tan x + \sqrt{3} = 0$$
$$\underline{\quad -\sqrt{3} \quad -\sqrt{3}}$$
$$\frac{3\tan x}{3} = \frac{-\sqrt{3}}{3}$$

$$\tan x = -\frac{\sqrt{3}}{3}$$

The reference angle for any solution of x is

$$\tan^{-1}\frac{\sqrt{3}}{3} = \frac{\pi}{6} = 30°.$$

We know that $\tan x < 0$ in quadrant II and quadrant IV. Using the reference angle, we find that

$$x = \underbrace{180° - 30° = 150°}_{\text{in quadrant II}} \quad \text{or} \quad x = \underbrace{360° - 30° = 330°}_{\text{in quadrant IV}}.$$

These are the only solutions in the interval $0° < x < 360°$ (why?).

2) $\sqrt{2}\cos\theta - 1 = 0$ in the interval $-360° < \theta < 360°$.

We will solve for $\cos\theta$ first.

$$\sqrt{2}\cos\theta - 1 = 0$$
$$\underline{\quad +1 \quad +1}$$
$$\frac{\sqrt{2}\cos\theta}{\sqrt{2}} = \frac{1}{\sqrt{2}}$$

$$\cos\theta = \frac{1}{\sqrt{2}}$$

The reference angle for any solution of θ is

$$\cos^{-1}\frac{1}{\sqrt{2}} = \frac{\pi}{4} = 45°.$$

Now, $\cos\theta > 0$ in quadrant I and quadrant IV. We already have a solution for θ in quadrant I, $\theta = 45°$. A solution of θ in quadrant IV is

$$\theta = 360° - 45° = 315°.$$

Therefore, any solution to the equation is of the form

$$\theta = 45° + 360°k \quad\text{or}\quad \theta = 315° + 360°k,$$

where k is any integer. However, we only want those solutions which are in the interval $-360° < \theta < 360°$. Observe:

When $k = 0$, we obtain $\theta = 45° + 360°\,(0) = 45°$ and $\theta = 315° + 360°\,(0) = 315°.$

When $k = 1$, we obtain $\underbrace{\theta = 45° + 360°\,(1) = 405°}_{\text{not in the interval } -360°<\theta<360°}$ and $\underbrace{\theta = 315° + 360°\,(1) = 675°}_{\text{not in the interval } -360°<\theta<360°}.$

When $k = -1$, we obtain $\theta = 45° + 360°\,(-1) = -315°$ and $\theta = 315° + 360°\,(-1) = -45°.$

When $k = -2$, we obtain $\underbrace{\theta = 45° + 360°\,(-2) = -675°}_{\text{not in the interval } -360°<\theta<360°}$ and $\underbrace{\theta = 315° + 360°\,(-2) = -405°}_{\text{not in the interval } -360°<\theta<360°}.$

Notice that the only values of θ which lie in the required interval are $\theta = 45°,\ 315°,\ -315°,$ and $-45°$. These are the solutions to the equation.

3) $\sin\left(\frac{3}{2}\theta - \pi\right) + 1 = 0$ in the interval $-4\pi \le \theta \le 4\pi$.

Let's solve for $\sin\left(\frac{3}{2}\theta - \pi\right)$ first.

$$\sin\left(\tfrac{3}{2}\theta - \pi\right) \cancel{+1} = 0$$
$$\frac{\cancel{1}\quad -1}{\sin\left(\tfrac{3}{2}\theta - \pi\right) = -1}$$

Now, observe that each solution of the equation $\sin x = -1$ is of the form $x = \frac{3\pi}{2} + 2\pi k$, where k is an integer. Therefore, if we replace x by $\frac{3}{2}\theta - \pi$, we find that

$$\sin\left(\frac{3}{2}\theta - \pi\right) = -1 \quad\text{becomes}\quad \frac{3}{2}\theta - \pi = \frac{3\pi}{2} + 2\pi k, \text{ where } k \text{ is an integer.}$$

We need to solve for θ.

$$\frac{3}{2}\theta - \pi = \frac{3\pi}{2} + 2\pi k$$
$$\frac{+\pi \qquad\qquad +\pi}{\frac{3}{2}\theta = \frac{5\pi}{2} + 2\pi k}$$

$$\frac{\cancel{2}}{\cancel{3}}\left(\frac{\cancel{3}}{\cancel{2}}\theta\right) = \frac{2}{3}\left(\frac{5\pi}{2} + 2\pi k\right)$$

$$\theta = \frac{5\pi}{3} + \frac{4\pi}{3}k$$

We only want those values of θ which lie in the interval $-4\pi \leq \theta \leq 4\pi$. Observe:

When $k = 0$, we obtain $\theta = \dfrac{5\pi}{3} + \dfrac{4\pi}{3}\,(0) = \dfrac{5\pi}{3}$.

When $k = 1$, we obtain $\theta = \dfrac{5\pi}{3} + \dfrac{4\pi}{3}\,(1) = \dfrac{9\pi}{3} = 3\pi$.

When $k = 2$, we obtain $\underbrace{\theta = \dfrac{5\pi}{3} + \dfrac{4\pi}{3}\,(2) = \dfrac{13\pi}{3}}_{\text{not in the interval } -4\pi \leq \theta \leq 4\pi}$.

When $k = -1$, we obtain $\theta = \dfrac{5\pi}{3} + \dfrac{4\pi}{3}\,(-1) = \dfrac{\pi}{3}$.

When $k = -2$, we obtain $\theta = \dfrac{5\pi}{3} + \dfrac{4\pi}{3}\,(-2) = \dfrac{-3\pi}{3} = -\pi$.

When $k = -3$, we obtain $\theta = \dfrac{5\pi}{3} + \dfrac{4\pi}{3}\,(-3) = -\dfrac{7\pi}{3}$.

When $k = -4$, we obtain $\theta = \dfrac{5\pi}{3} + \dfrac{4\pi}{3}\,(-4) = -\dfrac{11\pi}{3}$.

When $k = -5$, we obtain $\underbrace{\theta = \dfrac{5\pi}{3} + \dfrac{4\pi}{3}\,(-5) = -\dfrac{15\pi}{3} = -5\pi}_{\text{not in the interval } -4\pi \leq \theta \leq 4\pi}$.

Therefore, the solutions are $\theta = \frac{5\pi}{3},\ 3\pi,\ \frac{13\pi}{3},\ \frac{\pi}{3},\ -\pi,\ -\frac{7\pi}{3},$ and $-\frac{11\pi}{3}$.

4) $\cos 2x = 0.64$ in the interval $-90° \leq x < 180°$ (to the nearest degree).

This is an example of a multiple angle equation. Let's solve the equation $\cos\theta = 0.64$. We will begin by finding the reference angle for any solution of this equation. The calculator comes in handy.

$$\theta = \cos^{-1} 0.64 \approx 50°.$$

Another solution for θ can be found in quadrant IV (since $\cos\theta > 0$ in quadrant IV). We obtain

$$\theta = 360° - 50° = 310°.$$

And so any solution of the equation $\cos\theta = 0.64$ is of the form

$$\theta = 50° + 360°k \quad \text{or} \quad \theta = 310° + 360°k, \text{ where } k \text{ is an integer.}$$

Replacing θ by $2x$ gives us

$$\frac{\cancel{2}x}{\cancel{2}} = \frac{50° + 360°k}{2} \quad \text{or} \quad \frac{\cancel{2}x}{\cancel{2}} = \frac{310° + 360°k}{2}.$$

And so

$$x = 25° + 180°k \quad \text{or} \quad x = 155° + 180°k.$$

Now we need to find those values of x which lie within our interval $-90° \leq x < 180°$.

When $k = 0$, we obtain $x = 25° + 180°\,(0) = 25°$ and $x = 155° + 180°\,(0) = 155°$.

When $k = 1$, we obtain $\underbrace{x = 25° + 180°\,(1) = 205°}_{\text{not in the interval } -90° \leq x < 180°}$ and $\underbrace{x = 155° + 180°\,(1) = 335°}_{\text{not in the interval } -90° \leq x < 180°}$.

When $k = -1$, we obtain $\underbrace{x = 25° + 180°\,(-1) = -155°}_{\text{not in the interval } -90° \leq x < 180°}$ and $x = 155° + 180°\,(-1) = -25°$.

Therefore, the solutions are $x = 25°$, $155°$, and $-25°$.

5) $\cot(3\beta + 90°) = -3.4874$ in the interval $-180° < \beta < 180°$ (to the nearest degree).

We begin by solving the equation $\cot x = -3.4874$. Since cotangent is the reciprocal of tangent, we may rewrite this equation as

$$\frac{1}{\tan x} = \frac{-3.4874}{1}, \text{ which becomes } \tan x = \frac{1}{-3.4874} = -\frac{1}{3.4874}.$$

Let's find the reference angle for each solution of this equation:

$$\tan^{-1}\left(\frac{1}{3.4874}\right) \approx 16°$$

Since $\tan x < 0$ in quadrant II (and IV), we have

$$x = 180° - 16° = 164°.$$

Therefore, each solution of the equation

$$\tan x = -\frac{1}{3.4874}$$

has the form $x = 164° + 180°k$ for some integer k. Going back to our original equation, we have that

$$\cot(3\beta + 90°) = -3.4874 \quad \text{implies that} \quad 3\beta + 90° = 164° + 180°k, \text{ where } k \text{ is an integer.}$$

We now solve for β.

$$
\begin{aligned}
3\beta + \cancel{90°} &= 164° + 180°k \\
-\cancel{90°} \quad &\quad -90° \\
\hline
\frac{\cancel{3}\beta}{\cancel{3}} &= \frac{74° + 180°k}{3}
\end{aligned}
$$

$$\beta \approx 25° + 60°k$$

Now we need to find those values of x which lie within our interval $-180° < \beta < 180°$.

When $k = 0$, we obtain $\beta = 25° + 60°(0) = 25°$.

When $k = 1$, we obtain $\beta = 25° + 60°(1) = 85°$.

When $k = 2$, we obtain $\beta = 25° + 60°(2) = 145°$.

When $k = 3$, we obtain $\underbrace{\beta = 25° + 60°(3) = 205°}_{\text{not in the interval } -180° < \beta < 180°}$.

When $k = -1$, we obtain $\beta = 25° + 60°(-1) = -35°$.

When $k = -2$, we obtain $\beta = 25° + 60°(-2) = -95°$.

When $k = -3$, we obtain $\beta = 25° + 60°(-3) = -155°$.

When $k = -4$, we obtain $\underbrace{\beta = 25° + 60°(-4) = -215°}_{\text{not in the interval } -180° < \beta < 180°}$.

Therefore, the solutions are $\beta = 25°, 85°, 145°, -35°, -95°,$ and $-155°$.

Exercise 7.2

In Exercises 1-32, find the solutions to the equations. Express your answers in radian measure.

1. $2\cos\theta - 1 = 0$
2. $2\sin\theta - 1 = 0$
3. $2\sin\beta - \sqrt{3} = 0$
4. $\sqrt{2}\cos\beta - 1 = 0$

5. $2\tan\alpha - 2 = 0$
6. $\tan\alpha - \sqrt{3} = 0$
7. $2\cos x + \sqrt{3} = 0$
8. $\sqrt{2}\sin x + 1 = 0$

9. $\sin\theta + 1 = 0$
10. $\cos\theta - 1 = 0$
11. $3\tan t + \sqrt{3} = 0$
12. $\tan t + 1 = 0$

13. $\csc x - 2 = 0$
14. $\sec x - 1 = 0$
15. $\cot\alpha + \sqrt{3} = 0$
16. $\csc\alpha + \sqrt{2} = 0$

17. $\cos 3\alpha = 1$
18. $\sin 4\alpha = -1$
19. $\tan\left(x - \frac{\pi}{3}\right) = 0$
20. $\cos\left(x + \frac{5\pi}{4}\right) = 0$

21. $\sin\left(3\theta + \frac{\pi}{3}\right) = \frac{\sqrt{2}}{2}$
22. $\tan\left(5\theta - \frac{\pi}{4}\right) = \sqrt{3}$
23. $\cos\left(2\beta + \frac{\pi}{4}\right) = \frac{1}{2}$

24. $\cos\left(\frac{1}{2}\beta + \pi\right) = -\frac{\sqrt{3}}{2}$
25. $\tan\left(\frac{1}{3}x - \frac{5\pi}{6}\right) = -\frac{\sqrt{3}}{3}$
26. $\sin\left(\frac{1}{2}x - \frac{2\pi}{3}\right) = -\frac{\sqrt{2}}{2}$

27. $\sec 2t = \sqrt{2}$
28. $\cot 3t = 0$
29. $\csc\left(\frac{2}{3}\theta + \frac{\pi}{2}\right) = -2$

30. $\csc\left(\frac{3}{5}\theta - \pi\right) = -\sqrt{3}$
31. $\cot\left(6\alpha - \frac{\pi}{4}\right) = -1$
32. $\sec\left(2\beta + \frac{\pi}{3}\right) = -1$

In Exercises 33-60, find the solutions to each equation in the given interval.

33. $2\sin\theta - 1 = 0$; $0 \le \theta < 2\pi$
34. $2\sin\theta - \sqrt{3} = 0$; $0 \le \theta < 2\pi$
35. $6\cos\theta - 3 = 0$; $0 \le \theta < 2\pi$

36. $2\cos\theta - \sqrt{2} = 0$; $0 \le \theta < 2\pi$
37. $4\tan\theta + 4 = 0$; $0 \le \theta < 2\pi$
38. $3\tan\theta - \sqrt{3} = 0$; $0 \le \theta < 2\pi$

39. $2\cos\theta + 1 = 0$; $-\pi \le \theta < \pi$
40. $2\sin\theta + \sqrt{2} = 0$; $-\pi \le \theta < \pi$
41. $\sin\theta = -1$; $-\pi \le \theta \le \pi$

42. $\cos\theta = 1$; $-\pi \le \theta \le \pi$
43. $\cos\theta = 0$; $-\pi \le \theta \le \pi$
44. $\tan\theta = -\sqrt{3}$; $-\pi \le \theta \le \pi$

45. $\tan\left(\theta + \frac{\pi}{3}\right) = 1$; $0 \le \theta \le 2\pi$

46. $\cot\left(\theta + \frac{\pi}{4}\right) = \sqrt{3}$; $0 \le \theta \le 2\pi$

47. $\csc\left(\theta - \frac{3\pi}{4}\right) = -\sqrt{2}$; $0 \le \theta \le 2\pi$

48. $\sin\left(\theta - \frac{7\pi}{6}\right) = -\frac{1}{2}$; $0 \le \theta \le 2\pi$

49. $\sec\left(2\theta + \frac{\pi}{3}\right) = 2$; $-2\pi < \theta < 0$

50. $\cos\left(3\theta + \pi\right) = -\frac{\sqrt{2}}{2}$; $-2\pi < \theta < 0$

51. $\sin\left(4\theta - \pi\right) = -\frac{\sqrt{3}}{2}$; $-2\pi < \theta < 0$

52. $\csc\left(7\theta - \frac{5\pi}{2}\right) = \sqrt{2}$; $-2\pi < \theta < 0$

53. $\tan\left(\frac{1}{3}\theta + \frac{\pi}{6}\right) = -1$; $-2\pi < \theta < 2\pi$

54. $\cos\left(\frac{2}{3}\theta - \pi\right) = -\frac{1}{2}$; $-\pi < \theta < \pi$

55. $\tan\frac{2\theta}{3} = 0$; $-\pi \le \theta < \pi$

56. $\sin\frac{4\theta}{7} = 1$; $-\pi \le \theta \le \pi$

57. $\sec\frac{7\theta}{9} = -1$; $-2\pi < \theta < 2\pi$

58. $\cot\frac{5\theta}{4} = -\sqrt{3}$; $-2\pi < \theta < 2\pi$

59. $\csc\frac{9\theta}{10} = 1$; $-2\pi < \theta < 2\pi$

60. $\cos\frac{11\theta}{7} = 0$; $-2\pi < \theta < 2\pi$

In Exercises 61-76, find the solutions (to the nearest degree) to each equation in the interval $0° < \theta < 360°$.

61. $\sin\theta = 0.618$

62. $\cos\theta = 0.973$

63. $\tan\theta = 56.12$

64. $\sin\theta = 0.715$

65. $\cos\theta = -0.33$

66. $\tan\theta = -32.41$

67. $\sin\theta = -0.892$

68. $\cos\theta = -0.09$

69. $\cot\theta = 31.552$

70. $\csc\theta = 35.012$

71. $\sec\theta = 10.775$

72. $\cot\theta = 23.01$

73. $\csc\theta = -3$

74. $\sec\theta = -12.41$

75. $\cot\theta = -11.2$

76. $\csc\theta = -7.62$

Section 7.3   Second-Degree Trigonometric Equations

In this section, we will learn how to solve trigonometric equations which resemble second-degree (or quadratic) equations. Examples of such equations are

$$\underbrace{2\sin^2\theta - \sin\theta = 0}_{\text{Resembles } 2x^2 - x = 0.}, \quad \underbrace{\cos^2\alpha - 1 = 0}_{\text{Resembles } x^2 - 1 = 0.}, \quad \underbrace{2\tan^2\beta - 7\tan\beta + 3 = 0}_{\text{Resembles } 2x^2 - 7x + 3 = 0.}, \quad \text{and} \quad \underbrace{3\sec^2 t - 8\sec t + 2 = 0}_{\text{Resembles } 3x^2 - 8x + 2 = 0.}.$$

As with first-degree trigonometric equations, we solve a second-degree trigonometric equation by solving for the trigonometric function first (which is similar to solving for x in the examples above). The technique used for doing this depends upon the form that the equation takes. We will discuss each of these methods as we work on examples.

Section 7.3.1   Solving by Factoring

Suppose that we want to solve the equation $2\sin^2\theta - \sin\theta = 0$. Since the trigonometric function $\sin\theta$ appears in both terms on the left-hand side of the equation, we can replace it by the variable x and obtain the quadratic equation $2x^2 - x = 0$. Recall from algebra class that this equation can be solved by factoring $2x^2 - x$ and applying the zero product property (we'll remind ourselves of what this property is soon). Notice that

$$2x^2 - x = x(2x - 1) \quad \text{factors the same way as} \quad 2\sin^2\theta - \sin\theta = \sin\theta(2\sin\theta - 1).$$

This means that we can use the zero product property to split up the equation $\sin\theta\,(2\sin\theta - 1) = 0$ into two equations, $\sin\theta = 0$ and $2\sin\theta - 1 = 0$. We know how to solve these equations. Let's see how all of this is done by looking at some examples.

Examples. Find all of the solutions to the following equations. Express your answers in radian measure.

1) $2\sin^2\theta - \sin\theta = 0$

As it was shown above, we can factor $2\sin^2\theta - \sin\theta$ the same way as we factor $2x^2 - x$. We obtain the equation $\sin\theta\,(2\sin\theta - 1) = 0$ and we can apply the **Zero Product Property** (recall that this property states that if a and b are real numbers, then $ab = 0$ if and only if $a = 0$, or $b = 0$, or both). By the Zero Product Property, we have

$$\sin\theta\,(2\sin\theta - 1) = 0$$

$\sin\theta = 0$	$2\sin\theta - \cancel{1} = 0$
	$\cancel{1}\;\;+1$
	$\dfrac{\cancel{2}\sin\theta}{\cancel{2}} = \dfrac{1}{2}$
	$\sin\theta = \dfrac{1}{2}$

Now, the equation $\sin\theta = 0$ has solutions $\theta = \pi k$, where k is any integer. The equation $\sin\theta = \frac{1}{2}$ has solutions $\theta = \frac{\pi}{6} + 2\pi k$ or $\theta = \frac{5\pi}{6} + 2\pi k$, where k is any integer. Therefore, the set of solutions is

$$\left\{ \theta \mid \theta = \pi k,\; \theta = \frac{\pi}{6} + 2\pi k,\; \theta = \frac{5\pi}{6} + 2\pi k \right\}, \text{ where } k \text{ is any integer.}$$

2) $2\cos^2 t + \sqrt{2}\cos t = 0$

Notice that the equation resembles the quadratic equation $2x^2 + \sqrt{2}x = 0$, which can be solved by factoring x on the left-hand side of the equation and applying the Zero Product Property. Similarly, we can factor $\cos t$ on the left-hand side of $2\cos^2 t + \sqrt{2}\cos t = 0$ and apply the Zero Product Property. We obtain

$$\cos t\,(2\cos t + \sqrt{2}) = 0$$

$\cos t = 0$	$2\cos t + \cancel{\sqrt{2}} = 0$
	$-\cancel{\sqrt{2}}\;\;-\sqrt{2}$
	$\dfrac{\cancel{2}\cos t}{\cancel{2}} = \dfrac{-\sqrt{2}}{2}$
	$\cos t = -\dfrac{\sqrt{2}}{2}$

The equation $\cos t = 0$ has solutions $t = \frac{\pi}{2} + 2\pi k$ or $\frac{3\pi}{2} + 2\pi k$, where k is any integer. We can write these solutions more compactly as $t = \frac{(2k+1)\pi}{2}$, where k is any integer (why?).

The equation $\cos t = -\frac{\sqrt{2}}{2}$ has solutions $t = \frac{3\pi}{4} + 2\pi k$ or $t = \frac{5\pi}{4} + 2\pi k$, where k is any integer (note that the reference angle for any solution of the equation $\cos t = -\frac{\sqrt{2}}{2}$ is $\cos^{-1}\left(\frac{\sqrt{2}}{2}\right) = \frac{\pi}{4}$). Therefore, the set of solutions is

$$\left\{ t \mid t = \frac{(2k+1)\,\pi}{2},\; t = \frac{3\pi}{4} + 2\pi k,\; t = \frac{5\pi}{4} + 2\pi k \right\}, \text{ where } k \text{ is any integer.}$$

3) $2\cos^2\theta + 5\cos\theta - 3 = 0$

This is similar to the equation $2x^2 + 5x - 3 = 0$, which can be solved by factoring.

$$2\cos^2\theta + 5\cos\theta - 3 = 0$$
$$(2\cos\theta - 1)(\cos\theta + 3) = 0$$

$2\cos\theta - 1 = 0$	$\cos\theta + 3 = 0$
$\dfrac{2\cos\theta}{2} = \dfrac{1}{2}$	$\cos\theta = -3$
$\cos\theta = \dfrac{1}{2}$	

The equation $\cos\theta = \frac{1}{2}$ has solutions $t = \frac{\pi}{3} + 2\pi k$ or $\frac{5\pi}{3} + 2\pi k$, where k is any integer. The equation $\cos\theta = -3$ has no solutions since

$$-1 \le \cos\theta \le 1$$

for any value of θ. Therefore, the set of solutions is

$$\left\{\theta \mid \theta = \frac{\pi}{3} + 2\pi k,\ \theta = \frac{5\pi}{3} + 2\pi k\right\}, \text{ where } k \text{ is any integer.}$$

Examples. Find the solutions to the equations in the given interval.

1) $\tan^2 x - \tan x = 0$ in the interval $-2\pi < x < 2\pi$.

This is just like the equation $y^2 - y = 0$, which can be solved by factoring.

$$\tan^2 x - \tan x = 0 = 0$$
$$\tan x (\tan x - 1) = 0$$

$\tan x = 0$	$\tan x - 1 = 0$
	$\tan x = 1$

The equation $\tan x = 0$ has solutions $x = \pi k$, where k is any integer. The equation $\tan x = 1$ has solutions $x = \frac{\pi}{4} + \pi k$, where k is any integer. Let's find out which of these solutions are in the interval $-2\pi \le x \le 2\pi$.

When $k = 0$, we obtain $x = \pi(0) = 0$ and $x = \frac{\pi}{4} + \pi(0) = \frac{\pi}{4}$.

When $k = 1$, we obtain $x = \pi(1) = \pi$ and $x = \frac{\pi}{4} + \pi(1) = \frac{5\pi}{4}$.

When $k = 2$, we obtain $\underbrace{x = \pi(2) = 2\pi}_{\text{not in the interval } -2\pi < x < 2\pi}$ and $\underbrace{x = \frac{\pi}{4} + \pi(2) = \frac{9\pi}{4}}_{\text{not in the interval } -2\pi < x < 2\pi}$.

When $k = -1$, we obtain $x = \pi(-1) = -\pi$ and $x = \frac{\pi}{4} + \pi(-1) = -\frac{3\pi}{4}$.

When $k = -2$, we obtain $\underbrace{x = \pi(-2) = -2\pi}_{\text{not in the interval } -2\pi < x < 2\pi}$ and $x = \frac{\pi}{4} + \pi(-2) = -\frac{7\pi}{4}$.

Therefore, the set of solutions for x is

$$\left\{0, \ \frac{\pi}{4}, \ \pi, \ \frac{5\pi}{4}, \ -\pi, \ -\frac{3\pi}{4}, \ -\frac{7\pi}{4}\right\}.$$

2) $2\sin^2\alpha + \sqrt{3}\sin\alpha = 0$ in the interval $-\frac{3\pi}{2} \le \alpha \le \frac{3\pi}{2}$.

This resembles the quadratic equation $2x^2 + \sqrt{3}x = 0$, which can be solved by factoring.

$$2\sin^2\alpha + \sqrt{3}\sin\alpha = 0$$
$$\sin\alpha\left(2\sin\alpha + \sqrt{3}\right) = 0$$

$$
\begin{array}{c|c}
\sin\alpha = 0 & 2\sin\alpha + \sqrt{3} = 0 \\
& -\sqrt{3} \quad -\sqrt{3} \\
\hline
& \dfrac{\cancel{2}\sin\alpha}{\cancel{2}} = \dfrac{-\sqrt{3}}{2} \\
& \sin\alpha = -\dfrac{\sqrt{3}}{2}
\end{array}
$$

The equation $\sin\alpha = 0$ has solutions $\alpha = \pi k$, where k is any integer. The equation $\sin\alpha = -\frac{\sqrt{3}}{2}$ has solutions $\alpha = \frac{4\pi}{3} + 2\pi k$ and $\alpha = \frac{5\pi}{3} + 2\pi k$, where k is any integer (note that the reference angle for any solution of the equation $\sin\alpha = -\frac{\sqrt{3}}{2}$ is $\sin^{-1}\left(\frac{\sqrt{3}}{2}\right) = \frac{\pi}{3}$). Let's find out which of these solutions are in the interval $-\frac{3\pi}{2} \le \alpha \le \frac{3\pi}{2}$.

When $k = 0$, we obtain $\alpha = \pi(0) = 0$, $\alpha = \frac{4\pi}{3} + 2\pi(0) = \frac{4\pi}{3}$, and $\underbrace{x = \frac{5\pi}{3} + 2\pi(0) = \frac{5\pi}{3}}_{\text{not in the interval } -\frac{3\pi}{2} \le \alpha \le \frac{3\pi}{2}}$.

When $k = 1$, we obtain $\alpha = \pi(1) = \pi$, and $\underbrace{\alpha = \frac{4\pi}{3} + 2\pi(1) = \frac{10\pi}{3}}_{\text{not in the interval } -\frac{3\pi}{2} \le \alpha \le \frac{3\pi}{2}}$.

When $k = 2$, we obtain $\underbrace{\alpha = \pi(2) = 2\pi.}_{\text{not in the interval } -\frac{3\pi}{2} \le \alpha \le \frac{3\pi}{2}}$

When $k = -1$, we obtain $\alpha = \pi(-1) = -\pi$, $\alpha = \frac{4\pi}{3} + 2\pi(-1) = -\frac{2\pi}{3}$, and $\alpha = \frac{5\pi}{3} + 2\pi(-1) = -\frac{\pi}{3}$.

When $k = -2$, we obtain $\underbrace{\alpha = \pi(-2) = -2\pi}_{\text{not in the interval } -\frac{3\pi}{2} \le \alpha \le \frac{3\pi}{2}}$, $\underbrace{\alpha = \frac{4\pi}{3} + 2\pi(-2) = -\frac{8\pi}{3}}_{\text{not in the interval } -\frac{3\pi}{2} \le \alpha \le \frac{3\pi}{2}}$, and

$$\underbrace{\alpha = \frac{5\pi}{3} + 2\pi(-2) = -\frac{7\pi}{3}.}_{\text{not in the interval } -\frac{3\pi}{2} \le \alpha \le \frac{3\pi}{2}}$$

Therefore, the set of solutions for α is

$$\left\{0, \ \frac{4\pi}{3}, \ \pi, \ -\pi, \ -\frac{2\pi}{3}, \ -\frac{\pi}{3}\right\}.$$

3) $\cos^2 \beta - 3 \cos \beta + 2 = 0$ in the interval $-2\pi \leq \beta \leq 2\pi$.

This resembles the quadratic equation $x^2 + x - 2 = 0$, which can be solved by factoring.

$$\cos^2 \beta - 3 \cos \beta + 2 = 0$$
$$(\cos \beta - 1)(\cos \beta - 2) = 0$$

$\cos \beta - 1 = 0$	$\cos \beta + 2 = 0$
$+1 \quad +1$	$-2 \quad -2$
$\cos \beta = 1$	$\cos \beta = -2$

The equation $\cos \beta = 1$ has solutions $\beta = 2\pi k$, where k is any integer. The equation $\cos \beta = -2$ has no solutions since

$$-1 \leq \cos \beta \leq 1$$

for any value of β. Let's find out which of these solutions are in the interval $-2\pi \leq \beta \leq 2\pi$.

When $k = 0$, we obtain $\beta = 2\pi(0) = 0$.

When $k = 1$, we obtain $\beta = 2\pi(1) = 2\pi$.

When $k = 2$, we obtain $\underbrace{\beta = 2\pi(2) = 4\pi.}_{\text{not in the interval } -2\pi \leq \beta \leq 2\pi}$

When $k = -1$, we obtain $\beta = 2\pi(-1) = -2\pi$.

When $k = -2$, we obtain $\underbrace{\beta = 2\pi(-2) = -4\pi.}_{\text{not in the interval } -2\pi \leq \beta \leq 2\pi}$

Therefore, the set of solutions for β is

$$\{0, \ 2\pi, \ -2\pi\}.$$

4) $\csc^2 \theta - 2 \csc \theta + 1 = 0$ in the interval $-\pi < \theta < \pi$.

This looks like $x^2 - 2x + 1 = 0$, doesn't it? Let's solve this by factoring.

$$\csc^2 \theta - 2 \csc \theta + 1 = 0$$
$$(\csc \theta - 1)(\csc \theta - 1) = 0$$

$\csc \theta - 1 = 0$	$\csc \theta - 1 = 0$
$+1 \quad +1$	$+1 \quad +1$
$\csc \theta = 1$	$\csc \theta = 1$

Notice that $\csc \theta = 1$ is the same as $\dfrac{1}{\sin \theta} = 1$, which becomes $\sin \theta = 1$ after doing some cross multiplication. The solutions of the equations $\sin \theta = 1$ and $\csc \theta = 1$ are of the form $\theta = \frac{\pi}{2} + 2\pi k$, where k is any integer. Let's find out which of these solutions are in the interval $-\pi < \theta < \pi$.

When $k = 0$, we obtain $\theta = \dfrac{\pi}{2} + 2\pi(0) = \dfrac{\pi}{2}$.

When $k = 1$, we obtain $\underbrace{\theta = \dfrac{\pi}{2} + 2\pi(1) = \dfrac{5\pi}{2}}_{\text{not in the interval } -\pi < \theta < \pi}$.

When $k = -1$, we obtain $\underbrace{\theta = \dfrac{\pi}{2} + 2\pi(-1) = -\dfrac{3\pi}{2}}_{\text{not in the interval } -\pi < \theta < \pi}$.

Therefore, the only solution is $\theta = \frac{\pi}{2}$.

Try These (Set 6):

I) Find all of the solutions to the equations. Express your answers in radian measure.

1) $\sin^2 \alpha + \sin \alpha = 0$ 2) $2\cos^2 x - 3\cos x + 1 = 0$ 3) $\cot^2 x + 2\cot x + 1 = 0$

II) Find the solutions to the equations in the given interval.

1) $\cos^2 \theta - \cos \theta = 0$ in the interval $-2\pi \leq x \leq 2\pi$.   2) $\csc^2 x - 2\csc x = 0$ in the interval $-\pi < x < \pi$.

Section 7.3.2 Solving by Using the Square Root Property

Let's say that we want to solve the equation $\tan^2 \theta - 3 = 0$. If we replace $\tan \theta$ by the variable x, we obtain the quadratic equation $x^2 - 3 = 0$. This equation can be solved by using the **Square Root Property**. Recall that the Square Root Property states that if $n \geq 0$, then

$$x^2 = n \text{ implies that } x = \pm\sqrt{n}.$$

This property also holds if we allow n to be a negative number. In this case, we get complex numbers (which we are not concerned with here). We will now see examples which use the Square Root Property.

Examples. Find all of the solutions to the equations. Express your answers in radian measure.

1) $\cos^2 \theta - 1 = 0$

This equation resembles the equation $x^2 - 1 = 0$. This can be solved either by factoring or by using the Square Root Property. Let's use the property.

$$\begin{array}{c} \cos^2 \theta - \cancel{1} = 0 \\ \underline{\cancel{+1} \quad +1} \\ \cos^2 \theta = 1 \end{array}$$

$$\cos \theta = \pm\sqrt{1} = \pm 1$$

The solutions of the equation $\cos\theta = -1$ are of the form $\theta = \pi + 2\pi k = (2k+1)\pi$, where k is any integer. The solutions of the equation $\cos\theta = 1$ are of the form $\theta = 2\pi k$, where k is any integer. Therefore, the set of solutions is

$$\{\theta \mid \theta = (2k+1)\pi,\; \theta = 2\pi k\},\text{ where } k \text{ is any integer.}$$

This set can be written in the more simplified way

$$\{\theta \mid \theta = \pi k\},\text{ where } k \text{ is any integer.}$$

2) $3\tan^2\alpha - 1 = 0$

Notice that this resembles the equation $3x^2 - 1 = 0$. This can be solved by using the Square Root Property.

$$3\tan^2\alpha - 1 = 0$$
$$\underline{+1 \quad +1}$$
$$\frac{3\tan^2\alpha}{3} = \frac{1}{3}$$

$$\tan^2\alpha = \frac{1}{3}$$

$$\tan\alpha = \pm\sqrt{\frac{1}{3}} = \pm\frac{\sqrt{3}}{3}$$

The solutions of the equation $\tan\alpha = -\frac{\sqrt{3}}{3}$ are of the form $\alpha = \frac{5\pi}{6} + \pi k$, where k is any integer (since $\frac{\pi}{6} = \tan^{-1}\frac{\sqrt{3}}{3}$ is the reference angle for every solution of the equation). The solutions of the equation $\tan\alpha = \frac{\sqrt{3}}{3}$ are of the form $\alpha = \frac{\pi}{6} + \pi k$, where k is any integer. Therefore, the set of solutions is

$$\left\{\alpha \mid \alpha = \frac{5\pi}{6} + \pi k,\; \alpha = \frac{\pi}{6} + \pi k\right\},\text{ where } k \text{ is any integer.}$$

3) $\sin^2 t - \frac{3}{4} = 0$

Since this equation resembles the equation $x^2 - \frac{3}{4} = 0$, we will use the Square Root Property to solve it.

$$\sin^2 t - \frac{3}{4} = 0$$
$$\underline{+\frac{3}{4} \quad +\frac{3}{4}}$$
$$\sin^2 t = \frac{3}{4}$$

$$\sin t = \pm\sqrt{\frac{3}{4}} = \pm\frac{\sqrt{3}}{2}$$

Solutions of the equation $\sin t = -\frac{\sqrt{3}}{2}$ are of the form $t = \frac{4\pi}{3} + 2\pi k$ or $t = \frac{5\pi}{3} + 2\pi k$, where k is any integer (note that $\frac{\pi}{3} = \sin^{-1}\frac{\sqrt{3}}{2}$ is the reference angle for every solution of the equation). The solutions of the equation $\sin t = \frac{\sqrt{3}}{2}$ are of the form $t = \frac{\pi}{3} + 2\pi k$ or $t = \frac{2\pi}{3} + 2\pi k$, where k is any integer. Therefore, the set of solutions is

$$\left\{ t \mid t = \frac{\pi}{3} + \pi k, t = \frac{2\pi}{3} + \pi k \right\}, \text{ where } k \text{ is any integer.}$$

Examples. Find the solutions to the equations in the given interval.

1) $\sin^2 \alpha - \frac{1}{2} = 0$ in the interval $-2\pi \le \alpha \le 2\pi$.

We will use the Square Root Property.

$$\sin^2 \alpha - \frac{1}{2} = 0$$
$$\underline{+\frac{1}{2} \quad +\frac{1}{2}}$$
$$\sin^2 \alpha = \frac{1}{2}$$

$$\sin \alpha = \pm \sqrt{\frac{1}{2}} = \pm \frac{\sqrt{2}}{2}$$

Solutions of the equation $\sin \alpha = -\frac{\sqrt{2}}{2}$ are of the form $\alpha = \frac{5\pi}{4} + 2\pi k$ or $\alpha = \frac{7\pi}{4} + 2\pi k$, where k is any integer (note that $\frac{\pi}{4} = \sin^{-1} \frac{\sqrt{2}}{2}$ is the reference angle for every solution of the equation). The solutions of the equation $\sin \alpha = \frac{\sqrt{2}}{2}$ are of the form $\alpha = \frac{\pi}{4} + 2\pi k$ or $\alpha = \frac{3\pi}{4} + 2\pi k$, where k is any integer. Now let's find the solutions which lie in the interval $-2\pi \le \alpha \le 2\pi$.

When $k = 0$, we obtain
$$\alpha = \frac{5\pi}{4} + 2\pi (0) = \frac{5\pi}{4}, \ \alpha = \frac{7\pi}{4} + 2\pi (0) = \frac{7\pi}{4}, \ \alpha = \frac{\pi}{4} + 2\pi (0) = \frac{\pi}{4}, \text{ and } \alpha = \frac{3\pi}{4} + 2\pi (0) = \frac{3\pi}{4}.$$

When $k = 1$, we obtain
$$\underbrace{\alpha = \frac{5\pi}{4} + 2\pi (1) = \frac{13\pi}{4}}_{\text{not in the interval } -2\pi \le \alpha \le 2\pi}, \ \underbrace{\alpha = \frac{7\pi}{4} + 2\pi (1) = \frac{15\pi}{4}}_{\text{not in the interval } -2\pi \le \alpha \le 2\pi}, \ \underbrace{\alpha = \frac{\pi}{4} + 2\pi (1) = \frac{9\pi}{4}}_{\text{not in the interval } -2\pi \le \alpha \le 2\pi}, \text{ and } \underbrace{\alpha = \frac{3\pi}{4} + 2\pi (1) = \frac{11\pi}{4}}_{\text{not in the interval } -2\pi \le \alpha \le 2\pi}.$$

When $k = -1$, we obtain
$$\alpha = \frac{5\pi}{4} + 2\pi (-1) = -\frac{3\pi}{4}, \ \alpha = \frac{7\pi}{4} + 2\pi (-1) = -\frac{\pi}{4}, \ \alpha = \frac{\pi}{4} + 2\pi (-1) = -\frac{7\pi}{4}, \text{ and}$$

$$\alpha = \frac{3\pi}{4} + 2\pi (-1) = -\frac{5\pi}{4}.$$

When $k = -2$, we obtain
$$\underbrace{\alpha = \frac{5\pi}{4} + 2\pi (-2) = -\frac{11\pi}{4}}_{\text{not in the interval } -2\pi \le \alpha \le 2\pi}, \ \underbrace{\alpha = \frac{7\pi}{4} + 2\pi (-2) = -\frac{9\pi}{4}}_{\text{not in the interval } -2\pi \le \alpha \le 2\pi}, \ \underbrace{\alpha = \frac{\pi}{4} + 2\pi (-2) = -\frac{15\pi}{4}}_{\text{not in the interval } -2\pi \le \alpha \le 2\pi}, \text{ and}$$

$$\underbrace{\alpha = \frac{3\pi}{4} + 2\pi (-2) = -\frac{13\pi}{4}}_{\text{not in the interval } -2\pi \le \alpha \le 2\pi}.$$

Therefore, the set of solutions is

$$\left\{ t \mid t = \pm\frac{5\pi}{4}, \pm\frac{7\pi}{4}, \pm\frac{\pi}{4}, \pm\frac{3\pi}{4} \right\}.$$

2) $3\tan^2\left(2\theta + \frac{\pi}{3}\right) - 9 = 0$ in the interval $-\pi < \theta \le \pi$.

First let's solve the equation $3\tan^2 x - 9 = 0$ by using the Square Root Property.

$$3\tan^2 x - 9 = 0$$
$$\underline{+9 \quad +9}$$
$$\frac{3\tan^2 x}{3} = \frac{9}{3}$$
$$\tan^2 x = 3$$
$$\tan x = \pm\sqrt{3}$$

The solutions of the equation $\tan x = -\sqrt{3}$ are of the form $x = \frac{2\pi}{3} + \pi k$, where k is any integer (observe that $\frac{\pi}{3} = \tan^{-1}\sqrt{3}$ is the reference angle for every solution of the equation). The solutions of the equation $\tan x = \sqrt{3}$ are of the form $x = \frac{\pi}{3} + \pi k$, where k is any integer.

If we replace x by $2\theta + \frac{\pi}{3}$, we have that

$$2\theta + \frac{\pi}{3} = \frac{2\pi}{3} + \pi k \quad \text{and} \quad 2\theta + \frac{\pi}{3} = \frac{\pi}{3} + \pi k.$$

Let's solve for θ.

$$2\theta + \frac{\pi}{3} = \frac{2\pi}{3} + \pi k \qquad \text{and} \qquad 2\theta + \frac{\pi}{3} = \frac{\pi}{3} + \pi k$$
$$\underline{-\frac{\pi}{3} \quad -\frac{\pi}{3}} \qquad\qquad\qquad \underline{-\frac{\pi}{3} \quad -\frac{\pi}{3}}$$
$$2\theta = \frac{\pi}{3} + \pi k \qquad\qquad\qquad 2\theta = \pi k$$
$$\frac{1}{2}(2\theta) = \frac{1}{2}\left(\frac{\pi}{3} + \pi k\right) \qquad\qquad \frac{2\theta}{2} = \frac{\pi k}{2}$$
$$\theta = \frac{\pi}{6} + \frac{\pi}{2}k \qquad\qquad\qquad \theta = \frac{\pi k}{2}$$

Finally, we find those values of θ which lie in the interval $-\pi < \theta \le \pi$.

When $k = 0$, we obtain $\theta = \frac{\pi}{6} + \frac{\pi}{2}(0) = \frac{\pi}{6}$ and $\theta = \frac{\pi(0)}{2} = 0$.

When $k = 1$, we obtain $\theta = \frac{\pi}{6} + \frac{\pi}{2}(1) = \frac{2\pi}{3}$ and $\theta = \frac{\pi(1)}{2} = \frac{\pi}{2}$.

When $k = 2$, we obtain $\underbrace{\theta = \frac{\pi}{6} + \frac{\pi}{2}(2) = \frac{7\pi}{6}}_{\text{not in the interval } -\pi < \theta \le \pi}$ and $\theta = \frac{\pi(2)}{2} = \pi$.

When $k = -1$, we obtain $\theta = \frac{\pi}{6} + \frac{\pi}{2}(-1) = -\frac{\pi}{3}$ and $\theta = \frac{\pi(-1)}{2} = -\frac{\pi}{2}$.

When $k = -2$, we obtain $\theta = \frac{\pi}{6} + \frac{\pi}{2}(-2) = -\frac{5\pi}{6}$ and $\underbrace{\theta = \frac{\pi(-2)}{2} = -\pi}_{\text{not in the interval } -\pi < \theta \le \pi}$.

The solution set, therefore, is

$$\left\{ 0, \ \frac{\pi}{6}, \ \frac{2\pi}{3}, \ \frac{\pi}{2}, \ \pi, \ -\frac{\pi}{3}, \ -\frac{\pi}{2}, \ -\frac{5\pi}{6} \right\}.$$

3) $4\cos^2\left(\dfrac{t}{2}\right) - 3 = 0$ in the interval $-2\pi < t \le \pi$.

First let's solve the equation $4\cos^2 x - 3 = 0$ by using the Square Root Property.

$$4\cos^2 x - \cancel{3} = 0$$
$$\underline{\qquad +\cancel{3} \quad +3 \qquad}$$
$$\frac{\cancel{4}\cos^2 x}{\cancel{4}} = \frac{3}{4}$$
$$\cos^2 x = \frac{3}{4}$$
$$\cos x = \pm\sqrt{\frac{3}{4}} = \pm\frac{\sqrt{3}}{2}$$

The solutions of the equation $\cos x = -\frac{\sqrt{3}}{2}$ are of the form $x = \frac{5\pi}{6} + 2\pi k$ or $x = \frac{7\pi}{6} + 2\pi k$, where k is any integer (observe that $\frac{\pi}{6} = \cos^{-1}\frac{\sqrt{3}}{2}$ is the reference angle for every solution of the equation). The solutions of the equation $\cos x = \frac{\sqrt{3}}{2}$ are of the form $x = \frac{\pi}{6} + 2\pi k$ or $x = \frac{11\pi}{6} + 2\pi k$, where k is any integer.
If we now replace x by $\frac{t}{2}$, we have

$$\frac{t}{2} = \frac{5\pi}{6} + 2\pi k, \quad \frac{t}{2} = \frac{7\pi}{6} + 2\pi k, \quad \frac{t}{2} = \frac{\pi}{6} + 2\pi k, \quad \text{and} \quad \frac{t}{2} = \frac{11\pi}{6} + 2\pi k.$$

We solve for t by multiplying each equation by 2:

$$t = \frac{5\pi}{3} + 4\pi k, \quad t = \frac{7\pi}{3} + 4\pi k, \quad t = \frac{\pi}{3} + 4\pi k, \quad \text{and} \quad t = \frac{11\pi}{3} + 4\pi k.$$

Let's find those values of t which lie in the interval $-2\pi < t \le \pi$.

When $k = 0$, we obtain
$$t = \frac{5\pi}{3} + 4\pi\,(0) = \underbrace{\frac{5\pi}{3}}_{\text{not in the interval } -2\pi<t\le\pi}, \quad t = \frac{7\pi}{3} + 4\pi\,(0) = \underbrace{\frac{7\pi}{3}}_{\text{not in the interval } -2\pi<t\le\pi}, \quad t = \frac{\pi}{3} + 4\pi\,(0) = \frac{\pi}{3}, \quad \text{and} \quad t = \frac{11\pi}{3} + 4\pi\,(0) = \underbrace{\frac{11\pi}{3}}_{\text{not in the interval } -2\pi<t\le\pi}.$$

When $k = 1$, we obtain
$$t = \frac{5\pi}{3} + 4\pi\,(1) = \underbrace{\frac{17\pi}{3}}_{\text{not in the interval } -2\pi<t\le\pi}, \quad t = \frac{7\pi}{3} + 4\pi\,(1) = \underbrace{\frac{19\pi}{3}}_{\text{not in the interval } -2\pi<t\le\pi}, \quad t = \frac{\pi}{3} + 4\pi\,(1) = \underbrace{\frac{13\pi}{3}}_{\text{not in the interval } -2\pi<t\le\pi}, \quad \text{and} \quad t = \frac{11\pi}{3} + 4\pi\,(1) = \underbrace{\frac{23\pi}{3}}_{\text{not in the interval } -2\pi<t\le\pi}.$$

When $k = -1$, we obtain
$$t = \frac{5\pi}{3} + 4\pi\,(-1) = \underbrace{-\frac{7\pi}{3}}_{\text{not in the interval } -2\pi<t\le\pi}, \quad t = \frac{7\pi}{3} + 4\pi\,(-1) = \underbrace{-\frac{5\pi}{3}}_{}, \quad t = \frac{\pi}{3} + 4\pi\,(-1) = \underbrace{-\frac{11\pi}{3}}_{\text{not in the interval } -2\pi<t\le\pi}, \quad \text{and}$$

$$t = \frac{11\pi}{3} + 4\pi\,(-1) = -\frac{\pi}{3}.$$

When $k = -2$, we obtain

$$\underbrace{t = \frac{5\pi}{3} + 4\pi\,(-2) = -\frac{19\pi}{3},}_{\text{not in the interval } -2\pi<t\le\pi} \quad \underbrace{t = \frac{7\pi}{3} + 4\pi\,(-2) = -\frac{17\pi}{3},}_{\text{not in the interval } -2\pi<t\le\pi} \quad \underbrace{t = \frac{\pi}{3} + 4\pi\,(-2) = -\frac{23\pi}{3},}_{\text{not in the interval } -2\pi<t\le\pi}$$

$$\text{and } \underbrace{t = \frac{11\pi}{3} + 4\pi\,(-2) = -\frac{13\pi}{3}.}_{\text{not in the interval } -2\pi<t\le\pi}$$

The solution set is

$$\left\{ \frac{\pi}{3},\ -\frac{\pi}{3},\ -\frac{5\pi}{3} \right\}.$$

4) $5\csc^2\alpha - 9 = 0$ in the interval $-180° < \alpha < 450°$ (round off your answers to the nearest degree).

$$5\csc^2\alpha = \cancel{-9} = 0$$
$$\underline{\qquad\quad +\cancel{9}\quad +9\qquad}$$
$$\frac{\cancel{5}\csc^2\alpha}{\cancel{5}} \quad \frac{9}{5}$$
$$\csc^2\alpha = \frac{9}{5}$$
$$\csc\alpha = \pm\sqrt{\frac{9}{5}} = \pm\frac{3}{\sqrt{5}}$$

Since sine is the reciprocal of cosecant, we can write this as

$$\sin\alpha = \pm\frac{\sqrt{5}}{3} \approx \pm 0.745.$$

The solutions of the equation $\sin\alpha = -0.745$ are of the form $\alpha = 228° + 360°k$ or $\alpha = 312° + 360°k$, where k is any integer (observe that $48° \approx \sin^{-1} 0.745$ is the reference angle for every solution of the equation). The solutions of the equation $\sin\alpha = 0.745$ are of the form $\alpha = 48° + 360°k$ or $\alpha = 132° + 360°k$, where k is any integer.

Let's find out which of these solutions are in the interval $-180° < \alpha < 450°$.

When $k = 0$, we obtain
$\alpha = 228° + 360°\,(0) = 228°$, $\alpha = 312° + 360°\,(0) = 312°$, $\alpha = 48° + 360°\,(0) = 48°$, and $\alpha = 132° + 360°\,(0) = 132°$.

When $k = 1$, we obtain
$$\underbrace{\alpha = 228° + 360°\,(1) = 588°}_{\text{not in the interval } -180°<\alpha<450°},\quad \underbrace{\alpha = 312° + 360°\,(1) = 672°}_{\text{not in the interval } -180°<\alpha<450°},$$

$\alpha = 48° + 360°\,(1) = 408°$, and $\underbrace{\alpha = 132° + 360°\,(1) = 492°}_{\text{not in the interval } -180°<\alpha<450°}$.

When $k = -1$, we obtain
$\alpha = 228° + 360°\,(-1) = -132°$, $\alpha = 312° + 360°\,(-1) = -48°$,

$\underbrace{\alpha = 48° + 360°\,(-1) = -312°}_{\text{not in the interval } -180°<\alpha<450°}$, and $\underbrace{\alpha = 132° + 360°\,(-1) = -228°}_{\text{not in the interval } -180°<\alpha<450°}$.

Therefore, the solution set is

$$\{228°,\ 312°,\ 48°,\ 132°,\ 408°,\ -132°,\ -48°\}.$$

Try These (Set 7):

I) Find all of the solutions to the equations. Express your answers in radian measure.

1) $\tan^2 x - 1 = 0$ 2) $6\cos^2 \alpha - 3 = 0$ 3) $4\sin^2 \left(t + \frac{2\pi}{3}\right) - 3 = 0$

II) Find the solutions to the equations in the given interval. Round off any degree measures to the nearest degree.

1) $3\tan^2 x - 1 = 0$ in the interval $-2\pi < x < 2\pi$. 2) $14\sec^2 x - 200 = 0$ in the interval $-360° < x < 360°$.

Section 7.3.3 Solving by Using the Quadratic Formula

As we know, not all quadratic equations can be easily solved by either factoring or by using the Square Root Property. For such equations, we usually use the Quadratic Formula to determine the solutions. Recall that if $ax^2 + bx + c = 0$, $a \neq 0$, then

$$x = \frac{-b \pm \sqrt{b^2 - 4ac}}{2a}$$

is the Quadratic Formula. We will learn how to solve second-degree trigonometric equations which require the use of the Quadratic Formula.

Examples. Solve for θ in the interval $-360° \leq \theta \leq 360°$ (round off your answers to the nearest degree).

1) $\cos^2 \theta - 3\cos \theta + 1 = 0$

If we replace $\cos \theta$ by x, we get the equation $x^2 - 3x + 1 = 0$. Notice that $a = 1$, $b = -3$, and $c = 1$. Therefore,

$$\cos \theta = \frac{-b \pm \sqrt{b^2 - 4ac}}{2a}$$

$$= \frac{-(-3) \pm \sqrt{(-3)^2 - 4(1)(1)}}{2(1)}$$

$$= \frac{3 \pm \sqrt{5}}{2}$$

$$= \begin{cases} \dfrac{3 - \sqrt{5}}{2} \approx 0.381966 \\ \dfrac{3 + \sqrt{5}}{2} \approx 2.618034 \end{cases}$$

The solutions of the equation $\cos \theta = 0.381966$ are $\theta = 68° + 360°k$ or $\theta = 292° + 360°k$, where k is any integer. There are no solutions of the equation $\cos \theta = 2.618034$ since cosine cannot be larger than 1.

Now we need to find those solutions which lie in the given interval.

When $k = 0$, we obtain $\theta = 68° + 360° (0) = 68°$ and $\theta = 292° + 360° (0) = 292°$.

When $k = 1$, we obtain $\underbrace{\theta = 68° + 360° (1) = 428°}_{\text{not in the interval } -360° \leq \theta \leq 360°}$ and $\underbrace{\theta = 292° + 360° (1) = 652°}_{\text{not in the interval } -360° \leq \theta \leq 360°}$.

When $k = -1$, we obtain $\theta = 68° + 360° (-1) = -292°$ and $\theta = 292° + 360° (-1) = -68°$.

When $k = -2$, we obtain $\underbrace{\theta = 68° + 360° (-2) = -652°}_{\text{not in the interval } -360° \leq \theta \leq 360°}$ and $\underbrace{\theta = 292° + 360° (-2) = -428°}_{\text{not in the interval } -360° \leq \theta \leq 360°}$.

The solutions are $\theta = \pm 68°$ and $\theta = \pm 292°$.

2) $2 \sin^2 \theta + 6 \sin \theta - 1 = 0$

If we replace $\sin \theta$ by x, we get the equation $2x^2 + 6x - 1 = 0$. Notice that $a = 2$, $b = 6$, and $c = -1$. Therefore,

$$\sin \theta = \frac{-b \pm \sqrt{b^2 - 4ac}}{2a}$$

$$= \frac{-6 \pm \sqrt{(6)^2 - 4(2)(-1)}}{2(2)}$$

$$= \frac{-6 \pm \sqrt{44}}{4}$$

$$= \left\{ \begin{array}{l} \dfrac{-6 - \sqrt{44}}{4} \approx -3.158312 \\ \dfrac{-6 + \sqrt{44}}{4} \approx 0.158312 \end{array} \right\}$$

There are no solutions of the equation $\sin \theta = -3.158312$ since sine cannot be smaller than -1. The solutions of the equation $\sin \theta = 0.158312$ are $\theta = 9° + 360° k$ or $\theta = 171° + 360° k$, where k is any integer.

Now we need to find those solutions which lie in the given interval.

When $k = 0$, we obtain $\theta = 9° + 360° (0) = 9°$ and $\theta = 171° + 360° (0) = 171°$.

When $k = 1$, we obtain $\underbrace{\theta = 9° + 360° (1) = 369°}_{\text{not in the interval } -360° \leq \theta \leq 360°}$ and $\underbrace{\theta = 171° + 360° (1) = 531°}_{\text{not in the interval } -360° \leq \theta \leq 360°}$.

When $k = -1$, we obtain $\theta = 9° + 360° (-1) = -351°$ and $\theta = 171° + 360° (-1) = -189°$.

When $k = -2$, we obtain $\underbrace{\theta = 9° + 360° (-2) = -711°}_{\text{not in the interval } -360° \leq \theta \leq 360°}$ and $\underbrace{\theta = 171° + 360° (-2) = -549°}_{\text{not in the interval } -360° \leq \theta \leq 360°}$.

The solution set is

$$\{9°, \ 171°, \ -351°, \ -189°\}.$$

3) $\cos^2 \theta + 2.6 \cos \theta - 9.2 = 0$

The values which are needed for the Quadratic Formula are $a = 1$, $b = 2.6$, and $c = -9.2$.

$$
\begin{aligned}
\cos \theta &= \frac{-b \pm \sqrt{b^2 - 4ac}}{2a} \\
&= \frac{-2.6 \pm \sqrt{(2.6)^2 - 4(1)(-9.2)}}{2(1)} \\
&= \frac{-2.6 \pm \sqrt{43.56}}{2} \\
&= \left\{ \begin{array}{l} \dfrac{-2.6 - \sqrt{43.56}}{2} = -4.6 \\ \dfrac{-2.6 + \sqrt{43.56}}{2} = 2 \end{array} \right\}
\end{aligned}
$$

There are no solutions of both $\cos \theta = -4.6$ and $\cos \theta = 2$ since $-1 \leq \cos \theta \leq 1$ for any value of θ. Therefore, our given equation has no solution.

Try These (Set 8): Solve for θ in the interval $-360° \leq \theta \leq 360°$ (round off your answers to the nearest degree).

1) $\sin^2 \theta + 2 \sin \theta - 2 = 0$ $\qquad$ 2) $4 \tan^2 \theta - 7 \tan \theta - 1 = 0$

Exercise 7.3

In Exercises 1-22, find all of the solutions to the equations. Express your answers in radian measure.

1. $2 \cos^2 x + \cos x = 0$ $\qquad$ 2. $\cos^2 x - \cos x = 0$ $\qquad$ 3. $2 \sin^2 t - \sqrt{3} \sin t = 0$

4. $\sqrt{2} \sin^2 \theta + \sin \theta = 0$ $\qquad$ 5. $\tan^2 \alpha - \tan \alpha = 0$ $\qquad$ 6. $\tan \beta + \tan^2 \beta = 0$

7. $\sec^2 \theta + \sec \theta = 0$ $\qquad$ 8. $\csc^2 \alpha - \csc \alpha = 0$ $\qquad$ 9. $4 \cos^2 t - 1 = 0$

10. $2 \sin^2 t - 1 = 0$ $\qquad$ 11. $\tan^2 x - 3 = 0$ $\qquad$ 12. $\tan^2 x - 1 = 0$ $\qquad$ 13. $3 \sin^2 \theta - 3 = 0$

14. $4 \cos^2 \theta - 4 = 0$ $\qquad$ 15. $1 - 3 \tan^2 \beta = 0$ $\qquad$ 16. $1 - \cos^2 x = 0$ $\qquad$ 17. $2 - \csc^2 x = 0$

18. $2 - \sec^2 x = 0$ $\qquad$ 19. $\sin^2 \theta + 2 \sin \theta + 1 = 0$ $\qquad$ 20. $\cos^2 \theta - 2 \cos \theta + 1 = 0$

21. $2 \sin^2 x + 3 \sin x + 1 = 0$ $\qquad$ 22. $\sin^2 \beta + \sin \beta - 2 = 0$

In Exercises 23-44, solve for θ in the given interval. Express your answers in radian measure.

23. $2 \sin^2 \theta + \sin \theta = 0$; $0 < \theta \leq 2\pi$ $\qquad$ 24. $2 \cos^2 \theta - \cos \theta = 0$; $0 < \theta \leq 2\pi$ $\qquad$ 25. $\tan^2 \theta - 3 = 0$; $0 \leq \theta < 2\pi$

26. $2 \cos^2 \theta - 1 = 0$; $0 \leq \theta < 2\pi$ $\qquad$ 27. $3 - 4 \cos^2 \theta = 0$; $0 \leq \theta < 2\pi$ $\qquad$ 28. $1 - 3 \tan^2 \theta = 0$; $0 \leq \theta < 2\pi$

29. $4\cos^3\theta - 3\cos\theta = 0$; $-\pi \le \theta < \pi$

30. $4\sin^3\theta - 2\sin\theta = 0$; $-\pi \le \theta < \pi$

31. $2\sin^3\frac{\theta}{2} - \sin\frac{\theta}{2} = 0$; $0 \le \theta < 2\pi$

32. $12\cos^3 3\theta - 9\cos 3\theta = 0$; $0 \le \theta < 2\pi$

33. $4\cos^2\left(\theta + \frac{\pi}{6}\right) - 3 = 0$; $0 < \theta \le 2\pi$

34. $4\sin^2\left(\theta + \pi\right) - 3 = 0$; $0 < \theta \le 2\pi$

35. $\tan^2\left(4\theta - \frac{\pi}{2}\right) - 3 = 0$; $0 < \theta \le 2\pi$

36. $\cos^2\left(3\theta - \frac{\pi}{2}\right) - 1 = 0$; $0 < \theta \le 2\pi$

37. $\sin^2\left(\frac{\theta}{4} - \frac{3\pi}{2}\right) - 2 = 0$; $0 < \theta \le 2\pi$

38. $3\tan^2\left(\frac{\theta}{3} - \frac{3\pi}{4}\right) - 1 = 0$; $0 < \theta \le 2\pi$

39. $\cos^2\theta + 2\cos\theta + 1 = 0$; $0 < \theta \le 2\pi$

40. $\sin^2\theta - 2\sin\theta + 1 = 0$; $0 < \theta \le 2\pi$

41. $2\sin^2\theta + 3\sin\theta + 1 = 0$; $-2\pi \le \theta < 2\pi$

42. $2\cos^2\theta - 7\cos\theta + 3 = 0$; $-2\pi \le \theta < 2\pi$

43. $4\sin^2\theta - 12\sin\theta + 5 = 0$; $0 \le \theta < 2\pi$

44. $\cos^2\theta - \cos\theta - 2 = 0$; $0 \le \theta < 2\pi$

In Exercises 45-62, solve for θ in the interval $0° \le \theta \le 360°$. Round off your answers to the nearest degree.

45. $3\tan^2\theta + 3\tan\theta - 5 = 0$

46. $4\cos^2\theta - \cos\theta - 2 = 0$

47. $2\sin^2\theta - 6\sin\theta + 1 = 0$

48. $\tan^2\theta - 7\tan\theta - 3 = 0$

49. $3\cos^2\theta + 5\cos\theta - 4 = 0$

50. $4\sin^2\theta - 7\sin\theta + 2 = 0$

51. $2\tan^2\theta - \tan\theta - 10 = 0$

52. $6\sin^2\theta - 5\sin\theta + 2 = 0$

53. $7\cos^2\theta + 12\cos\theta + 5 = 0$

54. $4\tan^2\theta + 3\tan\theta - 1 = 0$

55. $5\csc^2\theta - 9 = 0$

56. $7\cot^2\theta - 10 = 0$

57. $3\sec^2\theta - \sec\theta - 9 = 0$

58. $2\csc^2\theta + 6\csc\theta - 1 = 0$

59. $\cot^2\theta + 5\cot\theta + 1 = 0$

60. $\sec^2\theta + 4\sec\theta - 2 = 0$

61. $\csc^2\theta + 6\csc\theta - 1 = 0$

62. $\cot^2\theta + 5\cot\theta + 1 = 0$

Section 7.4 Trigonometric Equations Involving Multiple Functions

Sometimes we may need to solve an equation which has more than one trigonometric function in it. In such a situation, we may need to use one or more of our trigonometric identities to produce an equation containing only a single trigonometric function. Another possible way of solving such an equation is by factoring as we did in Section 7.3. In this section, we will learn how to solve trigonometric equations which involve more than one trigonometric function.

Examples. Find all of the solutions to the equations. Express your answers in radian measure.

1) $2\cos\theta\sin\theta - \cos\theta = 0$

Notice that both terms on the left-hand side of the equation contain $\cos\theta$ and the right-hand side is 0. This suggests that we should solve it by factoring.

$$2\cos\theta\sin\theta - \cos\theta = 0$$

$$\cos\theta\,(2\sin\theta - 1) = 0$$

$\cos\theta = 0$	$2\sin\theta - 1 = 0$
	$+1\phantom{{}={}}+1$
	$\dfrac{2\sin\theta}{2} = \dfrac{1}{2}$
	$\sin\theta = \dfrac{1}{2}$

The solutions of the equation $\cos\theta = 0$ are of the form $\theta = \frac{(2k+1)\pi}{2}$, where k is any integer. The solutions of the equation $\sin\theta = \frac{1}{2}$ are of the form $\theta = \frac{\pi}{6} + 2\pi k$ or $\theta = \frac{5\pi}{6} + 2\pi k$, where k is any integer. Therefore, the solution to the equation can be written as

$$\left\{\theta \mid \theta = \frac{(2k+1)\,\pi}{2},\ \theta = \frac{\pi}{6} + 2\pi k, \theta = \frac{5\pi}{6} + 2\pi k\right\},\ \text{where } k \text{ is any integer.}$$

2) $3\sin\beta\tan\beta + 3\sin\beta = 0$

Since both terms on the left-hand side of the equation contain $\sin\beta$ and the right-hand side of the equation is 0, we will solve this equation by factoring.

$$3\sin\beta\tan\beta + 3\sin\beta = 0$$

$$3\sin\beta\,(\tan\beta + 1) = 0$$

$3\sin\beta = 0$	$\tan\beta + 1 = 0$
$\sin\beta = 0$	$-1\phantom{{}={}}-1$
	$\tan\beta = -1$

The solutions of the equation $\sin\beta = 0$ are of the form $\beta = \pi k$, where k is any integer. The solutions of the equation $\tan\beta = -1$ are of the form $\beta = \frac{3\pi}{4} + \pi k$ where k is any integer. Therefore, the solution to the equation may be written as

$$\left\{\beta \mid \beta = \pi k, \beta = \frac{3\pi}{4} + \pi k\right\},\ \text{where } k \text{ is any integer.}$$

3) $\cos^2 x + \sin x + 1 = 0$

We cannot solve this equation by factoring. Are there any identities we know of that relate sine and cosine? Well, one identity that comes to mind is $\sin^2 x + \cos^2 x = 1$. Observe that if we write this identity as

$$\cos^2 x = 1 - \sin^2 x,$$

we can replace $\cos^2 x$ in our equation by $1 - \sin^2 x$ and produce an equation which contains only sine. This is a good thing since we can then apply our factoring techniques to solve. Let's see how this all falls into place.

$$\cos^2 x + \sin x + 1 = 0$$
$$\left(1 - \sin^2 x\right) + \sin x + 1 = 0 \qquad \text{(substitute } 1 - \sin^2 x \text{ for } \cos^2 x\text{)}$$
$$-\sin^2 x + \sin x + 2 = 0 \qquad \text{(combine like terms)}$$
$$-1\left(\sin x - 2\right)\left(\sin x + 1\right) = 0 \qquad \text{(factor completely)}$$

$$\frac{\left(\sin x - 2\right)\left(\sin x + 1\right) = 0}{} \qquad \text{(divide by } -1\text{)}$$

$$
\begin{array}{c|c}
\sin x - \cancel{2} = 0 & \sin x + \cancel{1} = 0 \\
\underline{+\cancel{2} \quad +2} & \underline{\cancel{1} \quad -1} \\
\sin x = 2 & \sin x = -1
\end{array}
$$

Now, there are no solutions of the equation $\sin x = 2$ since the sine of an angle cannot be more than 1. The solutions of the equation $\sin x = -1$ are of the form $x = \frac{3\pi}{2} + 2\pi k$, where k is any integer. Therefore, the solution set of the original equation is

$$\left\{ \frac{3\pi}{2} + 2\pi k, \text{ where } k \text{ is any integer} \right\}.$$

4) $2 \tan^2 \theta - \sec^2 \theta = 0$

Notice that this cannot be solved by factoring. One of the Pythagorean identities states that

$$\tan^2 \theta + 1 = \sec^2 \theta.$$

We can use this to replace $\sec^2 \theta$ by $\tan^2 \theta + 1$ in our equation. After doing so, we will apply the Square Root Property.

$$2 \tan^2 \theta - \sec^2 \theta = 0$$
$$2 \tan^2 \theta - \left(\tan^2 \theta + 1\right) = 0$$

$$\tan^2 \theta - \cancel{1} = 0$$
$$\underline{\cancel{1} \quad +1}$$
$$\tan^2 \theta = 1$$

$$\tan \theta = \pm\sqrt{1} = \pm 1$$

The solutions of the equation $\tan \theta = -1$ are of the form $\theta = \frac{3\pi}{4} + \pi k$, where k is any integer. The solutions of the equation $\tan \theta = 1$ are of the form $\theta = \frac{\pi}{4} + \pi k$, where k is any integer. Therefore, the solution to the equation can be written as

$$\left\{ \theta \mid \theta = \frac{3\pi}{4} + \pi k, \theta = \frac{\pi}{4} + \pi k \right\}, \text{ where } k \text{ is any integer.}$$

5) $\sin \frac{\alpha}{2} - \cos \frac{\alpha}{2} = 0$

We cannot use a Pythagorean identity this time because there are no squares of sine or cosine present. We need to think of another identity which involves sine and cosine. One identity that comes to mind is

$$\frac{\sin \theta}{\cos \theta} = \tan \theta.$$

Can we use this somehow? Well, notice that we can add the cosine term to both sides, then divide both sides of the equation by it. This will produce an equation with only tangent in it. Let's give it a try and see what happens.

$$\sin \frac{\alpha}{2} - \cancel{\cos \frac{\alpha}{2}} = 0$$

$$\frac{+\cancel{\cos \frac{\alpha}{2}} \qquad + \cos \frac{\alpha}{2}}{\sin \frac{\alpha}{2} = \cos \frac{\alpha}{2}}$$

$$\frac{\sin \frac{\alpha}{2}}{\cos \frac{\alpha}{2}} = \frac{\cos \frac{\alpha}{2}}{\cos \frac{\alpha}{2}}$$

$$\tan \frac{\alpha}{2} = 1$$

This equation can easily be solved. Notice that the solutions of the equation $\tan x = 1$ are of the form $x = \frac{\pi}{4} + \pi k$, where k is any integer. If we replace x by $\frac{\alpha}{2}$, we will get

$$\frac{\alpha}{2} = \frac{\pi}{4} + \pi k, \quad \text{hence} \quad \alpha = 2 \left(\frac{\pi}{4} + \pi k \right) = \frac{\pi}{2} + 2\pi k, \text{ where } k \text{ is any integer.}$$

6) $\sec \theta = 2 \cos \theta$

How are secant and cosine related? Well, we know that they are reciprocals of each other. Let's use this identity to create an equation which contains only cosine. After doing so, we will apply the Square Root Property.

$$\sec \theta = 2 \cos \theta$$

$$\frac{1}{\cos \theta} = 2 \cos \theta$$

$$\cancel{\cos \theta} \left(\frac{1}{\cancel{\cos \theta}} \right) = \cos \theta \left(2 \cos \theta \right)$$

$$\frac{1}{2} = \frac{\cancel{2} \cos^2 \theta}{\cancel{2}}$$

$$\cos \theta = \pm \sqrt{\frac{1}{2}} = \pm \frac{\sqrt{2}}{2}$$

The solutions of the equation $\cos \theta = -\frac{\sqrt{2}}{2}$ are of the form $\theta = \frac{3\pi}{4} + 2\pi k$ or $\theta = \frac{5\pi}{4} + 2\pi k$, where k is any integer. The solutions of the equation $\cos \theta = \frac{\sqrt{2}}{2}$ are of the form $\theta = \frac{\pi}{4} + 2\pi k$ or $\theta = \frac{7\pi}{4} + 2\pi k$, where k is any integer. Therefore, the solution set is

$$\left\{ \frac{3\pi}{4} + \pi k, \frac{\pi}{4} + \pi k \right\}.$$

Examples. Solve for x in the given interval.

1) $\sin x - 2 \cos^2 x = -1$ in the interval $0 \le x \le 2\pi$.

We can replace $\cos^2 x$ by $1 - \sin^2 x$ since $\sin^2 x + \cos^2 x = 1$.

$$\sin x - 2\cos^2 x = -1$$
$$\sin x - 2\left(1 - \sin^2 x\right) = -1$$
$$\sin x - 2 + 2\sin^2 x = -1$$
$$\underline{ +1 +1}$$
$$2\sin^2 x + \sin x - 1 = 0$$

$$\left(2\sin x - 1\right)\left(\sin x + 1\right) = 0$$

$2\sin x - \cancel{1} = 0$	$\sin x + \cancel{1} = 0$
$\underline{+\cancel{1} \quad +1}$	$\underline{-\cancel{1} \quad -1}$
$\dfrac{\cancel{2}\sin x}{\cancel{2}} = \dfrac{1}{2}$	$\sin x = -1$

The solutions of the equation $\sin x = \frac{1}{2}$ in the interval $0 \le x \le 2\pi$ are $x = \frac{\pi}{6}$ and $x = \frac{5\pi}{6}$. The only solution of the equation $\sin x = -1$ in the interval $0 \le x \le 2\pi$ is $x = \frac{3\pi}{2}$. Therefore, the solution set of our equation is

$$\left\{\frac{\pi}{6}, \frac{5\pi}{6}, \frac{3\pi}{2}\right\}.$$

2) $\sin^2 x \cos x - \cos x = 0$ in the interval $0 \le x \le 2\pi$.

It is true that $\sin^2 x$ can be replaced by $1 - \cos^2 x$ and the equation can be solved as before. However, notice that both terms on the left-hand side of the equation contain $\cos x$. This means that we can use factoring immediately. Let's factor first.

$$\sin^2 x \cos x - \cos x = 0$$
$$\cos x \left(\sin^2 x - 1\right) = 0$$

$$\cos x \left(\sin x - 1\right)\left(\sin x + 1\right) = 0$$

$\cos x = 0$	$\sin x - \cancel{1} = 0$	$\sin x + \cancel{1} = 0$
	$\underline{+\cancel{1} \quad +1}$	$\underline{-\cancel{1} \quad -1}$
	$\sin x = 1$	$\sin x = -1$

In the interval $0 \le x \le 2\pi$, the equation $\cos x = 0$ has solutions $x = \frac{\pi}{2}$ and $\frac{3\pi}{2}$. Notice that $\frac{\pi}{2}$ is also the solution to $\sin x = 1$ and that $\frac{3\pi}{2}$ is also the solution to $\sin x = -1$. Therefore, the solution set of our equation is

$$\left\{\frac{\pi}{2}, \frac{3\pi}{2}\right\}.$$

3) $3\tan^2 2x \sec 3x = \sec 3x$ in the interval $-\pi < x \le \pi$.

The first thing we need to do is to get one side of the equation equal to zero. After this, we will be able to factor $\sec 3x$ on the left-hand side of the equation. Let's see what will happen.

$$3\tan^2 2x \sec 3x = \sec 3x$$
$$\underline{ -\sec 3x \quad -\sec 3x}$$
$$3\tan^2 2x \sec 3x - \sec 3x = 0$$

$$\sec 3x \left(3\tan^2 2x - 1\right) = 0$$

$\sec 3x = 0$	$3\tan^2 2x - \cancel{1} = 0$
	$\underline{+\cancel{1} \quad +1}$
	$\dfrac{\cancel{3}\tan^2 2x}{\cancel{3}} = \dfrac{1}{3}$
	$\tan 2x = \pm\sqrt{\dfrac{1}{3}} = \pm\dfrac{\sqrt{3}}{3}$

Now, the equation $\sec 3x = 0$ has no solutions since $|\sec \theta| \geq 1$ for any suitable value of θ. The solutions of $\tan 2x = \pm \frac{\sqrt{3}}{3}$ are of the form

$$2x = \frac{\pi}{6} + \pi k \quad \text{and} \quad 2x = \frac{5\pi}{6} + \pi k, \quad \text{where } k \text{ is any integer.}$$

Solving for x gives us

$$x = \frac{\pi}{12} + \frac{\pi}{2}k \quad \text{and} \quad x = \frac{5\pi}{12} + \frac{\pi}{2}k, \quad \text{where } k \text{ is any integer.}$$

Let's find the values of x which are in the interval $-\pi < x \leq \pi$.

When $k = 0$, we obtain $x = \frac{\pi}{12} + \frac{\pi}{2}(0) = \frac{\pi}{12}$ and $x = \frac{5\pi}{12} + \frac{\pi}{2}(0) = \frac{5\pi}{12}$.

When $k = 1$, we obtain $x = \frac{\pi}{12} + \frac{\pi}{2}(1) = \frac{7\pi}{12}$ and $x = \frac{5\pi}{12} + \frac{\pi}{2}(1) = \frac{11\pi}{12}$.

When $k = 2$, we obtain $x = \underbrace{\frac{\pi}{12} + \frac{\pi}{2}(2) = \frac{13\pi}{12}}_{\text{not in the interval } -\pi < x \leq \pi}$ and $x = \underbrace{\frac{5\pi}{12} + \frac{\pi}{2}(2) = \frac{17\pi}{12}}_{\text{not in the interval } -\pi < x \leq \pi}$.

When $k = -1$, we obtain $x = \frac{\pi}{12} + \frac{\pi}{2}(-1) = -\frac{5\pi}{12}$ and $x = \frac{5\pi}{12} + \frac{\pi}{2}(-1) = -\frac{\pi}{12}$.

When $k = -2$, we obtain $x = \frac{\pi}{12} + \frac{\pi}{2}(-2) = -\frac{11\pi}{12}$ and $x = \frac{5\pi}{12} + \frac{\pi}{2}(-2) = -\frac{7\pi}{12}$.

When $k = -3$, we obtain $x = \underbrace{\frac{\pi}{12} + \frac{\pi}{2}(-3) = -\frac{17\pi}{12}}_{\text{not in the interval } -\pi < x \leq \pi}$ and $x = \underbrace{\frac{5\pi}{12} + \frac{\pi}{2}(-3) = -\frac{13\pi}{12}}_{\text{not in the interval } -\pi < x \leq \pi}$.

The solution set of the equation is

$$\left\{ \pm \frac{\pi}{12}, \ \pm \frac{5\pi}{12}, \ \pm \frac{7\pi}{12}, \ \pm \frac{11\pi}{12} \right\}.$$

4) $\cos x - \sin x = \sqrt{2}$ in the interval $0 \leq x \leq 2\pi$.

There are a couple of ways of solving this equation. We will see how each method works.

Method 1. Whenever we have an equation of the form $a \cos x + b \sin x = c$, where at least one of the $a, b,$ or c equals either $\sqrt{3}, \sqrt{2}$ or 2, we multiply both sides of the equation by the reciprocal of that number and try to use a sum or difference of angles formula. In this example, we will multiply both sides of the equation by $\frac{1}{\sqrt{2}}$ and use the sum of angles formula for cosine to produce only cosine on the left hand side of the equation. Recall that $\cos(a + b) = \cos a \cos b - \sin a \sin b$.

$$\cos x - \sin x = \sqrt{2}$$

$$\frac{1}{\sqrt{2}} (\cos x - \sin x) = \frac{1}{\sqrt{2}} (\sqrt{2})$$

$$\frac{1}{\sqrt{2}}\cos x - \frac{1}{\sqrt{2}}\sin x = 1$$

$$\cos\frac{\pi}{4}\cos x - \sin\frac{\pi}{4}\sin x = 1$$

$$\cos\left(\frac{\pi}{4} + x\right) = 1$$

The equation $\cos\theta = 1$ has solutions of the form $\theta = 2\pi k$, where k is any integer. Therefore, we have that

$$\frac{\pi}{4} + x = 2\pi k.$$

And so, after solving for x, we find that the solutions of the equation $\cos\left(\frac{\pi}{4} + x\right) = 1$ are

$$x = 2\pi k - \frac{\pi}{4}.$$

In the interval $0 \leq x \leq 2\pi$, the only solution (when $k = 1$) is $x = 2\pi - \frac{\pi}{4} = \frac{7\pi}{4}$.

Method 2. We will square both sides of the equation and use the double angle formula for sine to produce only sine on the left hand side of the equation. Recall that $\sin^2 x + \cos^2 x = 1$ and $\sin 2x = 2\sin x \cos x$.

$$\cos x - \sin x = \sqrt{2}$$
$$(\cos x - \sin x)^2 = \left(\sqrt{2}\right)^2$$
$$\cos^2 x - 2\sin x \cos x + \sin^2 x = 2$$

$$\frac{\cancel{1} - \sin 2x = 2}{\cancel{1}\qquad\qquad -1}$$
$$\overline{\qquad -\sin 2x = 1\qquad}$$

$$\sin 2x = -1$$

Now, the solutions of the equation $\sin\theta = -1$ are of the form $\theta = \frac{3\pi}{2} + 2\pi k$, where k is any integer. Therefore, we have that

$$2x = \frac{3\pi}{2} + 2\pi k.$$

And so

$$x = \frac{3\pi}{4} + \pi k.$$

Now, the only solutions which lie in the interval are $x = \frac{3\pi}{4}$ (when $k = 0$) and $x = \frac{7\pi}{4}$ (when $k = 1$). We must make sure that we check BOTH of these answers since extraneous solutions can occur when we solve an equation by squaring both sides of the equation. Observe that

$$\underbrace{\cos\frac{3\pi}{4}}_{-\frac{\sqrt{2}}{2}} - \underbrace{\sin\frac{3\pi}{4}}_{\frac{\sqrt{2}}{2}} \neq \sqrt{2} \quad\text{and}\quad \underbrace{\cos\frac{7\pi}{4}}_{\frac{\sqrt{2}}{2}} - \underbrace{\sin\frac{7\pi}{4}}_{-\frac{\sqrt{2}}{2}} \overset{\checkmark}{=} \sqrt{2}.$$

Therefore, the only solution is $x = \frac{7\pi}{4}$ (just as we found by using Method 1).

Try These (Set 9): Solve for θ in the interval $0 \leq \theta \leq 2\pi$.

1) $5\csc\theta\cos\theta + 5\cos\theta = 0$ \qquad 2) $2\cos^2\theta - \sin\theta = 1$ \qquad 3) $\tan\frac{1}{2}\theta = \cot\frac{1}{2}\theta$

Exercise 7.4

In Exercises 1-12, find all of the solutions to the following equations. Express your answers in radian measure.

1. $\tan x \cos x - \cos x = 0$

2. $\sin x \tan x + \tan x = 0$

3. $\cos^2 x \sin x + \cos x \sin x = 0$

4. $\tan x \sin x - \tan^2 x \sin x = 0$

5. $2 \cos \theta \sin \theta - \sin \theta = 0$

6. $2 \cos \theta \sin \theta + 4 \cos \theta = 0$

7. $2 \tan \alpha \sin^2 \alpha - 2 \tan \alpha = 0$

8. $\cos^2 \alpha \tan \alpha - \cos \alpha \tan \alpha = 0$

9. $\cos \alpha \tan \alpha - 3 \tan \alpha = 0$

10. $\sin \theta \cos \theta + 4 \cos \theta = 0$

11. $\csc \theta \sec \theta - 2 \sec \theta = 0$

12. $\sec \alpha \cot \alpha + 2 \cot \alpha = 0$

In Exercises 13-36, solve for θ in the given interval. Express your answers in radian measure.

13. $2 \sin^2 \theta \cos \theta - \cos \theta = 0$; $-2\pi \leq \theta < 2\pi$

14. $2 \cos^2 \theta \tan \theta - \tan \theta = 0$; $-2\pi \leq \theta < 2\pi$

15. $\csc^2 \theta \cos \theta + \csc \theta \cos \theta = 0$; $0 < \theta \leq 2\pi$

16. $\sec^2 \theta \tan \theta - \sec \theta \tan \theta = 0$; $0 < \theta \leq 2\pi$

17. $4 \cot \theta \cos \theta - 12 \cot \theta = 0$; $-\pi < \theta < \pi$

18. $3 \tan \theta \csc \theta + 3 \tan \theta = 0$; $-\pi < \theta < \pi$

19. $2 \cos^2 \theta - \sin \theta - 1 = 0$; $0 < \theta \leq 2\pi$

20. $2 \cos^2 \theta + 3 \sin \theta - 3 = 0$; $0 < \theta \leq 2\pi$

21. $\tan \theta - \sec^2 \theta + 1 = 0$; $0 \leq \theta \leq 2\pi$

22. $4 \cot^2 \theta - \csc^2 \theta = 0$; $0 \leq \theta < 2\pi$

23. $\csc \theta - 1 = 2 \sin \theta$; $-2\pi < \theta < 2\pi$

24. $\sec \theta + 1 = 2 \cos \theta$; $-2\pi < \theta < 2\pi$

25. $\sec \theta - 2 \tan \theta = 0$; $0 \leq \theta < 2\pi$

26. $2 \cot \theta + \csc \theta = 0$; $0 \leq \theta < 2\pi$

27. $2 \sin^2 2\theta \cos \theta = \cos \theta$; $0 \leq \theta \leq 2\pi$

28. $\tan^2 \frac{\theta}{2} \csc \frac{\theta}{3} = \csc \frac{\theta}{3}$; $0 < \theta < 2\pi$

29. $\csc^2 \frac{\theta}{3} \sec \frac{\theta}{4} = 2 \sec \frac{\theta}{4}$; $0 < \theta < 2\pi$

30. $3 \tan^2 2\theta \sin 3\theta = \sin 3\theta$; $0 \leq \theta \leq 2\pi$

31. $\sin \theta + \cos \theta = \sqrt{2}$; $0 \leq \theta < 2\pi$

32. $\sin \theta - \cos \theta = \sqrt{2}$; $0 \leq \theta < 2\pi$

33. $\cos \theta + \sqrt{3} \sin \theta = \sqrt{3}$; $0 \leq \theta < 2\pi$

34. $\sin \theta - \sqrt{3} \cos \theta = 1$; $0 \leq \theta < 2\pi$

35. $5 \cos \theta - 5 \sin \theta = 0$; $0 < \theta < 2\pi$

36. $r \cos \theta = r \sin \theta$, where $r \neq 0$; $0 < \theta < 2\pi$

In Exercises 37-48, solve for θ (to the nearest degree) in the interval $0 \leq \theta \leq 2\pi$.

37. $\csc \theta - 1 = \sin \theta$

38. $\sec \theta + 1 = \cos \theta$

39. $2 \sec^2 \theta - 5 \tan \theta - 4 = 0$

40. $3 \sin^2 \theta + 4 \cos \theta - 1 = 0$

41. $2 \cos^2 \theta - 4 \sin \theta + 3 = 0$

42. $2 \tan^2 \theta - \sec \theta - 7 = 0$

43. $4 \sin \theta - 7 \cos \theta = 0$

44. $8 \sin \theta + 3 \cos \theta = 0$

45. $\csc \theta + \frac{5}{2} \cot \theta = 0$

46. $\tan \theta - \frac{2}{3} \sec \theta = 0$

47. $7 \tan \theta + 5 \cos \theta = \sec \theta$

48. $11 \sin \theta - 9 \csc \theta = 12 \cot \theta$

Section 7.5 Trigonometric Equations Involving Multiple Angles

We will learn how to solve trigonometric equations involving multiple angles. In Section 7.2, we have learned how to solve some simple equations which contain a multiple angle. As we will now see, many of our formulas (for example, the double angle formulas and the half angle formulas) will assist us in solving more complicated multiple angle equations.

Examples. Solve each equation.

1) $\sin 2\alpha \sin \alpha - \cos \alpha = 0$

Let's begin by replacing $\sin 2\alpha$ be $2 \sin \alpha \cos \alpha$ and see what will happen.

$$\sin 2\alpha \sin \alpha - \cos \alpha = 0$$
$$(2 \sin \alpha \cos \alpha) \sin \alpha - \cos \alpha = 0$$
$$2 \sin^2 \alpha \cos \alpha - \cos \alpha = 0$$

Notice that this equation can be solved by factoring.

$$2 \sin^2 \alpha \cos \alpha - \cos \alpha = 0$$
$$\cos \alpha \left(2 \sin^2 \alpha - 1\right) = 0$$

$$\cos \alpha = 0 \quad \Big| \quad 2 \sin^2 \alpha - \cancel{1} = 0$$
$$\Big| \qquad \quad +\cancel{1} \quad +1$$
$$\Big| \qquad \frac{\cancel{2} \sin^2 \alpha}{\cancel{2}} = \frac{1}{2}$$
$$\Big| \qquad \sin^2 \alpha = \frac{1}{2}$$
$$\Big| \qquad \sin \alpha = \pm \sqrt{\frac{1}{2}} = \pm \frac{\sqrt{2}}{2}$$

The solutions of the equation $\cos \alpha = 0$ are of the form $\alpha = \frac{(2k+1)\pi}{2}$, where k is any integer. The solutions of the equations $\sin \alpha = \pm \frac{\sqrt{2}}{2}$ are of the form $\alpha = \frac{(2k+1)\pi}{4}$, where k is any integer (why?). The solution set, therefore, is

$$\left\{ \frac{(2k+1)\,\pi}{2}, \ \frac{(2k+1)\,\pi}{4} \right\}, \text{ where } k \text{ is any integer.}$$

2) $\cos 2\theta - 3 \cos \theta - 1 = 0$

Recall that there are three formulas for $\cos 2\theta$. They are:

$$\cos 2\theta = \cos^2 \theta - \sin^2 \theta$$
$$\cos 2\theta = 2 \cos^2 \theta - 1$$
$$\cos 2\theta = 1 - 2 \sin^2 \theta$$

It makes sense to substitute $\cos 2\theta$ in our equation by $2 \cos^2 \theta - 1$ since this will produce an equation which contains only cosine.

$$\cos 2\theta - 3\cos\theta - 1 = 0$$
$$\left(2\cos^2\theta - 1\right) - 3\cos\theta - 1 = 0$$
$$2\cos^2\theta - 3\cos\theta - 2 = 0$$

$$\left(2\cos\theta + 1\right)\left(\cos\theta - 2\right) = 0$$

$2\cos\theta + 1 = 0$	$\cos\theta - 2 = 0$
$-1 \quad -1$	$+2 \quad +2$
$\dfrac{2\cos\theta}{2} = \dfrac{-1}{2}$	$\cos\theta = 2$
$\cos\theta = -\dfrac{1}{2}$	

The solutions of the equation $\cos\theta = -\frac{1}{2}$ are of the form $\theta = \frac{2\pi}{3} + 2\pi k$ or $\theta = \frac{4\pi}{3} + 2\pi k$, where k is any integer. There are no solutions of the equation $\cos\theta = 2$ since

$$-1 \le \cos\theta \le 1 \text{ for any value of } \theta.$$

3) $\cos^2\alpha - \sin^2\frac{\alpha}{2} = 0$

We will make use of the half-angle formula for sine:

$$\sin\frac{\alpha}{2} = \pm\sqrt{\frac{1 - \cos\alpha}{2}}$$

Notice that squaring both sides of this formula gives us

$$\sin^2\frac{\alpha}{2} = \frac{1 - \cos\alpha}{2}.$$

Therefore:

$$\cos^2\alpha - \sin^2\frac{\alpha}{2} = 0$$

$$\cos^2\alpha - \frac{1 - \cos\alpha}{2} = 0$$

$$2\left(\cos^2\alpha - \frac{1 - \cos\alpha}{2}\right) = 2\left(0\right)$$

$$2\cos^2\alpha - \left(1 - \cos\alpha\right) = 0$$
$$2\cos^2\alpha + \cos\alpha - 1 = 0$$

$$\left(2\cos\alpha - 1\right)\left(\cos\alpha + 1\right) = 0$$

$2\cos\alpha - 1 = 0$	$\cos\alpha + 1 = 0$
$+1 \quad +1$	$-1 \quad -1$
$\dfrac{2\cos\alpha}{2} = \dfrac{1}{2}$	$\cos\alpha = -1$
$\cos\alpha = \dfrac{1}{2}$	

The solutions of the equation $\cos\alpha = \frac{1}{2}$ are of the form $\alpha = \frac{\pi}{3} + 2\pi k$ or $\alpha = \frac{5\pi}{3} + 2\pi k$, where k is any integer. The solutions of the equation $\cos\alpha = -1$ are of the form $\alpha = (2k + 1)\pi$, where k is any integer.

4) $\sin 2x = \sin 3x$

We will group both terms on one side of the equation and use one of the sum-to-product formulas:

$$\sin A - \sin B = 2\cos\left(\frac{A+B}{2}\right)\sin\left(\frac{A-B}{2}\right)$$

$$\begin{array}{r} \sin 2x = \sin 3x \\ -\sin 3x \quad -\sin 3x \\ \hline \sin 2x - \sin 3x = 0 \end{array}$$

$$2\cos\left(\frac{2x+3x}{2}\right)\sin\left(\frac{2x-3x}{2}\right) = 0$$

$$2\cos\left(\frac{5x}{2}\right)\sin\left(-\frac{x}{2}\right) = 0$$

$$\cos\left(\frac{5x}{2}\right) = 0 \quad \text{and} \quad \sin\left(-\frac{x}{2}\right) = 0$$

The solutions of $\cos\left(\frac{5x}{2}\right) = 0$ satisfy the equation

$$\frac{5x}{2} = \frac{(2k+1)\pi}{2}, \text{ where } k \text{ is any integer.}$$

When we solve for x, we'll obtain

$$x = \frac{(2k+1)\pi}{5}, \text{ where } k \text{ is any integer.}$$

The solutions of $\sin\left(-\frac{x}{2}\right) = 0$ are the same as the solutions of the equation $\sin\frac{x}{2} = 0$ (why?), namely:

$$\frac{x}{2} = k\pi, \text{ where } k \text{ is any integer.}$$

Solving for x gives us

$$x = 2\pi k, \text{ where } k \text{ is any integer.}$$

Examples. Find the solutions of each equation in the given interval.

1) $\sin 2\theta \cos\theta + \cos^2\theta = 0$ in the interval $0 \le \theta < 2\pi$.

Let's substitute $\sin 2\theta$ by $2\sin\theta\cos\theta$ and solve the resulting equation by factoring.

$$\sin 2\theta \cos\theta + \cos^2\theta = 0$$
$$(2\sin\theta\cos\theta)\cos\theta + \cos^2\theta = 0$$
$$2\sin\theta\cos^2\theta + \cos^2\theta = 0$$

$$\cos^2\theta\,(2\sin\theta + 1) = 0$$

$\cos^2\theta = 0$	$2\sin\theta + \cancel{1} = 0$
$\cos\theta = 0$	$\cancel{-1} \quad -1$
	$\dfrac{\cancel{2}\sin\theta}{\cancel{2}} = \dfrac{-1}{2}$
	$\sin\theta = -\dfrac{1}{2}$

The solutions of the equation $\cos\theta = 0$ are of the form $\theta = \frac{(2k+1)\pi}{2}$, where k is any integer. The solutions of the equations $\sin\theta = -\frac{1}{2}$ are of the form $\theta = \frac{7\pi}{6} + 2\pi k$ or $\theta = \frac{11\pi}{6} + 2\pi k$, where k is any integer. Now, the solutions which are in the interval $0 \le \theta < 2\pi$ can be found by replacing k by the integers 0 and 1 as we have done in the previous examples. By doing so, we find that the solution set of our equation is

$$\left\{ \frac{\pi}{2}, \frac{3\pi}{2}, \frac{7\pi}{6}, \frac{11\pi}{6} \right\}.$$

2) $2\sin^2\frac{\theta}{2} + \sin^2\theta = 2$ in the interval $-2\pi \le \theta \le 2\pi$.

Notice that the half-angle formula for sine is useful here.

$$2\sin^2\frac{\theta}{2} + \sin^2\theta = 2$$

$$2\left(\pm\sqrt{\frac{1-\cos\theta}{2}}\right)^2 + \sin^2\theta = 2 \qquad \text{(half-angle formula for sine)}$$

$$2\left(\frac{1-\cos\theta}{2}\right) + \sin^2\theta = 2$$

$$1 - \cos\theta + \sin^2\theta = 2$$
$$1 - \cos\theta + \left(1 - \cos^2\theta\right) = 2 \qquad \text{(use } \sin^2\theta + \cos^2\theta = 1\text{)}$$
$$2 - \cos\theta - \cos^2\theta = 2$$
$$\underline{-2 \qquad\qquad\qquad -2}$$
$$-\cos\theta - \cos^2\theta = 0$$

$$-\cos\theta\,(1 + \cos\theta) = 0$$

$$
\begin{array}{c|c}
-\cos\theta = 0 & \cancel{1} + \cos\theta = 0 \\
\cos\theta = 0 & \underline{\cancel{1} \qquad\quad -1} \\
& \cos\theta = -1
\end{array}
$$

The solutions of the equation $\cos\theta = 0$ in the interval $-2\pi \le \theta \le 2\pi$ are $\theta = \pm\frac{3\pi}{2}$ and $\theta = \pm\frac{\pi}{2}$, and the solutions of the equation $\cos\theta = -1$ in the given interval are $\theta = \pm\pi$. Therefore, the solution set of our equation is

$$\left\{ \pm\frac{3\pi}{2}, \ \pm\frac{\pi}{2}, \ \pm\pi \right\}.$$

3) $\cos 2x + 5\cos x + 3 = 0$ in the interval $-\pi < x < \pi$.

We will use the double-angle formula for cosine and the factoring method to solve this equation. The version of the cosine formula that will work best for us is $\cos 2x = 2\cos^2 x - 1$ since our equation already has a $\cos x$ term in it.

$$\cos 2x + 5\cos x + 3 = 0$$
$$\left(2\cos^2 x - 1\right) + 5\cos x + 3 = 0$$
$$2\cos^2 x + 5\cos x + 2 = 0$$

$$(2\cos x + 1)(\cos x + 2) = 0$$

$$
\begin{array}{c|c}
2\cos x + 1 \cancel{=} 0 & \cos x + \cancel{2} = 0 \\
\underline{-\cancel{1} \quad -1} & \underline{-\cancel{2} \quad -2} \\
\dfrac{\cancel{2}\cos x}{\cancel{2}} = -\dfrac{1}{2} & \cos x = -2 \\
\cos x = -\dfrac{1}{2} &
\end{array}
$$

The solutions of the equation $\cos x = -\frac{1}{2}$ in the interval $-\pi < x < \pi$ are $x = \pm\frac{2\pi}{3}$. There are no solutions of the equation $\cos x = -2$.

4) $\tan 2t = -2\sin t$ in the interval $-\pi \leq t < \pi$.

The first step is to get one side of the equation equal to zero. Next, we will use the identity $\tan 2t = \frac{\sin 2t}{\cos 2t}$, along with the double-angle formulas for sine and cosine, to convert all of our terms into sines and cosines (this makes sense since we already have a term containing sine in our equation). Notice that we are not using the usual formula for $\tan 2t$ because it contains only terms with tangent, which is not what we want (however, this way of solving the problem will also give us what we want). After doing some algebraic manipulations and using the identities, we will solve the resulting equation.

$$\tan 2t = -2\sin t$$
$$\underline{+2\sin t \qquad +2\sin t}$$
$$\tan 2t + 2\sin t = 0$$

$$\frac{\sin 2t}{\cos 2t} + 2\sin t = 0$$

$$\frac{2\sin t\cos t}{2\cos^2 t - 1} + 2\sin t = 0$$

$$\left(2\cos^2 t - 1\right)\left(\frac{2\sin t\cos t}{2\cos^2 t - 1} + 2\sin t\right) = \left(2\cos^2 t - 1\right)(0)$$

$$2\sin t\cos t + 2\sin t\left(2\cos^2 t - 1\right) = 0$$
$$2\sin t\left[\cos t + \left(2\cos^2 t - 1\right)\right] = 0$$
$$2\sin t\left(2\cos^2 t + \cos t - 1\right) = 0$$

$$2\sin t\left(2\cos t - 1\right)\left(\cos t + 1\right) = 0$$

$2\sin t = 0$	$2\cos t - 1 = 0$	$\cos t + 1 = 0$
$\sin t = 0$	$+1 \quad +1$	$-1 \quad -1$
	$\dfrac{2\cos t}{2} = \dfrac{1}{2}$	$\cos t = -1$

In the interval $-\pi \leq t < \pi$, the solutions of $\sin t = 0$ are $t = -\pi$ and $t = 0$, the solutions of $\cos t = \frac{1}{2}$ are $t = \pm\frac{\pi}{3}$, and the solution of $\cos t = -1$ is $t = -\pi$. Therefore, the solution set of our equation is

$$\left\{-\pi,\ 0,\ -\frac{\pi}{3},\ \frac{\pi}{3}\right\}.$$

5) $4\cos^2\beta - \sin 2\beta - 1 = 0$ in the interval $0° \leq \beta \leq 360°$ (to the nearest degree).

Let's begin by replacing $\sin 2\beta$ by $2\sin\beta\cos\beta$ and 1 by $\sin^2\beta + \cos^2\beta$. This will produce an equation which can be solved by factoring.

$$4\cos^2\beta - \sin 2\beta - 1 = 0$$

$$4\cos^2\beta - 2\sin\beta\cos\beta - 1 = 0$$

$$4\cos^2\beta - 2\sin\beta\cos\beta - \left(\sin^2\beta + \cos^2\beta\right) = 0$$

$$4\cos^2\beta - 2\sin\beta\cos\beta - \sin^2\beta - \cos^2\beta = 0$$

$$3\cos^2\beta - 2\sin\beta\cos\beta - \sin^2\beta = 0$$

Observe that this could be solved by factoring since

$$3\cos^2\beta - 2\sin\beta\cos\beta - \sin^2\beta = (3\cos\beta + \sin\beta)(\cos\beta - \sin\beta).$$

Another method of solving this equation is to create a new equation that contains terms with only tangent. This is done by multiplying both sides of the equation by $\frac{1}{\cos^2\beta}$ and using one of our quotient identities. The resulting equation will be solvable by factoring as well. We will use this method (it is the easier one).

$$3\cos^2\beta - 2\sin\beta\cos\beta - \sin^2\beta = 0$$

$$\frac{1}{\cos^2\beta}\left(3\cos^2\beta - 2\sin\beta\cos\beta - \sin^2\beta\right) = \frac{1}{\cos^2\beta}(0)$$

$$\frac{3\cos^2\beta}{\cos^2\beta} - \frac{2\sin\beta\cos\beta}{\cos^2\beta} - \frac{\sin^2\beta}{\cos^2\beta} = 0$$

And now, using the identity $\dfrac{\sin\beta}{\cos\beta} = \tan\beta$, we have:

$$3 - 2\tan\beta - \tan^2\beta = 0$$

$$(3 + \tan\beta)(1 - \tan\beta) = 0$$

$3 + \tan\beta = 0$	$1 - \tan\beta = 0$
$-3 \qquad -3$	$+\tan\beta \quad +\tan\beta$
$\tan\beta = -3$	$1 = \tan\beta$

The reference angle for the solutions of $\tan x = 3$ is $x = \tan^{-1} 3 \approx 72°$. Therefore, the solutions of the equation $\tan\beta = -3$ are of the form

$$\beta = \underbrace{108°}_{180° - 72°} + 180°k, \text{ where } k \text{ is any integer.}$$

The solutions of the equation $\tan\beta = 1$ are of the form $\beta = 45° + 180°k$, where k is any integer. Therefore, in the given interval $0° \le \beta \le 360°$, our solution set is

$$\{108°, \ 288°, \ 45°, \ 225°\}.$$

Try These (Set 10):

I) Solve the equations.

1) $\sqrt{2}\cos\alpha + \sin 2\alpha = 0$ 2) $\cos 2\theta - \cos\theta = 0$ 3) $\cos x + \sin\frac{x}{2} = 1$

II) Solve for x in the interval $0 < x \le 2\pi$.

1) $\cos 2x - \sin x = 0$ 2) $\sin 2x \tan x - 1 = 0$ 3) $\cos 3x + \cos x = 0$

Exercise 7.5

In Exercises 1-10, find all of the solutions to the following equations. Express your answers in radian measure.

1. $\sin 2x = \cos x$ 2. $\sin 2x = \sin x$ 3. $\cos 2x - \cos x = 0$ 4. $\cos 2x - \cos x = -1$

5. $\cos 2\theta - 6\cos^2 \theta + 2 = 0$ 6. $\sin 2\theta \sin \theta - \cos \theta = 0$ 7. $\sin^2 \alpha - 3\sin^2 \frac{\alpha}{2} = 0$

8. $\sin^2 \frac{\alpha}{2} - 2\cos \alpha = 0$ 9. $\cos 3x + \cos x = 0$ 10. $\sin 3x + \sin 2x = 0$

In Exercises 11-34, find the solutions of each equation in the interval $0 \leq \theta < 2\pi$.

11. $\sin 2\theta + \sin \theta = 0$ 12. $\sin 2\theta - \cos \theta = 0$ 13. $\cos 2\theta - \sin \theta = 0$

14. $\cos 2\theta + \sin \theta = 1$ 15. $\cos 2\theta + 5\cos \theta + 3 = 0$ 16. $\cos 2\theta + \sin \theta - 3 = 0$

17. $\sin 2\theta + \sqrt{2}\cos \theta = 0$ 18. $\sin 2\theta - \sqrt{3}\cos \theta = 0$ 19. $\sin^2 \theta - \cos^2 \frac{\theta}{2} = 0$

20. $\cos^2 2\theta - \cos^2 \theta = 0$ 21. $\sin \frac{\theta}{2} - \cos \theta = 0$ 22. $\cos \frac{\theta}{2} - \cos \theta = 1$

23. $\sin 5\theta - \sin \theta = 0$ 24. $\sin 6\theta + \sin 4\theta = 0$ 25. $\cos 4\theta + \cos \theta = 0$

26. $\cos 2\theta - \cos 5\theta = 0$ 27. $4\sin 3\theta \cos 3\theta = \sqrt{3}$ 28. $\sin 5\theta \cos 5\theta = \frac{1}{4}$

29. $\cos^2 4\theta - \sin^2 4\theta = -1$ 30. $2\cos^2 3\theta - 1 = \sin 6\theta$

31. $\cos 2\theta \cos \theta - \sin 2\theta \sin \theta = 0$ 32. $\sin 5\theta \cos \theta - \cos 5\theta \sin \theta = -1$

33. $\sin 3\theta \cos 4\theta + \cos 3\theta \sin 4\theta = 1$ 34. $\cos 2\theta \cos 7\theta + \sin 2\theta \sin 7\theta = 1$

Section 7.6   Equations Involving Inverse Trigonometric Functions

In this section, we will learn how to solve equations which contain inverse trigonometric functions. Examples of such equations are

$$2\cos^{-1} x = 0, \; 3\arcsin x = \frac{\pi}{2}, \; \cos^{-1} x - \sin^{-1} x = \frac{\pi}{3}, \text{ and } \tan^{-1} \frac{\sqrt{3}}{6} = \cot^{-1} x.$$

To solve such an equation, the following properties of inverse trigonometric functions are useful:

$$\sin\left(\sin^{-1} x\right) = x, -1 \leq x \leq 1 \qquad \csc\left(\csc^{-1} x\right) = x, |x| \geq 1$$
$$\cos\left(\cos^{-1} x\right) = x, -1 \leq x \leq 1 \qquad \sec\left(\sec^{-1} x\right) = x, |x| \geq 1$$
$$\tan\left(\tan^{-1} x\right) = x, -\infty < x < \infty \qquad \cot\left(\cot^{-1} x\right) = x, -\infty < x < \infty$$

In terms of 'arc', we write

$$\sin\left(\arcsin x\right) = x, \qquad \cos\left(\arccos x\right) = x, \qquad \text{and} \qquad \tan\left(\arctan x\right) = x.$$

Examples. Solve each equation.

1) $2\cos^{-1} x = 0$

The first step is to get $\cos^{-1} x$ by itself on one side of the equation. Next, we will use one of the properties above to solve for x.

$$2\cos^{-1}x = 0$$

$$\frac{\cancel{2}\cos^{-1}x}{\cancel{2}} = \frac{0}{2}$$

$$\cos^{-1}x = 0$$

$$\cos\left(\cos^{-1}x\right) = \cos 0$$

$$x = \cos 0 = \frac{\pi}{2}$$

2) $3\arcsin x = \frac{\pi}{2}$

First we will solve for $\arcsin x$ by itself, then for x.

$$3\arcsin x = \frac{\pi}{2}$$

$$\frac{1}{\cancel{3}}\left(\cancel{3}\arcsin x\right) = \frac{1}{3}\left(\frac{\pi}{2}\right)$$

$$\arcsin x = \frac{\pi}{6}$$

$$\sin\left(\arcsin x\right) = \sin\frac{\pi}{6}$$

$$x = \sin\frac{\pi}{6} = \frac{1}{2}$$

3) $\sin^{-1}x - \cos^{-1}\left(\frac{\sqrt{3}}{5}\right) = 0$

To begin with, observe that we can isolate $\sin^{-1}x$ by itself by adding $\cos^{-1}\left(\frac{\sqrt{3}}{5}\right)$ to both sides of the equation. We will obtain

$$\sin^{-1}x = \cos^{-1}\left(\frac{\sqrt{3}}{5}\right), \text{ which means that}$$

$$\underbrace{\sin\left(\sin^{-1}x\right)}_{x} = \sin\left[\cos^{-1}\left(\frac{\sqrt{3}}{5}\right)\right].$$

We need to compute the right-hand side of this equation. Let $\cos^{-1}\left(\frac{\sqrt{3}}{5}\right) = \theta$. Then $\cos\theta = \frac{\sqrt{3}}{5}$ and angle θ lies in quadrant I, so $\sin\theta$ will be positive. Notice that

$$\sin\theta = \sqrt{1-\cos^2\theta} = \sqrt{1-\left(\frac{\sqrt{3}}{5}\right)^2} = \sqrt{1-\frac{3}{25}} = \sqrt{\frac{22}{25}} = \frac{\sqrt{22}}{5}.$$

Therefore,

$$x = \sin\left[\cos^{-1}\left(\frac{\sqrt{3}}{5}\right)\right] = \sin\theta = \frac{\sqrt{22}}{5}.$$

4) $\arctan\left(-\sqrt{3}\right) - \arccos x = \frac{4\pi}{3}$

Notice that $\arctan\left(-\sqrt{3}\right) = -\arctan\sqrt{3} = -\frac{\pi}{3}$. Therefore, after replacing $\arctan\left(-\sqrt{3}\right)$ by $-\frac{\pi}{3}$, our equation will become:

$$\frac{\cancel{\pi}}{3} - \arccos x = \frac{4\pi}{3}$$

$$\cancel{+\frac{\pi}{3}} \qquad\qquad +\frac{\pi}{3}$$

$$-\arccos x = \frac{5\pi}{3}$$

$$\arccos x = -\frac{5\pi}{3}$$

However, $\arccos x = -\frac{5\pi}{3}$ has no solution since $0 \le \arccos x \le \pi$ for all x-values such that $-1 \le x \le 1$. Therefore, this equation has no solution.

5) $\cos^{-1} x = \sin^{-1} x + \frac{5\pi}{6}$

Things become a bit more tedious now because two of the terms contain x. We need to come up with a plan. Well, what comes to mind is that if we take the cosine of both sides of the equation, we will get x by itself on the left-hand side. What will occur on the right-hand side? Let's find out.

$$\cos^{-1} x = \sin^{-1} x + \frac{5\pi}{6}$$

$$\cos\left(\cos^{-1} x\right) = \underbrace{\cos\left(\sin^{-1} x + \frac{5\pi}{6}\right)}_{\text{This is similar to } \cos(A+B).}$$

$$x = \cos\left(\sin^{-1} x\right)\cos\frac{5\pi}{6} - \sin\left(\sin^{-1} x\right)\sin\frac{5\pi}{6}$$

$$x = \cos\left(\sin^{-1} x\right)\left(-\frac{\sqrt{3}}{2}\right) - x\left(\frac{1}{2}\right)$$

$$x = -\frac{\sqrt{3}}{2}\cos\left(\sin^{-1} x\right) - \frac{1}{2}x$$

We need to figure out what $\cos(\sin^{-1} x)$ is. Let's go back to our original equation $\cos^{-1} x = \sin^{-1} x + \frac{5\pi}{6}$ for a moment. Since $0 \le \cos^{-1} x \le \pi$ for any x such that $-1 \le x \le 1$, we have:

$$0 \le \sin^{-1} x + \frac{\cancel{5\pi}}{6} \le \pi$$

$$-\frac{5\pi}{6} \qquad -\frac{\cancel{5\pi}}{6} \qquad -\frac{5\pi}{6}$$

$$-\frac{5\pi}{6} \le \sin^{-1} x \le \frac{\pi}{6}$$

However, we know that the definition of the inverse sine function requires that $-\frac{\pi}{2} \le \sin^{-1} x \le \frac{\pi}{2}$ for any x such that $-1 \le x \le 1$. Therefore, the solution(s) for x must satisfy

$$-\frac{\pi}{2} \le \sin^{-1} x \le \frac{\pi}{6}, \text{ which is equivalent to } -1 \le x \le \frac{1}{2}.$$

Now, if we let $\theta = \sin^{-1} x$, then $\sin \theta = x$. Observe that if $x < 0$, then θ lies in quadrant IV, and if $x > 0$, then θ lies in quadrant I. In both cases, we have that $\cos \theta > 0$. Furthermore, notice that

$$\underbrace{\cos \theta = +\sqrt{1 - \sin^2 \theta}}_{\text{since } \sin^2 \theta + \cos^2 \theta = 1} = \sqrt{1 - x^2},$$

irrespective of whether $x > 0$ or $x < 0$. Therefore, we may write

$$\cos\left(\sin^{-1} x\right) = \cos \theta = \sqrt{1 - x^2}.$$

Let's replace $\cos\left(\sin^{-x}\right)$ by $\sqrt{1 - x^2}$ and continue.

$$x = -\frac{\sqrt{3}}{2}\sqrt{1 - x^2} - \frac{1}{2}x$$

$$\frac{+\frac{1}{2}x \qquad\qquad\qquad +\frac{1}{2}x}{\frac{3}{2}x = -\frac{\sqrt{3}}{2}\sqrt{1 - x^2}}$$

$$2\left(\frac{3}{2}x\right) = 2\left(-\frac{\sqrt{3}}{2}\sqrt{1 - x^2}\right)$$

$$3x = -\sqrt{3} \cdot \sqrt{1 - x^2}.$$

If you look at this equation carefully, you will notice that any possible solution(s) for x must be negative because

$$-\underbrace{\sqrt{3} \cdot \sqrt{1 - x^2}}_{\text{This will be positive.}} < 0 \text{ implies that } 3x < 0, \text{ which means that } x < 0.$$

Getting back to our equation, we have:

$$3x = -\sqrt{3} \cdot \sqrt{1 - x^2}$$

$$(3x)^2 = \left(-\sqrt{3} \cdot \sqrt{1 - x^2}\right)^2$$

$$9x^2 = \left(-\sqrt{3}\right)^2 \left(\sqrt{1 - x^2}\right)^2$$

$$9x^2 = 3\left(1 - x^2\right)$$

$$9x^2 = 3 - 3x^2$$

$$\frac{+3x^2 \qquad +3x^2}{\frac{12x^2}{12} = \frac{3}{12}}$$

$$x^2 = \frac{1}{4}$$

$$x = \pm\sqrt{\frac{1}{4}} = \pm\frac{1}{2}$$

Since any solution for x must be negative, the only solution of the equation is $x = -\frac{1}{2}$.

Exercise 7.6

In Exercises 1-28, solve each equation.

1. $4\sin^{-1} x = 0$
2. $3\tan^{-1} x = 0$
3. $2\cos^{-1} x - \frac{\pi}{2} = 0$
4. $2\sin^{-1} x - \pi = 0$

5. $6\tan^{-1} x + \pi = 0$
6. $2\cos^{-1} x + \pi = 0$
7. $3\arcsin x - 5\pi = 0$

8. $4\arctan x - 7\pi = 0$
9. $5\arccos x - 5\pi = 0$
10. $7\arcsin x = 0$

11. $\sin^{-1} x - \cos^{-1}\left(\frac{\sqrt{2}}{4}\right) = 0$
12. $\cos^{-1} x - \sin^{-1}\left(\frac{\sqrt{3}}{5}\right) = 0$
13. $\arctan(-3) - \arcsin x = 0$

14. $\arccos x - \arctan\left(-\frac{8}{5}\right) = 0$
15. $\cos^{-1} x - \cos^{-1}\frac{9}{10} = 0$
16. $\sin^{-1} x - \sin^{-1}\frac{6}{7} = 0$

17. $\sin^{-1}\frac{\sqrt{3}}{2} - \tan^{-1} x = \frac{2\pi}{3}$
18. $\tan^{-1}\left(\frac{\sqrt{3}}{3}\right) - \cos^{-1} x = \frac{5\pi}{6}$
19. $\cos^{-1}\left(-\frac{1}{2}\right) - \sin^{-1} x = \frac{\pi}{3}$

20. $\sin^{-1}(-1) - \tan^{-1} x = \frac{5\pi}{4}$
21. $\arctan(-1) - \arcsin x = -\frac{3\pi}{4}$
22. $\arcsin x - \arccos\left(-\frac{\sqrt{2}}{2}\right) = -\frac{5\pi}{4}$

23. $\cos^{-1} x = \frac{\pi}{2} - \tan^{-1} x$
24. $\tan^{-1} x + \sin^{-1} x = 0$
25. $\cos^{-1} x - \sin^{-1} x = \pi$

26. $\cos^{-1} x - \sin^{-1} x = \frac{\pi}{6}$
27. $\arcsin x + \arctan x = \frac{3\pi}{4}$
28. $\arccos x - \arctan x = \pi$

Chapter 8: Applications of Trigonometry: Solving Oblique Triangles and Finding the Area of a Triangle

This chapter contains material on solving oblique triangles and area formulas for triangles. As we know, every triangle has three sides and three angles whose measures sum to 180°. If we are given any three of the six measures of a triangle (at least one measure is a side), we can use trigonometry to find the remaining three measures. This is known as **solving a triangle**.

In this chapter, we will learn how to solve a triangle for the case where the triangle doesn't contain a right angle. We call such a triangle an **oblique triangle**. To solve an oblique triangle, the two formulas which are used are the **Law of Sines** and the **Law of Cosines**. We must be given one of the following sets of data about the triangle in order to find the remaining measures:

<u>Case 1.</u> Two angles and one side (abbreviated as AAS or ASA).

When two angles and one side of a triangle are given, we can construct **exactly one** triangle with these measures (see the next figure). We say that two angles and one side **determine the triangle**. Using the Law of Sines, we can determine the unknown measures.

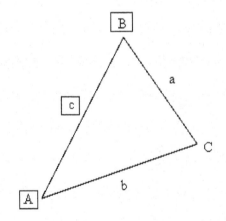

Given angles A and B and side c, there exists exactly one triangle with these measures.

This is an ASA case.

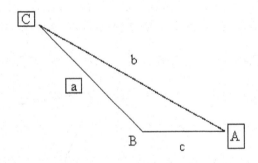

Given angles A and C and side a, there exists exactly one triangle with these measures.

This is an AAS case.

<u>Case 2.</u> Two sides and one angle opposite one of the given sides (abbreviated as SSA).

When two sides and one angle opposite one of the given sides are given, we may be able to construct one, two, or no triangles which contain these measures (see the next figure).

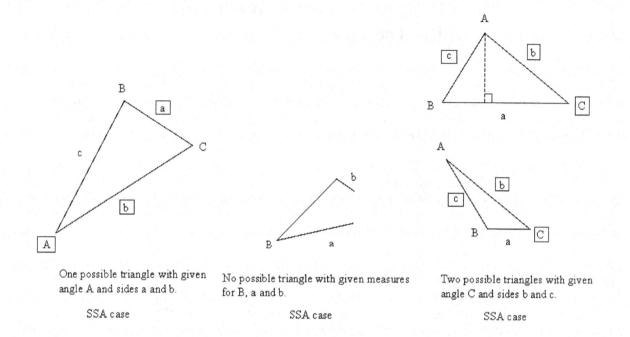

One possible triangle with given   No possible triangle with given measures   Two possible triangles with given
angle A and sides a and b.   for B, a and b.   angle C and sides b and c.

SSA case   SSA case   SSA case

The Law of Sines is used to determine the unknown measures. Since there are different possibilities which arise for SSA, we refer to this as the **ambiguous case of the Law of Sines**.

<u>**Case 3.**</u> Two sides and the angle between them (abbreviated as SAS).

Given two sides and the angle between them, **exactly one** triangle is constructible (see the next figure). To solve such an oblique triangle, we use the Law of Cosines and the Law of Sines.

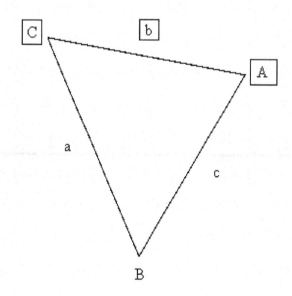

One possible triangle with given
angles A and C and side b.

SAS case

Case 4. Three sides (abbreviated as SSS).

Given three sides, **exactly one** triangle is constructible (see the next figure). Both the Law of Cosines and the Law of Sines are used to solve a triangle with three sides given.

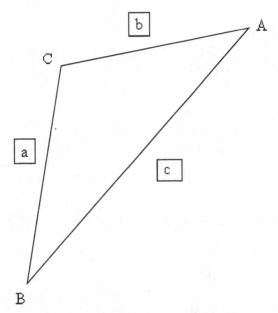

One possible triangle with given
sides a, b, and c.

SSS case

If we are given three angles of a triangle (AAA), there are infinitely many triangles which are constructible. In the next figure, all of the triangles have the same angle measurements.

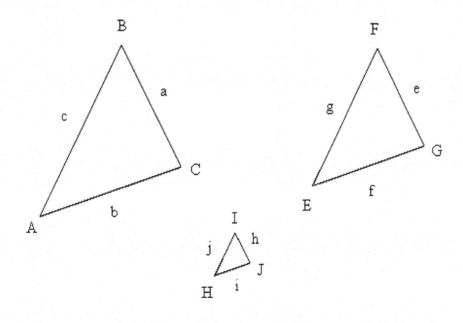

Notice that

$$m\angle A = m\angle E = m\angle H, \quad m\angle B = m\angle F = m\angle I, \quad \text{and} \quad m\angle C = m\angle G = m\angle J.$$

However,

$$a \neq e \neq h, \quad b \neq f \neq i, \quad \text{and} \quad c \neq g \neq j.$$

In Section 8.1, the Law of Sines will be introduced and used to solve an oblique triangle when ASA or AAS are given (Case 1). We will also use the Law of Sines to solve some application problems. The ambiguous case of the Law of Sines will be studied in Section 8.2. The Law of Sines is used to solve a triangle which satisfies the given data SSA (Case 2). We will learn how to determine the number of triangles that are constructible and satisfy the given data SSA. Section 8.3 deals with Case 3 (SAS) and Case 4 (SSS). The Law of Cosines is introduced and applied to solving these cases, as well as other application problems. Section 8.4 concludes the chapter with a study of different area formulas which allow us to find the area of a triangle. Deciding which area formula to use is based on the given information. If we are given an SAS triangle, we use a formula which contains the sine of the given angle. If we are given an SSS triangle, we use **Heron's Formula**.

Section 8.1 Solving AAS or ASA Oblique Triangles; the Law of Sines

An important relationship that exists between the sides and angles in any triangle is the **Law of Sines**. We will use it to solve AAS (or ASA) oblique triangles and other applied problems.

The Law of Sines

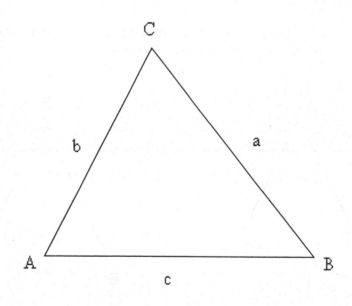

$$\frac{\sin A}{a} = \frac{\sin B}{b} = \frac{\sin C}{c}$$

$$\frac{a}{\sin A} = \frac{b}{\sin B} = \frac{c}{\sin C}$$

Proof: The proof is divided into two cases.

Case 1. If all of the angles of triangle ABC are acute angles.

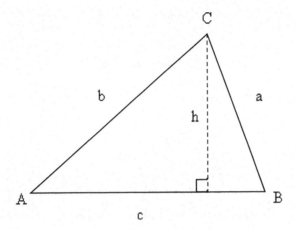

In the figure above, an altitude h is extended from C to $\overline{AB}$. We see that

$$\sin A = \frac{h}{b} \quad \text{and} \quad \sin B = \frac{h}{a}.$$

Solving for h in both equations gives us

$$h = b\sin A \quad \text{and} \quad h = a\sin B.$$

Since h appears on the left-hand side of each equation, we can set $b\sin A$ equal to $a\sin B$ and obtain

$$b\sin A = a\sin B$$

$$\frac{\not{b}\sin A}{a\not{b}} = \frac{\not{a}\sin B}{\not{a}b}$$

$$\frac{\sin A}{a} = \frac{\sin B}{b}$$

If we extend an altitude from A to $\overline{BC}$, we will obtain the relationship

$$\frac{\sin B}{b} = \frac{\sin C}{c}.$$

Therefore,

$$\frac{\sin A}{a} = \frac{\sin B}{b} = \frac{\sin C}{c}.$$

Case 2. If one of the angles of triangle ABC is an obtuse angle.

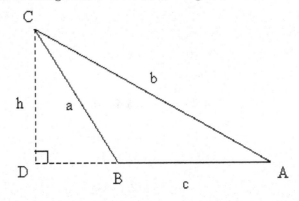

In the previous figure above, angle B is an obtuse angle. Notice that angle CBD has measure $180° - B$ since angle ABC and angle CBD add up to a straight angle (which has measure $180°$). This means that in triangle BCD, we have

$$\sin\left(180° - B\right) = \frac{h}{a}.$$

However,

$$\sin\left(180° - B\right) = \sin B$$

because B lies in quadrant II when in standard position. Therefore, we have the equation $\sin B = \frac{h}{a}$. Notice that in triangle ACD, we have that

$$\sin A = \frac{h}{b}.$$

And so

$$h = b\sin A \quad \text{and} \quad h = a\sin B.$$

We will simply repeat what has been done in Case 1 above. This completes the proof.

Examples.

1) In triangle ABC, $A = 30°$, $B = 80°$, and $a = 6.5$ inches. Find the length of side b to the nearest tenth.

The first thing that you should always do when working on a geometry problem is to draw a picture. Let's draw a rough sketch of triangle ABC described in the problem.

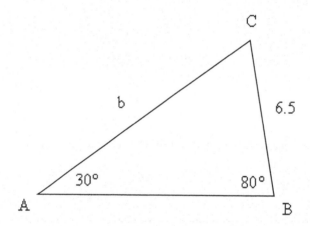

We can use the Law of Sines to find b. First, we will plug in the given values for A, B, and a. Next, we will solve for b. Once b is solved for, we will use the calculator to compute our answer.

$$\frac{\sin A}{a} = \frac{\sin B}{b}$$

$$\frac{\sin 30°}{6.5} = \frac{\sin 80°}{b}$$

$$b\sin 30° = 6.5\sin 80°$$

$$\frac{b\,\cancel{\sin 30°}}{\cancel{\sin 30°}} = \frac{6.5\sin 80°}{\sin 30°}$$

$$b \approx 12.8 \text{ inches}$$

2) Solve triangle ABC if $A = 46°$, $C = 52°$, and $b = 7.35$. Round off the values of a and c to the nearest hundredth.

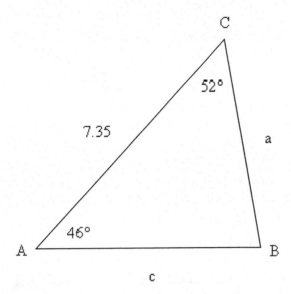

Recall that to **solve a triangle** means to find the measures of the unknown angle(s) and side(s). For this example, we need to find B, a, and c.

1. Find B: We know that $A + B + C = 180°$. Therefore,

$$
\begin{aligned}
B &= 180° - (A + C) \\
&= 180° - (46° + 52°) \\
&= 180° - 98° \\
&= 82°
\end{aligned}
$$

2. Find a: Since we know that $b = 7.35$, $A = 46°$, and $B = 82°$, we will use the Law of Sines.

$$\frac{\sin A}{a} = \frac{\sin B}{b}$$

$$\frac{\sin 46°}{a} = \frac{\sin 82°}{7.35}$$

$$7.35 \sin 46° = a \sin 82°$$

$$\frac{7.35 \sin 46°}{\sin 82°} = \frac{a \, \cancel{\sin 82°}}{\cancel{\sin 82°}}$$

$$a \approx 5.34$$

3. Find c: Again, we will use the Law of Sines. We can choose between $\dfrac{\sin A}{a} = \dfrac{\sin C}{c}$ or $\dfrac{\sin B}{b} = \dfrac{\sin C}{c}$ to solve for c. Since we have rounded off the value of a, it would be better to use the latter formula because our answer for c would be more accurate.

$$\frac{\sin B}{b} = \frac{\sin C}{c}$$

$$\frac{\sin 82°}{7.35} = \frac{\sin 52°}{c}$$

$$c \sin 82° = 7.35 \sin 52°$$

$$\frac{c \cancel{\sin 82°}}{\cancel{\sin 82°}} = \frac{7.35 \sin 52°}{\sin 82°}$$

$$c \approx 5.85$$

3) To determine the distance from Y to X across a river, a distance from Y to Z of 409 meters is measured on one side of the river (see diagram). If $Y = 109°$ and $Z = 18°40'$, find the distance from Y to X to the nearest hundredth of a meter.

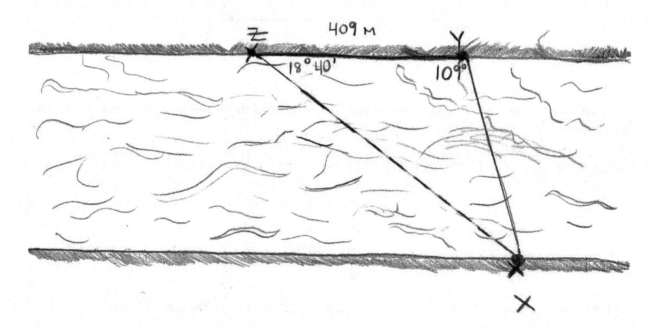

Solution: According to the diagram, the distance from Y to Z is $x = 409$ meters. We need to find z, the distance from Y to X. We will use the Law of Sines:

$$\frac{\sin Z}{z} = \frac{\sin X}{x}$$

First Let's find X.

$$
\begin{aligned}
X &= 180° - (Y + Z) \\
&= 180° - (109° + 18°40') \\
&= 180° - 127°40' \\
&= 52°20' \qquad \text{(recall that } 60' = 1°) \\
&\approx 52.333°
\end{aligned}
$$

Now, let's find z (observe that $Z = 18°40' \approx 18.667°$).

$$\frac{\sin Z}{z} = \frac{\sin X}{x}$$

$$\frac{\sin 18.667°}{z} = \frac{\sin 52.333°}{409}$$

$$409 \sin 18.667° = z \sin 52.333°$$

$$\frac{409 \sin 18.667°}{\sin 52.333°} = \frac{z \,\cancel{\sin 52.333°}}{\cancel{\sin 52.333°}}$$

$$z \approx 165.38 \text{ meters}$$

4) Ashley is standing several hundred feet away from a flagpole and looking at the U.S. flag which is attached to the flagpole. She observes that the angle of elevation from her foot to the top of the flagpole is 32°. After she has walked 200 feet further away, the angle of elevation to the top of the flagpole is 27° (see diagram). How far away from the flagpole was she when her first observation was made? Round off your answer to the nearest tenth of a foot.

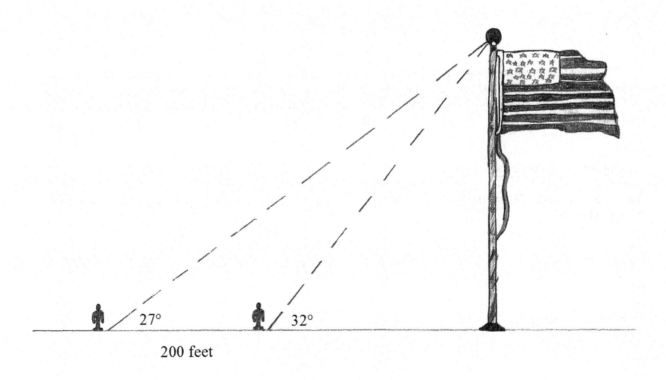

27°   32°

200 feet

Solution: If we label the angles and sides of the triangles in the given picture, we will obtain the following diagram:

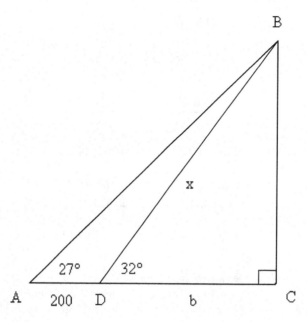

We need to come up with a plan which will help us solve for b. To begin with, notice that the quantities b and x in the diagram are related by the equation

$$\cos 32° = \frac{b}{x}.$$

This means that if we could find x, then we could find b. In order to find x, we must find the measure of angle DBA in triangle DBA and use the Law of Sines. The reason why this angle is important to know is because we know that the measure of its opposite side is 200 ft. This completes our plan. Let's now solve the problem.

1. Find the measure of angle DBA:

Observe that angle $BDA = 148°$ (since angle BDA and angle CDB make a straight angle and $148° + 32° = 180°$). Therefore,

$$
\begin{aligned}
\text{angle } DBA &= 180° - (148° + 27°) \\
&= 180° - 175° \\
&= 5°
\end{aligned}
$$

2. Find the value of x:

$$\frac{\sin 27°}{x} = \frac{\sin 5°}{200}$$

$$200 \sin 27° = x \sin 5°$$

$$\frac{200 \sin 27°}{\sin 5°} = \frac{x \cancel{\sin 5°}}{\cancel{\sin 5°}}$$

$$x \approx 1,041.79$$

3. <u>Find the value of b</u>:

$$\cos 32° \approx \frac{b}{1,041.79}$$

$$b \approx 1,041.79 \cos 32°$$

$$b \approx 883.5 \text{ feet}$$

Try These (Set 1):

1) In triangle ABC, $A = 36°$, $C = 28°$, and $c = 11$ inches. Find a to the nearest inch.

2) In triangle RST, $S = 72°30'$, $r = 29$, and $T = 41°$. Find R, s, and t.

3) Johnny and Anthony are standing $4,975$ feet apart on a straight, horizontal road. They notice a balloon between them directly above the road. The angle of elevation from Anthony is $65°$ and from Johnny is $72°$. Find the height of the balloon to the nearest tenth of a foot.

Section 8.2 Solving SSA Oblique Triangles; The Ambiguous Case of the Law of Sines

When we are given two sides of an oblique triangle and an angle opposite one of the sides, it is possible to have either 0, 1, or 2 triangles with these measurements. We refer to this as the **ambiguous case of the Law of Sines**. Let's examine each of these cases

Examples. Use the given information to solve triangle ABC (if it exists). Round off any decimals to the nearest hundredth.

1) $A = 60°$, $a = 12$, and $b = 10$

In order to solve the triangle, we need to find B, C, and c. By using the Law of Sines, we will determine B first. Once we find B, we can determine how many triangles with these measures are constructible and solve for these triangles.

1. Find B:

$$\frac{\sin B}{b} = \frac{\sin A}{a}$$

$$\frac{\sin B}{10} = \frac{\sin 60°}{12}$$

$$12 \sin B = 10 \sin 60°$$

$$\frac{\cancel{12} \sin B}{\cancel{12}} = \frac{10 \sin 60°}{12}$$

$$\sin B = \frac{10 \sin 60°}{12}$$

Now, there are **two possible answers** for angle B in triangle ABC, namely

$$B_1 = \sin^{-1}\left(\frac{10\sin 60°}{12}\right) = 46.19°$$

and

$$B_2 = 180° - 46.19° = 133.81°$$

(this is a possible answer because $\sin\theta = \sin(180° - \theta)$ for any angle θ). Let's see which of these work.

a) Observe that $A + B_1 = 60° + 46.19° = 106.19° < 180°$. This means that $B_1 = 46.19°$ could be the measure of one of the angles of triangle ABC.

b) Notice that $A + B_2 = 60° + 133.81° = 193.81° > 180°$, telling us that $B_2 = 133.81°$ could not be the measure of one of the angles of triangle ABC.

Therefore, $46.19°$ is the only possible measure for angle B (see the figure below). There is **only one triangle** that is constructible which has the given measures.

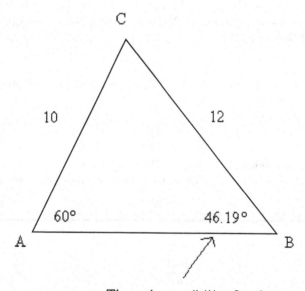

The only possibility for the measurement of B.

2. Find C: We know that $A + B + C = 180°$. Therefore,

$$\begin{aligned} C &= 180° - (A + B) \\ &= 180° - (60° + 46.19°) \\ &= 180° - 106.19° \\ &= 73.81°. \end{aligned}$$

3. Find c:

$$\frac{\sin C}{c} = \frac{\sin A}{a}$$

$$\frac{\sin 73.81°}{c} = \frac{\sin 60°}{12}$$

$$12 \sin 73.81° = c \sin 60°$$

$$\frac{12 \sin 73.81°}{\sin 60°} = \frac{c \,\cancel{\sin 60°}}{\cancel{\sin 60°}}$$

$$c = 13.31$$

2) $A = 55°$, $a = 25$, and $c = 30$

We need to find B, C, and b. By using the Law of Sines, we will determine C first. Once we find C, we can determine how many triangles with these measures are constructible and solve for these triangles just like in the previous example.

$$\frac{\sin C}{c} = \frac{\sin A}{a}$$

$$\frac{\sin C}{30} = \frac{\sin 55°}{25}$$

$$25 \sin C = 30 \sin 55°$$

$$\frac{\cancel{25} \sin C}{\cancel{25}} = \frac{30 \sin 55°}{25}$$

$$\sin C = \frac{30 \sin 55°}{25}$$

As before, there are **two possible answers** for angle C in triangle ABC, namely

$$C_1 = \sin^{-1}\left(\frac{30 \sin 55°}{25}\right) = 79.41°$$

and

$$C_2 = 180° - 79.41° = 100.59°$$

(again, this is a possible answer because $\sin \theta = \sin(180° - \theta)$ for any angle θ). Let's see which of these work.

a) Notice that $A + C_1 = 55° + 79.41° = 134.41° < 180°$, so $C_1 = 79.41°$ could be the measure of one of the angles of triangle ABC.

b) Similarly, $A + C_2 = 55° + 100.59° = 155.59° < 180°$, so $C_2 = 100.59°$ could **also** be the measure of one of the angles of triangle ABC.

Therefore, both $79.41°$ and $100.59°$ are possible measures for angle C. This means that there are **two triangles** that are constructible which has the given measures. Let's solve each triangle. We will call them triangles $A_1B_1C_1$ and $A_2B_2C_2$, where $A_1 = A_2 = 55°$, $a_1 = a_2 = 25$ and $c_1 = c_2 = 30$ (see the next figure).

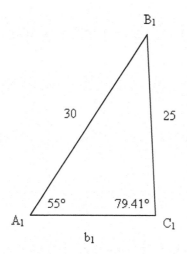

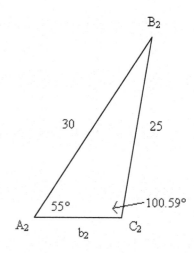

I) Solve $\triangle A_1 B_1 C_1$: We have that $A_1 = 55°$, $C_1 = 79.41°$, $a_1 = 25$, and $c_1 = 30$. Let's find B_1 and b_1.

1. Find B_1:

$$
\begin{aligned}
B_1 &= 180° - (A_1 + C_1) \\
&= 180° - (55° + 79.41°) \\
&= 180° - 134.41° \\
&= 45.59°
\end{aligned}
$$

2. Find b_1:

$$
\begin{aligned}
\frac{\sin B_1}{b_1} &= \frac{\sin A_1}{a_1} \\
\frac{\sin 45.59°}{b_1} &= \frac{\sin 55°}{25} \\
25 \sin 45.59° &= b_1 \sin 55° \\
\frac{25 \sin 45.59°}{\sin 55°} &= \frac{b_1 \,\cancel{\sin 55°}}{\cancel{\sin 55°}} \\
b_1 &= 21.80
\end{aligned}
$$

II) Solve $\triangle A_2 B_2 C_2$: We have that $A_2 = 55°$, $C_2 = 100.59°$, $a_2 = 25$, and $c_2 = 30$. Let's find B_2 and b_2.

1. Find B_2:

$$
\begin{aligned}
B_2 &= 180° - (A_2 + C_2) \\
&= 180° - (55° + 100.59°) \\
&= 180° - 155.59° \\
&= 24.41°
\end{aligned}
$$

2. Find b_2:

$$\frac{\sin B_2}{b_2} = \frac{\sin A_2}{a_2}$$

$$\frac{\sin 24.41°}{b_2} = \frac{\sin 55°}{25}$$

$$25 \sin 24.41° = b_2 \sin 55°$$

$$\frac{25 \sin 24.41°}{\sin 55°} = \frac{b_2 \,\cancel{\sin 55°}}{\cancel{\sin 55°}}$$

$$b_2 = 12.61$$

3) $B = 30°$, $b = 3$, and $c = 9$

We need to find A, C, and a. By using the Law of Sines, we will determine C first. Once we find C, we can determine how many triangles with these measures are constructible and solve for these triangles.

$$\frac{\sin B}{b} = \frac{\sin C}{c}$$

$$\frac{\sin 30°}{3} = \frac{\sin C}{9}$$

$$9 \sin 30° = 3 \sin C$$

$$\frac{\overset{3}{\cancel{9}} \sin 30°}{\underset{1}{\cancel{3}}} = \frac{\overset{1}{\cancel{3}} \sin C}{\underset{1}{\cancel{3}}}$$

$$\sin C = 3 \sin 30° = 3\left(\frac{1}{2}\right) = \frac{3}{2}$$

Since $\sin C = \frac{3}{2} > 1$, there are **no triangles** which have the given measures (recall that $0 < \sin\theta < 1$ for every acute angle θ). See the figure below.

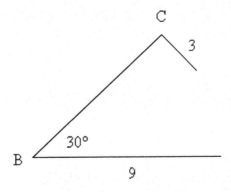

No possible measurement for angle C would give a triangle.

Notice that the three examples are all solved by following the same steps.

Steps For Solving The Ambiguous Case

Suppose that we are given angle A and sides a and b. To solve triangle ABC, we proceed as follows:

Step I: Solve for angle B by using the Law of Sines.

$$\frac{\sin A}{a} = \frac{\sin B}{b} \quad \text{yields} \quad B_1 = \sin^{-1}\left(\frac{b\sin A}{a}\right) \text{ and } B_2 = 180° - B_1 \text{ (if } B_1 \text{ exists)}.$$

Step II: Determine how many triangles are constructible.

Case 1. If $A + B_1 < 180°$ and $A + B_2 > 180°$, there is **one triangle.**
Case 2. If $A + B_1 < 180°$ and $A + B_2 < 180°$, there are **two triangles.**
Case 3. If B_1 doesn't exist, there are **zero triangles.**

Step III: Find the remaining measures and solve the triangle.

For Case 1. Find $C = 180° - (A + B)$, then find c using the Law of Sines.
For Case 2. Find $C_1 = 180° - (A + B_1)$, then find c_1 using the Law of Sines.
  Next find $C_2 = 180° - (A + B_2)$ and c_2 (using the Law of Sines).
For Case 3. There is no triangle to solve.

Sometimes we are interested knowing how many triangles are constructible without using the Law of Sines and going through so much work. The table below summarizes the different situations which can occur and how many triangles are constructible for each case. The proofs of these results will not be given. However, the diagrams that accompany each case should convince you that these results are true.

Suppose that we are given angle A and sides a and b. Let h be the altitude from vertex C. In each triangle for which h is labeled, notice that we have the relationship $h = b\sin A$.

Conditions	Diagram	Number of Constructible Triangles
$A < 90°$ and $a = h$		1
$A < 90°$ and $a \geq b$		1

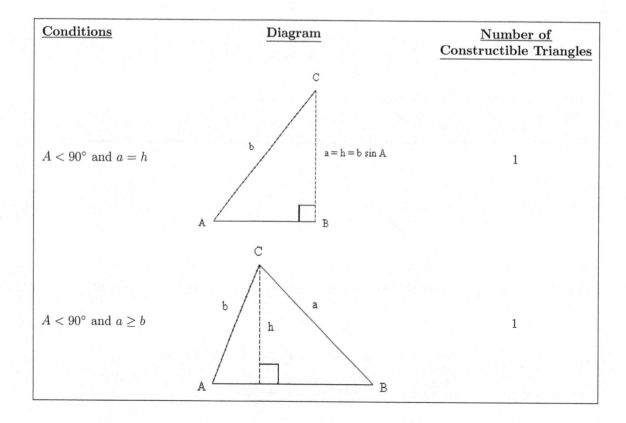

continued

Conditions	Diagram	Number of Constructible Triangles
$A > 90°$ and $a > b$	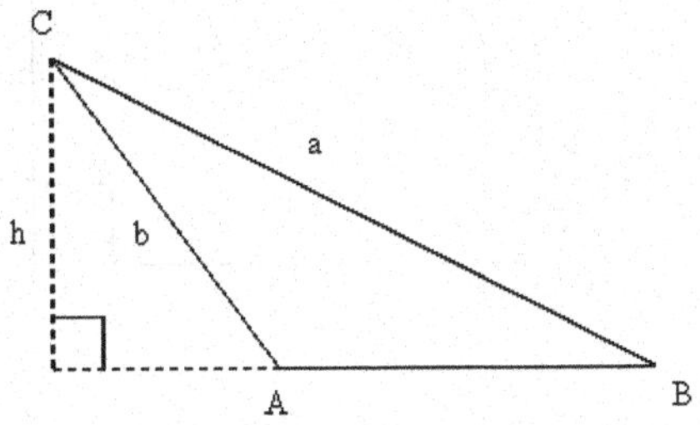	1
$A < 90°$ and $h < a < b$	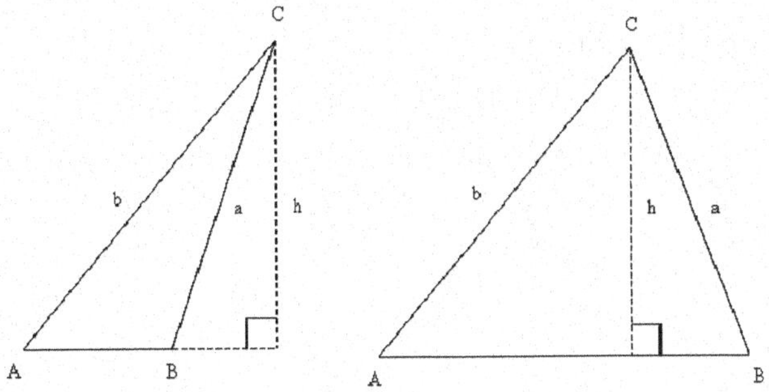	2
$A < 90°$ and $a < h$	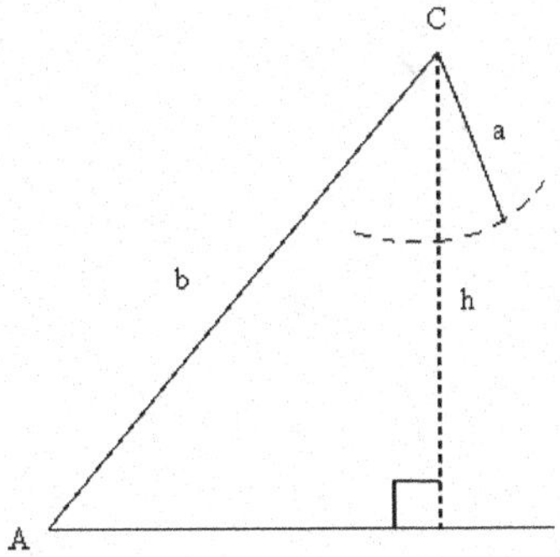	0
$A > 90°$ and $a < b$	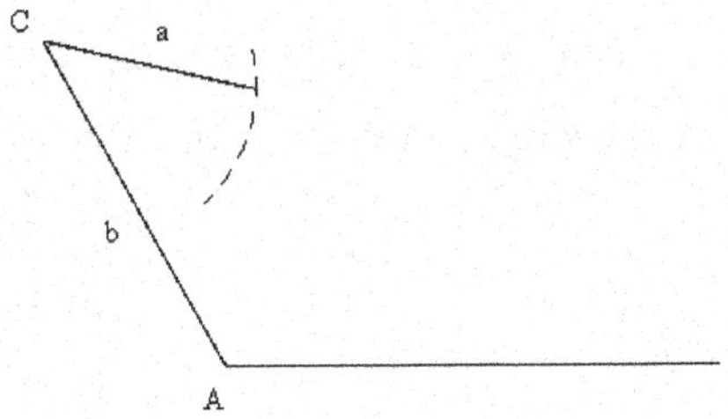	0

Examples. Determine the number of triangles which can be constructed with the given measures.

1) $A = 30°$, $a = 5$, and $b = 10$

Let h be the altitude from vertex C. Then

$$h = b \sin A = 10 \sin 30° = 5.$$

Since $a = h = 5$ and $A = 30° < 90°$, there is one triangle (see the next figure). Observe that angle B is a right angle when $a = h$.

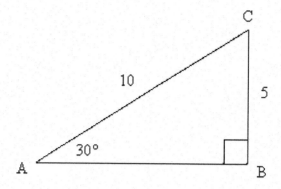

2) $A = 47°$, $a = 3$, and $b = 7$

Let h be the altitude from vertex C. Then

$$h = b \sin A = 7 \sin 47° = 5.12.$$

Since $a < h$ and $A = 47° < 90°$, there is no triangle that can be constructed (see the figure below).

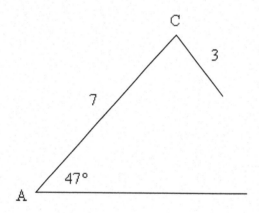

3) $A = 50°$, $a = 9$, and $b = 11$

Let h be the altitude from vertex C. Then

$$h = b \sin A = 11 \sin 50° = 8.43.$$

Since $h < a < b$ and $A = 50° < 90°$, there are two triangles that can be constructed (see the figure below).

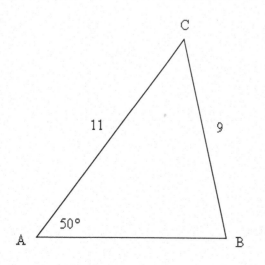 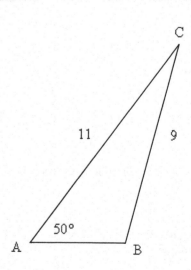

4) $A = 135°$, $a = 17$, and $b = 13$

Since $a > b$ and $A = 135° > 90°$, there is one triangle that can be constructed (see the figure below).

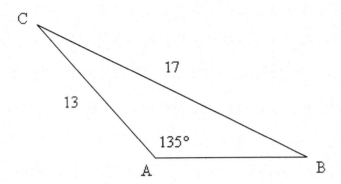

5) $A = 29°$, $a = b = 4$

Since $a = b$ and $A = 29° < 90°$, there is one triangle that can be constructed (see the figure below).

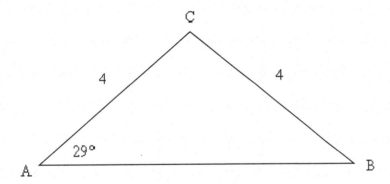

In the previous examples, you may have found it difficult to remember all of the conditions to determine the number of constructible triangles. It may be easier for you to solve such examples by following the steps mentioned before (especially when the angles and sides are not labeled as A, B, C, a, b, and c). Let's try some more examples.

Examples.

1) Determine the number of triangles ABC which can be constructed when $B = 34°$, $a = 6$, and $b = 11$.

We will do this the long (but easier) way. First, we have to find A (this makes sense since we cannot find anything else at this point).

$$\frac{\sin A}{a} = \frac{\sin B}{b}$$

$$\frac{\sin A}{6} = \frac{\sin 34°}{11}$$

$$11 \sin A = 6 \sin 34°$$

$$\frac{\cancel{11} \sin A}{\cancel{11}} = \frac{6 \sin 34°}{11}$$

$$\sin A = \frac{6 \sin 34°}{11}$$

There are two possibilities for A, namely

$$A_1 = \sin^{-1}\left(\frac{6\sin 34°}{11}\right) = 17.76°$$

and

$$A_2 = 180° - 17.76° = 162.24°.$$

Case 1: Observe that $B + A_1 = 34° + 17.76° = 51.76° < 180°$, so A_1 can be the measure of an angle of the triangle.

Case 2: Notice that $B + A_2 = 34° + 162.24° = 196.24° > 180°$, so A_2 cannot be the measure of an angle of the triangle.

Therefore, only one triangle is possible.

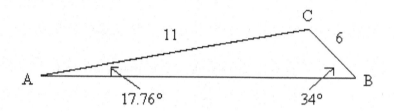

2) Determine the number of triangles RST which can be constructed when $R = 155°$, $s = 14.05$, and $r = 9.62$.

We have to find S (the angle which is opposite side s).

$$\frac{\sin R}{r} = \frac{\sin S}{s}$$

$$\frac{\sin 155°}{9.62} = \frac{\sin S}{14.05}$$

$$14.05\sin 155° = 9.62\sin S$$

$$\frac{14.05\sin 155°}{9.62} = \frac{\cancel{9.62}\sin S}{\cancel{9.62}}$$

$$\sin A = \frac{14.05\sin 155°}{9.62}$$

There are two possibilities for S, namely

$$S_1 = \sin^{-1}\left(\frac{14.05\sin 155°}{9.62}\right) = 38.11°$$

and

$$S_2 = 180° - 38.11° = 141.89°.$$

Case 1: Notice that $R + S_1 = 155° + 38.11° = 193.11° > 180°$, so S_1 cannot be the measure of an angle of the triangle.

Case 2: Since $R + S_2 = 155° + 141.89° = 296.89° > 180°$, S_2 cannot be the measure of an angle of the triangle.

Therefore, no triangles can be constructed.

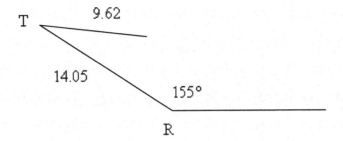

3) Determine the number of triangles WXY which can be constructed when $Y = 40°$, $w = 32.16$, and $y = 23.18$.

We need to find W (the angle which is opposite side w).

$$\frac{\sin W}{w} = \frac{\sin Y}{y}$$

$$\frac{\sin W}{32.16} = \frac{\sin 40°}{23.18}$$

$$23.18 \sin W = 32.16 \sin 40°$$

$$\frac{\cancel{23.18}\sin W}{\cancel{23.18}} = \frac{32.16 \sin 40°}{23.18}$$

$$\sin W = \frac{32.16 \sin 40°}{23.18}$$

The two possibilities for W are

$$W_1 = \sin^{-1}\left(\frac{32.16 \sin 40°}{23.18}\right) = 63.1°$$

and

$$W_2 = 180° - 63.1° = 116.9°.$$

Case 1: Observe that $Y + W_1 = 40° + 63.1° = 103.1° < 180°$, so W_1 can be the measure of an angle of the triangle.

Case 2: Notice that $Y + W_2 = 40° + 116.9° = 156.9° < 180°$, so W_2 can be the measure of an angle of the triangle.

Therefore, two triangles are possible.

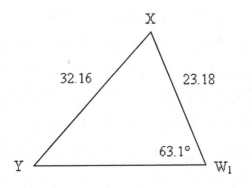

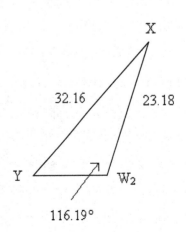

Try These (Set 2):

1) Solve triangle ABC if $A = 75°$, $a = 18$, inches, and $b = 13$ inches. Round off your answers to the nearest whole numbers.

2) Solve triangle RST if $T = 122°45'$, $r = 5.92$, and $t = 12.16$. Round off your answers to the nearest whole numbers.

3) How many triangles EFG can be made if $E = 36°30'$, $e = 5.92$, and $g = 9.8$?

Section 8.3   Solving SAS and SSS Oblique Triangles; the Law of Cosines

In this section, we will solve SAS and SSS oblique triangles. The Law of Cosines will allow us to achieve this.

The Law of Cosines

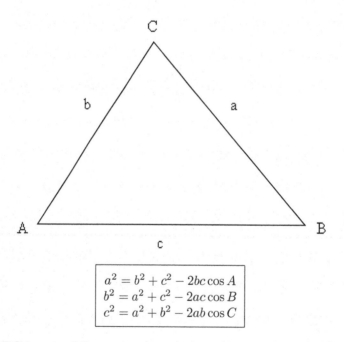

$$a^2 = b^2 + c^2 - 2bc \cos A$$
$$b^2 = a^2 + c^2 - 2ac \cos B$$
$$c^2 = a^2 + b^2 - 2ab \cos C$$

Proof: Let triangle ABC be any oblique triangle and place the triangle in the Cartesian Plane in such a way that vertex A is at the origin and $\overline{AC}$ lies on the positive x-axis (in the next diagram, both an acute triangle and an obtuse triangle are shown). Let (x, y) denote the coordinates of vertex B. Then, by our definitions of sine and cosine, we have that

$$\sin A = \frac{y}{r} = \frac{y}{c} \qquad \text{(which becomes } y = c \sin A)$$

and

$$\cos A = \frac{x}{r} = \frac{x}{c} \qquad \text{(which becomes } x = c \cos A)$$

where r represents the distance from $(0,\ 0)$ to $(x,\ y)$, which is just c in each of the triangles in the diagram below. We can, therefore, represent the coordinates $(x,\ y)$ of vertex B as $(c\cos A,\ c\sin A)$.

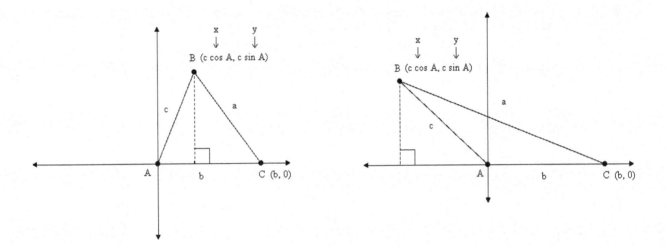

According to the diagram above, the distance between the points $(b,\ 0)$ and $(c\cos A,\ c\sin A)$ is a. We may relate these quantities by using the Distance Formula.

$$
\begin{aligned}
d &= \sqrt{(x_2 - x_1)^2 + (y_2 - y_1)^2} \\[2mm]
a &= \sqrt{(c\cos A - b)^2 + (c\sin A - 0)^2} \\[2mm]
a^2 &= \left(\sqrt{(c\cos A - b)^2 + (c\sin A)^2}\right)^2 \\[2mm]
&= (c\cos A - b)^2 + (c\sin A)^2 \\[2mm]
&= c^2\cos^2 A - 2bc\cos A + b^2 + c^2\sin^2 A \\[2mm]
&= c^2\left(\cos^2 A + \sin^2 A\right) - 2bc\cos A + b^2 \\[2mm]
&= c^2\left(1\right) - 2bc\cos A + b^2 \\[2mm]
&= b^2 + c^2 - 2bc\cos A
\end{aligned}
$$

To prove the other two formulas we simply repeat this proof, but place B or C at the origin instead of A.

Notice that if one of the angles is a right angle, then the Law of Cosines reduces to the Pythagorean theorem. For example, if $C = 90°$, then

$$
\begin{aligned}
c^2 &= a^2 + b^2 - 2ab\cos C \\
c^2 &= a^2 + b^2 - 2ab\cos 90° \\
c^2 &= a^2 + b^2 - 2ab\left(0\right) \\
c^2 &= a^2 + b^2
\end{aligned}
$$

where c is the hypotenuse in this case.

We will now use the Law of Cosines to solve SAS and SSS oblique triangles, as well as some applications. Before doing so, we should list some important facts about triangles which will come in handy.

1. Opposite the **smallest angle** of a triangle is the **smallest side** of the triangle.
2. Opposite the **largest angle** of a triangle is the **largest side** of the triangle.
3. The sum of any two sides of a triangle is always **greater than** the remaining side.

Examples.

1) In triangle ABC, $B = 60°$, $a = 12$, and $c = 5$. Find b to the nearest tenth.

We use the Law of Cosines.

$$
\begin{aligned}
b^2 &= a^2 + c^2 - 2ac\cos B \\
&= 12^2 + 5^2 - 2(12)(5)\cos 60° \\
&= 144 + 25 - 60 \\
&= 109
\end{aligned}
$$

Therefore, $b = \sqrt{109} = 10.4$. Notice that $b \neq -\sqrt{109} = -10.4$ since b represents the measure of a side of a triangle.

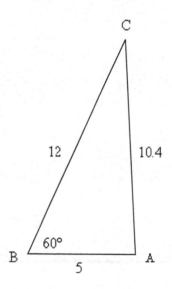

2) In triangle PQR, $R = 145°$, $p = 9$, and $q = 17$. Find r to the nearest hundredth.

We use the Law of Cosines.

$$
\begin{aligned}
r^2 &= p^2 + q^2 - 2pq\cos R \\
&= 9^2 + 17^2 - 2(9)(17)\cos 145° \\
&= 81 + 289 - (-250.66) \\
&= 620.66
\end{aligned}
$$

Therefore, $r = \sqrt{620.66} = 24.91$.

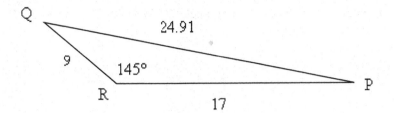

3) Solve triangle ABC, where $A = 29°$, $b = 21$, and $c = 13$. Round off any decimals to the nearest hundredth.

Whenever we solve an SAS problem, there is always **exactly one** triangle which can be constructed. We begin by finding the value of a by using the Law of Cosines. Notice that angle C is smaller than angle B since c (the side opposite C) is smaller than b (the side opposite B). Therefore, once we find a, we will use the Law of Sines to find angles C and B in **exactly this order**.

> **We always find the smaller of the two remaining angles after we find the side opposite the given angle.**

1. Find a:

$$
\begin{aligned}
a^2 &= b^2 + c^2 - 2bc \cos A \\
&= 21^2 + 13^2 - 2\,(21)\,(13) \cos 29° \\
&= 441 + 169 - 477.54 \\
&= 132.46
\end{aligned}
$$

And so $a = \sqrt{132.46} = 11.51$.

2. Find C:

$$
\frac{\sin C}{c} = \frac{\sin A}{a}
$$

$$
\frac{\sin C}{13} = \frac{\sin 29°}{11.51}
$$

$$
11.51 \sin C = 13 \sin 29°
$$

$$
\frac{\cancel{11.51} \sin C}{\cancel{11.51}} = \frac{13 \sin 29°}{11.51}
$$

$$
\sin C = \frac{13 \sin 29°}{11.51}
$$

Therefore, $C = \sin^{-1}\left(\dfrac{13 \sin 29°}{11.51}\right) = 33.2°$.

3. Find B:

$$
\begin{aligned}
B &= 180° - (A + C) \\
&= 180° - (29° + 33.2°) \\
&= 180° - 62.2° \\
&= 117.8°
\end{aligned}
$$

Why did we have to find angle C before finding angle B? Well, if we found angle B before angle C by using the Law of Sines, we would have obtained:

$$\frac{\sin B}{b} = \frac{\sin A}{a}$$

$$\frac{\sin B}{21} = \frac{\sin 29°}{11.51}$$

$$11.51 \sin B = 21 \sin 29°$$

$$\frac{\cancel{11.51} \sin B}{\cancel{11.51}} = \frac{21 \sin 29°}{11.51}$$

$$\sin B = \frac{21 \sin 29°}{11.51}$$

and there are two solutions for B, namely $B_1 = \sin^{-1}\left(\dfrac{21 \sin 29°}{11.51}\right) = 62.2°$ and $B_2 = 180° - 62.19° = 117.8°$. Which one of these answers should we choose for B? Well, we know that $B = 117.8°$ is correct **only** because we originally found C first. Otherwise, we would have to do more work before finding out that $B = 62.2°$ cannot satisfy our triangle. Again, I stress the fact that we **always find the smaller of the two remaining angles after we find the side opposite the given angle.**

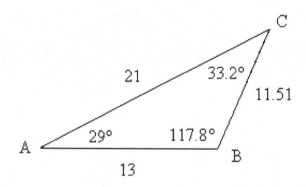

4) Find the angles of triangle EFG (to the nearest degree) if $e = 7$, $f = 12$, and $g = 9$.

Whenever we solve a SSS problem, there is always **exactly one** triangle which can be constructed. We begin by finding the value of F (the side opposite F) by using the Law of Cosines. Notice that angle F is largest of the angles since f (the side opposite F) is larger than e (the side opposite E) and g (the side opposite G). Once we find F, we will use the Law of Sines to find angles E and G in any order we'd like.

We always find the largest angle first.

---

1. Find F:

$$f^2 = e^2 + g^2 - 2eg \cos F$$

$$12^2 = 7^2 + 9^2 - 2(7)(9) \cos F$$

$$144 = 49 + 81 - 126 \cos F$$

$$144 = \cancel{130} - 126\cos F$$
$$\underline{-130 \quad \cancel{-130}}$$
$$\frac{114}{-126} = \frac{\cancel{-126}\cos F}{\cancel{-126}}$$

$$\frac{114}{-126} = \cos F$$

$$F = \cos^{-1}\left(-\frac{114}{126}\right) \approx 155°$$

2. Find E:

$$\frac{\sin E}{e} = \frac{\sin F}{f}$$

$$\frac{\sin E}{7} = \frac{\sin 155°}{12}$$

$$7\sin 155° = 12\sin E$$

$$\frac{7\sin 155°}{12} = \frac{\cancel{12}\sin E}{\cancel{12}}$$

$$\sin E = \frac{7\sin 155°}{12}$$

$$E = \sin^{-1}\left(\frac{7\sin 155°}{12}\right) \approx 14°$$

3. Find G:

$$G = 180° - (E + F)$$
$$= 180° - (14° + 155°)$$
$$= 180° - 169°$$
$$= 11°$$

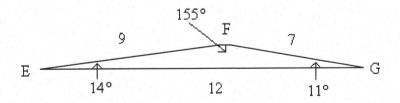

5) Solve triangle PQR if $p = 16$, $q = 13$, and $r = 13$ (round off your answers to the nearest degree).

Since the largest side is $p = 16$, we will begin by finding P by using the Law of Cosines. Notice that $Q = R$ because $q = r = 13$. Triangle PQR is an **isosceles triangle** (it has two equal sides/angles).

1. Find P:

$$p^2 = q^2 + r^2 - 2qr \cos P$$
$$16^2 = 13^2 + 13^2 - 2(13)(13) \cos P$$
$$256 = 169 + 169 - 338 \cos P$$
$$256 = \cancel{338} - 338 \cos P$$
$$\underline{-338 \quad \cancel{-338}}$$
$$\frac{-82}{-338} = \frac{\cancel{-338} \cos P}{\cancel{-338}}$$
$$\frac{82}{338} = \cos P$$
$$P = \cos^{-1}\left(\frac{82}{338}\right) \approx 76°$$

2. Find Q (and R): Since $Q = R$, we don't need to use the Law of Sines to find Q (and R) as in the previous example. Observe that:

$$P + Q + R = 180°$$
$$76° + Q + R = 180°$$
$$\underline{-76° \qquad\qquad -76°}$$
$$Q + R = 104°$$

And so $Q = R = 52°$.

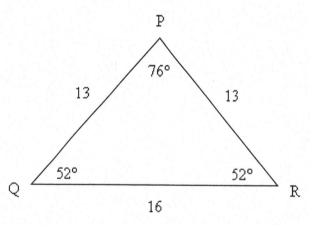

6) A ship at sea is 82 miles from one radio transmitter and 146 miles from another. The angle between the signals sent to the ship by the transmitters is 102.45°. How far apart are the transmitters from one another? Round off your answer to the nearest mile.

The first step is to sketch a rough diagram of the situation.

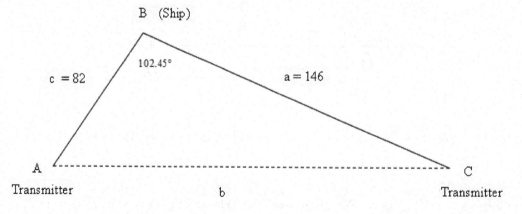

According to the diagram, we want to find side b.

$$
\begin{aligned}
b^2 &= a^2 + c^2 - 2ac\cos B \\[2mm]
&= 146^2 + 82^2 - 2\,(146)\,(82)\cos 102.45° \\[2mm]
&\approx 21,316 + 6,724 - (-5,162.03) \\[2mm]
&= 33,166.03
\end{aligned}
$$

Therefore, $b \approx \sqrt{33,166.03} \approx 182$ miles.

7) A tower 550 feet high is located on a ground in such a way that one side of the tower lies on a part of the ground which slopes upward with an angle of elevation of 9° (see diagram). A rope is to be extended from the top of the tower to a point on the sloped side of the ground 112 feet from the base of the tower. What should the length of rope be?

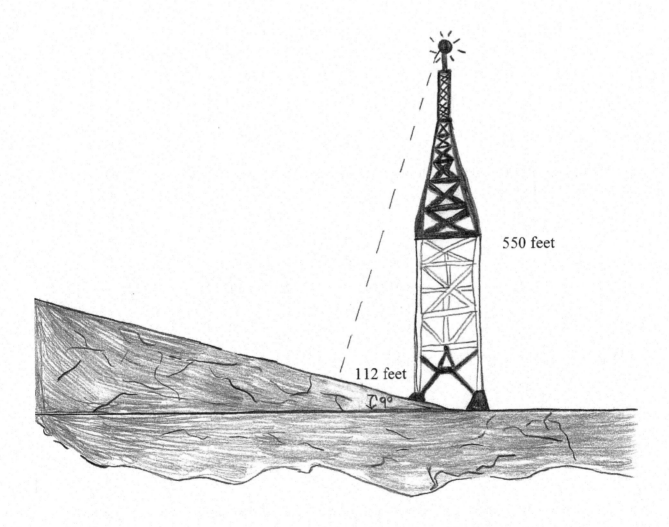

If we focus our attention on the triangle which contains the given information, we obtain the diagram on next page.

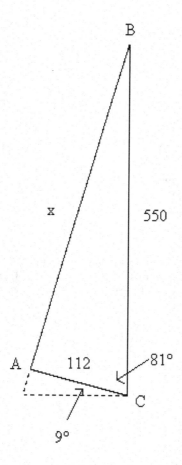

Observe that angle $C = 81°$ since the tower is perpendicular to the horizontal ground and $90° - 9° = 81°$. We use the Law of Cosines.

$$
\begin{aligned}
x^2 &= a^2 + b^2 - 2ab \cos C \\
&= 550^2 + 112^2 - 2\,(550)\,(112) \cos 81° \\
&\approx 302,500 + 12,544 - 19,272.7261 \\
&= 295,771.2739
\end{aligned}
$$

Therefore, $x \approx \sqrt{295,771.2739} \approx 544$ feet.

Try These (Set 3):

1) Solve triangle ABC, where $A = 56°$, $b = 10$ feet, and $c = 7$ feet. Round off your answers to the nearest tenth.

2) Solve triangle LMN, where $l = 5$, $m = 9$, and $n = 10$. Round off your answers to the nearest tenth.

3) The diagonals of a parallelogram are 90 meters and 86 meters and the shorter side of the parallelogram is 35 meters. Find the acute angle formed by the two diagonals to the nearest tenth of a degree (note that the diagonals of a parallelogram bisect each other).

Section 8.4 The Area of a Triangle

Trigonometry comes in handy when we want to find the area of a triangle. Let's begin by recalling the well known area formula for a triangle with a given base and height.

Area Formula (I)

The area A of a triangle with base b and height h is

$$A = \frac{1}{2}bh.$$

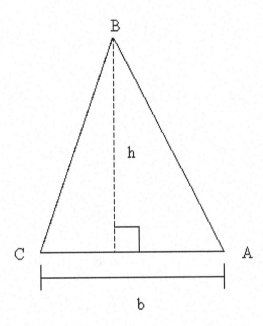

Area Formula (I) is useful when the base and height are known and is used to find the area of any triangle. What if we are given two sides, b and c, of triangle ABC and the angle between them, angle A. How would we find the area of triangle ABC? Well, suppose that angle A is an acute angle (see the next figure). If we let h be the altitude to b, then we have

$$\sin A = \frac{h}{c} \text{ or, equivalently, } h = c\sin A.$$

And so formula (I) becomes

$$A = \frac{1}{2}bh = \frac{1}{2}bc\sin A.$$

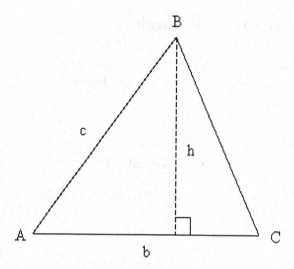

Similarly, we can verify that

$$A = \frac{1}{2}ab\sin C$$

and

$$A = \frac{1}{2}ac\sin B$$

if we drop the altitude from the other vertices. If angle A is an obtuse triangle, then the same formulas arise. For example, in the figure below, we see that

$$\sin\left(180° - A\right) = \frac{h}{c} \text{ or, equivalently, } h = c\sin\left(180° - A\right).$$

Since $\sin\left(180° - A\right) = \sin A$, we have

$$h = c\sin\left(180° - A\right) = c\sin A.$$

And so

$$A = \frac{1}{2}bh = \frac{1}{2}bc\sin A$$

as before.

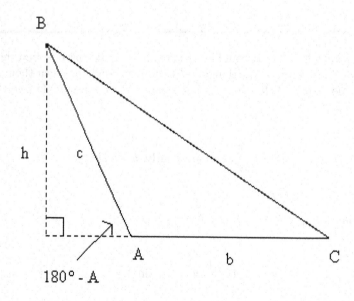

Area Formulas (II)

If we are given two sides of triangle ABC and the angle between them, then the area A is

$$A = \frac{1}{2}ab\sin C \ \text{ or } \ A = \frac{1}{2}ac\sin B \ \text{ or } \ A = \frac{1}{2}bc\sin A.$$

Examples.

1) Find the area of triangle ABC, where $B = 60°$, $a = 12$ inches, and $c = 5$ inches. Leave your answer in simplified radical form.

Notice that angle B is between sides a and c. We can use Formula (II) to find the area.

$$A = \frac{1}{2}ac\sin B = \frac{1}{2}(12)(5)\underbrace{\sin 60°}_{\frac{\sqrt{3}}{2}} = 30\left(\frac{\sqrt{3}}{2}\right) = 15\sqrt{3} \text{ square inches.}$$

2) Find the area of triangle EFG, where $G = 121°$, $e = 19$ feet, and $f = 33$ feet. Round off your answer to the nearest integer.

Using Formula (II), we have

$$A = \frac{1}{2}ef\sin G = \frac{1}{2}(19)(33)\sin 121° \approx 269 \text{ square feet.}$$

Our next formula is used to find the area of a triangle when we are given all three sides. It is known as **Heron's Formula.**

Heron's Formula

The area A of triangle ABC with sides a, b, and c is

$$A = \sqrt{s(s-a)(s-b)(s-c)}, \text{ where } s = \frac{1}{2}(a+b+c).$$

Proof: We will use several formulas to derive this formula. To begin with, we know that the Law of Cosines states that

$$c^2 = a^2 + b^2 - 2ab\cos C, \text{ which can be written as } \cos C = \frac{a^2+b^2-c^2}{2ab}\text{(why?).}$$

Recall that the half-angle formula for $\sin\frac{C}{2}$ is

$$\sin\frac{C}{2} = \pm\sqrt{\frac{1-\cos C}{2}}, \text{ which becomes } \sin^2\frac{C}{2} = \frac{1-\cos C}{2}.$$

Now, using the given information that $2s = a + b + c$, we find that

$$\sin^2 \frac{C}{2} = \frac{1 - \cos C}{2} = \frac{1 - \dfrac{a^2 + b^2 - c^2}{2ab}}{2}$$

$$= \frac{1(2ab) - \dfrac{a^2 + b^2 - c^2}{2ab}(2ab)}{2(2ab)} = \frac{2ab - a^2 - b^2 + c^2}{4ab}$$

$$= \frac{c^2 - (a^2 - 2ab + b^2)}{4ab} = \frac{c^2 - (a - b)^2}{4ab}$$

$$= \frac{(c + a - b)(c - a + b)}{4ab} = \frac{(2s - 2b)(2s - 2a)}{4ab} \qquad \text{(since } 2s = a + b + c\text{)}$$

$$= \frac{\overset{1}{\cancel{2}}(s - b) \cdot \overset{1}{\cancel{2}}(s - a)}{\underset{1}{\cancel{4}ab}} = \frac{(s - b)(s - a)}{ab}.$$

And so $\sin \dfrac{C}{2} = \sqrt{\dfrac{(s - b)(s - a)}{ab}}.$

Similarly, using the half-angle formula for cosine,

$$\cos \frac{C}{2} = \pm\sqrt{\frac{1 + \cos C}{2}}, \text{ which becomes } \cos^2 \frac{C}{2} = \frac{1 + \cos C}{2},$$

we find that

$$\cos^2 \frac{C}{2} = \frac{s(s - c)}{ab}.$$

And so $\cos \dfrac{C}{2} = \sqrt{\dfrac{s(s - c)}{ab}}.$

Now we use Formula (II) to find the area. Using the identity $\sin C = \sin\left[2\left(\frac{C}{2}\right)\right] = 2\sin\frac{C}{2}\cos\frac{C}{2}$, we have:

$$A = \frac{1}{2}ab\sin C$$

$$= \frac{1}{\cancel{2}}\underset{1}{ab}\left(\overset{1}{\cancel{2}}\sin\frac{C}{2}\cos\frac{C}{2}\right) = ab\left(\sqrt{\frac{(s - b)(s - a)}{ab}} \cdot \sqrt{\frac{s(s - c)}{ab}}\right)$$

$$= ab \cdot \sqrt{\frac{s(s - a)(s - b)(s - c)}{(ab)^2}} = ab \cdot \frac{\sqrt{s(s - a)(s - b)(s - c)}}{\sqrt{(ab)^2}}$$

$$= \frac{\overset{1}{\cancel{ab}}}{1} \cdot \frac{\sqrt{s(s - a)(s - b)(s - c)}}{\underset{1}{\cancel{ab}}} \qquad \text{(Note that } \sqrt{(ab)^2} = |ab| = ab \text{ since } a > 0 \text{ and } b > 0.\text{)}$$

$$= \sqrt{s(s - a)(s - b)(s - c)}$$

And this is Heron's formula.

Examples. Find the area of a triangle with the given sides to the nearest integer.

1) $a = 6$, $b = 7$, and $c = 11$.

We first need to find the value of s.

$$
\begin{aligned}
s &= \frac{1}{2}(a + b + c) \\[2mm]
&= \frac{1}{2}(6 + 7 + 11) \\[2mm]
&= \frac{1}{2}(24) = 12
\end{aligned}
$$

Now we use Heron's formula.

$$
\begin{aligned}
A &= \sqrt{s(s - a)(s - b)(s - c)} \\[2mm]
&= \sqrt{12(12 - 6)(12 - 7)(12 - 11)} \\[2mm]
&= \sqrt{12(6)(5)(1)} \approx 19
\end{aligned}
$$

2) $h = 21$, $g = 19$, and $k = 36$.

We first need to find the value of s. Rather than using a, b, and c in Heron's formula, we will use h, g, and k.

$$
\begin{aligned}
s &= \frac{1}{2}(h + g + k) \\[2mm]
&= \frac{1}{2}(21 + 19 + 36) \\[2mm]
&= \frac{1}{2}(76) = 38
\end{aligned}
$$

Now we use Heron's formula.

$$
\begin{aligned}
A &= \sqrt{s(s - h)(s - g)(s - k)} \\[2mm]
&= \sqrt{38(38 - 21)(38 - 19)(38 - 36)} \\[2mm]
&= \sqrt{38(17)(19)(2)} \approx 157
\end{aligned}
$$

Try These (Set 4):

1) Find the area of triangle ABC if $C = 101°$, $a = 19$, and $b = 7$. Round off your answer to the nearest tenth.

2) Find the area of a triangle whose sides measure 10 feet, 31 feet, and 22 feet.

3) The area of triangle ABC is 120 m^2. Find the length of the side included between angle $A = 40°$ and angle $B = 115°$.

Exercise 8

In Exercises 1-6, find the values of the remaining sides and angles of each triangle. Round off any decimals to the nearest hundredth.

1.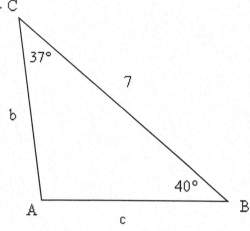

2.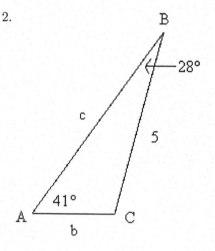

3.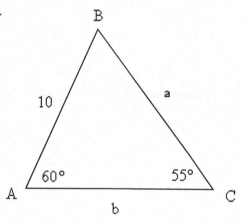

4.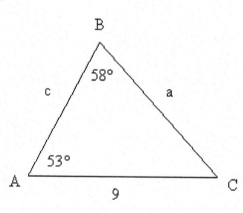

5.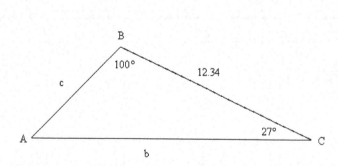

6.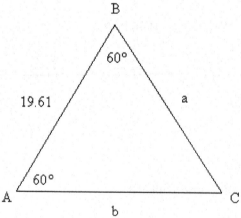

In Exercises 7-14, find the values of the remaining sides and angles of $\triangle ABC$. Round off any decimals to the nearest hundredth.

7. $A = 25°$, $B = 92°$, $a = 13$ in.

8. $A = 104°$, $B = 42°$, $b = 8$ ft.

9. $B = 29°$, $C = 81°$, $b = 49.38$ ft.

10. $A = 72°$, $C = 56°$, $a = 14.65$ m.

11. $A = 68.6°$, $c = 91.8$ m., $B = 18.9°$ 12. $A = 54.7°$, $b = 12.48$ yd., $C = 66.2°$

13. $B = 36°20'$, $a = 17.34$ cm., $C = 102°30'$ 14. $B = 141°29'$, $c = 51.16$ ft., $A = 20°$

In Exercises 15-32, use the given information to solve $\triangle ABC$ (if it exists). Round off any decimals to the nearest hundredth.

15. $A = 40°$, $a = 2$, $b = 5$ 16. $A = 65°$, $a = 3$, $b = 6$ 17. $A = 68°$, $a = 13$, $b = 4$

18. $A = 34°$, $a = 1$, $b = 1$ 19. $A = 127°$, $a = 8.16$, $b = 2.11$ 20. $A = 95°$, $a = 19.03$, $b = 27.46$

21. $A = 25°$, $a = 6$, $b = 8$ 22. $A = 62°$, $a = 3$, $b = 2.8$ 23. $A = 140°$, $a = 13$, $b = 16$

24. $A = 93°$, $a = 7$, $b = 15$ 25. $A = 80°$, $a = 20.35$, $b = 20.6$ 26. $A = 51°$, $a = 6.55$, $b = 7.65$

27. $A = 45°$, $a = 2\sqrt{2}$, $b = 4$ 28. $A = 60°$, $a = \frac{7\sqrt{3}}{2}$, $b = 7$ 29. $A = 34°$, $a = 5.6$, $b = 14$

30. $A = 19°$, $a = 11.18$, $b = 40.3$ 31. $A = 133°$, $a = 4$, $b = 3$ 32. $A = 169°$, $a = 5$, $b = 2$

In Exercises 33-44, determine the number of triangles ABC which can be constructed that contain the given measures.

33. $A = 33°$, $a = b = 5$ 34. $A = 52°$, $a = b = 3$ 35. $B = 95°$, $b = 48$, $c = 26$

36. $C = 102°$, $a = 29$, $c = 13$ 37. $C = 162°$, $b = 2.5$, $c = 1.3$ 38. $B = 107°$, $a = 4.4$, $b = 5.61$

39. $B = 30°$, $b = 14$, $c = 12$ 40. $C = 135°$, $a = 4$, $c = 2.5$ 41. $A = 60°$, $a = 10$, $b = 9$

42. $C = 120°$, $b = 10$, $c = 19$ 43. $A = 30°$, $a = 9$, $c = 15$ 44. $B = 115°$, $a = 8$, $b = 7.6$

In Exercises 45-50, find the values of the remaining sides and angles of each triangle. Round off any decimals to the nearest hundredth.

45.
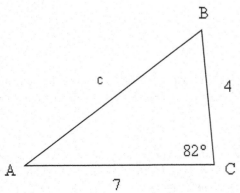

46.
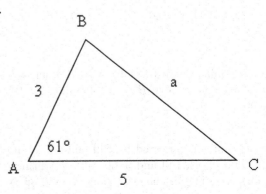

47.

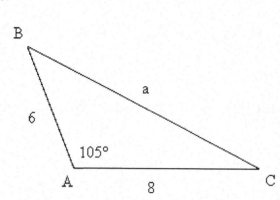

48.

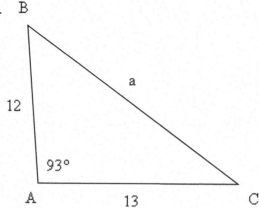

49.

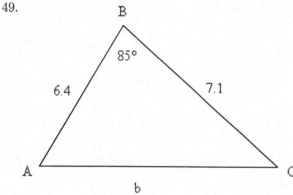

50.

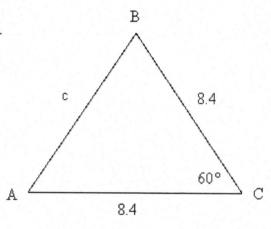

In Exercises 51-68, use the given information to solve $\triangle ABC$. Round off any decimals to the nearest hundredth.

51. $A = 30°$, $b = 6$, $c = 10$ 52. $A = 65°$, $b = 11$, $c = 5$ 53. $C = 75°$, $a = 3$, $b = 8$

54. $B = 52°$, $a = 19$, $c = 12$ 55. $B = 107°$, $a = 9$, $c = 14$ 56. $C = 124°$, $a = 16$, $b = 23$

57. $C = 42°$, $a = 6.85$, $b = 4.15$ 58. $B = 86°$, $a = 3.14$, $c = 17.2$ 59. $A = 116°$, $b = 25.09$, $c = 31.66$

60. $A = 144°$, $b = 18.72$, $c = 29.04$ 61. $a = 10$, $b = 9$, $c = 6$ 62. $a = 15$, $b = 21$, $c = 8$

63. $a = 9.8$, $b = 14.7$, $c = 16.3$ 64. $a = 20.3$, $b = 17.1$, $c = 3.6$ 65. $a = 8$, $b = 8$, $c = 13$

66. $a = 11$, $b = 11$, $c = 26$ 67. $a = 3$, $b = 5$, $c = 4$ 68. $a = 5$, $b = 13$, $c = 12$

69. To determine the distance from B to A across a river, a distance from B to C of 357 meters is measured on one side of the river. If $B = 112°45'$ and $C = 19°$, find the distance from B to A to the nearest hundredth of a meter.

70. A helicopter is observed by Bill and John who are 950 feet apart. As the helicopter flies over the line joining them, both Bill and John take a sighting of the angle of elevation to the helicopter (see the next diagram). How high is the helicopter? Round off your answer to the nearest foot.

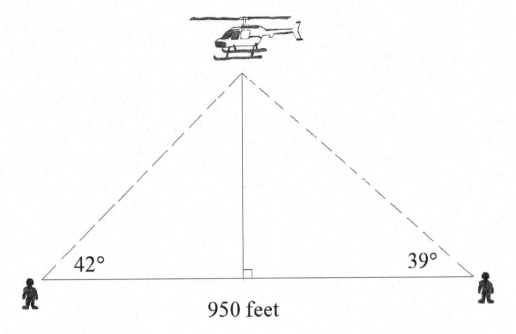

71. Angelina is standing near a radio station antenna and notices that the angle of elevation to the top of the antenna is 65°. After walking 115 feet further away from the antenna, she noticed that the angle of elevation to the top of the antenna is 43° (see diagram below). Find the height of the antenna to the nearest foot.

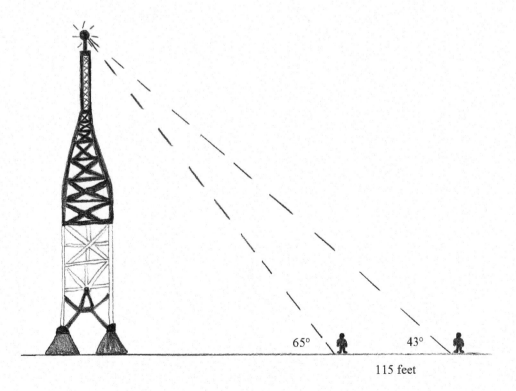

72. Anne is standing on the street. She looks up to the top of a building and figures that the angle of elevation is 36°. She walks 460 feet further away from the building and notices that the angle of elevation to the top of the building is 29°. How far away from the building was Anne when she made her first observation? Round off your answer to the nearest foot.

73. A ski lift begins at ground level 0.75 miles from the base of a mountain whose face has an angle of elevation of 53°. The ski lift ascends in a straight line at an angle of 22° (see the next diagram). Find the length of the ski lift from the beginning of the ski lift to the top of the mountain. Round off your answer to the nearest tenth of a mile.

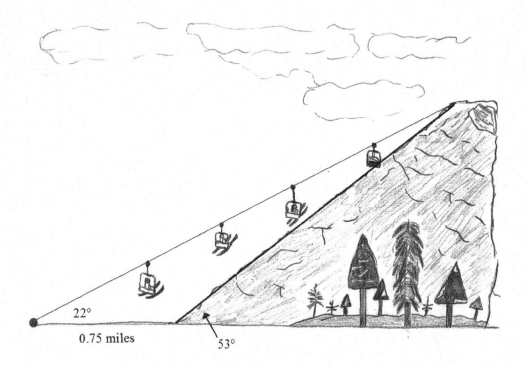

74. To find the distance across a canyon, a surveying team locates points M and N on one side of the canyon and point P on the other side of the canyon. The distance between M and N is 79 yards. The measure of $\angle PMN$ is 72° and the measure of $\angle PNM$ is 69°. Find the distance across the canyon.

75. Kaitlyn spends a day out on her sailboat. While she is sailing, Kaitlyn sees a lighthouse and calculates that the angle of elevation to the top of the lighthouse is 4°. When she sails her boat 690 feet closer to the lighthouse, she figures out that the angle of elevation is now 7°. How tall is the lighthouse? Round off your answer to the nearest hundredth of a foot.

76. Michael is standing on the ground and looking at a 30 foot flagpole which is standing vertically on top of a hill (see the next diagram). He observes that the angle of elevation to the bottom of the pole is 33° and the pole subtends an angle of 0.9°. Find the height of the hill to the nearest tenth of a foot.

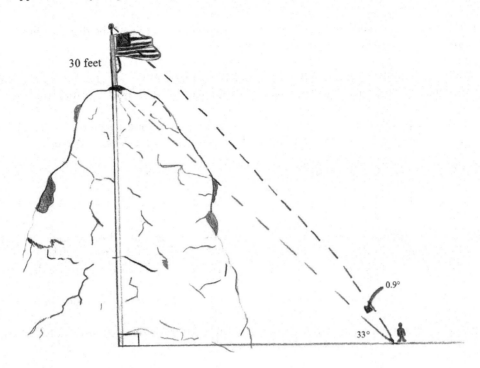

77. Avram is a surveyor who is mapping a triangular plot of land He measures two sides to be 375 yards and 250 yards. The angle formed by these two sides measures 55°. What is the measure of the third side of the plot of land to the nearest tenth of a yard.

78. Thomas is the captain of a ship. One day, he takes the ship out to sea and observes that the ship is 97 miles from one radio transmitter and 122 miles from another. The angle between the signals sent to the ship by the transmitters is 100.94°. How far apart are the transmitters from one another? Round off your answer to the nearest mile.

79. The pitcher's mound on a baseball field is 43 feet from second base and the distance between the bases is 58 feet (note that the pitcher's mound is **not** in the center of the field). Approximately how far is the pitcher's mound from third base?

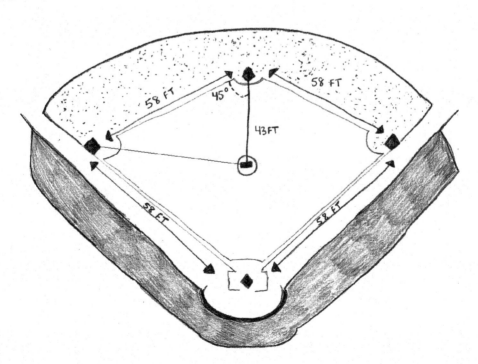

80. The pitcher's mound on a baseball field is 54.75 feet from home plate and the distance between the bases is 85 feet. Approximately how far is the pitcher's mound from first base?

81. The diagonals of a parallelogram are 80 meters and 76 meters and the shorter side of the parallelogram is 25 meters. Find the acute angle formed by the two diagonals to the nearest tenth of a degree.

82. The diagonals of a parallelogram are 34 feet and 40 feet and the longer side of the parallelogram is 76 feet. Find the acute angle formed by the two diagonals to the nearest tenth of a degree.

In Exercises 83-92, find the area of $\triangle ABC$.

83. $B = 30°$, $a = 10$ inches, and $c = 6$ inches.

84. $A = 45°$, $b = 12$ feet, and $c = 8$ feet.

85. $C = 125°$, $a = 4$ yards, and $b = 17$ yards.

86. $B = 136°$, $a = 9$ miles, and $c = 11$ miles.

87. $A = 45.62°$, $b = 12$ feet, and $c = 18$ feet.

88. $C = 71.48°$, $a = 4$ yards, and $b = 13$ yards.

89. $a = 8$ inches, $b = 11$ inches, and $c = 5$ inches.

90. $a = 7$ miles, $b = 16$ miles, and $b = 15$ miles.

91. $a = 4$ meters, $b = 9$ meters, and $c = 6$ meters.

92. $a = 2$ feet, $b = 19$ feet, and $b = 4$ feet.

SOLUTIONS TO 'TRY THESE' EXAMPLES

Chapter 1, Set 1

I) 1) $\frac{1}{8}$ revolution

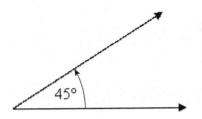

2) $\frac{7}{12}$ revolution

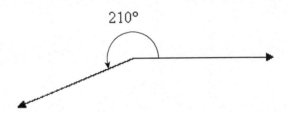

3) $3\frac{1}{8}$ revolutions

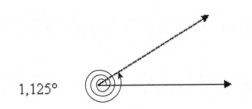

II) 1) 88.1236°   2) 180.9839°   3) 0.6503°

III) 1) 103°40'30"   2) 11°24'7"   3) 450°1'5"

Chapter 1, Set 2

1) 6π yards   2) 3.9 feet   3) 5.5 radians

Chapter 1, Set 3

I) 1) π radians   2) $\frac{13\pi}{4}$ radians   3) $-\frac{4\pi}{3}$ radians   4) $-\frac{\pi}{30}$ radians

II) 1) 120°   2) 1,035°   3) $-150°$ 4) 0°

Chapter 1, Set 4

1) $\frac{100\pi}{3}$ square inches   2) about 15.27 feet/minute   3) 359.1 feet   4) 48,000 radians/hour

---

Chapter 2, Set 1

1) $\sin B = \dfrac{\sqrt{2}}{2}$, $\cos B = \dfrac{\sqrt{2}}{2}$, $\tan B = 1$, $\csc B = \sqrt{2}$, $\sec B = \sqrt{2}$, $\cot B = 1$

2) $\sin \beta = \dfrac{3\sqrt{134}}{67}$, $\cos \beta = \dfrac{7\sqrt{67}}{67}$, $\tan \beta = \dfrac{3\sqrt{2}}{7}$, $\csc \beta = \dfrac{\sqrt{134}}{6}$, $\sec \beta = \dfrac{\sqrt{67}}{7}$, $\cot \beta = \dfrac{7\sqrt{2}}{6}$

Chapter 2, Set 2

I) 1) 0 2) 3 3) 7

II) $\sin \beta = \dfrac{\sqrt{33}}{11}$, $\cos \beta = \dfrac{2\sqrt{22}}{11}$, $\csc \beta = \dfrac{\sqrt{33}}{3}$, $\sec \beta = \dfrac{\sqrt{22}}{4}$, $\cot \beta = \dfrac{2\sqrt{6}}{3}$

Chapter 2, Set 3

I) 1) $\csc 49°$ 2) $\cos 78°$ 3) $\cot \dfrac{3\pi}{10}$ 4) $\sec \dfrac{9\pi}{26}$

II) 1) 0 2) 4 3) 1

Chapter 2, Set 4

1) $\dfrac{2 + \sqrt{3}}{2}$ 2) $-\dfrac{5}{4}$ 3) $\dfrac{\sqrt{6}}{6}$

Chapter 2, Set 5

1) 0.951 2) 0.94 3) 0.80 4) 8.77

Chapter 2, Set 6

1) approximately 6.47 2) approximately 61.73 feet

Chapter 3, Set 1

1) $\sin \theta = -\dfrac{3}{5}$, $\cos \theta = \dfrac{4}{5}$, $\tan \theta = -\dfrac{3}{4}$, $\csc \theta = -\dfrac{5}{3}$, $\sec \theta = \dfrac{5}{4}$, $\cot \theta = -\dfrac{4}{3}$

2) $\sin \theta = -\dfrac{\sqrt{6}}{9}$, $\cos \theta = -\dfrac{5\sqrt{3}}{9}$, $\tan \theta = \dfrac{\sqrt{2}}{5}$, $\csc \theta = -\dfrac{3\sqrt{6}}{2}$, $\sec \theta = -\dfrac{3\sqrt{3}}{5}$, $\cot \theta = \dfrac{5\sqrt{2}}{2}$

3) $\sin \theta = 0$, $\cos \theta = 1$, $\tan \theta = 0$, $\csc \theta$ does not exist, $\sec \theta = 1$, $\cot \theta$ does not exist

Chapter 3, Set 2

1) $\cot x$ 2) $\dfrac{1}{\sin^2 x} = \csc^2 x$ 3) $|\cos \beta|$

Chapter 3, Set 3

I)   quadrant III

II)   1) $-\dfrac{\sqrt{3}}{2}$ 2) 1 3) $\dfrac{\sqrt{2}}{2}$ 4) $-\dfrac{\sqrt{3}}{3}$ 5) $\dfrac{1}{2}$

6) $-\sqrt{2}$ 7) $\sqrt{3}$ 8) $\sqrt{2}$

III) $\sin\alpha = -\dfrac{2\sqrt{2}}{5}$, $\tan\alpha = -\dfrac{2\sqrt{34}}{17}$, $\csc\alpha = -\dfrac{5\sqrt{2}}{4}$, $\cot\alpha = -\dfrac{\sqrt{34}}{4}$, $\sec\alpha = \dfrac{5\sqrt{17}}{17}$

Chapter 3, Set 4

1) $\dfrac{\sqrt{2}}{2}$ 2) $\dfrac{\sqrt{3}}{2}$ 3) $-\sqrt{3}$ 4) 1

Chapter 4, Set 1

1) $\sin t = -\dfrac{\sqrt{2}}{2}$, $\cos t = -\dfrac{\sqrt{2}}{2}$, $\tan t = 1$, $\csc t = -\sqrt{2}$, $\sec t = -\sqrt{2}$, $\cot t = 1$

2) $\sin t = \dfrac{\sqrt{15}}{4}$, $\cos t = \dfrac{1}{4}$, $\tan t = \sqrt{15}$, $\csc t = \dfrac{4\sqrt{15}}{15}$, $\sec t = 4$, $\cot t = \dfrac{\sqrt{15}}{15}$

3) $\sin t = 1$, $\cos t = 0$, $\tan t$ does not exist, $\csc t = 1$, $\sec t$ does not exist, $\cot t = 0$

Chapter 4, Set 2

1) $\sin A = -\dfrac{\sqrt{10}}{5}$, $\cos A = \dfrac{\sqrt{15}}{5}$, $\tan A = -\dfrac{\sqrt{6}}{3}$, $\csc A = -\dfrac{\sqrt{10}}{2}$, $\sec A = \dfrac{\sqrt{15}}{3}$, $\cot A = -\dfrac{\sqrt{6}}{2}$

2) $\sin\alpha = 0$, $\tan\alpha = 0$, $\cos\alpha = -1$, $\csc\alpha$ does not exist, $\sec\alpha = -1$, $\cot\alpha$ does not exist

Chapter 4, Set 3

1) yes   2) no   3) no   4) yes   5) yes   6) no   7) no   8) yes

Chapter 4, Set 4

1) $-\dfrac{3}{4}$ 2) 19.135   3) 5.13   4) 2.07

Chapter 5, Set 1

1)

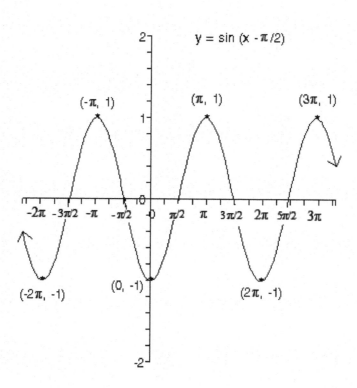

2)

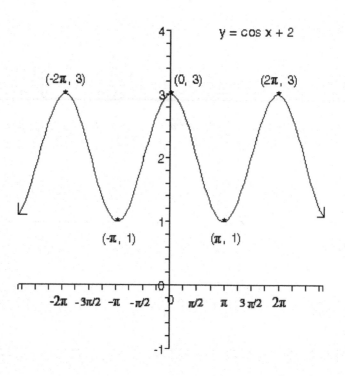

3)

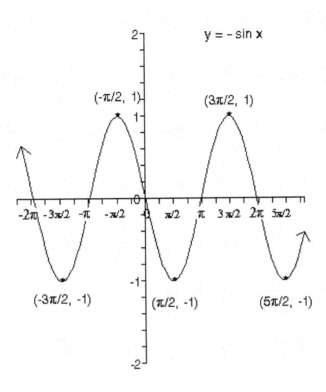

$$y = -\sin x$$

Chapter 5, Set 2

1) The amplitude is 2 and the period is 4π.

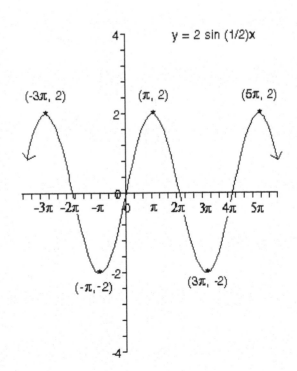

$$y = 2 \sin (1/2)x$$

2) The amplitude is 1 and the period is 1.

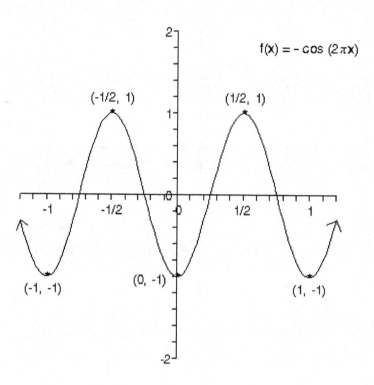

$$f(x) = -\cos(2\pi x)$$

Chapter 5, Set 3

1) The amplitude is 1, the period is 4π, and the phase shift is 2π.

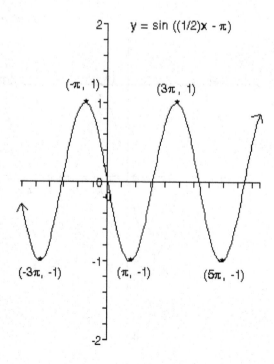

$$y = \sin\left(\tfrac{1}{2}x - \pi\right)$$

2) The amplitude is 2, the period is π, and the phase shift is $-\dfrac{\pi}{6}$.

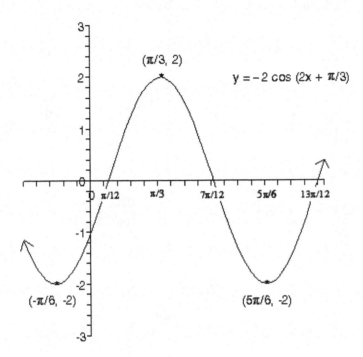

Chapter 6, Set 1

1) $6 \sin x - 9 \cos x$ 2) $-3 \sin^2 A - 5 \sin A + 8$ 3) $-3 \tan 2\theta - 2$

4) $-5 \csc^2 (x+1) + 5 \csc (x-1) + 4 \csc (x+1)$

Chapter 6, Set 2

1) $-24 \sin^3 \theta \cos^8 \theta$ 2) $6 \cos^2 \beta - 11 \cos \beta + 4$ 3) $4 \tan x + 2$ 4) $-4 \csc A \sec^2 A + \csc^3 A$

Chapter 6, Set 3

1) $\tan x \left(\tan^2 x + 6 \right)$ 2) $\sin \theta \cos \theta \left(3 \cos \theta - \sin \theta \right)$ 3) $(\csc \alpha + 7)(\csc \alpha - 9)$

4) $(\cot A + \sin A)(\cot A - \sin A)$ 5) $\sin (3-x) \left[(3 \cos (5x-1) + 2)(\cos (5x-1) - 7) \right]$

Chapter 6, Set 4

1) $\dfrac{2 \cos x}{\sin x} - 3$ 2) $\dfrac{\tan \theta - 2}{\tan \theta - 12}$ 3) $\dfrac{\sec \theta}{5 \sec \theta - \csc \theta}$

Chapter 6, Set 5

1) $\dfrac{4 \tan \alpha}{7 \cos^2 \beta}$

2) $\dfrac{2}{3 \left(5 \sin x - 3\right)}$

3) $\dfrac{\sec \theta + 5}{\sec \theta - 3}$

Chapter 6, Set 6

1) $\dfrac{13 \sin x - 3 \cos x}{\sin x + 2 \cos x}$

2) $-\dfrac{1}{\cot \alpha + 4}$

3) $\sec A$

4) $\dfrac{- \sec^2 \theta - 8 \sec \theta + 8}{2 \sec \theta \left(\sec \theta - 3\right) \left(\sec \theta - 4\right)}$

Chapter 6, Set 7

1) $\dfrac{\tan^2 \alpha - 2}{4 \tan \alpha}$

2) $\dfrac{4 \cos x \left(\csc x + \sin x\right)}{2 \cos x \sin x + 3}$

3) $\dfrac{2 \cos A - 5}{6 \left(\cos A + 3\right)}$

Chapter 6, Set 8

1) $\dfrac{1}{\sin \alpha \cos \alpha}$

2) $\cos^2 \alpha$

3) $\dfrac{1}{\cos \alpha} - \sin \alpha$

4) $\cos^2 \alpha$

Chapter 6, Set 9

1) $\sin x \sec x = \sin x \left(\dfrac{1}{\cos x}\right) = \dfrac{\sin x}{\cos x} = \tan x = \dfrac{1}{\cot x}$

2) $\tan \beta + \cot \beta = \dfrac{\sin \beta}{\cos \beta} + \dfrac{\cos \beta}{\sin \beta} = \left(\dfrac{\sin \beta}{\sin \beta}\right) \dfrac{\sin \beta}{\cos \beta} + \left(\dfrac{\cos \beta}{\cos \beta}\right) \dfrac{\cos \beta}{\sin \beta} = \dfrac{\sin^2 \beta + \cos^2 \beta}{\sin \beta \cos \beta}$

$$= \dfrac{1}{\sin \beta \cos \beta} = \dfrac{1}{\sin \beta} \cdot \dfrac{1}{\cos \beta} = \csc \beta \sec \beta$$

3) $\dfrac{1 - \cos \theta}{\sin^2 \theta} = \dfrac{1 - \cos \theta}{1 - \cos^2 \theta} = \dfrac{1 - \cos \theta}{\left(1 + \cos \theta\right) \left(1 - \cos \theta\right)} = \dfrac{1}{1 + \cos \theta} = \left(\dfrac{\sec \theta}{\sec \theta}\right) \dfrac{1}{1 + \cos \theta} = \dfrac{\sec \theta}{\sec \theta + 1}$

Chapter 6, Set 10

1) $\dfrac{2\sqrt{15} - \sqrt{5}}{12}$

2) $\dfrac{1}{2}$

3) $\cos \left(\pi + \theta\right) = \cos \pi \cos \theta - \sin \pi \sin \theta = -1 \left(\cos \theta\right) - 0 \left(\sin \theta\right) = - \cos \theta$

Chapter 6, Set 11

1) $\dfrac{-3\sqrt{22} - 12\sqrt{11}}{55}$

2) $\dfrac{1}{2}$

3)

$$\sin\left(\frac{\pi}{4}+t\right)+\sin\left(\frac{\pi}{4}-t\right)=\left(\sin\frac{\pi}{4}\cos t+\cos\frac{\pi}{4}\sin t\right)+\left(\sin\frac{\pi}{4}\cos t-\cos\frac{\pi}{4}\sin t\right)$$

$$=\frac{\sqrt{2}}{2}\cos t+\frac{\sqrt{2}}{2}\sin t+\frac{\sqrt{2}}{2}\cos t-\frac{\sqrt{2}}{2}\sin t$$

$$=\sqrt{2}\cos t$$

Chapter 6, Set 12

1) $\dfrac{3\sqrt{5}+\sqrt{7}}{3+\sqrt{35}}$
    2) $-\dfrac{\sqrt{3}}{3}$
    3) $\tan\left(2\pi-x\right)=\underbrace{\dfrac{\tan 2\pi-\tan x}{1+\tan 2\pi\tan x}}_{\tan 2\pi=0}=\dfrac{-\tan x}{1}=\dfrac{-\tan x}{1}$

Chapter 6, Set 13

1) $\dfrac{\sin\left(A+B\right)}{\cos A\cos B}=\dfrac{\sin A\cos B+\cos A\sin B}{\cos A\cos B}=\dfrac{\sin A\cos B}{\cos A\cos B}+\dfrac{\cos A\sin B}{\cos A\cos B}=\dfrac{\sin A}{\cos A}+\dfrac{\sin B}{\cos B}=\tan A+\tan B$

2)

$$\frac{\sin\left(\alpha+\beta\right)}{\cos\left(\alpha-\beta\right)}=\frac{\sin\alpha\cos\beta+\cos\alpha\sin\beta}{\cos\alpha\cos\beta+\sin\alpha\sin\beta}=\left(\frac{\dfrac{1}{\sin\alpha\sin\beta}}{\dfrac{1}{\sin\alpha\sin\beta}}\right)\left(\frac{\sin\alpha\cos\beta+\cos\alpha\sin\beta}{\cos\alpha\cos\beta+\sin\alpha\sin\beta}\right)$$

$$=\frac{\dfrac{\sin\alpha\cos\beta}{\sin\alpha\sin\beta}+\dfrac{\cos\alpha\sin\beta}{\sin\alpha\sin\beta}}{\dfrac{\cos\alpha\cos\beta}{\sin\alpha\sin\beta}+\dfrac{\sin\alpha\sin\beta}{\sin\alpha\sin\beta}}=\frac{\dfrac{\cos\beta}{\sin\beta}+\dfrac{\cos\alpha}{\sin\alpha}}{\dfrac{\cos\alpha}{\sin\alpha}\cdot\dfrac{\cos\beta}{\sin\beta}+1}$$

$$=\frac{\cot\beta+\cot\alpha}{\cot\alpha\cot\beta+1}$$

Chapter 6, Set 14

1) $-\dfrac{19}{27}$
    2) $\dfrac{\sqrt{3}}{3}$
    3) $-\dfrac{3\sqrt{7}}{8}$

Chapter 6, Set 15

1) $\left(\sin A-\cos A\right)^2=\sin^2 A-2\sin A\cos A+\cos^2 A=1-\sin 2A$

2)

$$\cos 4\theta=\cos\left[2\left(2\theta\right)\right]=2\cos^2 2\theta-1$$

$$=2\left(2\cos^2\theta-1\right)^2-1=2\left(4\cos^4\theta-4\cos^2\theta+1\right)-1$$

$$=8\cos^4\theta-8\cos^2\theta+1$$

Chapter 6, Set 16

1) $\sin\dfrac{\theta}{2} = \sqrt{\dfrac{\sqrt{5}+1}{2\sqrt{5}}}$, $\cos\dfrac{\theta}{2} = -\sqrt{\dfrac{\sqrt{5}-1}{2\sqrt{5}}}$, $\tan\dfrac{\theta}{2} = -\dfrac{\sqrt{5}+1}{2}$ 　　　2) $-\dfrac{\sqrt{2-\sqrt{3}}}{2}$

Chapter 6, Set 17

1) $\csc^2\dfrac{\theta}{2} = \dfrac{1}{\sin^2\dfrac{\theta}{2}} = \dfrac{1}{\dfrac{1-\cos\theta}{2}} = \dfrac{2}{1-\cos\theta} = \left(\dfrac{\sec\theta}{\sec\theta}\right)\left(\dfrac{2}{1-\cos\theta}\right) = \dfrac{2\sec\theta}{\sec\theta-1}$

2)

$$\dfrac{2\tan\dfrac{x}{2}}{1+\tan^2\dfrac{x}{2}} = \dfrac{2\left(\dfrac{\sin x}{1+\cos x}\right)}{1+\left(\pm\sqrt{\dfrac{1-\cos x}{1+\cos x}}\right)^2} = \dfrac{\dfrac{2\sin x}{1+\cos x}}{1+\dfrac{1-\cos x}{1+\cos x}}$$

$$= \left(\dfrac{1+\cos x}{1+\cos x}\right)\left(\dfrac{\dfrac{2\sin x}{1+\cos x}}{1+\dfrac{1-\cos x}{1+\cos x}}\right) = \dfrac{2\sin x}{1+\cos x+1-\cos x}$$

$$= \dfrac{2\sin x}{2} = \sin x$$

Chapter 6, Set 18

1) $\dfrac{1}{2}\cos 7x + \dfrac{1}{2}\cos x$ 　　　2) $3\cos 6\theta - 3\cos 8\theta$ 　　　3) $-\dfrac{1}{2}\sin 11t + \dfrac{1}{2}\sin 7t$

Chapter 6, Set 19

1) $2\cos 6x\cos 2x$ 　　　2) $-2\cos 4\beta\sin 3\beta$ 　　　3) $-2\sin 2A\sin A$

Chapter 6, Set 20

1) $\dfrac{\sin A - \sin B}{\cos A - \cos B} = \dfrac{2\cos\left(\dfrac{A+B}{2}\right)\sin\left(\dfrac{A-B}{2}\right)}{-2\sin\left(\dfrac{A+B}{2}\right)\sin\left(\dfrac{A-B}{2}\right)} = -\dfrac{\cos\left(\dfrac{A+B}{2}\right)}{\sin\left(\dfrac{A+B}{2}\right)} = -\cot\left(\dfrac{A+B}{2}\right)$

2) $\dfrac{\sin x + \sin 3x}{4\sin x\cos x} = \dfrac{2\sin\left(\dfrac{x+3x}{2}\right)\cos\left(\dfrac{x-3x}{2}\right)}{4\sin x\cos x} = \underbrace{\dfrac{2\sin 2x\cos(-x)}{4\sin x\cos x} = \dfrac{2(2\sin x\cos x)\cos x}{4\sin x\cos x}}_{\sin 2x = 2\sin x\cos x\ \text{and}\ \cos(-x)=\cos x.} = \cos x$

Chapter 7, Set 1

1) $\dfrac{\pi}{3}$ 2) $-\dfrac{\pi}{4}$ 3) $-\dfrac{7}{9}$ 4) $\dfrac{\pi}{3}$

Chapter 7, Set 2

1) $\dfrac{\pi}{4}$ 2) $\dfrac{2\pi}{3}$ 3) $-\dfrac{3}{4}$ 4) $\dfrac{5\pi}{6}$

Chapter 7, Set 3

1) $\dfrac{\pi}{3}$ 2) $-\dfrac{\pi}{4}$ 3) 4.71   4) $-\dfrac{\pi}{6}$

Chapter 7, Set 4

I)   1) $\dfrac{2\pi}{3}$ 2) $\dfrac{5\sqrt{5}-2}{3\sqrt{26}}$ 3) $-\dfrac{7}{18}$ 4) $\dfrac{\sqrt{10}}{4-\sqrt{6}}$

II)   1) Let $\cos^{-1} x = \theta$. Observe that $0 \le \theta \le \pi$, $\theta \ne \dfrac{\pi}{2}$. Then $\cos\theta = x$, so

$$\tan\left(\cos^{-1} x\right) = \tan\theta = \frac{\sin\theta}{\cos\theta} = \frac{+\sqrt{1-\cos^2\theta}}{\cos\theta} = \frac{\sqrt{1-x^2}}{x}.$$

     2) Let $\sin^{-1} x = \theta$. Then $\sin\theta = x$, so

$$\begin{aligned}
\sin\left(\sin^{-1} x - \frac{\pi}{2}\right) &= \sin\left(\theta - \frac{\pi}{2}\right) = \sin\theta\cos\frac{\pi}{2} - \cos\theta\sin\frac{\pi}{2}\\
&= -\cos\theta = -\sqrt{1-\sin^2\theta} = -\sqrt{1-x^2}.
\end{aligned}$$

Chapter 7, Set 5

1) $\dfrac{\pi}{6}$ 2) $-\dfrac{\pi}{6}$ 3) π 4) $\dfrac{\sqrt{3}}{2}$

Chapter 7, Set 6

In all of the solutions below, k represents any integer.

I)   1) $\left\{\pi k,\ \dfrac{3\pi}{2} + 2\pi k\right\}$ 2) $\left\{2\pi k,\ \dfrac{\pi}{3} + 2\pi k,\ \dfrac{5\pi}{3} + 2\pi k\right\}$ 3) $\dfrac{3\pi}{4} + \pi k$

II)   1) $\left\{\pm\dfrac{3\pi}{2},\ \pm\dfrac{\pi}{2},\ \pm 2\pi,\ 0\right\}$ 2) $\left\{\dfrac{\pi}{6},\ \dfrac{5\pi}{6}\right\}$

Chapter 7, Set 7

In all of the solutions below, k represents any integer.

I)   1) $\left\{ \dfrac{\pi}{4} + \pi k, \; \dfrac{3\pi}{4} + \pi k \right\}$ 2) $\left\{ \dfrac{\pi}{4} + 2\pi k, \; \dfrac{3\pi}{4} + 2\pi k, \; \dfrac{5\pi}{4} + 2\pi k, \; \dfrac{7\pi}{4} + 2\pi k \right\}$

      3) $\left\{ -\dfrac{\pi}{3} + 2\pi k, \; 2\pi k, \; \dfrac{2\pi}{3} + 2\pi k, \; \pi + 2\pi k \right\}$

II)   1) $\left\{ \pm \dfrac{\pi}{6}, \; \pm \dfrac{5\pi}{6} \right\}$ 2) $\{ \pm 75°, \; \pm 285° \}$

Chapter 7, Set 8

1) $\{ 47°, \; 133°, \; -313°, \; -227° \}$ 2) $\{ -298°, \; -188°, \; -118°, \; -8°, \; 62°, \; 172°, \; 242°, \; 352° \}$

Chapter 7, Set 9

1) $\left\{ \dfrac{\pi}{2}, \; \dfrac{3\pi}{2} \right\}$ 2) $\left\{ \dfrac{\pi}{6}, \; \dfrac{5\pi}{6}, \; \dfrac{3\pi}{2} \right\}$ 3) $\left\{ \dfrac{\pi}{2}, \; \dfrac{3\pi}{2} \right\}$

Chapter 7, Set 10

In all of the solutions below, k represents any integer.

I)   1) $\left\{ \dfrac{\pi}{2} + 2\pi k, \; \dfrac{3\pi}{2} + 2\pi k, \; \dfrac{5\pi}{4} + 2\pi k, \; \dfrac{7\pi}{4} + 2\pi k \right\}$ 2) $\left\{ \pi + 2\pi k, \; \dfrac{\pi}{3} + 2\pi k, \; \dfrac{2\pi}{3} + 2\pi k \right\}$

      3) $\left\{ \dfrac{\pi}{3} + 2\pi k, \; \dfrac{2\pi}{3} + 2\pi k, \; 2\pi k \right\}$

II)   1) $\left\{ \dfrac{\pi}{6}, \; \dfrac{5\pi}{6}, \; \dfrac{3\pi}{2} \right\}$ 2) $\left\{ \dfrac{\pi}{4}, \; \dfrac{3\pi}{4}, \; \dfrac{5\pi}{4}, \; \dfrac{7\pi}{4} \right\}$ 3) $\left\{ \dfrac{\pi}{2}, \; \dfrac{3\pi}{2}, \; \dfrac{\pi}{4}, \; \dfrac{3\pi}{4} \right\}$

Chapter 8, Set 1

1) 14 inches   2) $R = 66°30'$, $s = 30$, $t = 21$ 3) $6,287.7$ feet

Chapter 8, Set 2

1) $B = 44°$, $C = 61°$, $c = 16$ inches   2) $R = 24°$, $S = 31.25°$, $s = 8$ 3) 2 triangles

Chapter 8, Set 3

1) $B = 80.7°$, $C = 43.3°$, $a = 8.4$ feet   2) $L = 29.9°$, $M = 63.9°$, $N = 86.2°$ 3) $46.8°$

Chapter 8, Set 4

1) 65.3   2) 56.7 square feet   3) 13.19 m

SOLUTIONS TO ODD NUMBERED EXERCISES

Chapter R Exercise R.1

Exercises 1-19 odd

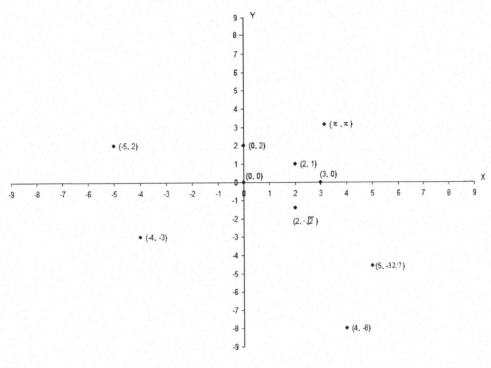

21. 5   23. 10   25. $\sqrt{26}$ 27. $\left(\frac{7}{2}, 3\right)$ 29. $(-3, 0)$ 31. $(4, 2)$

Chapter R Exercise R.2

1.

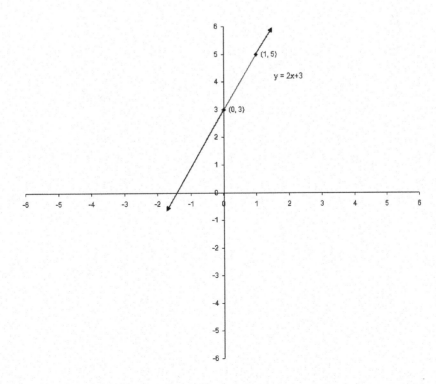

3.

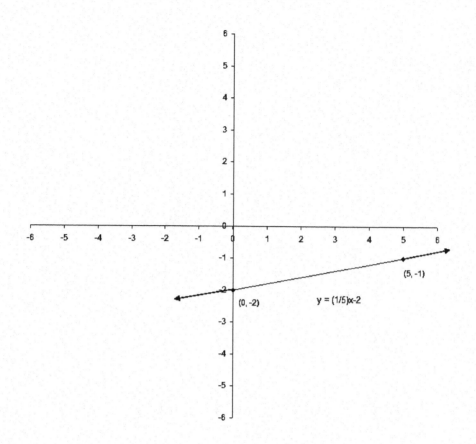

5.

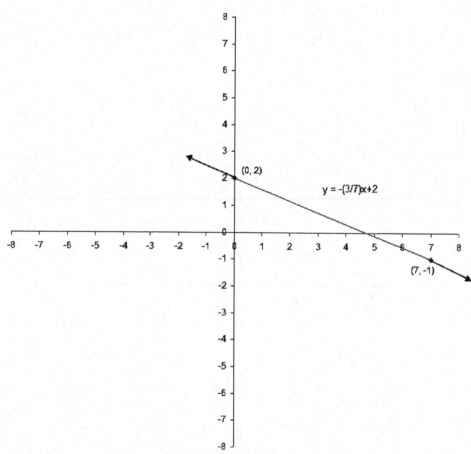

7.

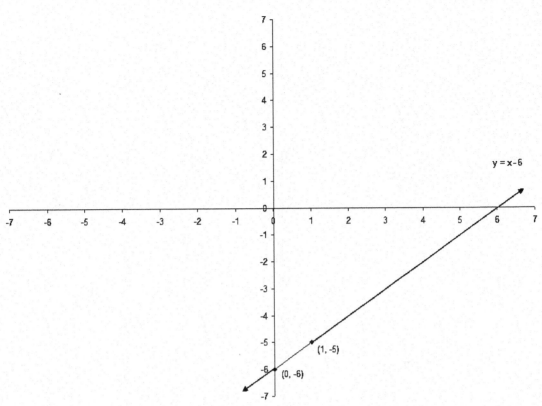

9.

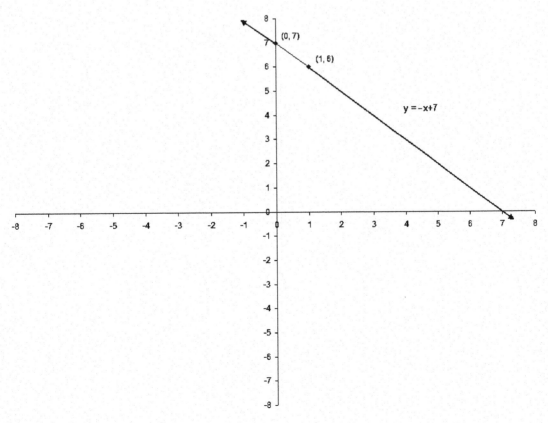

11.

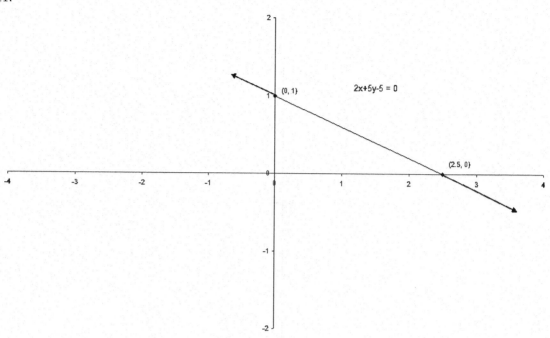

13.

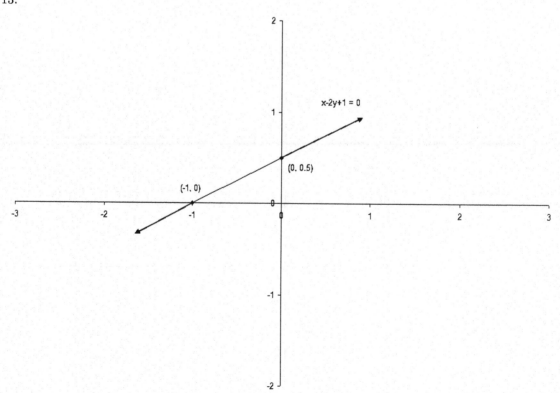

15.

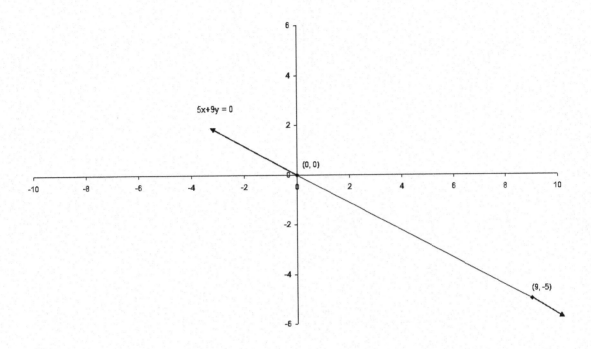

17.

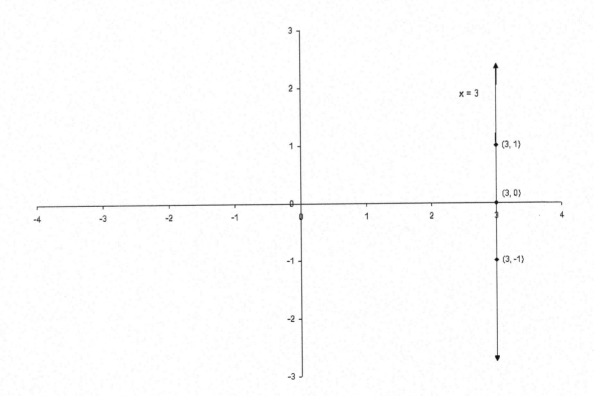

19.

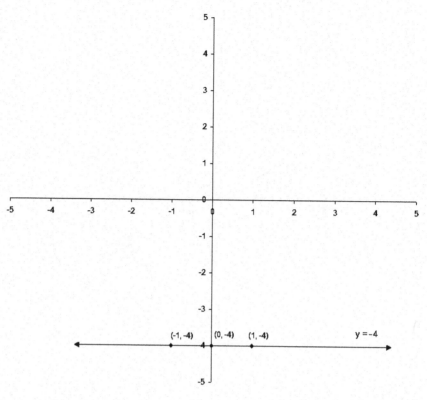

21. $(x - 4)^2 + (y - 1)^2 = 9$ 23. $(x - 6)^2 + (y + 3)^2 = 25$ 25. $x^2 + y^2 = 4$

27. $(x + 9)^2 + (y + 8)^2 = 28$ 29. center $(0, 0)$ and radius 7   31. center $(0, 0)$ and radius 2

33. center $(6, 5)$ and radius 8   35. center $(-8, 0)$ and radius 3   37. center $(3, -1)$ and radius 4

39. center $(6, 0)$ and radius $\sqrt{43}$

41.

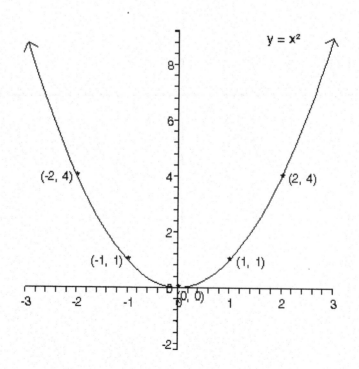

43.

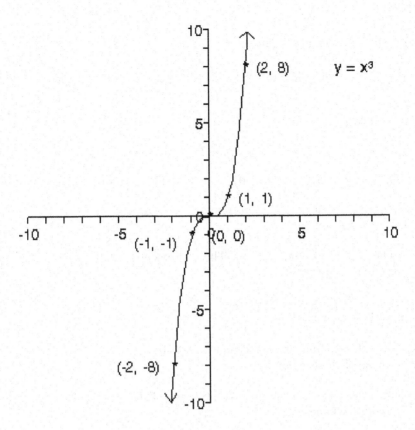

45.

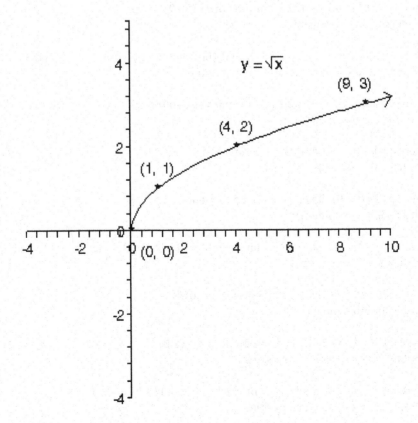

47. yes: $5 = 3(4) - 7$ 49. yes: $-6 = (0) - 6$ 51. no: $3 \neq -\frac{3}{5}(5) + 2$

53. yes: $9 = (5)^2 - 16$ 55. no: $-8 \neq \sqrt{64}$ 57. yes: $0 = \sqrt{4} - 2$

59. yes: $-2 = \frac{1}{-0.5}$ 61. yes: $13.7089 = (2.17)^2 + 9$ 63. yes: $363 = (7.2)^3 - 10.248$

Chapter R Exercise R.3

1. *a*) The *y*-intercept is $(0, 3)$.   *b*) The graph has *y*-axis symmetry.

3. *a*) The *x*-intercept and *y*-intercept are $(0, 0)$.   *b*) The graph has origin symmetry.

5. *a*) The *x*-intercept is $(2, 0)$ and the *y*-intercepts are $(0, -3)$ and $(0, 3)$.
   b) The graph has *x*-axis symmetry.

7. *a*) The *x*-intercepts are $(-2, 0)$ and $(-2, 0)$. The *y*-intercept is $(0, 16)$.
   b) The graph has *y*-axis symmetry.

9. *a*) Both the *y*-intercept and the *x*-intercept are $(0, 0)$.
   b) The graph has origin symmetry.

11. *a*) The *y*-intercept is $(0, 18)$ and the *x*-intercept is $(-3, 0)$.
    b) The graph has none of these symmetries.

13. *a*) The *y*-intercept is $(0, -16)$ and the *x*-intercepts are $(-4, 0)$ and $(4, 0)$.
    b) The graph has *y*-axis symmetry.

15. *a*) The *y*-intercept is $(0, 8)$ and there are no *x*-intercepts.
    b) The graph has *y*-axis symmetry.

17. *a*) There are no *y*-intercepts and the *x*-intercept is $(5, 0)$.
    b) The graph has *x*-axis symmetry.

19. *a*) The *y*-intercepts are $(0, -5)$ and $(0, 5)$ and the *x*-intercepts are $(-5, 0)$ and $(5, 0)$.
    b) The graph has *x*-axis, *y*-axis and origin symmetry.

21. *a*) The *y*-intercepts are $\left(0, -\frac{5}{2}\right)$ and $\left(0, \frac{5}{2}\right)$ and the *x*-intercepts are $(-5, 0)$ and $(5, 0)$.
    b) The graph has origin symmetry.

23. *a*) The *y*-intercept is $(0, -4)$ and the *x*-intercept is $(-8, 0)$.
    b) The graph has none of these symmetries.

25. *a*) The *y*-intercept is $(0, 6)$. There are no *x*-intercepts.
    b) The graph has *y*-axis symmetry.

27. *a*) The *y*-intercept is $(0, -9)$ and the *x*-intercepts are $(-9, 0)$ and $(9, 0)$.
    b) The graph has *y*-axis symmetry.

29. *a*) Both the *y*-intercept and the *x*-intercept are $(0, 0)$.
    b) The graph has origin symmetry.

31. *a*) The *y*-intercept is $(0, 3)$ and the *x*-intercept is $\left(-\frac{9}{2}, 0\right)$.
    b) The graph has none of these symmetries.

33. *a*) The *y*-intercept is $(0, -1)$ and the *x*-intercepts are $(-11, 0)$ and $(1, 0)$.
    b) The graph has none of these symmetries.

35. *a)* The y-intercept is $(0,\ 10)$. There are no x-intercepts.
   b) The graph has y-axis symmetry.

37. *a)* There are no y-intercepts. The x-intercepts are $(-4,\ 0)$ and $(4,\ 0)$.
   b) The graph has x-axis, y-axis and origin symmetry.

39. *a)* There are no y-intercepts and there are no x-intercepts.
   b) The graph has origin symmetry.

Chapter R Exercise R.4

1. It is a function with domain {Steve, Tom, Avi} and range {34, 35, 36}.

3. It is not a function since John $\longrightarrow$ dog and John $\longrightarrow$ bird.

5. It is a function with domain {7, 1, 8} and range {2, -4, 3}.

7. It is a function with domain {1, 4, 9, 16} and range {-1, -2, -3, -4}.

9. It is not a function since $5 \longrightarrow 0$ and $5 \longrightarrow -2$.

11. $f(-2) = -5$, $f(0) = 1$, and $f(5) = 16$.

13. $g(-2) = 17$, $g(0) = 3$, and $g(5) = -32$.

15. $f(-2) = -12$, $f(0) = -10$, and $f(5) = 30$.

17. $f(-2) = -\dfrac{4}{11}$, $f(0) = -\dfrac{4}{5}$, and $f(5) = \dfrac{2}{5}$.

19. $R(-2) = -\dfrac{7}{3}$, $R(0) = \dfrac{5}{3}$, and $R(5) = 0$.

21. $f(-2) = 0$, $f(0) = 2$, and $f(5) = \sqrt{14}$.

23. $f(-2) = \sqrt{22}$, $f(0) = 4$, and $f(5) = 1$,

25. $p(-2) = -\dfrac{\sqrt{2}}{3}$, $p(0) = 2$, and $p(5) = -\dfrac{1}{8}$.

27. y is an implicit function of x.

29. y is an implicit function of x.

31. y is not an implicit function of x.

33. y is not an implicit function of x.

35. y is an implicit function of x.

37. y is an implicit function of x.

39. y is not an implicit function of x.

41. The domain of f is the set of all real numbers.

43. The domain of g is the set of all real numbers.

45. The domain of g is the set of all real numbers.

47. The domain of g is $\{x \mid x \neq -8\}$.

49. The domain of h is $\{x \mid x \neq 4\}$.

51. The domain of g is $\{x \mid x \neq 4, 5\}$.

53. The domain of f is $\{x \mid x \neq -4, 4\}$.

55. The domain of f is the set of all real numbers.

57. The domain of g is $\{x \mid x \geq 9\}$.

59. The domain of f is $\{x \mid x \leq -2 \text{ or } x \geq 2\}$.

61. The domain of f is $\{x \mid -7 \leq x \leq 7\}$.

63. The domain of f is $\{x \mid x \leq -4 \text{ or } x > 3\}$.

65. The domain of f is the set of all real numbers.

67. Yes. It passes the vertical line test.   69. No. It fails the vertical line test.

71. Yes. It passes the vertical line test.

73. a) The domain of f is $\{x \mid -\infty < x < \infty\}$.
    b) The range of f is $\{y \mid y \le -2\}$.
    c) The y-intercept is $(0, -3)$.
    d) No symmetry (x-axis, y-axis, or origin).
    e) f is increasing on $(-\infty, -1)$ and decreasing on $(-1, \infty)$.

75. a) The domain of f is $\{x \mid -\infty < x < \infty\}$.
    b) The range of f is $\{y \mid -\infty < y < \infty\}$.
    c) The y-intercept is $(0, 0)$, and the x-intercepts are $\left(-\sqrt{3}, 0\right)$, $(0, 0)$, and $\left(\sqrt{3}, 0\right)$.
    d) The graph has origin symmetry.
    e) f is increasing on $(-\infty, -1) \cup (1, \infty)$ and decreasing on $(-1, 1)$.

77. a) The domain of f is $\{x \mid -\infty < x < \infty\}$.
    b) The range of f is $\{y \mid y \ge 3\}$.
    c) The y-intercept is $(0, 5)$.
    d) No symmetry (x-axis, y-axis, or origin).
    e) f is decreasing on $(-\infty, 2)$ and increasing on $(2, \infty)$.

79. a) The domain of f is $\{x \mid -5 < x \le 5\}$.
    b) The range of f is $\{y \mid 2 \le y \le 4\}$.
    c) The y-intercept is $(0, 2)$.
    d) No symmetry (x-axis, y-axis, or origin).
    e) f is decreasing on $(-5, -1)$, constant on $(-1, 1)$, and increasing on $(1, 5)$.

81. $f(x) = 2x^2 + 4$ is even.

83. $f(x) = x^3 + 6x$ is odd.

85. $f(x) = x^3 - 7x^2$ is neither even nor odd.

87. $g(x) = 8x$ is odd.

89. $h(x) = \sqrt{x - 7}$ is neither even nor odd.

91. $g(x) = \dfrac{x^2}{x^2 + 4}$ is even.

93. $g(x) = \dfrac{5x}{x^2 - 10}$ is odd.

95. $g(x) = \dfrac{x + 2}{2x - 5}$ is neither even nor odd.

97. $h(x) = x^4 + 12x^2$ is even.

99. $g(x) = -x^3 + 3x^2$ is neither even nor odd.

101. $f(x) = x^3 - 1$ is neither even nor odd.

103. $f(x) = |x| - 7$ is even.

105. $f(x) = |x - 7|$ is neither even nor odd.

Chapter R Exercise R.5

1. $f(x) = x^2$ is the **square function**.

3. $y = x^3$ is the **cube function**.

5. $g(x) = |x|$ is the **absolute value function**.

7. $y = \dfrac{1}{x}$ is the **reciprocal function**.

9. a) $f(1) = 2$ b) $f(-4) = -8$ c) $f(3) = -4$

d)

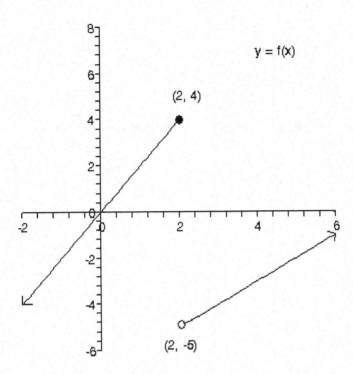

11. a) $f(1) = 1$ b) $f(-4) = 5$ c) $f(3) = 9$

d)

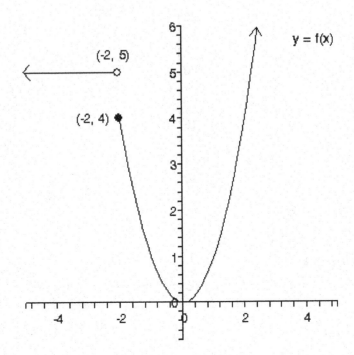

13. a) $f(1) = 1$ b) $f(-4) = -64$ c) $f(3) = \sqrt{3}$

d)

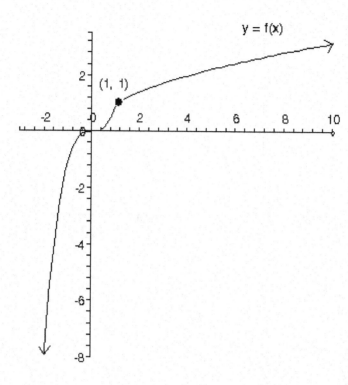

15. a) $f(1) = 0$ b) $f(-4) = 2$ c) $f(3) = -2$

d)

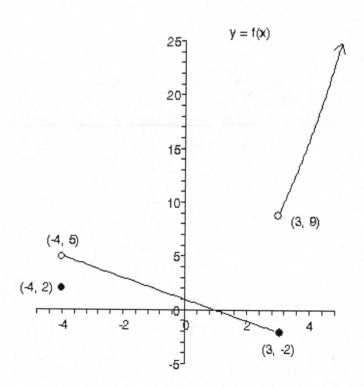

17. a) $f(1) = 1$ b) $f(-4) = -1$ c) $f(3) = -1$

    d)

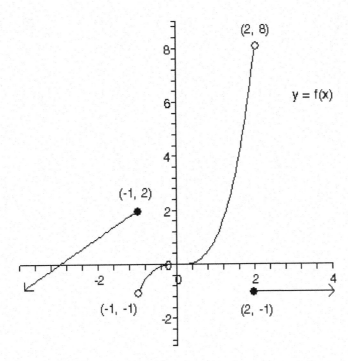

19. a) $f(1) = 4$ b) $f(-4) = -\dfrac{1}{4}$ c) $f(3) = 10$

    d)

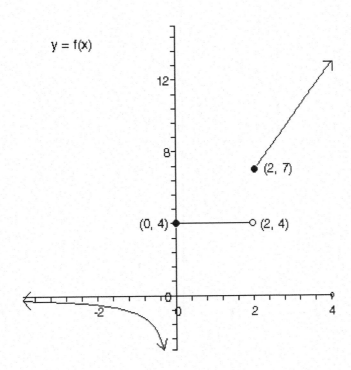

21.

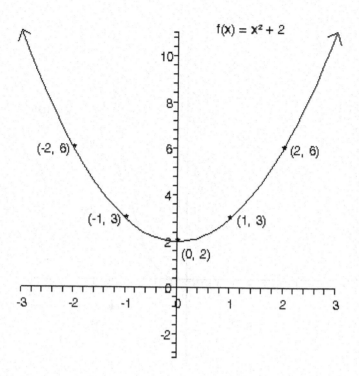

23.

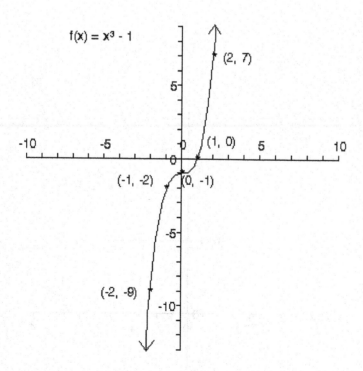

25.

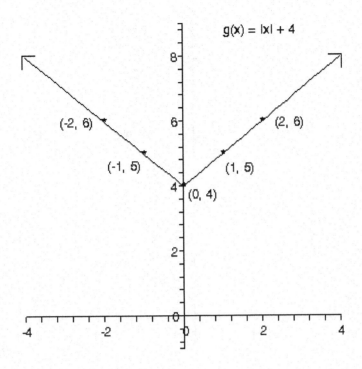

27.

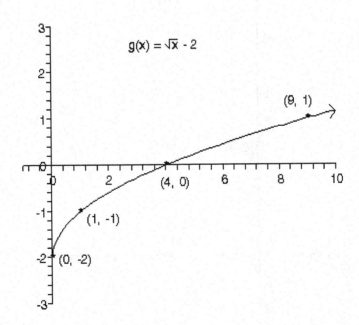

29.

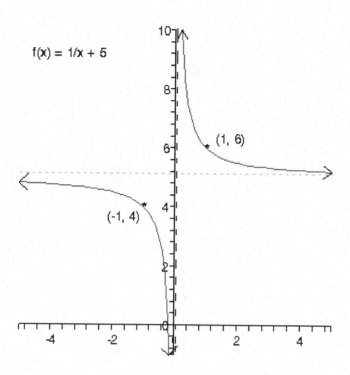

31.

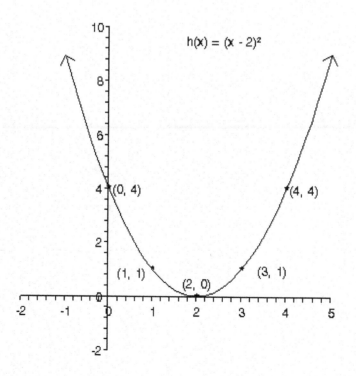

33.

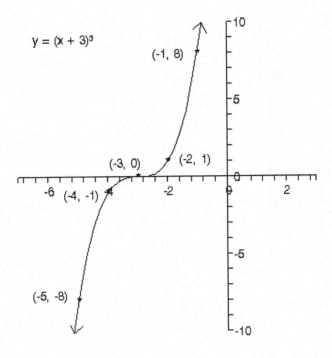

$y = (x + 3)^3$

(-1, 8)

(-3, 0) (-2, 1)

-6 (-4, -1)

(-5, -8)

35.

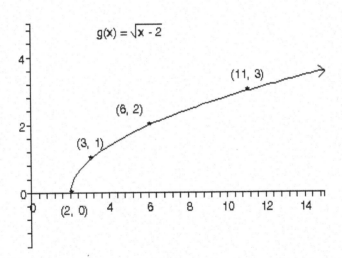

$g(x) = \sqrt{x - 2}$

(11, 3)

(6, 2)

(3, 1)

(2, 0)

37.

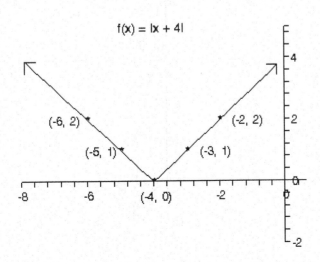

$f(x) = |x + 4|$

(-6, 2) (-2, 2)

(-5, 1) (-3, 1)

(-4, 0)

39.

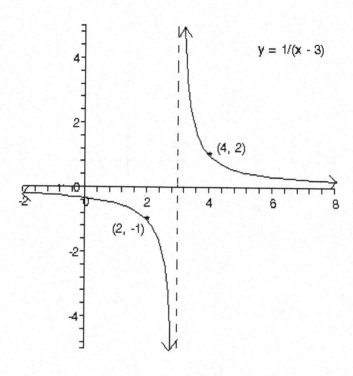

$y = 1/(x - 3)$

(4, 2)

(2, -1)

41.

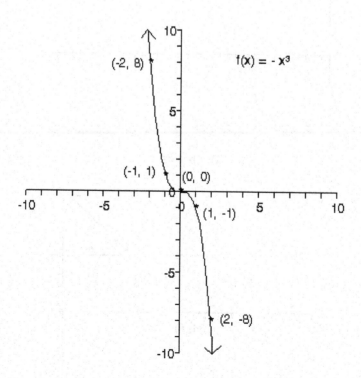

$f(x) = -x^3$

(-2, 8)

(-1, 1)   (0, 0)

(1, -1)

(2, -8)

43.

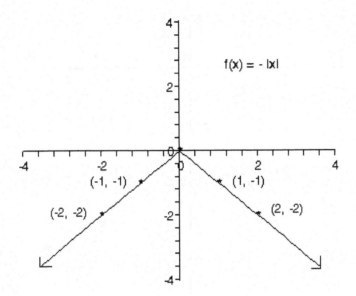

45.

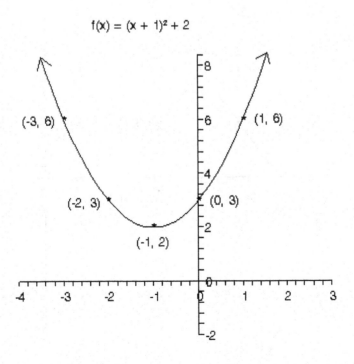

47.

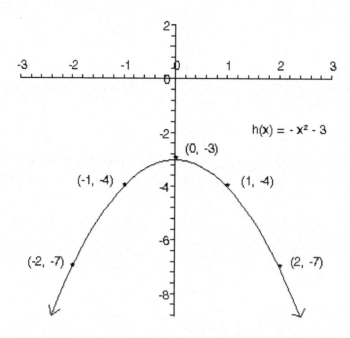

$h(x) = -x^2 - 3$

49.

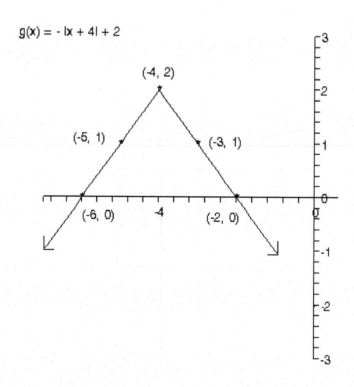

$g(x) = -|x + 4| + 2$

51.

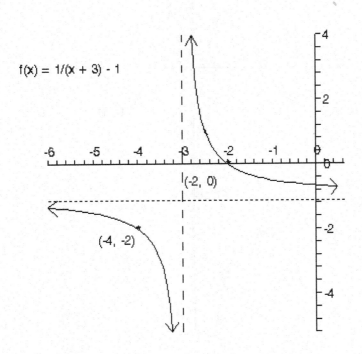

53.

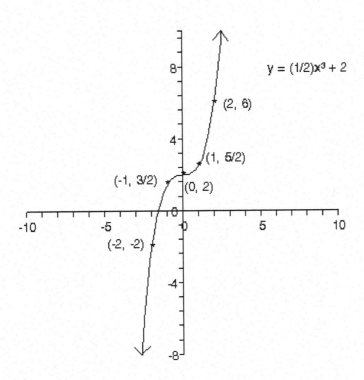

55.

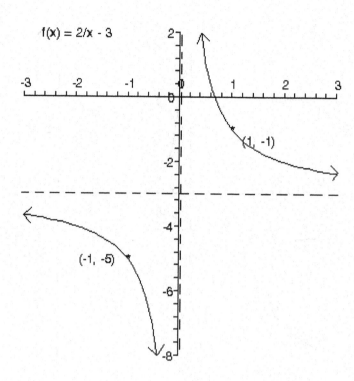

f(x) = 2/x - 3

(1, -1)

(-1, -5)

Chapter R Exercise R.6

1. $(f + g)(x) = -3x + |x| + 7$. The domain of $f + g$ is the set of all real numbers.

3. $(f - h)(x) = \dfrac{-3x^2 + 13x - 18}{x - 3}$. The domain of $f - h$ is $\{x \mid x \neq 3\}$.

5. $(f \cdot g)(x) = -3x\,|x| - 6x + 5\,|x| + 10$. The domain of $f \cdot g$ is the set of all real numbers.

7. $\left(\dfrac{g}{f}\right)(x) = \dfrac{|x| + 2}{-3x + 5}$. The domain of $\dfrac{g}{f}$ is $\left\{x \mid x \neq \dfrac{5}{3}\right\}$.

9. $(h + g)(6) = 11$ 11. $(f - h)(9) = -24$ 13. $(f \cdot g)(-2) = 44$

15. $\left(\dfrac{h}{g}\right)(0) = -\dfrac{1}{2}$ 17. $(f - g)(x) = x - 8 - \sqrt{x}$. The domain of $f - g$ is $\{x \mid x \geq 0\}$.

19. $(f + h)(x) = x - 3$. The domain of $f + h$ is the set of all real numbers.

21. $(f \cdot f)(x) = x^2 - 16x + 64$. The domain of $f \cdot f$ is the set of all real numbers.

23. $(g \cdot g)(x) = x$. The domain of $g \cdot g$ is $\{x \mid x \geq 0\}$.

25. $\left(\dfrac{g}{f}\right)(x) = \dfrac{\sqrt{x}}{x - 8}$. The domain of $\dfrac{g}{f}$ is $\{x \mid x \geq 0 \text{ and } x \neq 8\}$.

27. $(f + g)(25) = 22$ 29. $(h - g)(4) = 3$ 31. $(g \cdot f)(1) = -7$

33. $(h \cdot f)(0) = -40$ 35. $\left(\dfrac{f}{h}\right)(-7) = -3$ 37. $\left(\dfrac{f}{f}\right)(2) = 1$

39. $(f \circ g)(x) = 4\sqrt{x} - 1$. The domain of $f \circ g$ is $\{x \mid x \geq 0\}$.

41. $(h \circ f)(x) = \dfrac{2x + 1}{2x - 2}$. The domain of $h \circ f$ is $\{x \mid x \neq 1\}$.

43. $(f \circ f)(x) = 16x - 5$. The domain of $f \circ f$ is the set of all real numbers.

45. $(h \circ h)(x) = \dfrac{2x - 3}{-x + 6}$. The domain of $h \circ h$ is $\{x \mid x \neq 3,\ x \neq 6\}$.

47. $(h \circ g)(16) = 7$ 49. $(g \circ h)(5) = 2$ 51. $(f \circ f)(0) = -5$ 53. $(h \circ h)(9) = -5$

55. $(f \circ g)(x) = -3$ 57. $(h \circ f)(x) = 17$ 59. $(f \circ f)(x) = -3$ 61. $(g \circ h)(-3) = 21$

63. $(f \circ h)(-6) = -3$ 65. $(h \circ h)(0) = -8$ 67. $(g \circ g)(-7) = 7$

69. a) $(f \circ g)(x) = 3x - 6$ b) $(g \circ f)(x) = 3x - 2$ c) $(f \circ f)(x) = 9x$ d) $(g \circ g)(x) = x - 4$

71. a) $(f \circ g)(x) = -3x + 11$ b) $(g \circ f)(x) = -3x + 5$ c) $(f \circ f)(x) = x$ d) $(g \circ g)(x) = 9x - 28$

73. a) $(f \circ g)(x) = 2$ b) $(g \circ f)(x) = 11$ c) $(f \circ f)(x) = 2$ d) $(g \circ g)(x) = 16x + 15$

75. a) $(f \circ g)(x) = \sqrt{5x + 7}$ b) $(g \circ f)(x) = 5\sqrt{x} + 7$ c) $(f \circ f)(x) = \sqrt{\sqrt{x}}$

   d) $(g \circ g)(x) = 25x + 42$

77. a) $(f \circ g)(x) = \dfrac{2}{2 + x}$ b) $(g \circ f)(x) = \dfrac{2x + 2}{x}$ c) $(f \circ f)(x) = \dfrac{x}{2x + 1}$ d) $(g \circ g)(x) = x$

79. a) $(f \circ g)(x) = \dfrac{3x - 1}{9x - 6}$ b) $(g \circ f)(x) = \dfrac{-x + 1}{x}$ c) $(f \circ f)(x) = \dfrac{4x + 1}{3x + 3}$ d) $(g \circ g)(x) = 9x - 8$

81. a) $(f \circ g)(x) = x^4 + 6x^2 + 5$ b) $(g \circ f)(x) = x^4 - 8x^2 + 19$ c) $(f \circ f)(x) = x^4 - 8x^2 + 12$

   d) $(g \circ g)(x) = x^4 + 6x^2 + 12$

83. a) $(f \circ g)(x) = x^2 + 4$ b) $(g \circ f)(x) = x^2 + 8|x| + 16$ c) $(f \circ f)(x) = |x| + 8$

   d) $(g \circ g)(x) = x^4$

85. a) $(f \circ g)(x) = \dfrac{4x - 9}{8x - 17}$ b) $(g \circ f)(x) = \dfrac{x + 2}{-9x - 14}$ c) $(f \circ f)(x) = \dfrac{x + 2}{2x + 5}$

   d) $(g \circ g)(x) = \dfrac{4x - 9}{-36x + 85}$

Chapter R Exercise R.7

1. The set of ordered pairs for the inverse is $\{(-6,\ -2),\ (0,\ 0),\ (3,\ 1)\}$. The inverse is a function.

3. The set of ordered pairs for the inverse is $\{(9,\ 2),\ (3,\ 1)\}$. The inverse is a function.

5. The set of ordered pairs for the inverse is $\{(1,\ -1),\ (1,\ 1),\ (16,\ 4),\ (9,\ -3)\}$.
   The inverse is not a function.

7. The set of ordered pairs for the inverse is $\{(0,\ 9),\ (4,\ 3),\ (4,\ 0),\ (12,\ -7)\}$.
   The inverse is not a function.

9. The set of ordered pairs for the inverse is $\{(1,\ 1),\ (-3,\ 2),\ (-7,\ 3)\}$. The inverse is a function.

11. The set of ordered pairs for the inverse is $\{(12,\ 0),\ (0,\ 4)\}$. The inverse is a function.

13. The set of ordered pairs for the inverse is $\{(-1,\ 0),\ (5,\ 2),\ (-1,\ 4)\}$. The inverse is not a function.

15. $f(x) = x - 3$ is one-to-one.   17. $h(x) = -3x + 3$ is one-to-one.

19. $f(x) = x^2 + 1$ is not one-to-one.   21. $f(x) = (x-3)^2$, $x \geq 3$, is one-to-one.

23. $f(x) = x^2 + 2$, $x \geq -1$, is not one-to-one.   25. $f(x) = 5$ is not one-to-one.

27. $f(x) = \sqrt{x} + 4$ is one-to-one.   29. $h(x) = \sqrt{x - 6}$ is one-to-one.

31. $g(x) = \dfrac{1}{x - 2}$ is one-to-one.   33. $g(x) = \dfrac{1}{x} + 5$ is one-to-one.

35. $g(x) = |x - 3|$ is not one-to-one.

37. $(f \circ g)(x) = f(g(x)) = f(x+5) = (x+5) - 5 = x$ and

$(g \circ f)(x) = g(f(x)) = g(x-5) = (x-5) + 5 = x.$

39. $(f \circ g)(x) = f(g(x)) = f\left(\dfrac{x}{4}\right) = 4\left(\dfrac{x}{4}\right) = x$ and $(g \circ f)(x) = g(f(x)) = g(4x) = \dfrac{4x}{4} = x.$

41. $(f \circ g)(x) = f(g(x)) = f\left(\dfrac{1}{3}x - 1\right) = 3\left(\dfrac{1}{3}x - 1\right) + 3 = x - 3 + 3 = x$ and

$(g \circ f)(x) = g(f(x)) = g(3x + 3) = \dfrac{1}{3}(3x + 3) - 1 = x + 1 - 1 = x.$

43. $(f \circ g)(x) = f(g(x)) = f\left(\dfrac{1}{9}x + \dfrac{2}{9}\right) = 9\left(\dfrac{1}{9}x + \dfrac{2}{9}\right) - 2 = x + 2 - 2 = x$ and

$(g \circ f)(x) = g(f(x)) = g(9x - 2) = \dfrac{1}{9}(9x - 2) + \dfrac{2}{9} = x - \dfrac{2}{9} + \dfrac{2}{9} = x.$

45. $(f \circ g)(x) = f(g(x)) = f\left(\dfrac{6}{5}x - \dfrac{2}{5}\right) = \dfrac{5}{6}\left(\dfrac{6}{5}x - \dfrac{2}{5}\right) + \dfrac{1}{3} = x - \dfrac{1}{3} + \dfrac{1}{3} = x$ and

$(g \circ f)(x) = g(f(x)) = g\left(\dfrac{5}{6}x + \dfrac{1}{3}\right) = \dfrac{6}{5}\left(\dfrac{5}{6}x + \dfrac{1}{3}\right) - \dfrac{2}{5} = x + \dfrac{2}{5} - \dfrac{2}{5} = x.$

47. $(f \circ g)(x) = f(g(x)) = f(\sqrt{x-1}) = (\sqrt{x-1})^2 + 1 = x - 1 + 1 = x$ and

$(g \circ f)(x) = g(f(x)) = g(x^2 + 1) = \sqrt{(x^2 + 1) - 1} = \sqrt{x^2} = \underbrace{|x| = x}_{\text{since } x \geq 0}.$

49. $(f \circ g)(x) = f(g(x)) = f(\sqrt{x} + 4) = ((\sqrt{x} + 4) - 4)^2 = (\sqrt{x})^2 = x$ and

$(g \circ f)(x) = g(f(x)) = g\left((x - 4)^2\right) = \sqrt{(x - 4)^2} + 4 = \underbrace{|x - 4| + 4 = x - 4 + 4}_{\text{since } x \geq 4} = x.$

51. $(f \circ g)(x) = f(g(x)) = f\left(-\sqrt{x+6}\right) = \left(-\sqrt{x+6}\right)^2 - 6 = x + 6 - 6 = x$ and

$(g \circ f)(x) = g(f(x)) = g(x^2 - 6) = -\sqrt{(x^2 - 6) + 6} = -\sqrt{x^2} = \underbrace{-|x| = -(-x)}_{\text{since } x \leq 0} = x.$

53. $(f \circ g)(x) = f(g(x)) = f(\sqrt[3]{x} + 9) = ((\sqrt[3]{x} + 9) - 9)^3 = (\sqrt[3]{x})^3 = x$ and

$(g \circ f)(x) = g(f(x)) = g\left((x-9)^3\right) = \sqrt[3]{(x-9)^3} + 9 = x - 9 + 9 = x.$

55. $(f \circ g)(x) = f(g(x)) = f\left(\dfrac{3}{x}\right) = \dfrac{3}{\frac{3}{x}} = \dfrac{3(x)}{\frac{3}{x}(x)} = \dfrac{3x}{3} = x$ and $(g \circ f)(x)$ is the same.

57. The inverse function is $f^{-1}(x) = \frac{1}{2}y - 4$. The domain and range are both the set of all real numbers.

59. The inverse function is $g^{-1}(x) = -\frac{1}{7}x$. The domain and range are both the set of all real numbers.

61. The inverse function is $h^{-1}(x) = \frac{3}{2}x + \frac{15}{2}$. The domain and range are both the set of all real numbers.

63. The inverse function is $g^{-1}(x) = \sqrt[3]{x} - 8$. The domain and range are both the set of all real numbers.

65. The inverse function is $f^{-1}(x) = \dfrac{1 - 3x}{x}$. The domain is $\{x \mid x \neq 0\}$ and the range is $\{y \mid y \neq -3\}$.

67. The inverse function is $g^{-1}(x) = \dfrac{1}{x + 6}$. The domain is $\{x \mid x \neq -6\}$ and the range is $\{y \mid y \neq 0\}$.

69. The inverse function is $f^{-1}(x) = \dfrac{2x + 4}{x - 1}$. The domain is $\{x \mid x \neq 1\}$ and the range is $\{y \mid y \neq 2\}$.

71. The inverse function is $f^{-1}(x) = \dfrac{-x + 3}{3x + 2}$. The domain is $\left\{x \mid x \neq -\frac{2}{3}\right\}$ and the range is $\left\{y \mid y \neq -\frac{1}{3}\right\}$.

73. The inverse function is $f^{-1}(x) = x^2 - 3$. The domain is $\{x \mid x \geq 0\}$ and the range is $\{y \mid y \geq -3\}$.

75. The inverse function is $f^{-1}(x) = (x - 3)^2$. The domain is $\{x \mid x \geq 3\}$ and the range is $\{y \mid y \geq 0\}$.

77. The inverse function is $f^{-1}(x) = \sqrt{x + 9}$. The domain is $\{x \mid x \geq -9\}$ and the range is $\{y \mid y \geq 0\}$.

79. The inverse function is $f^{-1}(x) = -\sqrt{x - 3}$. The domain is $\{x \mid x \geq 3\}$ and the range is $\{y \mid y \leq 0\}$.

81. The inverse function is $f^{-1}(x) = \sqrt{x} + 5$. The domain is $\{x \mid x \geq 0\}$ and the range is $\{y \mid y \geq 5\}$.

83. The inverse function is $f^{-1}(x) = -\sqrt{x} - 8$. The domain is $\{x \mid x \geq 0\}$ and the range is $\{y \mid y \leq -8\}$.

85.

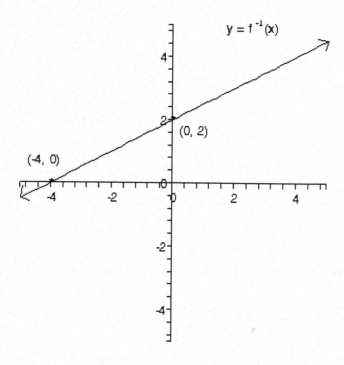

87.

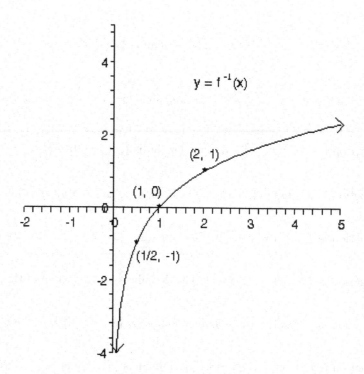

89.

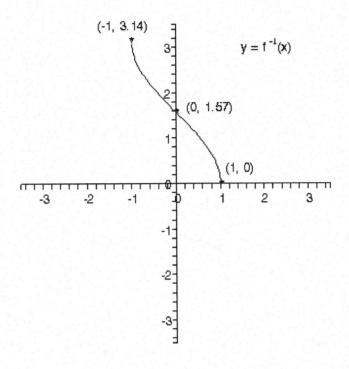

Chapter 1 Exercise 1

1. 0 revolutions

3. $\frac{1}{6}$ revolution

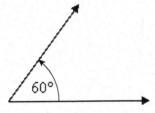

5. $\frac{1}{4}$ revolution

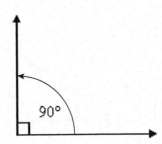

7. $\frac{1}{3}$ revolution

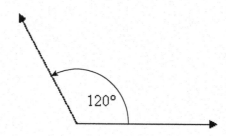

9. $\frac{7}{12}$ revolution

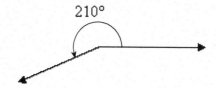

11. $\frac{5}{6}$ revolution

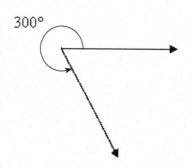

13. $\frac{1}{4}$ revolution in the clockwise direction.

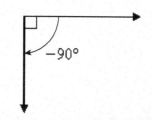

15. $\frac{5}{12}$ revolution in the clockwise direction.

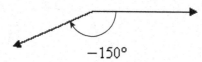

17. $\frac{7}{8}$ revolution in the clockwise direction.

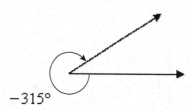

19. $\frac{1}{8}$ revolution

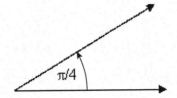

21. $\frac{3}{4}$ revolution

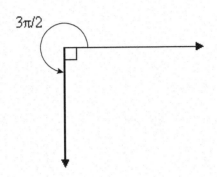

23. $\frac{5}{12}$ revolution

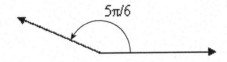

25. $\frac{3}{2}$ revolution

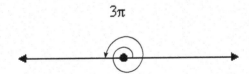

27. $\frac{9}{8}$ revolution clockwise.

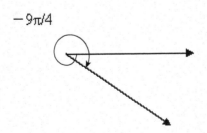

29. $\frac{13}{12}$ revolution clockwise.

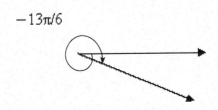

31. 70.5042°   33. 154.4686°   35. 53.1622°   37. 179.0038°

39. 16°8'24"   41. 76°49'52"   43. 35°59'28"   45. 22'5"

47. $s = 2$ inches   49. $s = 18.850$ meters   51. $\theta = 3$ radians

53. $\theta = 4.189$ radians   55. $s = 0.681$ feet   57. $r = 12.527$ meters

59. $\frac{\pi}{6}$ 61. $\frac{3\pi}{4}$ 63. $\frac{11\pi}{6}$ 65. $\frac{2\pi}{3}$ 67. $-\frac{\pi}{2}$ 69. -2π

71. 4π 73. $\frac{25\pi}{4}$ 75. $\frac{35\pi}{3}$ 77. 45°   79. 135°   81. 75°

83. 70°   85. 54°   87. $-180°$ 89. 390°   91. 900°   93. $1,980°$

95. $s = \frac{3\pi}{4}$ inches and $A = \frac{9\pi}{8}$ square inches.   97. $s = 6\pi$ meters and $A = 18\pi$ square meters.

99. 26.18 in/sec   101. 18.85 inches   103. 7.32 inches

105. 2.492 radians $\approx 142.78°$ 107. 5 in/sec   109. $\frac{\pi}{6}$ rad/sec

111. 667.8 feet   113. 324 ft/min   115. $5,877$ rad/min

Chapter 2 Exercise 2

1. $\sin\theta = \frac{4}{5}$, $\cos\theta = \frac{3}{5}$, $\tan\theta = \frac{4}{3}$, $\csc\theta = \frac{5}{4}$, $\sec\theta = \frac{5}{3}$, $\cot\theta = \frac{3}{4}$

3. $\sin\alpha = \frac{\sqrt{2}}{2}$, $\cos\alpha = \frac{\sqrt{2}}{2}$, $\tan\alpha = 1$, $\csc\alpha = \sqrt{2}$, $\sec\alpha = \sqrt{2}$, $\cot\alpha = 1$

5. $\sin\beta = \frac{\sqrt{6}}{3}$, $\cos\beta = \frac{\sqrt{3}}{3}$, $\tan\beta = \sqrt{2}$, $\csc\beta = \frac{\sqrt{6}}{2}$, $\sec\beta = \sqrt{3}$, $\cot\beta = \frac{\sqrt{2}}{2}$

7. $\sin A = \frac{\sqrt{13}}{7}$, $\cos A = \frac{6}{7}$, $\tan A = \frac{\sqrt{13}}{6}$, $\csc A = \frac{7\sqrt{13}}{13}$, $\sec A = \frac{7}{6}$, $\cot A = \frac{6\sqrt{13}}{13}$

9. $\sin\theta = \frac{4\sqrt{118}}{59}$, $\cos\theta = \frac{3\sqrt{177}}{59}$, $\tan\theta = \frac{4\sqrt{6}}{9}$, $\csc\theta = \frac{\sqrt{118}}{8}$, $\sec\theta = \frac{\sqrt{177}}{9}$, $\cot\theta = \frac{3\sqrt{6}}{8}$

11. 1   13. 1   15. 1   17. 0   19. 1   21. -1 23. -1

25. 3   27. 0   29. 0   31. 1   33. 0   35. 0   37. 0

39. 1   41. 1   43. -1 45. $\frac{1}{4}$ 47. $\frac{2}{3}$ 49. 0   51. $\frac{3}{2}$

53. $\frac{1}{7}$ 55. $\frac{1}{2}$ 57. $\frac{\sqrt{41}}{6}$ 59. $\frac{\sqrt{91}}{3}$ 61. $\cos\theta = \frac{\sqrt{35}}{6}$ and $\tan\theta = \frac{\sqrt{35}}{35}$.

63. $\sin\gamma = \frac{\sqrt{3}}{3}$ and $\cot\gamma = \sqrt{2}$.   65. $\frac{2\sqrt{2}}{3}$ 67. $\frac{2\sqrt{6}}{5}$ 69. $\frac{\sqrt{3}}{2}$ 71. $\frac{3\sqrt{3}}{4}$

73. $\frac{3\sqrt{7}}{8}$ 75. $\frac{2\sqrt{11}}{7}$ 77. (a) $\frac{2\sqrt{3}}{3}$ (b) $\frac{\sqrt{3}}{2}$ (c) $\frac{1}{4}$ (d) 2   (e) 3   (f) $\frac{1}{3}$

79. (a) $\frac{1}{x}$ (b) x (c) $1 - x^2$ (d) $\frac{1-x^2}{x^2}$ (e) $\frac{\sqrt{1-x^2}}{x}$ (f) $\frac{1}{x}$

81. $\dfrac{1}{2}$ 83. $\dfrac{2+\sqrt{3}}{\sqrt{3}}$ 85. $-\dfrac{1}{12}$ 87. $\dfrac{1}{3}$ 89. $\dfrac{1-2\sqrt{2}}{2}$ 91. $\dfrac{1}{3}$

93. $\dfrac{2+\sqrt{2}}{2}$ 95. 0.554   97. 0.326   99. 1.079   101. 6.314   103. 0.809

105. 0.842   107. 1.189   109. 0.630   111. 5.35   113. 5.22   115. 34.28

117. 30.02   119. 79.39   121. 158.71   123. 19.24   125. 84.56

Chapter 3 Exercise 3

1. $\sin\theta = \dfrac{4}{5}$, $\cos\theta = \dfrac{3}{5}$, $\tan\theta = \dfrac{4}{3}$, $\csc\theta = \dfrac{5}{4}$, $\sec\theta = \dfrac{5}{3}$, $\cot\theta = \dfrac{3}{4}$

3. $\sin\theta = -\dfrac{1}{3}$, $\cos\theta = \dfrac{2\sqrt{2}}{3}$, $\tan\theta = \dfrac{-\sqrt{2}}{4}$, $\csc\theta = -3$, $\sec\theta = \dfrac{3\sqrt{2}}{4}$, $\cot\theta = -2\sqrt{2}$

5. $\sin\theta = 0$, $\cos\theta = -1$, $\tan\theta = 0$, $\csc\theta$ is undefined, $\sec\theta = -1$, $\cot\theta$ is undefined

7. $\sin\theta = -\dfrac{\sqrt{2}}{2}$, $\cos\theta = -\dfrac{\sqrt{2}}{2}$, $\tan\theta = 1$, $\csc\theta = -\sqrt{2}$, $\sec\theta = -\sqrt{2}$, $\cot\theta = 1$

9. $\csc x$ 11. $\cos^2\theta$ 13. 1   15. $\dfrac{1}{2}$ 17. 1   19. $-10\tan\theta$ 21. $\cos\theta$

23. -1 25. -1 27. $45°$ 29. $30°$ 31. $30°$ 33. $45°$ 35. $60°$

37. $60°$ 39. $60°$ 41. $45°$ 43. $\dfrac{\pi}{4}$ 45. $\dfrac{\pi}{6}$ 47. $\dfrac{\pi}{4}$ 49. $\dfrac{\pi}{3}$

51. $\dfrac{1}{2}$ 53. $\dfrac{\sqrt{2}}{2}$ 55. $-\sqrt{3}$ 57. -2 59. $\dfrac{\sqrt{3}}{3}$ 61. $-\dfrac{2\sqrt{3}}{3}$

63. $\dfrac{\sqrt{2}}{2}$ 65. $\dfrac{\sqrt{3}}{3}$ 67. $\sqrt{2}$ 69. -1 71. $-\dfrac{\sqrt{3}}{2}$ 73. -1

75. 2   77. $-\sqrt{3}$ 79. $\sqrt{2}$ 81. $-\dfrac{1}{2}$ 83. $\dfrac{\sqrt{2}}{2}$ 85. $\dfrac{\sqrt{3}}{3}$

87. -1 89. $-\dfrac{\sqrt{2}}{2}$ 91. $\dfrac{1}{2}$ 93. $-\dfrac{\sqrt{3}}{3}$ 95. $-\dfrac{2\sqrt{3}}{3}$ 97. $\sqrt{3}$

99. $\dfrac{\sqrt{3}}{2}$ 101. $\dfrac{\sqrt{3}}{3}$ 103. $\dfrac{\sqrt{3}}{2}$ 105. $-\dfrac{2\sqrt{3}}{3}$ 107. $-\sqrt{3}$ 109. 0

111. 0   113. 0   115. 1   117. -1 119. 0   121. -1 123. 1

125. 0   127. -1 129. 0   131. 0   133. 0   135. 1

137. quadrant I   139. quadrant III   141. quadrant II   143. quadrant IV

145. $\sin A = \dfrac{4}{5}$, $\cos A = \dfrac{3}{5}$, $\csc A = \dfrac{5}{4}$, $\sec A = \dfrac{5}{3}$, $\cot A = \dfrac{3}{4}$

147. $\sin A = -\dfrac{\sqrt{21}}{5}$, $\tan A = \dfrac{\sqrt{21}}{2}$, $\csc A = -\dfrac{5\sqrt{21}}{21}$, $\sec A = -\dfrac{5}{2}$, $\cot A = \dfrac{2}{\sqrt{21}}$

149. $\sin A = \dfrac{\sqrt{22}}{11}$, $\cos A = -\dfrac{3\sqrt{11}}{11}$, $\csc A = \dfrac{\sqrt{22}}{2}$, $\sec A = -\dfrac{\sqrt{11}}{3}$, $\cot A = -\dfrac{3\sqrt{2}}{2}$

151. $\cos A = \dfrac{\sqrt{11}}{4}$, $\tan A = -\dfrac{\sqrt{55}}{11}$, $\csc A = -\dfrac{4\sqrt{5}}{5}$, $\sec A = \dfrac{4\sqrt{11}}{11}$, $\cot A = -\dfrac{\sqrt{55}}{5}$

153. $\sin A = -\dfrac{2\sqrt{6}}{5}$, $\cos A = -\dfrac{1}{5}$, $\tan A = 2\sqrt{6}$, $\csc A = -\dfrac{5\sqrt{6}}{12}$, $\cot A = \dfrac{\sqrt{6}}{12}$

155. $\sin A = \dfrac{\sqrt{6}}{4}$, $\tan A = \dfrac{\sqrt{15}}{5}$, $\csc A = \dfrac{2\sqrt{6}}{3}$, $\sec A = \dfrac{2\sqrt{10}}{5}$, $\cot A = \dfrac{\sqrt{15}}{3}$

157. $\sin A = -\dfrac{3\sqrt{10}}{10}$, $\cos A = \dfrac{\sqrt{10}}{10}$, $\csc A = \dfrac{r}{b} = -\dfrac{\sqrt{10}}{3}$, $\sec A = \sqrt{10}$, $\cot A = -\dfrac{1}{3}$

Chapter 4 Exercise 4

1. $\sin t = -\dfrac{\sqrt{3}}{2}$, $\cos t = a = \dfrac{1}{2}$, $\tan t = -\sqrt{3}$, $\csc t = -\dfrac{2\sqrt{3}}{3}$, $\sec t = 2$, $\cot t = -\dfrac{\sqrt{3}}{3}$

3. $\sin t = 0$, $\cos t = -1$, $\tan t = 0$, $\csc t$ is undefined, $\sec t = -1$, $\cot t$ is undefined

5. $\sin t = \dfrac{\sqrt{35}}{6}$, $\cos t = \dfrac{1}{6}$, $\tan t = \sqrt{35}$, $\csc t = \dfrac{6\sqrt{35}}{35}$, $\sec t = 6$, $\cot t = \dfrac{\sqrt{35}}{35}$

7. $\sin t = -\dfrac{\sqrt{6}}{3}$, $\cos t = -\dfrac{\sqrt{3}}{3}$, $\tan t = \sqrt{2}$, $\csc t = -\dfrac{\sqrt{6}}{2}$, $\sec t = -\sqrt{3}$, $\cot t = \dfrac{\sqrt{2}}{2}$

9. $\sin \theta = -\dfrac{2\sqrt{5}}{5}$, $\cos \theta = \dfrac{\sqrt{5}}{5}$, $\tan \theta = -2$, $\csc \theta = -\dfrac{\sqrt{5}}{2}$, $\sec \theta = \sqrt{5}$, $\cot \theta = -\dfrac{1}{2}$

11. $\sin \theta = \dfrac{\sqrt{26}}{26}$, $\cos \theta = -\dfrac{5\sqrt{26}}{26}$, $\tan \theta = -\dfrac{1}{5}$, $\csc \theta = \sqrt{26}$, $\sec \theta = -\dfrac{\sqrt{26}}{5}$, $\cot \theta = -5$

13. $\sin \theta = \dfrac{\sqrt{10}}{10}$, $\cos \theta = \dfrac{3\sqrt{10}}{10}$, $\tan \theta = \dfrac{1}{3}$, $\csc \theta = \sqrt{10}$, $\sec \theta = \dfrac{\sqrt{10}}{3}$, $\cot \theta = 3$

15. $\sin \theta = -\dfrac{\sqrt{6}}{3}$, $\cos \theta = -\dfrac{\sqrt{3}}{3}$, $\tan \theta = \sqrt{2}$, $\csc \theta = -\dfrac{\sqrt{6}}{2}$, $\sec \theta = -\sqrt{3}$, $\cot \theta = \dfrac{\sqrt{2}}{2}$

17. The domain of the cosine function is the set of all real numbers.

19. The domain of the cotangent function is the set $\{x \mid x \ne n\pi, \text{ where } n \text{ is any integer}\}$.

21. The range of the tangent function is the set of all real numbers.

23. The range of the sine function is the set $\{y \mid -1 \le y \le 1\}$.

25. $\sin x = 0$ for any x-value of the form $x = n\pi$, where n is any integer.

27. $\tan x$ undefined for all x-values of the form $x = \dfrac{n\pi}{2}$, where n is any odd integer.

29. $f(\theta) = \sin \theta$ is odd.   31. The period of $f(x) = \cos x$ is 2π.   33. The period of $y = \tan x$ is π.

35. $\dfrac{2}{3}$ 37. -3 39. -0.76

Chapter 5 Exercise 5

1.

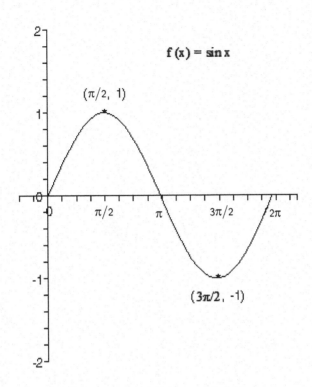

$f(x) = \sin x$

$(\pi/2, 1)$

$(3\pi/2, -1)$

3.

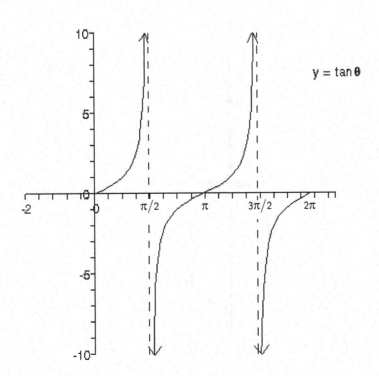

$y = \tan \theta$

5.

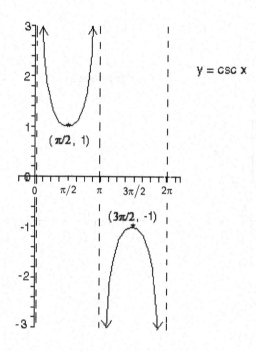

$y = \csc x$

$(\pi/2, 1)$

$(3\pi/2, -1)$

7.

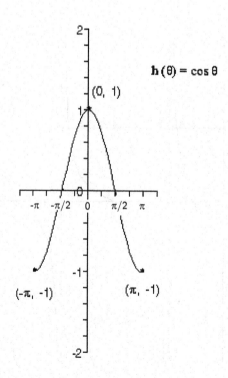

$\mathbf{h}(\theta) = \cos \theta$

$(0, 1)$

$(-\pi, -1)$

$(\pi, -1)$

9.

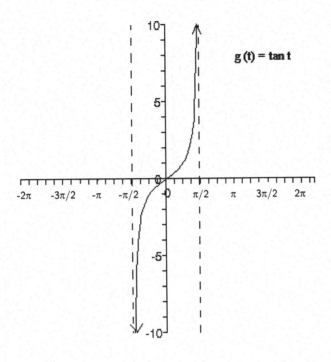

11.

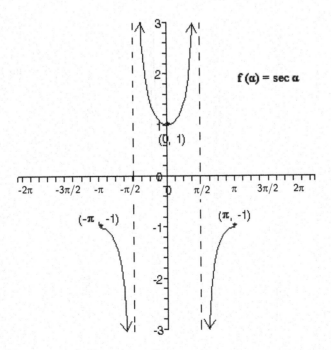

13.

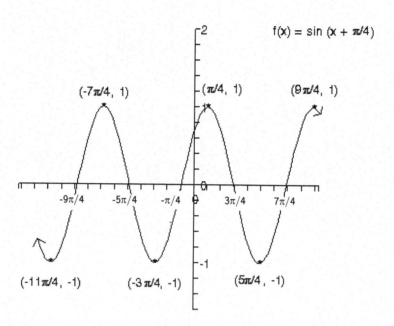

15.

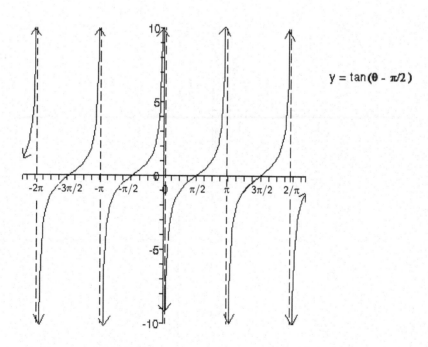

17.

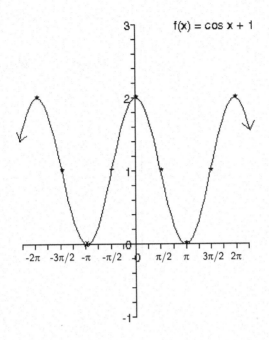

19.

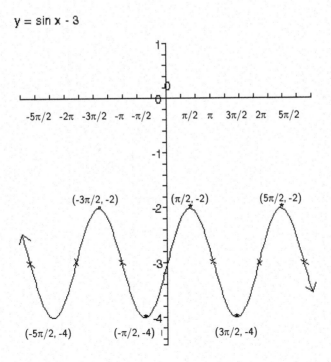

21.

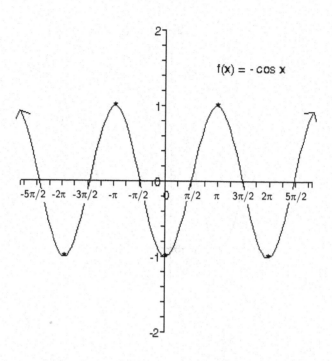

23.

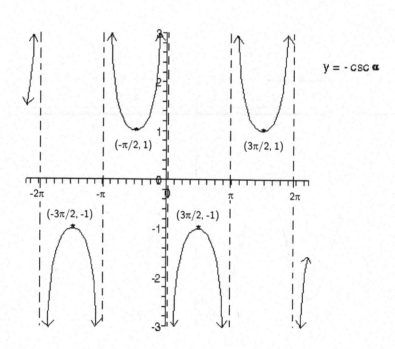

25.

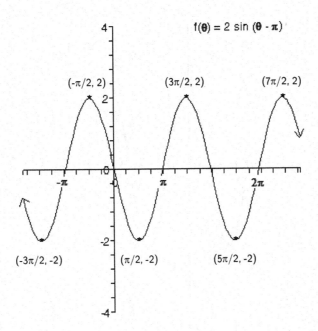

27.

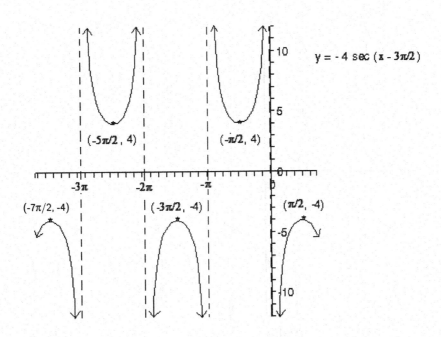

29.

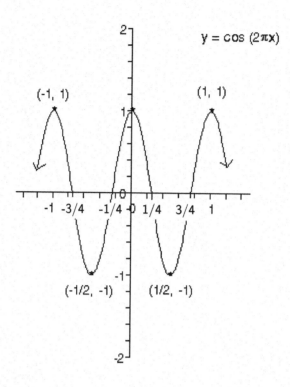

y = cos (2πx)

31.

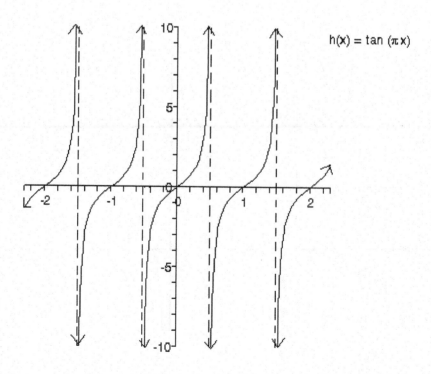

h(x) = tan (πx)

33. $y = \sin 2x$ has amplitude 1 and period π.

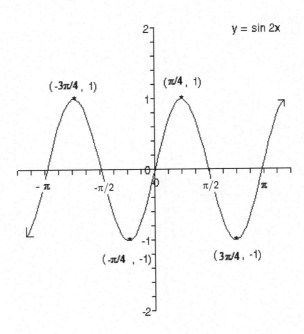

35. $y = 2\cos\frac{1}{2}x$ has amplitude 2 and period 4π.

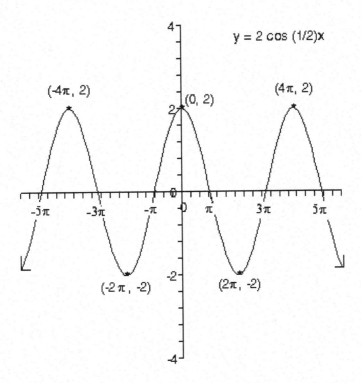

37. $f(x) = \frac{1}{3} \sin 4x$ has amplitude $\frac{1}{3}$ and period $\frac{\pi}{2}$.

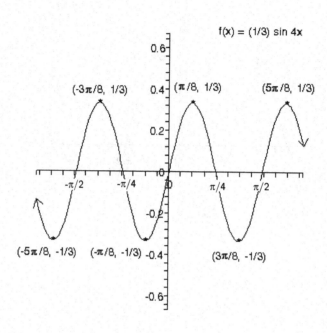

39. $f(\theta) = 3 \cos(\pi\theta)$ has amplitude 3 and period 2.

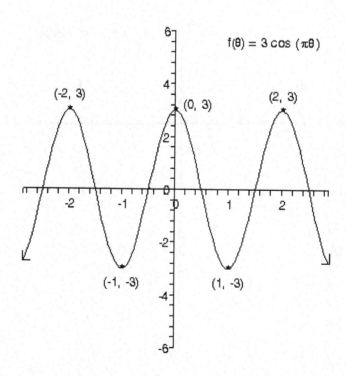

41. $y = -2\cos 2x$ has amplitude 2 and period π.

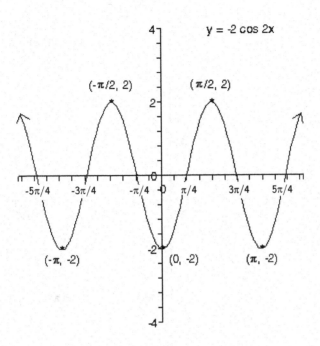

43. $f(t) = -\sin\left(\frac{\pi}{2}t\right)$ has amplitude 1 and period 4.

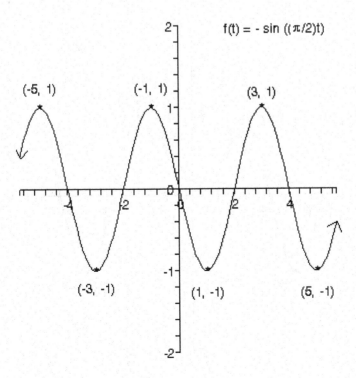

45. The period is π, the phase shift is $\frac{\pi}{2}$, and the amplitude is 1.

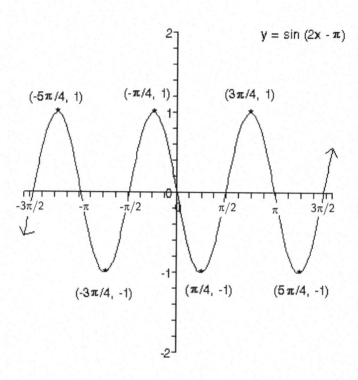

47. The period is $\frac{\pi}{2}$, the phase shift is $-\frac{\pi}{4}$, and the amplitude is 2.

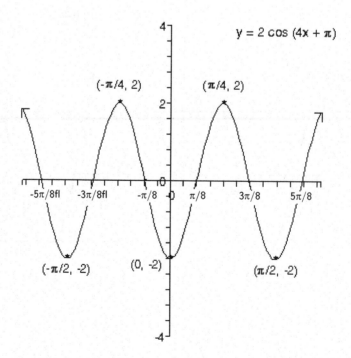

49. The period is $\frac{2\pi}{3}$, the phase shift is $\frac{\pi}{6}$, and the amplitude is $\frac{1}{4}$.

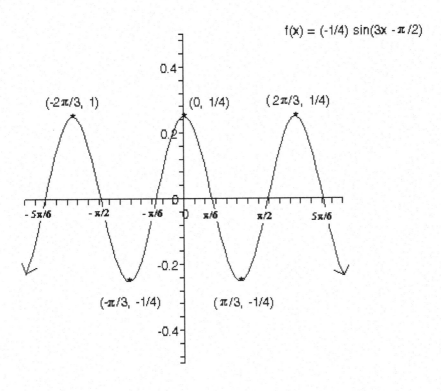

$f(x) = (-1/4) \sin(3x - \pi/2)$

51. The period is 2, the phase shift is $-\frac{1}{\pi}$, and the amplitude is 2.

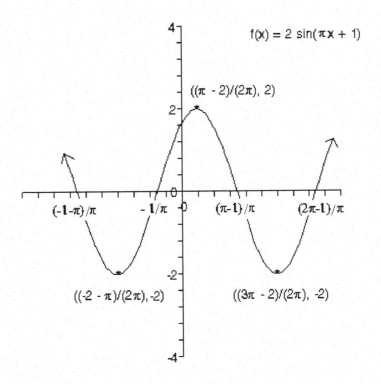

$f(x) = 2 \sin(\pi x + 1)$

53. The period is 1, the phase shift is $-\frac{1}{\pi}$, and the amplitude is 1.

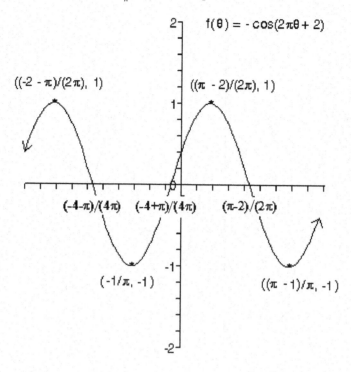

55. The period is π, the phase shift is $\frac{\pi}{4}$, and the amplitude is 1.

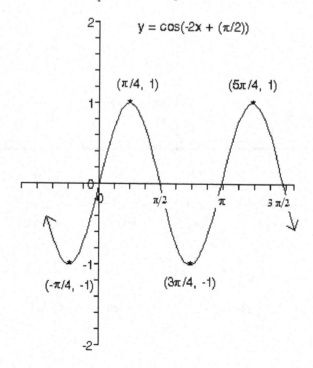

Chapter 6 Exercise 6.1

1. $13\sin\theta$ 3. $-4\tan x$ 5. $-8\cos 2\alpha$ 7. $13\cot^2 x$ 9. $\sin A + 5\cos A$

11. $-4\sec^2 x + 4\csc y$ 13. $6\sin^2 A + 3\sin A - 6$ 15. $6\sec^2 4\alpha + 12\sec 4\alpha + 17$

17. $11\tan(5x-1) - 6\cot 6x$ 19. $7\cos^2(5x-1) - 23\cos^2(5x+1)$ 21. $24\sin^3\theta\cos^4\theta$

23. $18\cos^6\alpha\csc^8\alpha$ 25. $4\sin^2 x + 5\sin x$ 27. $63\tan^2\theta - 14\tan\theta$

29. $6\sin^2\beta + 23\sin\beta + 20$ 31. $8\cot^2\theta - 18\cot\theta + 9$ 33. $\sin^2 x + \cos^2 x$

35. $\sin^2 x - 4\sin x + 4$ 37. $25\csc^2 A + 30\csc A + 9$ 39. $9\sin x + 1$

41. $10\tan\theta - 2$ 43. $\sin x + 3$ 45. $6\csc B\tan B - 5$

47. $-4\cos^2 A\sin A + 2\cos A$ 49. $\sin x(\sin x + 2)$ 51. $3\cos\theta(2\cos\theta - 3)$

53. $(\cot\theta + \sin\theta)(\cot\theta - \sin\theta)$ 55. $(3\sec\alpha + 2)(3\sec\alpha - 2)$ 57. $\sin\theta\cos\theta(5\sin\theta + 4\cos^2\theta)$

59. $6\tan^2 x\csc x(2 - 3\tan x\csc^3 x)$ 61. $(\tan\alpha + 3)(\tan\alpha - 5)$ 63. $(\cos\theta - 3)(\cos\theta - 4)$

65. $(2\sin\theta + 1)(\sin\theta - 1)$ 67. $(3\tan x - 2)(\tan x + 1)$ 69. $(\cos 5x + 7)(\cos 5x - 4)$

71. $(\cot(x+4) + 3)^2$ 73. $\sin 5\alpha(\sin 5\alpha + 4)(\sin 5\alpha - 4)$ 75. $\cos^2\theta(3\cos\theta + 1)(3\cos\theta - 1)$

77. $\tan\theta + 8\sec\theta$ 79. $\dfrac{\cos x - 3}{\cos x - 7}$ 81. $\sin A - \cos A$ 83. $\dfrac{\tan B}{3\tan B + \csc B}$

85. $\dfrac{3\sin 4\alpha - 2}{\sin 4\alpha(\sin 4\alpha - 1)}$ 87. $\dfrac{\cos 2\beta - 3}{\sin 2\beta}$ 89. $\dfrac{4\sin^2 A}{3\cos B}$ 91. $-\dfrac{55\cot^2 y}{8}$

93. $\dfrac{1}{2\csc u(4\csc u + 5)}$ 95. $\dfrac{4(\cos\beta - \sin\beta)}{3(\sin\beta - 2)}$ 97. $\dfrac{8\sin^2 x}{3\cos^2 y}$ 99. $\dfrac{28\tan A}{3\cot^3 B}$

101. $\dfrac{8\tan\alpha}{9(\tan\alpha + 6)}$ 103. $\dfrac{2(\cos\theta - 8)}{\cos\theta - 2}$ 105. $\dfrac{11\cos y - 5}{1 + 2\cos y}$ 107. $\dfrac{1 - \sin\theta}{\cos\theta}$

109. $\dfrac{-2\tan x + 4\sin x}{\sin x + 2\cos x}$ 111. $\dfrac{\csc^2 A + 1}{\csc A - 1}$ 113. $\dfrac{2(3\sec x + 4)}{\sec x - 2}$ 115. $\dfrac{1}{4 - \cos x}$

117. $\dfrac{\cos x\cos y + \sin x\sin y}{\sin y\cos y}$ 119. $\dfrac{\cos^2\theta - \sin^2\theta - \sin\theta}{\cos\theta(1 + \sin\theta)}$ 121. $\dfrac{5\csc A - \cos A}{(\csc A + \cos A)(\csc A - \cos A)}$

123. $\dfrac{4\sin x\cos x}{(\sin x - \cos x)(\sin x + \cos x)}$ 125. $\dfrac{1}{\cos y} = \sec y$ 127. $\dfrac{15\sin^2\theta - 2}{5\sin\theta}$

129. 0 131. $\dfrac{4\sin A + 5\tan^2 A}{6\sin^2 A\tan^3 A}$ 133. $\dfrac{-5\sin x\cos^2 x + 4\sin x + 7\cos x}{14\cos^2 x\sin^2 x}$

135. $\dfrac{7\tan A - 6}{\tan A(\tan A + 6)(\tan A - 6)}$ 137. $\dfrac{2\cot^2\theta + 2\cot\theta + 21}{(\cot\theta - 3)(\cot\theta + 2)(\cot\theta - 2)}$

139. $\dfrac{\cos^2 t + 3\cos t - 3}{(\cos t + 5)(\cos t - 5)}$ 141. $\dfrac{5\tan^2 A - 59\tan A + 6}{(\tan A + 2)(\tan A - 2)(\tan A - 10)}$

143. $\dfrac{\sin^2 x + 2}{3\sin x}$ 145. $\dfrac{\sin\theta(\cos\theta - 2\sin\theta)}{8}$

147. $\dfrac{3\csc x(\csc x + 2\cos x)}{24\csc x - 5}$ 149. $\dfrac{2(13 - 3\tan A)}{\tan A(7\tan A - 27)}$

151. $\dfrac{\cos x}{\sin x} = \tan x$

Chapter 6 Exercise 6.2

1. $\sin x$ 3. $\dfrac{1}{\sin^2 x}$ 5. $\sin x + 1$ 7. $-\sin x \cos x$ 9. -1

11. $\dfrac{\sin x - \cos x}{\sin x \cos x}$ 13. $\cos x$ 15. $\cos x$ 17. $1 - \sin^2 x$ 19. $\dfrac{1 + \sin x}{\cos x}$

21. $\dfrac{\sin^2 x - \cos^2 x}{\sin x \cos x}$ 23. 1 25. $\cos^2 x$ 27. $\dfrac{1}{\cos^3 x}$

29. $\csc\theta\cos\theta = \dfrac{1}{\sin\theta}\left(\dfrac{\cos\theta}{1}\right) = \dfrac{\cos\theta}{\sin\theta} = \cot\theta$

31. $\tan\alpha\cot\alpha - \cos^2\alpha = \tan\alpha\left(\dfrac{1}{\tan\alpha}\right) - \cos^2\alpha = 1 - \cos^2\alpha = \sin^2\alpha$

33. $\cos x\,(\tan x + \sec x) = \cos x\tan x + \cos x\sec x = \cos x\left(\dfrac{\sin x}{\cos x}\right) + \cos x\left(\dfrac{1}{\cos x}\right) = \sin x + 1$

35. $(\sin A + \cos A)^2 = \underbrace{\sin^2 A + 2\sin A\cos A + \cos^2 A}_{\sin^2 A + \cos^2 A = 1} = 1 + 2\sin A\cos A$

37. $(\cos x + \sin x)(\cos x - \sin x) = \cos^2 x - \sin^2 x = \underbrace{1 - \sin^2 x}_{\sin^2 x + \cos^2 x = 1} - \sin^2 x = 1 - 2\sin^2 x$

39. $\cos^4\beta - \sin^4\beta = \underbrace{\left(\cos^2\beta + \sin^2\beta\right)}_{1}\left(\cos^2\beta - \sin^2\beta\right) = 1\left(\cos^2\beta - \sin^2\beta\right) = \cos^2\beta - \sin^2\beta$

41. $\sin\alpha\cot\alpha = \dfrac{\sin\alpha}{1}\left(\dfrac{\cos\alpha}{\sin\alpha}\right) = \cos\alpha = \dfrac{1}{\sec\alpha}$

43. $\dfrac{\tan A}{\sec A} = \dfrac{\frac{1}{\cot A}}{\frac{1}{\cos A}} = \dfrac{\frac{\cos A\cot A}{1}\left(\frac{1}{\cot A}\right)}{\frac{\cos A\cot A}{1}\left(\frac{1}{\cos A}\right)} = \dfrac{\cos A}{\cot A}$

45. $\dfrac{\cos B - \tan B}{\sin B} = \underbrace{\dfrac{\cos B}{\sin B} - \dfrac{\tan B}{\sin B}}_{\tan B = \frac{\sin B}{\cos B}} = \cot B - \dfrac{1}{\cos B} = \cot B - \sec B$

47. $\dfrac{\sin x + 1}{\tan x} = \underbrace{\dfrac{\sin x}{\tan x} + \dfrac{1}{\tan x}}_{\tan x = \frac{\sin x}{\cos x}} = \cos x + \cot x$

49. $\dfrac{\sec\beta}{\tan\beta + \cot\beta} = \dfrac{\frac{1}{\cos\beta}}{\frac{\sin\beta}{\cos\beta} + \frac{\cos\beta}{\sin\beta}} = \dfrac{\frac{\sin\beta\cos\beta}{1}\left(\frac{1}{\cos\beta}\right)}{\frac{\sin\beta\cos\beta}{1}\left(\frac{\sin\beta}{\cos\beta}\right) + \frac{\sin\beta\cos\beta}{1}\left(\frac{\cos\beta}{\sin\beta}\right)}$

$$= \dfrac{\sin\beta}{\sin^2\beta + \cos^2\beta} = \dfrac{\sin\beta}{1} = \sin\beta$$

51. $\dfrac{1 + \sin\alpha}{1 - \sin\alpha} = \dfrac{\csc\alpha}{\csc\alpha}\left(\dfrac{1 + \sin\alpha}{1 - \sin\alpha}\right) = \dfrac{\csc\alpha + \csc\alpha\sin\alpha}{\csc\alpha - \csc\alpha\sin\alpha} = \dfrac{\csc\alpha + \left(\frac{1}{\sin\alpha}\right)\sin\alpha}{\csc\alpha - \left(\frac{1}{\sin\alpha}\right)\sin\alpha} = \dfrac{\csc\alpha + 1}{\csc\alpha - 1}$

53. $\dfrac{\cos\theta}{1-\sin\theta} + \dfrac{1-\sin\theta}{\cos\theta} = \dfrac{\cos\theta\,(\cos\theta) + (1-\sin\theta)\,(1-\sin\theta)}{\cos\theta\,(1-\sin\theta)} = \dfrac{\cos^2\theta + 1 - 2\sin\theta + \sin^2\theta}{\cos\theta\,(1-\sin\theta)}$

$\qquad = \dfrac{1 + 1 - 2\sin\theta}{\cos\theta\,(1-\sin\theta)} = \dfrac{2 - 2\sin\theta}{\cos\theta\,(1-\sin\theta)} = \dfrac{2\,(1-\sin\theta)}{\cos\theta\,(1-\sin\theta)} = \dfrac{2}{\cos\theta} = 2\left(\dfrac{1}{\cos\theta}\right) = 2\sec\theta$

55. $\underbrace{\dfrac{(1-\sin x)^2}{\cos^2 x} = \dfrac{(1-\sin x)^2}{1-\sin^2 x}}_{\sin^2 x + \cos^2 x = 1} = \dfrac{(1-\sin x)^2}{(1+\sin x)\,(1-\sin x)} = \dfrac{1-\sin x}{1+\sin x}$

57. $\underbrace{\dfrac{\tan^2 y - 1}{\tan^2 y + 1} + 2\cos^2 y = \dfrac{\tan^2 y - 1}{\sec^2 y} + 2\cos^2 y}_{\tan^2 y + 1 = \sec^2 y} = \dfrac{\tan^2 y - 1}{\sec^2 y} + \dfrac{2\cos^2 y}{1}\left(\dfrac{\sec^2 y}{\sec^2 y}\right)$

$\qquad\qquad = \dfrac{\tan^2 y - 1 + \overbrace{2\cos^2 y \sec^2 y}^{1}}{\sec^2 y} = \dfrac{\tan^2 y - 1 + 2}{\sec^2 y}$

$\qquad\qquad = \dfrac{\tan^2 y + 1}{\sec^2 y} = \dfrac{\sec^2 y}{\sec^2 y} = 1$

59. $\dfrac{1+\cos\beta}{1-\cos\beta} - \dfrac{1-\cos\beta}{1+\cos\beta} = \dfrac{(1+\cos\beta)^2 - (1-\cos\beta)^2}{(1+\cos\beta)\,(1-\cos\beta)} = \dfrac{1 + 2\cos\beta + \cos^2\beta - (1 - 2\cos\beta + \cos^2\beta)}{(1+\cos\beta)\,(1-\cos\beta)}$

$\qquad = \dfrac{1 + 2\cos\beta + \cos^2\beta - 1 + 2\cos\beta - \cos^2\beta}{(1+\cos\beta)\,(1-\cos\beta)} = \dfrac{4\cos\beta}{(1+\cos\beta)\,(1-\cos\beta)}$

$\qquad = \dfrac{4\cos\beta}{1-\cos^2\beta} = \dfrac{4\cos\beta}{\sin^2\beta} = 4\left(\dfrac{\cos\beta}{\sin\beta}\right)\left(\dfrac{1}{\sin\beta}\right) = 4\cot\beta\csc\beta$

61. $\dfrac{1-\tan^2\alpha}{\cos^2\alpha - \sin^2\alpha} = \dfrac{1 - \dfrac{\sin^2\alpha}{\cos^2\alpha}}{\cos^2\alpha - \sin^2\alpha} = \dfrac{(\cos^2\alpha)\,(1) - \cos^2\alpha\left(\dfrac{\sin^2\alpha}{\cos^2\alpha}\right)}{\cos^2\alpha\,(\cos^2\alpha - \sin^2\alpha)} = \dfrac{\cos^2\alpha - \sin^2\alpha}{\cos^2\alpha\,(\cos^2\alpha - \sin^2\alpha)}$

$\qquad = \dfrac{1}{\cos^2\alpha} = \sec^2\alpha$

Chapter 6 Exercise 6.3

1. $\dfrac{\sqrt{2}+\sqrt{6}}{4}$ 　　　3. $\dfrac{\sqrt{2}+\sqrt{6}}{4}$ 　　　5. $\dfrac{-\sqrt{2}-\sqrt{6}}{4}$ 　　　7. $\dfrac{\sqrt{2}+\sqrt{6}}{4}$

9. $-2-\sqrt{3}$ 　　　11. $-2-\sqrt{3}$ 　　　13. $\dfrac{\sqrt{2}-\sqrt{6}}{4}$ 　　　15. $\dfrac{\sqrt{2}-\sqrt{6}}{4}$

17. 0 　　19. $-\dfrac{\sqrt{2}}{2}$ 　　21. -1 　　23. $\dfrac{\sqrt{2}}{2}$ 　　25. $\dfrac{\sqrt{3}}{2}$ 　　27. 0 　　29. $\dfrac{\sqrt{3}}{3}$

31. (a) $\dfrac{6\sqrt{2}+4\sqrt{17}}{25}$ 　　(b) $\dfrac{8\sqrt{2}+3\sqrt{17}}{25}$ 　　(c) $\dfrac{8\sqrt{2}-3\sqrt{17}}{6\sqrt{2}+4\sqrt{17}}$ 　　(d) $\dfrac{6\sqrt{2}-4\sqrt{17}}{25}$

33. (a) $\dfrac{19\sqrt{17}}{85}$ 　　(b) $-\dfrac{8\sqrt{17}}{85}$ 　　(c) $\dfrac{16}{13}$ 　　(d) $-\dfrac{13\sqrt{17}}{85}$

35. (a) $\dfrac{-4\sqrt{10}-5\sqrt{3}}{15}$ 　　(b) $\dfrac{-10\sqrt{2}+2\sqrt{15}}{15}$ 　　(c) $\dfrac{4\sqrt{5}+2\sqrt{6}}{8-\sqrt{30}}$ 　　(d) $\dfrac{-4\sqrt{10}+5\sqrt{3}}{15}$

37. $\cos\left(\frac{\pi}{2} + x\right) = \cos\frac{\pi}{2}\cos x - \sin\frac{\pi}{2}\sin x = 0\,(\cos x) - 1\,(\sin x) = -\sin x$

39. $\sin\left(\pi - A\right) = \sin\pi\cos A - \cos\pi\sin A = 0\,(\cos A) - (-1)\sin A = \sin A$

41. $\cos\left(\pi + \theta\right) = \cos\pi\cos\theta - \sin\pi\sin\theta = (-1)\cos\theta - 0\,(\sin\theta) = -\cos\theta$

43. $\sin\left(\frac{3\pi}{2} + \alpha\right) = \sin\frac{3\pi}{2}\cos\alpha + \cos\frac{3\pi}{2}\sin\alpha = -1\,(\cos\alpha) + 0\,(\sin\alpha) = -\cos\alpha$

45. $\tan\left(\pi + x\right) = \dfrac{\tan\pi + \tan x}{1 - \tan\pi\tan x} = \dfrac{0 + \tan x}{1 - 0\,(\tan x)} = \dfrac{\tan x}{1} = \tan x$

47. $\tan\left(\frac{3\pi}{2} - \alpha\right) = \dfrac{\sin\left(\frac{3\pi}{2} - \alpha\right)}{\cos\left(\frac{3\pi}{2} - \alpha\right)} = \dfrac{\sin\frac{3\pi}{2}\cos\alpha - \cos\frac{3\pi}{2}\sin\alpha}{\cos\frac{3\pi}{2}\cos\alpha + \sin\frac{3\pi}{2}\sin\alpha} = \dfrac{-\cos\alpha}{-\sin\alpha} = \cot\alpha$

49. $\sin\left(x + y\right) + \sin\left(x - y\right) = (\sin x\cos y + \cos x\sin y) + (\sin x\cos y - \cos x\sin y) = 2\sin x\cos y$

51. $\cos\left(x + y\right) - \cos\left(x - y\right) = (\cos x\cos y - \sin x\sin y) - (\cos x\cos y + \sin x\sin y) = -2\sin x\sin y$

53. $\dfrac{\sin\left(A + B\right)}{\sin\left(A - B\right)} = \dfrac{\sin A\cos B + \cos A\sin B}{\sin A\cos B - \cos A\sin B} = \dfrac{\dfrac{\sin A\cos B}{\cos A\cos B} + \dfrac{\cos A\sin B}{\cos A\cos B}}{\dfrac{\sin A\cos B}{\cos A\cos B} - \dfrac{\cos A\sin B}{\cos A\cos B}} = \dfrac{\tan A + \tan B}{\tan A - \tan B}$

55. $\dfrac{\cos\left(A - B\right)}{\sin A\cos B} = \dfrac{\cos A\cos B + \sin A\sin B}{\sin A\cos B} = \dfrac{\cos A\cos B}{\sin A\cos B} + \dfrac{\sin A\sin B}{\sin A\cos B} = \tan B + \cot A$

57. $\sec\left(\theta + \alpha\right) = \dfrac{1}{\cos\left(\theta + \alpha\right)} = \dfrac{1}{\cos\theta\cos\alpha - \sin\theta\sin\alpha} = \dfrac{\dfrac{1}{\sin\theta\sin\alpha}}{\dfrac{\cos\theta\cos\alpha}{\sin\theta\sin\alpha} - \dfrac{\sin\theta\sin\alpha}{\sin\theta\sin\alpha}} = \dfrac{\csc\theta\csc\alpha}{\cot\theta\cot\alpha - 1}$

59. $\tan\left(\alpha + \beta\right) + \tan\left(\alpha - \beta\right) = \dfrac{\tan\alpha + \tan\beta}{1 - \tan\alpha\tan\beta} + \dfrac{\tan\alpha - \tan\beta}{1 + \tan\alpha\tan\beta}$

$\qquad = \left(\dfrac{1 + \tan\alpha\tan\beta}{1 + \tan\alpha\tan\beta}\right)\dfrac{\tan\alpha + \tan\beta}{1 - \tan\alpha\tan\beta} + \left(\dfrac{1 - \tan\alpha\tan\beta}{1 - \tan\alpha\tan\beta}\right)\dfrac{\tan\alpha - \tan\beta}{1 + \tan\alpha\tan\beta}$

$\qquad = \dfrac{(1 + \tan\alpha\tan\beta)(\tan\alpha + \tan\beta) + (1 - \tan\alpha\tan\beta)(\tan\alpha - \tan\beta)}{(1 + \tan\alpha\tan\beta)(1 - \tan\alpha\tan\beta)}$

$\qquad = \dfrac{\tan\alpha + \tan\beta + \tan^2\alpha\tan\beta + \tan\alpha\tan^2\beta + \tan\alpha - \tan\beta - \tan^2\alpha\tan\beta + \tan\alpha\tan^2\beta}{(1 + \tan\alpha\tan\beta)(1 - \tan\alpha\tan\beta)}$

$\qquad = \dfrac{2\tan\alpha + 2\tan\alpha\tan^2\beta}{(1 + \tan\alpha\tan\beta)(1 - \tan\alpha\tan\beta)} = \dfrac{2\tan\alpha\left(1 + \tan^2\beta\right)}{(1 + \tan\alpha\tan\beta)(1 - \tan\alpha\tan\beta)}$

$\qquad = \dfrac{2\tan\alpha\sec^2\beta}{1 - \tan^2\alpha\tan^2\beta}$

61. $\cos\left(\theta + k\pi\right) = \cos\theta\underbrace{\cos k\pi}_{(-1)^k} - \sin\theta\underbrace{\sin k\pi}_{0} = (-1)^k\cos\theta$

63. $\tan\left(\alpha + k\pi\right) = \underbrace{\dfrac{\tan\alpha + \tan k\pi}{1 - \tan\alpha\tan k\pi}}_{\tan k\pi = 0} = \dfrac{\tan\alpha}{1} = \tan\alpha$

65. $\dfrac{f(x+h)-f(x)}{h} = \dfrac{\cos(x+h)-\cos x}{h} = \dfrac{\cos x \cos h - \sin x \sin h - \cos x}{h}$

$\qquad = \dfrac{-\sin x \sin h - \cos x + \cos x \cos h}{h} = \dfrac{-\sin x \sin h - \cos x(1-\cos h)}{h}$

$\qquad = \dfrac{-\sin x \sin h}{h} - \dfrac{\cos x(1-\cos h)}{h} = -\sin x\left(\dfrac{\sin h}{h}\right) - \cos x\left(\dfrac{1-\cos h}{h}\right)$

Chapter 6 Exercise 6.4

1. $\dfrac{\sqrt{2}}{2}$ 3. $\dfrac{\sqrt{3}}{2}$ 5. $-\dfrac{\sqrt{3}}{2}$ 7. $\dfrac{\sqrt{3}}{3}$ 9. (a) $\dfrac{120}{169}$ (b) $\dfrac{119}{169}$ (c) $\dfrac{120}{119}$

11. (a) $\dfrac{2\sqrt{2}}{3}$ (b) $-\dfrac{1}{3}$ (c) $-2\sqrt{2}$ 13. (a) $-\dfrac{2\sqrt{66}}{25}$ (b) $-\dfrac{19}{25}$ (c) $\dfrac{2\sqrt{66}}{19}$

15. (a) $-\dfrac{5}{13}$ (b) $-\dfrac{12}{13}$ (c) $\dfrac{5}{12}$ 17. (a) $\dfrac{5\sqrt{39}}{32}$ (b) $-\dfrac{7}{32}$ (c) $\dfrac{5\sqrt{39}}{7}$

19. (a) $-\dfrac{6\sqrt{14}}{25}$ (b) $-\dfrac{21}{25}$ (c) $\dfrac{6\sqrt{14}}{11}$

21. $(\cos\theta - \sin\theta)^2 = (\cos\theta - \sin\theta)(\cos\theta - \sin\theta) = \underbrace{\cos^2\theta - 2\sin\theta\cos\theta + \sin^2\theta = 1 - \sin 2\theta}_{\cos^2\theta + \sin^2\theta = 1 \text{ and } 2\sin\theta\cos\theta = 2\sin\theta.}$

23. $(\cos x + \sin x)(\cos x - \sin x) = \cos^2 x - \sin^2 x = \cos 2x$

25. $\cos 2\beta = 2\cos^2\beta - 1 = \underbrace{2\left(\dfrac{1}{\sec^2\beta}\right) - \dfrac{\sec^2\beta}{\sec^2\beta} = \dfrac{2}{\sec^2\beta} - \dfrac{\sec^2\beta}{\sec^2\beta} = \dfrac{2-\sec^2\beta}{\sec^2\beta}}_{\cos\beta = \frac{1}{\sec\beta} \text{ gives us } \cos^2\beta = \frac{1}{\sec^2\beta}.}$

27. $\csc 2A = \dfrac{1}{\sin 2A} = \dfrac{1}{2\sin A \cos A} = \dfrac{1}{2\sin A} \cdot \dfrac{1}{\cos A} = \dfrac{1}{2\sin A} \cdot \sec A = \dfrac{\sec A}{2\sin A}$

29. $\dfrac{\tan\theta - \cot\theta}{\tan\theta + \cot\theta} = \left(\dfrac{\tan\theta}{\tan\theta}\right)\left(\dfrac{\tan\theta - \cot\theta}{\tan\theta + \cot\theta}\right) = \dfrac{\tan^2\theta - \tan\theta\cot\theta}{\tan^2\theta + \tan\theta\cot\theta} = \underbrace{\dfrac{\tan^2\theta - 1}{\tan^2\theta + 1} = \dfrac{\tan^2\theta - 1}{\sec^2\theta}}_{\tan^2\theta + 1 = \sec^2\theta}$

$\qquad = \dfrac{\tan^2\theta}{\sec^2\theta} - \dfrac{1}{\sec^2\theta} = \dfrac{\frac{\sin^2\theta}{\cos^2\theta}}{\frac{1}{\cos^2\theta}} - \dfrac{1}{\sec^2\theta} = \dfrac{\sin^2\theta}{1} - \dfrac{1}{\sec^2\theta} = \sin^2\theta - \cos^2\theta = -\cos 2\theta$

31. $\cos^4 x - \sin^4 x = (\cos^2 x - \sin^2 x)\underbrace{(\cos^2 x + \sin^2 x)}_{1} = \cos^2 x - \sin^2 x = \cos 2x$

33. $\frac{1}{2} - \frac{1}{2}\cos 2x = \frac{1}{2} - \frac{1}{2}(1 - 2\sin^2 x) = \frac{1}{2} - \frac{1}{2} + \sin^2 x = \sin^2 x$

35. $\cos 3\theta = \cos(2\theta + \theta) = \underbrace{\cos 2\theta \cos\theta - \sin 2\theta \sin\theta = (2\cos^2\theta - 1)\cos\theta - 2\sin\theta\cos\theta(\sin\theta)}_{\cos 2\theta = 2\cos^2\theta - 1 \text{ and } \sin 2\theta = 2\sin\theta\cos\theta.}$

$\qquad = \underbrace{2\cos^3\theta - \cos\theta - 2\sin^2\theta\cos\theta = 2\cos^3\theta - \cos\theta - 2(1-\cos^2\theta)\cos\theta}_{\sin^2\theta + \cos^2\theta = 1, \text{ so } \sin^2\theta = 1 - \cos^2\theta.}$

$\qquad = 2\cos^3\theta - \cos\theta - 2\cos\theta + 2\cos^3\theta = 4\cos^3\theta - 3\cos\theta$

37. $\tan 3x = \tan(2x + x) = \dfrac{\tan 2x + \tan x}{1 - \tan 2x \tan x} = \dfrac{\dfrac{2\tan x}{1 - \tan^2 x} + \tan x}{1 - \left(\dfrac{2\tan x}{1 - \tan^2 x}\right)\tan x}$

$\qquad = \left(\dfrac{\dfrac{1 - \tan^2 x}{1}}{\dfrac{1 - \tan^2 x}{1}}\right)\left(\dfrac{\dfrac{2\tan x}{1 - \tan^2 x} + \tan x}{1 - \left(\dfrac{2\tan x}{1 - \tan^2 x}\right)\tan x}\right) = \dfrac{2\tan x + \tan x\left(1 - \tan^2 x\right)}{1 - \tan^2 x - 2\tan x\left(\tan x\right)}$

$\qquad = \dfrac{2\tan x + \tan x - \tan^3 x}{1 - \tan^2 x - 2\tan^2 x} = \dfrac{3\tan x - \tan^3 x}{1 - 3\tan^2 x} = \dfrac{\tan^3 x - 3\tan x}{3\tan^2 x - 1}$

39. $\sin 4A = \underbrace{\sin 2\,(2A)}_{\text{Use } \sin 2x = 2\sin x \cos x.} = 2\sin 2A \cos 2A = 2\left(2\sin A \cos A\right)\left(1 - 2\sin^2 A\right) = 4\sin A \cos A\left(1 - 2\sin^2 A\right)$

$\qquad = 4\sin A \cos A - 8\sin^3 A \cos A$

41. $\dfrac{2\cot x}{1 + \cot^2 x} = \dfrac{2\left(\dfrac{\cos x}{\sin x}\right)}{\csc^2 x} = \dfrac{\dfrac{2\cos x}{\sin x}}{\dfrac{1}{\sin^2 x}} = \left(\dfrac{\dfrac{\sin^2 x}{1}}{\dfrac{\sin^2 x}{1}}\right)\left(\dfrac{\dfrac{2\cos x}{\sin x}}{\dfrac{1}{\sin^2 x}}\right) = \dfrac{2\sin x \cos x}{1}$

43. $\sin^4 x = \left(\sin^2 x\right)^2 = \left(\frac{1}{2} - \frac{1}{2}\cos 2x\right)^2 = \frac{1}{4} - \frac{1}{2}\cos 2x + \frac{1}{4}\cos^2 2x = \frac{1}{4} - \frac{1}{2}\cos 2x + \frac{1}{4}\left(\frac{1}{2} + \frac{1}{2}\cos 4x\right)$

$\qquad = \frac{1}{4} - \frac{1}{2}\cos 2x + \frac{1}{8} + \frac{1}{8}\cos 4x = \frac{3}{8} - \frac{1}{2}\cos 2x + \frac{1}{8}\cos 4x$

Chapter 6 Exercise 6.5

1. $\dfrac{\sqrt{2 + \sqrt{3}}}{2}$ 3. $\dfrac{\sqrt{2 + \sqrt{3}}}{2}$ 5. $2 - \sqrt{3}$ 7. $\dfrac{\sqrt{2 + \sqrt{2}}}{2}$

9. $\dfrac{\sqrt{2 - \sqrt{2}}}{2}$ 11. $-\sqrt{2} + 1$ 13. $-\dfrac{\sqrt{2 - \sqrt{2}}}{2}$

15. (a) $\sin\dfrac{x}{2} = \dfrac{\sqrt{10}}{10}$ (b) $\cos\dfrac{x}{2} = \dfrac{3\sqrt{10}}{10}$ (c) $\tan\dfrac{x}{2} = \dfrac{1}{3}$

17. (a) $\sin\dfrac{x}{2} = \dfrac{\sqrt{74 + 8\sqrt{74}}}{2\sqrt{37}}$ (b) $\cos\dfrac{x}{2} = -\dfrac{\sqrt{74 - 8\sqrt{74}}}{2\sqrt{37}}$ (c) $\tan\dfrac{x}{2} = -\dfrac{\sqrt{185} + 4\sqrt{10}}{5}$

19. (a) $\sin\dfrac{x}{2} = \sqrt{\dfrac{5 + \sqrt{3}}{10}}$ (b) $\cos\dfrac{x}{2} = -\sqrt{\dfrac{5 - \sqrt{3}}{10}}$ (c) $\tan\dfrac{x}{2} = -\dfrac{5\sqrt{22} + \sqrt{66}}{22}$

21. (a) $\sin\dfrac{x}{2} = \dfrac{\sqrt{26 - \sqrt{26}}}{2\sqrt{13}}$ (b) $\cos\dfrac{x}{2} = -\dfrac{\sqrt{26 + \sqrt{26}}}{2\sqrt{13}}$ (c) $\tan\dfrac{x}{2} = \dfrac{1 - \sqrt{26}}{5}$

23. (a) $\sin\dfrac{x}{2} = \sqrt{\dfrac{7 + 3\sqrt{5}}{14}}$ (b) $\cos\dfrac{x}{2} = \sqrt{\dfrac{7 - 3\sqrt{5}}{14}}$ (c) $\tan\dfrac{x}{2} = \dfrac{7 + 3\sqrt{5}}{2}$

25. (a) $\sin\dfrac{x}{2} = \sqrt{\dfrac{\sqrt{217} + 8\sqrt{3}}{2\sqrt{217}}}$ (b) $\cos\dfrac{x}{2} = -\sqrt{\dfrac{\sqrt{217} - 8\sqrt{3}}{2\sqrt{217}}}$ (c) $\tan\dfrac{x}{2} = -\dfrac{\sqrt{217} + 8\sqrt{3}}{5}$

27. $\sin^2\dfrac{x}{2} = \dfrac{1 - \cos x}{2} = \left(\dfrac{\csc x}{\csc x}\right)\left(\dfrac{1 - \cos x}{2}\right) = \dfrac{\csc x - \csc x \cos x}{2\csc x} = \dfrac{\csc x - \dfrac{\cos x}{\sin x}}{2\csc x} = \dfrac{\csc x - \cot x}{2\csc x}$

29. $\csc^2 \dfrac{\alpha}{2} = \dfrac{1}{\sin^2 \frac{\alpha}{2}} = \dfrac{1}{\frac{1-\cos\alpha}{2}} = \dfrac{2}{1-\cos\alpha}$

31. $\tan \dfrac{\alpha}{2} = \dfrac{1-\cos\alpha}{\sin\alpha} = \dfrac{1}{\sin\alpha} - \dfrac{\cos\alpha}{\sin\alpha} = \csc\alpha - \cot\alpha$

33. $\tan^2 \dfrac{A}{2} = \left(\dfrac{\sin A}{1+\cos A}\right)^2 = \dfrac{\sin^2 A}{(1+\cos A)^2}$

35. $\cot \dfrac{\alpha}{2} + \tan \dfrac{\alpha}{2} = \dfrac{\sin\alpha}{1-\cos\alpha} + \dfrac{1-\cos\alpha}{\sin\alpha} = \dfrac{\sin\alpha}{\sin\alpha}\left(\dfrac{\sin\alpha}{1-\cos\alpha}\right) + \left(\dfrac{1-\cos\alpha}{1-\cos\alpha}\right)\left(\dfrac{1-\cos\alpha}{\sin\alpha}\right)$

$= \underbrace{\dfrac{\sin^2\alpha + 1 - 2\cos\alpha + \cos^2\alpha}{\sin\alpha(1-\cos\alpha)}}_{\sin^2\alpha + \cos^2\alpha = 1} = \dfrac{2 - 2\cos\alpha}{\sin\alpha(1-\cos\alpha)} = \dfrac{2(1-\cos\alpha)}{\sin\alpha(1-\cos\alpha)} = \dfrac{2}{\sin\alpha} = 2\csc\alpha$

37. $2\cos \dfrac{x}{2} = \dfrac{2\cos\frac{x}{2}\sin\frac{x}{2}}{\sin\frac{x}{2}} = \underbrace{\dfrac{1}{\sin\frac{x}{2}} \cdot \dfrac{2\cos\frac{x}{2}\sin\frac{x}{2}}{1} = \csc\dfrac{x}{2} \cdot \sin 2\left(\dfrac{x}{2}\right)}_{\text{Use } 2\cos\theta\sin\theta = \sin 2\theta.} = \sin x\csc\dfrac{x}{2}$

Chapter 6 Exercise 6.6

1. $\dfrac{1}{2}(\sin 10x + \sin 4x)$
3. $3(\cos 3\theta - \cos 7\theta)$
5. $\dfrac{1}{2}(\cos 7x + \cos 5x)$

7. $\dfrac{1}{2}(\sin 10t - \sin 6t)$
9. $\dfrac{1}{2}(\cos 3\alpha - \cos 9\alpha)$
11. $\dfrac{3}{2}(\cos 8x + \cos 4x)$

13. $2\cos 4x\cos 2x$
15. $-2\sin 3A\sin 2A$
17. $2\sin\dfrac{7\theta}{2}\cos\dfrac{\theta}{2}$

19. $-2\cos\dfrac{13\beta}{2}\sin\dfrac{9\beta}{2}$
21. $\sin\dfrac{11x}{2}\sin\dfrac{5x}{2}$
23. $\dfrac{1}{4}\sin 5\theta\cos\theta$

25. $-\dfrac{1}{2}\sin\dfrac{15A}{2}\sin\dfrac{A}{2}$
27. $\dfrac{\sqrt{3}-1}{4}$
29. $-\dfrac{1}{4}$
31. $\dfrac{1}{4}$

33. $\dfrac{\sqrt{3}-1}{4}$
35. $\dfrac{\sqrt{2}}{2}$
37. $-\dfrac{\sqrt{2}}{2}$

39. $\dfrac{\cos 3x + \cos x}{2\cos 2x} = \dfrac{2\cos\left(\frac{3x+x}{2}\right)\cos\left(\frac{3x-x}{2}\right)}{2\cos 2x} = \dfrac{2\cos 2x\cos x}{2\cos 2x} = \cos x$

41. $\dfrac{\cos 4\theta - \cos 6\theta}{\sin 4\theta + \sin 6\theta} = \dfrac{-2\sin\left(\frac{4\theta+6\theta}{2}\right)\sin\left(\frac{4\theta-6\theta}{2}\right)}{2\sin\left(\frac{4\theta+6\theta}{2}\right)\cos\left(\frac{4\theta-6\theta}{2}\right)} = \underbrace{\dfrac{-2\sin 5\theta\sin(-\theta)}{2\sin 5\theta\cos(-\theta)} = \dfrac{2\sin 5\theta\sin\theta}{2\sin 5\theta\cos\theta}}_{\sin(-\theta)=-\sin\theta \text{ and } \cos(-\theta)=\cos\theta.} = \tan\theta$

43. $\dfrac{\sin 3\alpha - \sin\alpha}{\cos\alpha - \cos 3\alpha} = \dfrac{2\cos\left(\frac{3\alpha+\alpha}{2}\right)\sin\left(\frac{3\alpha-\alpha}{2}\right)}{-2\sin\left(\frac{\alpha+3\alpha}{2}\right)\sin\left(\frac{\alpha-3\alpha}{2}\right)} = \underbrace{\dfrac{2\cos 2\alpha\sin\alpha}{-2\sin 2\alpha\sin(-\alpha)} = \dfrac{2\cos 2\alpha\sin\alpha}{2\sin 2\alpha\sin\alpha}}_{\sin(-\alpha)=-\sin\alpha}$

$= \dfrac{\cos 2\alpha}{\sin 2\alpha} = \cot 2\alpha$

45. $\tan\left(\dfrac{A+B}{2}\right)\cot\left(\dfrac{A-B}{2}\right) = \dfrac{\sin\left(\dfrac{A+B}{2}\right)}{\cos\left(\dfrac{A+B}{2}\right)} \cdot \dfrac{\cos\left(\dfrac{A-B}{2}\right)}{\sin\left(\dfrac{A-B}{2}\right)} = \dfrac{\sin\left(\dfrac{A+B}{2}\right)\cos\left(\dfrac{A-B}{2}\right)}{\cos\left(\dfrac{A+B}{2}\right)\sin\left(\dfrac{A-B}{2}\right)}$

$$= \dfrac{2\sin\left(\dfrac{A+B}{2}\right)\cos\left(\dfrac{A-B}{2}\right)}{2\cos\left(\dfrac{A+B}{2}\right)\sin\left(\dfrac{A-B}{2}\right)} = \dfrac{\sin A + \sin B}{\sin A - \sin B}$$

51. $\cot\left(\dfrac{x+y}{2}\right) = \dfrac{\cos\left(\dfrac{x+y}{2}\right)}{\sin\left(\dfrac{x+y}{2}\right)} = \dfrac{\cos\left(\dfrac{x+y}{2}\right)}{\sin\left(\dfrac{x+y}{2}\right)} \cdot \dfrac{2\cos\left(\dfrac{x-y}{2}\right)}{2\sin\left(\dfrac{x-y}{2}\right)}$

$$= \dfrac{2\cos\left(\dfrac{x+y}{2}\right)\cos\left(\dfrac{x-y}{2}\right)}{2\sin\left(\dfrac{x+y}{2}\right)\sin\left(\dfrac{x-y}{2}\right)} = \dfrac{\cos x + \cos y}{\sin x + \sin y}$$

Chapter 7 Exercise 7.1

1. $\dfrac{\pi}{6}$ 3. $\dfrac{\pi}{3}$ 5. $\dfrac{\pi}{6}$ 7. $-\dfrac{\pi}{2}$ 9. 0 11. $-\dfrac{\pi}{6}$ 13. $\dfrac{2\pi}{3}$

15. $-\dfrac{\pi}{6}$ 17. 0 19. $\dfrac{\pi}{3}$ 21. $\dfrac{\pi}{3}$ 23. $\dfrac{2\pi}{3}$ 25. $-\dfrac{\pi}{2}$ 27. $\dfrac{2}{3}$

29. $\dfrac{5}{2}$ 31. $\dfrac{4}{7}$ 33. $-\dfrac{\sqrt{11}}{2}$ 35. $-\dfrac{7}{10}$ 37. $\dfrac{\pi}{3}$ 39. π 41. $\dfrac{\pi}{4}$

43. $\dfrac{2\pi}{3}$ 45. $-\dfrac{\pi}{4}$ 47. 0 49. $\dfrac{\pi}{6}$ 51. $\dfrac{\pi}{4}$ 53. $\dfrac{\pi}{3}$ 55. $\dfrac{\pi}{4}$

57. $\dfrac{3\pi}{4}$ 59. $-\dfrac{\pi}{2}$ 61. $\dfrac{\sqrt{3}}{2}$ 63. $\dfrac{1}{2}$ 65. $\dfrac{\sqrt{2}}{2}$ 67. $-\dfrac{\sqrt{3}}{3}$ 69. $\dfrac{7}{9}$

71. $\dfrac{\sqrt{39}}{8}$ 73. $-\dfrac{3}{11}$ 75. $-\dfrac{21}{20}$ 77. $-\dfrac{4}{3}$ 79. $\sqrt{\dfrac{5-\sqrt{21}}{10}}$

81. $\sqrt{\dfrac{\sqrt{11}+2}{2\sqrt{11}}}$ 83. $\dfrac{-2\sqrt{3}}{7+\sqrt{37}}$ 85. $\dfrac{2\sqrt{5}}{5}$ 87. $\dfrac{\sqrt{21}}{7}$ 89. $\dfrac{2+2\sqrt{10}}{9}$

91. $\dfrac{\sqrt{51}+4\sqrt{102}}{51}$ 93. $\dfrac{-35-3\sqrt{15}}{21-5\sqrt{15}}$ 95. $\dfrac{-7}{3}$ 97. $-\dfrac{33}{65}$ 99. $y\sqrt{1-x^2} + x\sqrt{1-y^2}$

101. $\dfrac{x\sqrt{1-y^2}+y}{\sqrt{1+x^2}}$ 103. $\dfrac{\sqrt{1-x^2}\cdot\sqrt{1-y^2}+xy}{x\sqrt{1-y^2}-y\sqrt{1-x^2}}$ 105. $2x^2-1$ 107. $2x\sqrt{1-x^2}$

109. Let $\sin^{-1} x = \theta$. Then $\sin\theta = x$ and $\cos\theta = \sqrt{1-\sin^2\theta} = \sqrt{1-x^2}$, so

$$\tan\left(\sin^{-1} x\right) = \tan\theta = \frac{\sin\theta}{\cos\theta} = \frac{x}{\sqrt{1-x^2}}.$$

111. Let $\sin^{-1} x = \theta$. Then $\sin\theta = x$ and $\cos\theta = \sqrt{1-\sin^2\theta} = \sqrt{1-x^2}$, so

$$\cos\left(\sin^{-1} x\right) = \cos\theta = \sqrt{1-x^2}.$$

113. Observe that $\sin\left(\frac{\pi}{2} - \theta\right) = \cos\theta$ since

$$\sin\left(\frac{\pi}{2} - \theta\right) = \sin\frac{\pi}{2}\cos\theta - \cos\frac{\pi}{2}\sin\theta = \cos\theta.$$

If we let $\cos\theta = x$, then $\theta = \cos^{-1}x$. However, this is the same as $\sin\left(\frac{\pi}{2} - \theta\right) = x$, which implies that $\sin^{-1}x = \frac{\pi}{2} - \theta$. When we replace θ by $\cos^{-1}x$, we obtain

$$\sin^{-1}x = \frac{\pi}{2} - \cos^{-1}x, \text{ or equivalently, } \sin^{-1}x + \cos^{-1}x = \frac{\pi}{2}.$$

115. Let $\tan^{-1}x = \theta$. Then $\tan\theta = x$. This implies that $\sin\theta = \dfrac{x}{\sqrt{1-x^2}}$ and $\cos\theta = \dfrac{1}{\sqrt{1-x^2}}$ (why?).

Therefore,

$$\sin\left(2\tan^{-1}x\right) = \sin 2\theta = 2\sin\theta\cos\theta = 2\left(\frac{x}{\sqrt{1-x^2}}\right)\left(\frac{1}{\sqrt{1-x^2}}\right) = \frac{2x}{1+x^2}.$$

Chapter 7 Exercise 7.2

NOTE: In every solution set that follows, k represents any integer.

1. $\left\{\dfrac{\pi}{3} + 2\pi k,\ \dfrac{5\pi}{3} + 2\pi k\right\}$

3. $\left\{\dfrac{\pi}{3} + 2\pi k,\ \dfrac{2\pi}{3} + 2\pi k\right\}$

5. $\left\{\dfrac{\pi}{4} + \pi k\right\}$

7. $\left\{\dfrac{5\pi}{6} + 2\pi k,\ \dfrac{7\pi}{6} + 2\pi k\right\}$

9. $\left\{\dfrac{3\pi}{2} + 2\pi k\right\}$

11. $\left\{\dfrac{5\pi}{6} + \pi k\right\}$

13. $\left\{\dfrac{\pi}{6} + 2\pi k,\ \dfrac{5\pi}{6} + 2\pi k\right\}$

15. $\left\{\dfrac{5\pi}{6} + \pi k\right\}$

17. $\left\{\dfrac{2\pi k}{3}\right\}$

19. $\left\{\dfrac{\pi}{3} + \pi k\right\}$

21. $\left\{-\dfrac{\pi}{36} + \dfrac{2\pi k}{3},\ \dfrac{5\pi}{36} + \dfrac{2\pi k}{3}\right\}$

23. $\left\{\dfrac{\pi}{24} + \pi k,\ \dfrac{17\pi}{24} + \pi k\right\}$

25. $\{5\pi + 3\pi k\}$

27. $\left\{\dfrac{\pi}{8} + \pi k,\ \dfrac{7\pi}{8} + \pi k\right\}$

29. $\{\pi + 3\pi k,\ 2\pi + 3\pi k\}$

31. $\left\{\dfrac{\pi k}{6}\right\}$

33. $\left\{\dfrac{\pi}{6},\ \dfrac{5\pi}{6}\right\}$

35. $\left\{\dfrac{\pi}{3},\ \dfrac{5\pi}{3}\right\}$

37. $\left\{\dfrac{3\pi}{4},\ \dfrac{7\pi}{4}\right\}$

39. $\left\{-\dfrac{2\pi}{3},\ \dfrac{2\pi}{3}\right\}$

41. $\left\{-\dfrac{\pi}{2}\right\}$

43. $\left\{-\dfrac{\pi}{2},\dfrac{\pi}{2}\right\}$

45. $\left\{\dfrac{11\pi}{12},\ \dfrac{23\pi}{12}\right\}$

47. $\{0,\ 2\pi\}$

49. $\left\{-\pi,\ -\dfrac{\pi}{3},\ -\dfrac{4\pi}{3}\right\}$

51. $\left\{-\dfrac{5\pi}{12},\ -\dfrac{11\pi}{12},\ -\dfrac{17\pi}{12},\ -\dfrac{23\pi}{12},\ -\dfrac{\pi}{3},\ -\dfrac{5\pi}{6},\ -\dfrac{4\pi}{3},\ -\dfrac{11\pi}{6}\right\}$

53. $\left\{\dfrac{7\pi}{4},\ -\dfrac{5\pi}{4}\right\}$

55. $\{0\}$

57. $\left\{-\dfrac{9\pi}{7},\ \dfrac{9\pi}{7}\right\}$

59. $\left\{-\dfrac{5\pi}{3},\ \dfrac{5\pi}{9}\right\}$

61. $\{38°,\ 152°\}$

63. $\{89°,\ 169°\}$

65. $\{109°,\ 251°\}$

67. $\{243°,\ 297°\}$

69. $\{2°,\ 182°\}$

71. $\{85°,\ 275°\}$

73. $\{199°,\ 341°\}$

75. $\{175°,\ 355°\}$

Chapter 7 Exercise 7.3

NOTE: In every solution set that follows, k represents any integer.

1. $\left\{\dfrac{\pi}{2}+\pi k,\ \dfrac{2\pi}{3}+2\pi k,\ \dfrac{4\pi}{3}+2\pi k\right\}$ 3. $\left\{\pi k,\ \dfrac{\pi}{3}+2\pi k,\ \dfrac{2\pi}{3}+2\pi k\right\}$

5. $\left\{\pi k,\ \dfrac{\pi}{4}+\pi k\right\}$ 7. $\{\pi+2\pi k\}$ 9. $\left\{\dfrac{\pi}{3}+2\pi k,\ \dfrac{2\pi}{3}+2\pi k,\ \dfrac{4\pi}{3}+2\pi k,\ \dfrac{5\pi}{3}+2\pi k\right\}$

11. $\left\{\dfrac{\pi}{3}+\pi k,\ \dfrac{2\pi}{3}+\pi k\right\}$ 13. $\left\{\dfrac{\pi}{2}+\pi k,\right\}$ 15. $\left\{\dfrac{\pi}{6}+\pi k,\ \dfrac{5\pi}{6}+\pi k\right\}$

17. $\left\{\dfrac{\pi}{4}+2\pi k,\ \dfrac{3\pi}{4}+2\pi k,\ \dfrac{5\pi}{4}+2\pi k,\ \dfrac{7\pi}{4}+2\pi k\right\}$ 19. $\left\{\dfrac{3\pi}{2}+2\pi k\right\}$

21. $\left\{\dfrac{7\pi}{6}+2\pi k,\ \dfrac{11\pi}{6}+2\pi k,\ \dfrac{3\pi}{2}+2\pi k\right\}$ 23. $\left\{\pi,\ 2\pi,\ \dfrac{7\pi}{6},\ \dfrac{11\pi}{6}\right\}$

25. $\left\{\dfrac{\pi}{3},\ \dfrac{4\pi}{3},\ \dfrac{2\pi}{3},\ \dfrac{5\pi}{3}\right\}$ 27. $\left\{\dfrac{\pi}{6},\ \dfrac{5\pi}{6},\ \dfrac{7\pi}{6},\ \dfrac{11\pi}{6}\right\}$ 29. $\left\{\pm\dfrac{\pi}{2},\ \pm\dfrac{\pi}{6},\ \pm\dfrac{5\pi}{6}\right\}$

31. $\left\{0,\ \dfrac{\pi}{2},\ \dfrac{3\pi}{2}\right\}$ 33. $\left\{\pi,\ 2\pi,\ \dfrac{2\pi}{3},\ \dfrac{5\pi}{3}\right\}$

35. $\left\{\dfrac{\pi}{24},\dfrac{5\pi}{24},\dfrac{7\pi}{24},\dfrac{11\pi}{24},\dfrac{13\pi}{24},\dfrac{17\pi}{24},\dfrac{19\pi}{24},\dfrac{23\pi}{24},\dfrac{25\pi}{24},\dfrac{29\pi}{24},\dfrac{31\pi}{24},\dfrac{35\pi}{24},\dfrac{37\pi}{24},\dfrac{41\pi}{24},\dfrac{43\pi}{24},\dfrac{47\pi}{24}\right\}$

37. No solution.   39. $\{\pi\}$ 41. $\left\{\dfrac{7\pi}{6},\ \dfrac{11\pi}{6},\ \dfrac{3\pi}{2},\ -\dfrac{5\pi}{6},\ -\dfrac{\pi}{6},\ -\dfrac{\pi}{2}\right\}$ 43. $\left\{\dfrac{\pi}{6},\ \dfrac{5\pi}{6}\right\}$

45. $\{41°,\ 118°,\ 221°,\ 298°\}$ 47. $\{10°,\ 170°\}$ 49. $\{54°,\ 306°\}$

51. $\{68°,\ 117°,\ 248°,\ 297°\}$ 53. $\{136°,\ 180°,\ 224°\}$ 55. $\{48°,\ 132°,\ 228°,\ 312°\}$

57. $\{58°,\ 129°,\ 231°,\ 302°\}$ 59. $\{102°,\ 168°,\ 282°,\ 348°\}$ 61. $\{189°,\ 351°\}$

Chapter 7 Exercise 7.4

NOTE: In every solution set that follows, k represents any integer.

1. $\left\{\dfrac{\pi}{4}+\pi k,\ \dfrac{\pi}{2}+\pi k\right\}$ 3. $\left\{\dfrac{\pi}{2}+2\pi k,\ \dfrac{3\pi}{2}+2\pi k,\ \pi k\right\}$ 5. $\left\{\pi k,\ \dfrac{\pi}{3}+2\pi k,\ \dfrac{5\pi}{3}+2\pi k\right\}$

7. $\left\{\pi k,\ \dfrac{\pi}{2}+2\pi k,\ \dfrac{3\pi}{2}+2\pi k\right\}$ 9. $\{\pi k\}$ 11. $\left\{\dfrac{\pi}{6}+2\pi k,\ \dfrac{5\pi}{6}+2\pi k\right\}$

13. $\left\{\pm\dfrac{\pi}{2},\ \pm\dfrac{3\pi}{2},\ \pm\dfrac{\pi}{4},\ \pm\dfrac{3\pi}{4},\ \pm\dfrac{5\pi}{4},\ \pm\dfrac{7\pi}{4}\right\}$ 15. $\left\{\dfrac{\pi}{2},\ \dfrac{3\pi}{2}\right\}$ 17. $\left\{-\dfrac{\pi}{2},\ \dfrac{\pi}{2}\right\}$

19. $\left\{\dfrac{\pi}{6},\ \dfrac{5\pi}{6},\ \dfrac{3\pi}{2}\right\}$ 21. $\left\{0,\ \pi,\ 2\pi,\ \dfrac{\pi}{4},\ \dfrac{5\pi}{4}\right\}$ 23. $\left\{\dfrac{\pi}{6},\ \dfrac{5\pi}{6},\ \dfrac{3\pi}{2},\ \dfrac{-\pi}{2},\ \dfrac{-11\pi}{6},\ \dfrac{-7\pi}{6}\right\}$ 25. $\left\{\dfrac{\pi}{6},\ \dfrac{5\pi}{6}\right\}$

27. $\left\{\dfrac{\pi}{8},\ \dfrac{3\pi}{8},\ \dfrac{5\pi}{8},\ \dfrac{7\pi}{8},\ \dfrac{9\pi}{8},\ \dfrac{11\pi}{8},\ \dfrac{13\pi}{8},\ \dfrac{15\pi}{8}\right\}$ 29. $\left\{\dfrac{3\pi}{4}\right\}$ 31. $\left\{\dfrac{\pi}{4}\right\}$ 33. $\left\{\dfrac{\pi}{6},\ \dfrac{\pi}{2}\right\}$

35. $\left\{\dfrac{\pi}{4}, \dfrac{5\pi}{4}\right\}$ 37. $\{38°,\ 142°\}$ 39. $\{71°,\ 161°,\ 251°,\ 341°\}$ 41. $\{61°,\ 119°\}$

43. $\{30°,\ 210°\}$ 45. $\{114°,\ 246°\}$ 47. $\{206°,\ 334°\}$

Chapter 7 Exercise 7.5

NOTE: In every solution set that follows, k represents any integer.

1. $\left\{\dfrac{\pi}{2} + 2\pi k,\ \dfrac{3\pi}{2} + 2\pi k,\ \dfrac{\pi}{6} + 2\pi k,\ \dfrac{5\pi}{6} + 2\pi k\right\}$ 3. $\left\{\dfrac{2\pi}{3} + 2\pi k,\ \dfrac{4\pi}{3} + 2\pi k,\ 2\pi k\right\}$

5. $\left\{\dfrac{\pi}{3} + 2\pi k,\ \dfrac{2\pi}{3} + 2\pi k,\ \dfrac{4\pi}{3} + 2\pi k,\ \dfrac{5\pi}{3} + 2\pi k\right\}$ 7. $\left\{\dfrac{\pi}{3} + 2\pi k,\ \dfrac{5\pi}{3} + 2\pi k,\ 2\pi k\right\}$

9. $\left\{\dfrac{\pi}{4} + \pi k,\ \dfrac{3\pi}{4} + \pi k,\ \dfrac{\pi}{2} + \pi k\right\}$ 11. $\left\{0,\ \pi,\ \dfrac{2\pi}{3},\ \dfrac{4\pi}{3}\right\}$ 13. $\left\{\dfrac{\pi}{6},\ \dfrac{5\pi}{6},\ \dfrac{3\pi}{2}\right\}$

15. $\left\{\dfrac{2\pi}{3},\ \dfrac{4\pi}{3}\right\}$ 17. $\left\{\dfrac{\pi}{2},\ \dfrac{3\pi}{2},\ \dfrac{5\pi}{4},\ \dfrac{7\pi}{4}\right\}$ 19. $\left\{\dfrac{\pi}{3},\ \pi,\ \dfrac{5\pi}{3}\right\}$ 21. $\left\{\dfrac{\pi}{3},\ \dfrac{5\pi}{3}\right\}$

23. $\left\{0, \pi,\ \dfrac{\pi}{6},\ \dfrac{5\pi}{6},\ \dfrac{3\pi}{2},\ \dfrac{\pi}{2},\ \dfrac{7\pi}{6},\ \dfrac{11\pi}{6}\right\}$ 25. $\left\{\dfrac{\pi}{5},\ \dfrac{3\pi}{5},\ \pi,\ \dfrac{7\pi}{5},\ \dfrac{9\pi}{5},\ \dfrac{\pi}{3},\ \dfrac{5\pi}{3}\right\}$

27. $\left\{\dfrac{\pi}{18},\ \dfrac{\pi}{9},\ \dfrac{7\pi}{18},\ \dfrac{4\pi}{9},\ \dfrac{13\pi}{18},\ \dfrac{7\pi}{9},\ \dfrac{19\pi}{18},\ \dfrac{10\pi}{9},\ \dfrac{25\pi}{18},\ \dfrac{13\pi}{9},\ \dfrac{31\pi}{18},\ \dfrac{16\pi}{9}\right\}$

29. $\left\{\dfrac{\pi}{8},\ \dfrac{3\pi}{8},\ \dfrac{5\pi}{8},\ \dfrac{7\pi}{8},\ \dfrac{9\pi}{8},\ \dfrac{11\pi}{8},\ \dfrac{13\pi}{8},\ \dfrac{15\pi}{8}\right\}$ 31. $\left\{\dfrac{\pi}{6},\ \dfrac{\pi}{2},\ \dfrac{5\pi}{6},\ \dfrac{7\pi}{6},\ \dfrac{3\pi}{2},\ \dfrac{11\pi}{6}\right\}$

33. $\left\{\dfrac{\pi}{14},\ \dfrac{5\pi}{14},\ \dfrac{9\pi}{14},\ \dfrac{13\pi}{14},\ \dfrac{17\pi}{14},\ \dfrac{3\pi}{2},\ \dfrac{25\pi}{14}\right\}$

Chapter 7 Exercise 7.6

1. 0   3. $\dfrac{\sqrt{2}}{2}$ 5. $\dfrac{\sqrt{3}}{3}$ 7. No Solution.   9. -1

11. $\dfrac{\sqrt{14}}{4}$ 13. $-\dfrac{3\sqrt{10}}{10}$ 15. $\dfrac{9}{10}$ 17. $-\sqrt{3}$ 19. $\dfrac{\sqrt{3}}{2}$

21. 1   23. 0   25. $-\dfrac{\sqrt{2}}{2}$ 27. 1

Chapter 8 Exercise 8

1. $A = 103°$, $b = 4.32$, $c = 4.62$ 3. $B = 65°$, $a = 10.57$, $b = 11.06$

5. $A = 53°$, $b = 15.22$, $c = 7.01$ 7. $C = 63°$, $b = 30.71$, $c = 27.41$

9. $A = 70°$, $a = 95.71$, $c = 100.6$ 11. $C = 92.5°$, $a = 85.55$, $b = 29.76$

13. $A = 41°10'$, $b = 15.73$, $c = 25.72$ 15. No triangle exists.

17. $A = 68°$, $B = 16.58°$, $C = 95.42°$, $a = 13$, $b = 4$, $c = 13.96$

19. $A = 127°$, $B = 11.92°$, $C = 41.08°$, $a = 8.16$, $b = 2.11$, $c = 6.71$

21. Triangle 1: $A = 25°$, $B = 34.3°$, $C = 120.7°$, $a = 6$, $b = 8$, $c = 12.21$
    Triangle 2: $A = 25°$, $B = 145.7°$, $C = 9.3°$, $a = 6$, $b = 8$, $c = 2.29$

23. No triangle exists.

25. Triangle 1: $A = 80°$, $B = 85.49°$, $C = 14.51°$, $a = 20.35$, $b = 20.6$, $c = 5.18$
    Triangle 2: $A = 80°$, $B = 94.51°$, $C = 5.49°$, $a = 20.35$, $b = 20.6$, $c = 1.98$

27. $A = 45°$, $B = 90°$, $C = 45°$, $a = 2\sqrt{2}$, $b = 4$, $c = 2\sqrt{2}$

29. No triangle exists.

31. $A = 133°$, $B = 33.27°$, $C = 13.73°$, $a = 4$, $b = 3$, $c = 1.3$

33. 1 triangle   35. 1 triangle   37. 0 triangles   39. 1 triangle

41. 1 triangle   43. 2 triangles   45. $c = 8.53$, $A = 27.67°$, $B = 70.33°$

47. $a = 8.67$, $C = 41.95°$, $B = 33.05°$ 49. $b = 9.14$, $A = 44.2°$, $C = 50.8°$

51. $a = 5.66$, $B = 32°$, $C = 118°$ 53. $c = 7.78$, $A = 21.87°$, $B = 83.13°$

55. $b = 18.73$, $A = 27.36°$, $C = 45.64°$ 57. $c = 4.68$, $A = 101.6°$, $B = 36.4°$

59. $a = 48.25$, $B = 27.86°$, $C = 36.14°$ 61. $A = 80.94°$, $B = 62.72°$, $C = 36.34°$

63. $A = 36.4°$, $B = 62.88°$, $C = 80.72°$ 65. $A = 35.66°$, $B = 35.66°$, $C = 108.68°$

67. $A = 36.87°$, $B = 90°$, $C = 53.13°$ 69. 152.28 meters   71. 190 feet

73. 1.2 miles   75. 112.1 feet   77. 309.2 yards   79. 41 feet

81. 37.3°   83. 15 square inches   85. 27.9 square yards

87. 77.2 square feet   89. 18.3 square inches   91. 9.6 square meters

Index